STRUCTURAL GEOLOGY

International Series in the Earth Sciences

ROBERT R. SHROCK, *Consulting Editor*

STRUCTURAL GEOLOGY

L. U. DE SITTER

Professor of Structural and Applied Geology
University of Leiden

FIRST EDITION

McGRAW-HILL BOOK COMPANY, INC.

LONDON · NEW YORK · TORONTO

1956

STRUCTURAL GEOLOGY

© McGraw-Hill Publishing Co. Ltd.

Library of Congress Catalog Card Number: 56-8646

1st impression — 1956
2nd impression — 1957
3rd impression — 1959
4th impression — 1961

16574

Printed in the Netherlands

Preface

This book is intended for the trained geologist rather than the layman or the first-year student; it presupposes a certain familiarity with the elements of structural geology and with its terminology.

Through the vast spread of accurate geological mapping which has been carried out for economic and scientific purposes, an enormous mass of facts about the forms of tectonic features has been accumulated, but we have only a rather crude and antiquated method with which to attempt to marshal these facts into a comprehensible system. Clearly there is a need to elaborate the system of comparative structural geology so as to show the genetic relations between the multitude of tectonic shapes.

There are, of course, numerous theories of diastrophism of the earth's crust, but because these are based on insufficient and unsystematized knowledge of the deformations themselves they are distinctly disappointing. None of the many hypotheses on orogenesis gives an adequate indication of why and how the major diastrophisms took place.

This book, therefore, is primarily concerned with systematizing our detailed knowledge so that we may be able to distinguish genetic relationships. It tries to show that we really have advanced beyond the argument about the sealing-wax which you can break with your hands but which will still flow when left alone; beyond the point where folds and faults are synonymous with flow and rupture; where underthrust and overthrust are opposite; where gravity is either ignored or presented as the one and only force, and where images conceal facts.

Theories of orogenesis have developed side by side with, rather than out of, our large store of practical knowledge. There is a very good reason for this. The man who is most intimately familiar with the enormous diversity of structural forms is the field geologist, but, submerged as he is in the ocean of facts, he seldom feels the urge to theorize. It is extremely rare for a geologist to go out into the field to investigate a particular tectonic problem as opposed to doing regional fieldwork, but when this happens it can be of great value to the progress of structural geology.

The aim of this book, then, is to establish a link between theory and practice. Starting with the physical properties of rocks (Part I), it deals in considerable detail with comparative structural geology, proceeding from simple to more complex structures. Finally, in Part III, an attempt is made to define some characteristics of the largest structural units and to discuss theories concerning their origin. The comparative method predominates throughout, for in a young science such as ours, hampered in its development by the vastness and inaccessibility of its subject, theorizing must remain a secondary function and to a certain extent a luxury, for some time to come.

As a field geologist I tend to believe what I see more than what I read. This book must therefore undoubtedly have a personal flavour and be limited in content, and I beg the forgiveness of those colleagues whose work has not received the attention it deserves. I hope they will let me know my omissions.

Finally I want to express my very sincere thanks to Mr A. J. Butler, O.B.E., of the Geological Survey and Museum, London, who has given me so much invaluable assistance in the preparation of this book.

L. U. DE SITTER

LEIDEN
March, 1956

Contents

Part One

Theoretical Structural Geology

Chapter I

Introduction

STRUCTURAL GEOLOGY IN RELATION TO OTHER EARTH SCIENCES

Structural Geology and Stratigraphy. Structural Geology is concerned with analysing the deformation of sedimentary strata. Before this object can be attained it is essential to know the depositional sequence of the strata involved. When folding is relatively mild the stratigraphical sequence is clear from the law of super-position. When, however, the layers are thoroughly disturbed by steep folds, or by thrusts or other great disturbances one must either know the stratigraphical sequence beforehand, or find fossil or sedimentary evidence of the sequence in the structures themselves.

In other words, the tectonics of a particular region cannot be elucidated without a basic knowledge of its stratigraphy; and the stratigraphy cannot be worked out without a general knowledge of the structures. In mapping a region and solving its geological problems, stratigraphical and tectonic investigations must proceed hand in hand.

The influence of movements of the earth's crust may be either simultaneous with or subsequent to the deposition of sedimentary strata or to intrusion of igneous rocks; or, as often happens, there may be both simultaneous and subsequent effects. One of the most difficult problems to solve by structural analysis is the precise relationship between tectonics and stratigraphy.

In the simplest case, that of quiet sedimentation and no subsequent folding or large-scale faulting, we can deduce the epeirogenic motion of the crust by a careful analysis of the thickness and facies variations over a relatively large area. Thus the degree of sinking of a basin-floor can be determined by measuring the increase of thickness towards the centre of the basin. The mid-continental region of the United States is particularly rich in examples because of the intensive search for oil there. Much drilling, combined with gravitational and seismic

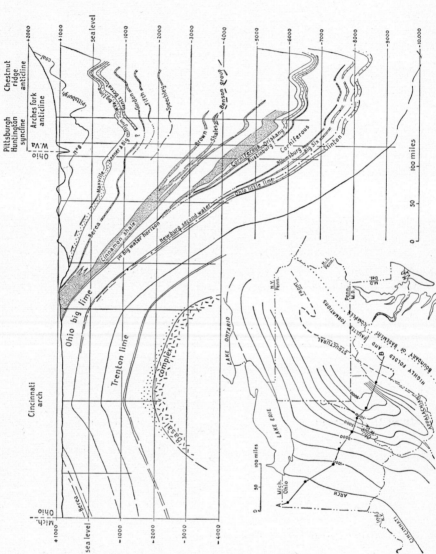

Fig. 1. Appalachian Basin, section from Ohio to West Virginia. (*After Appalachian Geological Society. Published by permission of the American Association of Petroleum Geologists.*)

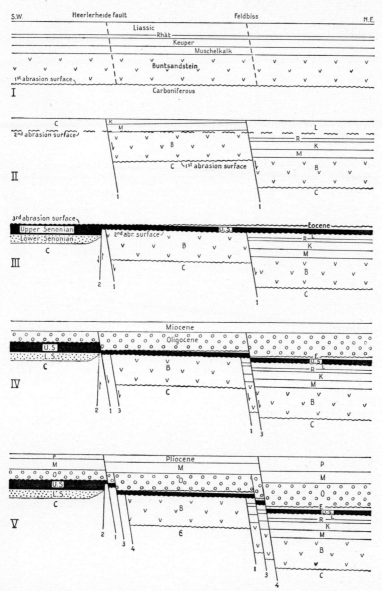

Fig. 2. Schematic cross-section across step-faults showing development of Roer Valley rift in south-east Netherlands. Each major movement along the two main faults is represented by a new parallel fault, although in nature all the movement occurred more or less along the same fault-plane. Vertical scale exaggerated. *(After de Sitter. Published by permission of Med. Jaarversl. Geol. Bureau Heerlen.)*

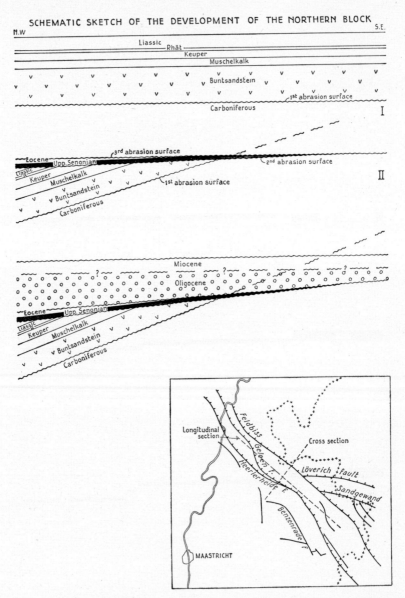

Fig. 3. Schematic longitudinal section development on tilted fault-step along
Roer Valley rift. Vertical scale exaggerated. (*After de Sitter. Published by
permission of Med. Jaarversl. Geol. Bureau Heerlen.*)

work, has established the existence of numerous basins with but slight subsequent disturbances. In a section through the Appalachian basin (Fig. 1) we can follow the epeirogenic sinking as if enacted in a film. Of particular interest are intraformational unconformities, demonstrated by the wedging-out of certain strata towards the basin-edge.

Another interesting example in which much of the structural evidence is derived solely from stratigraphical data is offered by the survey of the Roer Valley rift in the SE of the Netherlands. This deep rift is flanked to the NE and SW by more stable blocks; the latter, however, in the course of their Mesozoic history of regression and transgression, have been uniformly tilted to slope north-eastward. Figures 2 and 3 give a synopsis of the combined movement of sinking of the rift valley and tilting of the flanking blocks. The movement occurred in three main phases: a first Kimmeric (Jurassic) phase of down-faulting and tilting, a second Laramide (Cretaceous) phase of uplift of a formerly down-faulted block and a third Tertiary phase in the same sense as the first movement. The last phase is probably still active, as is indicated by occasional earthquakes (de Sitter, 1942; Muller, 1945). In this instance the subsequent tilting of earlier abrasion surfaces is of particular interest (Fig. 3).

In these quiet regions the epeirogenic disturbances of the crust can be followed step by step because no later folding has complicated the original structure. When later folding does occur, the interpretation is no longer so simple.

When, for instance, thrusts and unconformities remain unrecognized, serious errors in correlation are likely to result. Such difficulties arise especially in strongly folded regions with abrupt facies-changes, a combination which often occurs since both phenomena arise from the instability of the region. When the facies-change is, for example, from a massive off-shore reef limestone to a thick soft marl of deeper-water facies, the facies boundary is often extremely abrupt. Subsequent folding will invariably cause disturbances along the facies boundary because the two rock-types are so different in their reaction to stress. In such a case it is often almost impossible to evaluate the amount of movement along these predisposed surfaces; attempted interpretations are apt to range widely—from the supposition of large overthrusts to the supposition of but minor faults with little throw.

The same kind of uncertainty can arise when low-angle overthrusts or glided nappes are suspected in a region where the stratigraphy is insufficiently known. A typical example can be found in the "Cantabric

nappes" of Northern Spain proposed by Mengaud in 1920. At that time
nappe-structures were much in favour, and on the sole evidence of
unfossiliferous black schists of supposedly Albian age cropping out
below a Carboniferous limestone, the existence of an enormous "Picos
de Europa nappe" was suggested (Léon Bertrand and Mengaud, 1912;
Mengaud, 1920). Sampelayo (1928), however, found plant remains
with *Calamites* in the black schists, and thus refuted the hypothesis.
Finally Mengaud had to admit in 1932 that all his nappe constructions
were in error, mostly because of faulty interpretation of the stratigraphy. In other instances, such as the Marctic overthrust (E. Cloos
and Hietanen, 1941), it is impossible to gather enough irrefutable
stratigraphical evidence either to prove or to disprove the nappe
hypothesis, either because of the metamorphic state of the rocks or
of the complete absence of fossils.

The interdependence of stratigraphical and structural knowledge is
well known to every field geologist; but recent progress in sedimentology is as yet less widely used by structural geologists. The older methods of determining the top and bottom of a layer have been augmented
by new ones, such as the graded texture of sandstone beds, and the cyclic
nature of a succession of beds; and in particular by a better understanding of the characteristics of the bottom of a sandbed. It has been
known for a long time that even the cleavage or schistosity of the
bedding can help us in defining the bottom and top of a bed, and this
is of particular use in low-grade metamorphic rocks. But to supplement
this well-known tool, modern sedimentology has given us a much better
insight into the filling of a basin, and therefore into its structural
history as well. The recognition of the mechanism of turbidity currents,
and the determination of the current direction by flow-markings,
current-bedding, etc., if applied much more generally and systematically than hitherto, will certainly teach us much about the development
of a basin.

Finally, it will be shown that variations in lithological succession
have a strong influence on the subsequent fold-structures. The alternation of incompetent and competent beds, the total thickness of the
whole series, the thickness of its components, and their lateral changes
of facies determine to a very large degree the shape and locality of folds.

Thus we find that structural geology, in all its aspects, is always
dependent on the stratigraphy of the rock-sequence.

Structural Geology and Physiography. Structure depends largely on
stratigraphy; and physiography depends largely on structure. But

the older the structure, the less marked is its physiographical expression. Pre-Cambrian orogenic belts seldom coincide with present mountain ranges, and Hercynian structures are often obscured by Tertiary movements. The facial expression of geotectonics is therefore almost exclusively due to Tertiary movements, even in cases such as the Late Palaeozoic Appalachians where a mountain chain which began to rise in the Cretaceous, is the basis, again uplifted later, of the present mountain system. There still remains a secondary relation between the original folded belt and the present mountain system. This applies to most Tertiary orogenic belts as well. We have to distinguish, as we shall see later, between a folding or orogenic period and a later morphogenic period of uplift, often after a prolonged period of denudation. But in

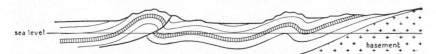

Fig. 4.   First-order morphology. Anticlines and synclines appear as rows of hills and valleys.

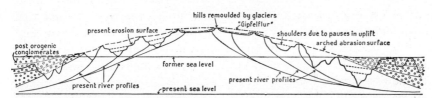

Fig. 5.   Second-order morphology. (1) Orogenic phase. Folding causing strong upheaval of central region of mountain chain and subsidence of marginal troughs filled up in later stages of folding. (2) Morphogenic phase. After peneplenization rhythmic uplift of aplanation surface in big arch, followed by remodelling by river and glacial erosion.

less severely compressed areas, such as basins and their peripheries, no later uplift intervenes between the folding and erosion, and we find the direct physiographic expression of structure. The basin is still a basin surrounded by its uplifted borders.

Thus we can distinguish between a first-order relationship, in which structural features gave rise directly to geomorphological features (Fig. 4); and a second-order relationship, in which peneplanation intervened between the creation of structures and the creation of the geomorphological features connected with them (Fig. 5).

Large geomorphological features of the first order are commonly of negative form, e.g. sinking parts of the crust are reflected as basins, deep-sea furrows, ocean-basins, etc. Most orogenic belts are second-order structures, but some are believed to be of the first order. The arcuate island belts of the Western Pacific, the Indonesian island arcs and their prolongation in Malaya, and perhaps the Himalayan orogenic belt in part, are regarded as first-order structures. Besides these major first-order structures, smaller structures in moderately folded regions are often of the first order. Late-Tertiary anticlines and synclines in basins are almost invariably first-order structures all over the world (Fig. 4). The anticlines form rows of hills, the synclines contain the swamps. Even if the relief has been reversed, and we find synclinal ridges and subsequent anticlinal rivers, they still may be of the first order. What has been said of folds is equally true of faults in so far as they are connected with folding. Block-faulted areas, on the other hand, and in particular the great rift valleys of the earth, are all relatively young, or rejuvenated structures. They generally possess very pronounced geomorphological features and have often been recognized in the first place by these features and not by geological structure. For many of the great rift valleys, the Lower Rhine Valley rift and the African rifts, for instance, it has been proved that the structure originated early in the Mesozoic and was progressively accentuated by subsequent similar movements which continued into recent times. The geomorphological expression is of course mainly due to the latest movement.

The reason for the fact that no large rift valleys of Hercynian or earlier age are known remains obscure.

We need not enter here into a detailed description of the physiography produced by folds or faults. Any textbook on geomorphology treats this matter *in extenso*, but I should like to make a few remarks on the role of physiographical evidence in structural mapping.

When one has come to understand the structure of a region in detail it becomes clear that almost every feature of its topography is caused by some particular structural item, but one cannot understand the geomorphology unless the structure is known in great detail beforehand. In other words, structural analysis of geomorphological features in the field and on the map is possible only when the structure is known in advance. Without such knowledge the method almost invariably leads to serious errors, except in the case of recent block-faulting. Nevertheless, a good eye for topographical features is very useful in tracing the prolongation of observed structural features through unexposed areas.

Structural analysis from aerial photographs, however, can be surprisingly accurate, particularly in regions which have been disturbed only once, e.g. in regions which have experienced only Tertiary or Mesozoic folding. This method has therefore become a most important tool in mapping work. It should even precede the fieldwork, and the photographs should be consulted again during and after the fieldwork. Many features, particularly faults, show better on photographs than in the field; often the photographs reveal structural details which can be found and checked only with great difficulty in the field. But every structural inference from aerial photographs ought nevertheless to be checked in the field, for misinterpretations are common. I know personally of an exceptional case in which three geologists independently analysed a structure clearly standing in the photograph as an anticline. In the field it proved to be a syncline! Structural analysis of aerial photographs is a valuable tool in the hands of an experienced field geologist, but it can never replace the fieldwork.

In the typical sequence of events which mould a mountain chain there is first the folding which forms the primary structure; then denudation, which reduces the axial zone to an old mellow relief and fills the marginal troughs with thick conglomeratic sediments; and then the morphogenic phase — a succession of uplifts with intervals of repose. During this phase consequent streams develop on the flanks of the resuscitated chain. They flow away from its axis, their headwaters cut back towards it, and the uplifted old surface at the axis becomes reshaped by glaciers.

In such a sequence the mountain tops will represent the hill tops of the old mellow relief before the morphogenic phase. There is no reason or need to presume that this level (Gipfelflur) represents a still older surface of erosion. The old relief is sometimes well preserved in the axial zone, but in many instances it has been destroyed almost completely by the later episodes of erosion. When it is still recognizable it indicates the total uplift during the morphogenic phase.

The succession of uplifts is discernible in the shoulders on the slopes of the valleys. By careful correlation of these features the history of the morphogenic phase can be established.

During the rejuvenation of the old mountain chain its structural peculiarities again affect the geomorphology; but the main consequent river systems retain the courses they have already established.

In this connexion it is interesting to observe that in Tertiary mountain chains structural control of the physiography remains pronounced, whereas in Hercynian mountain chains refolded in Tertiary times this control is much weaker. In Hercynian mountain chains which have been rejuvenated by an Alpine morphogenic phase, but not by an Alpine folding phase, the structures are still well represented by the morphology. Analyses of aerial photographs bring out the difference particularly well. The Hercynian Appalachians, for instance, which have not been submitted to any Tertiary folding, show a pronounced structural control; the Pyrenees, in contrast, show it only very incompletely. It appears that a second orogenic period of folding largely destroys the different resistance of the various rock types to erosion.

Structural Geology and Petrology. Petrology and structural geology are often so completely interwoven that it is impossible to say whether one is studying a petrological problem by structural methods or a structural problem by petrological methods. The little we know of the mechanism of the internal deformation of rocks has clearly demonstrated that the texture and structure of the rock determine to a large degree the kind of deformation which will take place under certain stress conditions. If we also take account of the all-important factor of the temperature-rise during deformation, and also of the possible lubricating effect of circulating vapours or liquids of magmatic origin, we have arrived in the midst of the controversial subjects of metamorphism and granitization. Such phenomena are very properly regarded as petrological problems, but they are also extremely important structural problems. The purely structural evidence should be taken into account by the petrologist, and vice versa. We shall see further on that a complete orogenic cycle contains three or four magmatic phases of different character: an initial or geosynclinal ultrabasic phase, a syntectonic leucocratic granite phase, a late tectonic granodioritic phase, and a post-tectonic volcanic phase. Moreover we can distinguish, in addition to orogenic magmatism, a non-orogenic or kratogenic magmatic activity of basaltic character, very similar to the magmatic activity connected with block-faulting of the rift valley type.

As soon as we advance beyond the limits of purely descriptive structural geology, an intimate knowledge of the petrology of both sedimentary and igneous rocks is therefore a prerequisite.

Structural geology has even created its own method of study, the petrofabric technique. This allows us to determine the directions of the principal stresses which have affected a rock by measuring the orientation of recrystallized and original crystals, on the assumption that a systematic rearrangement of the originally random orientation is produced by the stress-field. The results of this method are perhaps not as yet very striking from a tectonic point of view. This is probably because on the one hand the orientation of the stress-field itself is rather variable during a single orogenic phase, and on the other hand because we still know very little about the mechanical and chemical mobility of mineral grains under stress. Structural petrology based on these methods has become a science in itself and will be treated only briefly in this book.

Structural Geology and Economic Geology. The relationship between structural geology and the geology of economic mineral deposits is a matter of degree of "structural control", of how far the distribution of the economic mineral is related to structural features. It is obvious that the disposition of a coal seam, as of any other sedimentary bed, is wholly determined by the structure of the region and by the original lateral extent of the seam. In oil geology a similar relation exists, although the actual oil content of a reservoir rock is a secondary feature determined largely by the permeability of the reservoir. Both oil- and coal-geologists must always employ structural geology in their daily work.

Structural control of bedded sedimentary ores is comparable with that of coal. Alluvial and eluvial ores are only superficially related to structure.

The structural control of magmatic ores, whether of hydrothermal, pneumatolytic or another mode of deposition, is much more complicated. In the first place the magmatic activities which produce the ore are in their turn almost invariably of orogenic origin. Secondly, the host rock may have been prepared to receive the ore by orogenic forces, either by the shattering of the rock or by the creation of minimum stress-, tension-, or fracture-zones where the mineralizing agent could penetrate. In the third place, the fault pattern, which in itself is also an expression of the stress field to which the rock has been submitted, may act in various ways as channels for the ore-bodies. It is frequently found that, in a particular region, some fault directions are sterile whereas others are mineralized, and this is a strong indication that the mineralization occurred more or less simultaneously with the faulting. Recurrent mineralization may show that the faults were also active during several succeeding phases, and in the same sense.

Finally, structural deformation after mineralization may be an important factor for the present distribution of the ore-bodies.

Structural Geology and Geophysics. The science of applied geophysics has been extensively developed as a means of determining hidden structures, and has become an important tool in the hand of the tectonician. The seismic reflection method, for instance, measures strike and dip at depth. Electrical resistivity measurements in boreholes enable detailed correlation from one hole to the next, and thus facilitate determination of the structure. Other methods, such as seismic refraction, and gravity measurements of various kinds, give the broad outline and sometimes also the details of raised and subsided regions of the earth crust and so contribute to our knowledge of its deeper layers. It is no overstatement to say that only since geophysical methods have been employed to explore basins for oil have we obtained positive knowledge of their structure.

Applied geophysics is of great value in the elucidation of structures in the upper crust; in the purely scientific study of the earth's interior, geophysical methods assume an even greater importance. Seismic evidence from earthquakes is almost the only factual evidence we have concerning the mantle and the core. Together with general conclusions from measurements of the earth's gravity and of its magnetic field, it provides the basis for the current theories about the interior, from which all orogenic forces originate.

This brief review of the relationships between structural geology and other earth sciences has shown on the one hand that structural geology leans heavily on information from its brother sciences, and on the other hand that it serves as a basis for many inquiries into the nature of our globe. Since structural geology has developed its own methods of investigation and its own systematic classification of the data with which it is concerned, it has earned the right to be regarded as a full-grown member of the assembly of earth sciences.

OUTLINE OF A CLASSIFICATION OF STRUCTURAL PHENOMENA

Structural geology is concerned with all aspects of the earth's crustal distortion. It is a descriptive science which needs its own systematic classification of rock deformation, i.e. comparative structural geology. Since it also aims to explain how the crust has been distorted, it needs a theoretical and experimental background. This is found in theoretical and experimental structural geology. Finally, it must explain why the earth's crust has been deformed at all, which necessitates an analysis of the distribution and interrelations of structural features all over the earth's crust. This is the concern of the science of geotectonics.

Comparative structural geology is concerned in the first place with the outward shapes of the disturbances, and classifies them into groups as folds and faults with various different characteristics. By observing the distribution and frequency of the separate groups of the classification within structural units of larger size, within basins and mountain chains, for instance, a distinct correlation appears. This leads to the following broad outline of structural regions:

1. Block-faulted regions, where faults separate blocks which have moved in relation to one another, without major disturbance of the unit blocks.

2. Paratectonic regions, where simple inter-related folds occur in relatively large regions, all of them composed of rocks of roughly the same age (folded basins, for instance).

3. Orthotectonic regions, where complicated inter-related structures occur in relatively large regions, subdivided into longitudinal belts of different ages and different structural features (mountain chains).

Block–faulted Regions. Faults bounding the blocks may be either of normal (horst and rift structure) or of wrench-fault type. In both cases the movement of the blocks may have created folds (Saxonic type of folding) but the folds are only secondary features.

Paratectonic Regions contain curved folds, predominantly of concentric type without thickening of the strata in the hinges, accompanied by faulting which is secondary to the folding. Folding is restricted to sedimentary basins and the basin structure is not destroyed by the folding. The absence of important magmatic activity within the region is typical. Folding has been continuously in progress, slowly and gently, with occasional times of greater activity. Detailed analysis of the phases of folding reveals more and more of them, distributed irregularly in time and space and without distinct correlation with the phases in other paratectonic regions. Physiographic expression of the structure is usually a first-order morphology.

Orthotectonic Regions. Mountain chains are distinguished by very intense folding of a characteristic type, usually accompanied by development of cleavage and schistosity. Magmatic phases are an essential part of the orogeny. The original basin is completely destroyed and can be reconstructed only by linking up different sections. The folding, although probably continuous, is chiefly concentrated in a few very large paroxysms which can be correlated in time with similar phases in other orogenies. The orogenies are always built up in longitudinal belts, each characterized by a particular style of deformation.

The physiography is often of the second order, i.e. a subsequent morphogenic phase of uplift rejuvenates the eroded chain.

This subdivision into three different styles of structural regions is far from being absolute; there are all kinds of transitional regions, as, for instance, the marginal troughs of orogenies, which are characterized by paratectonic features although they undoubtedly belong to an orthotectonic unit. Although a later uplift, separated from the last orogenic paroxysmal phase by a period of erosion, is typical of orthotectonic regions, it is by no means restricted to them. Some paratectonic regions show the same kind of morphogenic phase. On the other hand first-order physiographic expression of folds and faults is typical of paratectonic regions. The same is true of very young or still moving orthotectonic regions (islands arcs, for instance). Nevertheless, the broad outline of this classification is not arbitrary. On the contrary it has a fundamental basis, which will be more fully discussed in Part III of this book.

METHODS IN STRUCTURAL GEOLOGY

The study of the distortion of rocks can take several courses. The most common kind of investigation is the study of structural shapes, which leads to a comparison of observed features on the one hand and to a classification into related groups on the other. This comparative structural geology is mostly concerned with external features, and without the help of other methods of approach leads only to superficial conclusions about the origin and development of the structures.

This has led to other methods of approach, first of all the theoretical, which, as a physical science, tries as far as is possible to isolate in the laboratory the various properties of rocks. This is done by reducing the number of factors which are involved in natural deformation in order to get a clearer picture of each of them successively and separately. Such purely theoretical study has not yet been developed and is still completely in the exploratory experimental stage. For instance, the experimental evidence that rock deformation takes place in the elastico-viscous field has nowhere been treated from a theoretical point of view. The present attempt in that direction is therefore necessarily rather tentative and certainly needs considerable amplification.

Secondly, an investigation of much more detailed character has been developed by microscopical study of the preferred orientation of mineral grains in deformed rocks. This technique of structural petrology using petrofabrics as its basis has evolved enormously since 1930, the date of Sander's first treatise on this subject. It still suffers however from the same lack of theoretical and experimental background as does simple comparative tectonics. It has given us a wealth of information but we are very ignorant of the way to use it. The science works with concepts of "flow", "flattening", and "shear" structures, but as the reader will perceive for himself, the exact sense of these words for motions which need thousands of years to develop in solid material under the influence of elastic stresses, is still obscure.

Quite another kind of approach to the understanding of structural shapes is the imitative experiment, which in spite of a lack of theoretical background has blundered into quite surprising results. None the less its limitations are now clearly visible, and we do not believe it can ever bring us much fundamental knowledge.

Finally the most fascinating subject of structural geology, the geotectonical synthesis of all structural knowledge, is at the same time in a certain sense its most unsatisfactory branch, because so many totally unknown and untested properties of the deeper crust, the mantle, and the core of the earth are involved. It is the territory of the most unchecked and flamboyant fantasy, built up by piling hypotheses on theories, shored by very rare and thin reeds of geophysical facts. Even the factual geological data are woefully inadequate for a geotectonic description of our earth's surface and too many immense regions are totally unknown, or only superficially known. Nevertheless it seems useful to marshal those facts which are known, and those which can be directly interpolated from them, into one comprehensive picture. My effort in this direction is contained in Part III; its usefulness perhaps lies principally in bringing out the flimsiness of all present geotectonic concepts, including my own.

Chapter 2

Physical Properties of Rocks

The deformations which a geologist observes at the surface of the earth's crust can either be studied from the point of view of the shapes that have been created by external stresses, or as a problem of internal deformation of rock material. Both points of view pose a physical-mechanical problem but nevertheless differ in their way of approach. The study of rock deformation needs first of all a knowledge of the physical properties of rocks, in relation to deformation. These properties are concerned either with elastic or with plastic deformation or with rupture. We shall see in the course of our investigation that nearly all the deformations in which we are interested lie in a zone between the plastic and elastic fields, and that rupture and plastic deformation can hardly be distinguished from a physical point of view.

Until recently our knowledge about the physical properties of rocks had been inferred principally from experiments performed by civil engineers, and as these people do not construct buildings to last millions of years, and use a large safety-margin anyway, their findings are usually little concerned with the time-factor. Only very recently have laboratory experiments been made from a purely geological point of view. It then soon became apparent that even in relatively short experiments time plays a predominant role. In other words the boundary between the elastic and plastic field has become very ill defined. It is therefore important to study these fields carefully before developing any theories about deformation either of the earth's crust as a whole or of a special layer of it.

ELASTIC PROPERTIES OF ROCKS

An elastic deformation is defined as one which disappears again when the load which caused the deformation has been removed. Ideal elasticity would exist if the deformation on loading and its disappearance on unloading were both instantaneous. This is never quite

18

realized in actual materials, however, since there is always some retardation, known as hysteresis, in the unloading process.

With a purely elastic deformation the strain is a linear function of the stress (Hooke's law), or in the case of a bar of the length l and diameter of 1 cm², stretched by the stress σ acting in the direction of the bar

$$\text{the strain } \varepsilon = \frac{\Delta l}{l} = \frac{\sigma}{E}$$

Δl is the change in length, and E the *elasticity* or *Young's modulus*

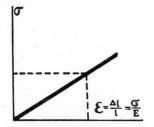

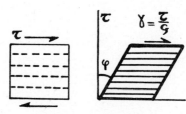

Fig. 6. Elasticity—or Young's modulus. *E*.

Fig. 7. Rigidity, *G*.

a constant for the material of the bar. Since E is a constant, the deformation curve in a stress/strain diagram is a straight line (Fig. 6).

Instead of using a normal stress σ we may use a shearing stress τ. In that case the deformation will be of another type (Fig. 7), known as simple shear. When the deformation is purely elastic we shall have:

$$\gamma = \tan \varphi = \frac{dx}{dy} = \frac{\tau}{G}$$

where G is known as the shear modulus or *rigidity*, which is also a constant for the material.

When a body is subjected to a change of hydrostatic stress, the volume change per unit pressure change is called the *compressibility*:

$$K = \frac{dV}{dP}$$

where V is the volume and P the hydrostatic stress.

These three constants, E, G, and K define the elastic properties of the material but they are not independent of one another. The relation between them may be expressed in terms of the Poisson's ratio (μ), which is the ratio of the lateral contraction to the longitudinal extension in the case of a bar lengthened elastically by a tensile stress.

It must be remembered that in these considerations tensile and compressive stresses differ only in sign. In Fig. 8 the compressive stresses σ_1, σ_2 and σ_3 are taken as variable.

When $\sigma_3 < \sigma_1 = \sigma_2$ the elastic deformation of the body would be a stretching in the direction of σ_3. When $\sigma_3 = \sigma_2 = \sigma_1$ we should consider the stress condition as a hydrostatic (or confining) pressure, and when $\sigma_3 > \sigma_1 = \sigma_2$ we should have an elastic shortening of the cylinder.

The deformative stress which results from a stress condition when $\sigma_3 > \sigma_2 > \sigma_1$ (see Fig. 8) is:

$$\Delta\sigma = \sigma_3 - \frac{\sigma_2 + \sigma_1}{2}$$

or when $\sigma_2 = \sigma_1$

$$\Delta\sigma = \sigma_3 - \sigma_1$$

the sign being positive when the stress is directed towards the specimen, and negative when in the opposite direction. We can now return to the constant of Poisson and the relation between E, G, and K. Experimentally, it has been shown that elastic shortening in one direction is accompanied by an elastic lengthening in both perpendicular directions, or a lengthening of Δl is accompanied by a shortening of $-\mu\Delta l$. The volume after the elastic deformation is then $(1+\Delta)(1-\mu\Delta)^2$, that is, the ratio of the final volume V' to the initial volume is closely equal to

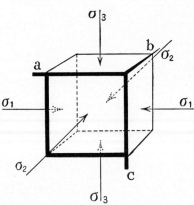

$$\frac{V'}{V} = 1 + (1 - 2\mu)\Delta$$

Fig. 8.   Unit cube in a stress-field.

because Δ is very small. When we consider the edges a, b, and c, of the cube in question (Fig. 8) after elastic deformation under the stress condition of σ_1, σ_2 and σ_3, we shall find that the stress σ_1 has added the following values to a, b, and c:

$$-\frac{\sigma_1}{E}a, \quad +\mu\frac{\sigma_1}{E}b, \quad +\mu\frac{\sigma_1}{E}c$$

and the stress σ_2

$$+\mu\frac{\sigma_2}{E}a, \quad -\frac{\sigma_2}{E}b, \quad +\mu\frac{\sigma_2}{E}c$$

and the stress σ_3

$$+\mu\frac{\sigma_3}{E}a, \quad +\mu\frac{\sigma_3}{E}b, \quad -\frac{\sigma_3}{E}c$$

The change of the length of edge a is the algebraic sum of the change due to each principal stress, or

$$a_1 = a - \frac{\sigma_1 - \mu(\sigma_2 + \sigma_3)}{E} a$$

and

$$b_1 = b - \frac{\sigma_2 - \mu(\sigma_1 + \sigma_3)}{E} b$$

$$c_1 = c - \frac{\sigma_3 - \mu(\sigma_1 + \sigma_2)}{E} c$$

and when $\sigma_1 = \sigma_2 = \sigma_3$

$$a_1 = a \left(1 - \frac{\sigma(1 - 2\mu)}{E}\right)$$

and the volume has become

$$V_1 = a_1 b_1 c_1 = abc \left\{1 - \frac{3(1 - 2\mu)}{E} \sigma\right\}$$

when we neglect the higher powers of the small second term.

The compressibility is therefore

$$K = \frac{3(1 - 2\mu)}{E} \quad \text{or} \quad E = 3 \frac{1 - 2\mu}{K}$$

In a similar way one can derive the relation between the rigidity and the constant of Poisson, the result being:

$$G = \frac{1}{2} \frac{E}{1 + \mu}$$

The four elastic constants — the elasticity modulus E, the compressibility K, the rigidity G, and the constant of Poisson — are not independent of one another: there exist only two independent constants, which we may choose from the four at our disposal. Perhaps the natural choice is to select the compressibility (resistance to change in volume) on the one hand and the rigidity (resistance to change in shape) on the other. From the relation between E, K, and μ it follows that μ must be positive but smaller than 0.5 (otherwise E would become negative, which would mean a shortening by a tensile stress).

Table I gives the constants of some different rocks (after Ide, 1936).

The application of the principles concerning the elastic properties of rocks to tectonic problems has not, as yet, led to any important results. Both Smoluchowski and Vening Meinesz used elasticity equations for the calculation of the necessary stress and the wavelength of a fold concerning the whole earth's crust, and both came to the conclusion that folds of this kind could develop only when the earth's crust was layered. Their numerical values for the physical properties are, however, very uncertain. A question arises as to whether considerations of elasticity can be used in describing deformations of the earth's crust, which obviously have a permanent and therefore plastic character.

Table I

		E		G		
		$P=1$	$P=4000$	$P=1$	$P=4000$	μ
Granite:	Rockport, Mass.	3.54–4.34	8.36	1.71	3.36	.180
	Quincy, Mass.	2.38–6.05	4.49	1.55–2.9	3.45	.045–.124
Diabase:	Vinal Haven	10.20–10.70	11.40	4.17–4.21	4.46	.258–.275
Gneiss:	Hell Gate, N.Y.	–	–	1.64–1.82	3.38	–
Schist:	Chlorite	7.05	–	3.15	4.13	.81
Sandstone:	Quartzitic, Penn.	6.36	9.6	3.24	4.42	.115
Slate:	Everett, Mass.	4.87	–	2.18	2.72	.115
Limestone:	Solenhofen	5.77–6.27	6.3	2.31	2.47	.25
Dolomite:	Penn.	7.1	–	3.23	–	–

E = Young's modulus in 10^{11} dynes. cm^{-2}, G = rigidity in 10^{11} dynes. cm^{-2},
μ = Poisson's ratio
P = Hydrostatic pressure in kg cm^{-2}
From: Handbook of Phys. Constants. Sp. pap. No. 36, 1942. Geol. Soc. of Am

Although on first consideration the answer would seem to be negative, we perceive on second thoughts that a modified application of the laws of elasticity might perhaps be possible, for our experiments on the strain of rock, both elastic and permanent, have shown that the elastic properties of a specimen which has been plastically deformed are not destroyed. We may therefore assume that during the tectonic deformation each unit volume of the rock is partially in a condition of elastic strain, and it may well be that this elastic condition controls the orientation and magnitude of the principal stresses in the rock. In that case each successive minute change of shape is fundamentally an elastic strain which eventually becomes permanent. Hence it would appear that the premises of Vening Meinesz and others were entirely warranted. Vening Meinesz concluded that the force needed to bend the crust is so large that the rocks would have been crushed long before bending, unless the crust were layered — in which case each layer could be considered as an independent elastic sheet.

Because this assumption is obviously very improbable, the theory has been rejected. In Chapter 5 we shall see, however, that an initial very slight bending will spontaneously cause shear-planes parallel to the upper and lower surface, and that the whole thick sheet of the solid crust will become layered in as many layers as the elastic curvature dictates. Hence a bending of the crust with a stress below the crushing strength is certainly possible. Whether the numerical values of strength and other physical properties of rocks which Vening Meinesz and others have adopted in their calculations are trustworthy is, however, very doubtful. In the next chapter we shall learn that it is very difficult to obtain a definite experimental value for the strength of a particular rock, and even in these cases where we get a reasonable answer it is still doubtful whether the results may be applied to conditions in the earth's crust. The hydrostatic pressure in the experiment is given by a fluid under high pressure surrounding the rock specimen; but in nature the rock specimen is surrounded in every direction by more rock which does not yield like a fluid. The elastic properties of rocks are moreover of great importance for seismology, because the propagation of shock waves is a purely elastic phenomenon.

For longitudinal waves we have for the velocity

$$V_{\text{long}} = \sqrt{\frac{1/K + {}^4/_3 G}{D}}$$

and for transverse waves:

$$V_{\text{trans}} = \sqrt{\frac{G}{D}}$$

(D being the density of the rocks). Because transverse shock waves cannot traverse the core of the earth it is assumed that the matter there has no rigidity. Deep-focus earth-quakes prove that rigidity for a shock wave is still present to a depth of 700 km.

RUPTURE, STRENGTH, AND SHEARING

The field of elastic strain of rocks is not unlimited. With a rise of the deformative or differential stress, rocks rupture along certain planes, and under high confining pressure slip-planes develop and shearing takes place along them. Permanent deformation sets in after a certain limit of elasticity has been passed. In the next chapter we shall see that many different kinds of permanent deformation exist, but that all of them are subject to the condition of the internal stress of the rock, which we shall consider later.

The slip-planes which develop in the rock specimen make a certain angle α with the deformative stress P (Fig. 9.) On the plane ab two forces are active, a normal stress σ and a shearing stress τ, which are expressed in terms of P and α by:

$$\sigma = P\,\frac{\sin\alpha}{1/\sin\alpha} = P\sin{}^2\alpha = {}^1/_2\,P\,(1-\cos 2\alpha)$$

$$\tau = P\sin\alpha\cos\alpha = {}^1/_2\,P\sin 2\alpha$$

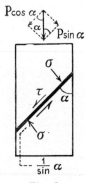

Fig. 9.

Normal stress σ and shearing stress τ on oblique shear-plane.

The shearing stress τ will have a maximum value when $\sin 2\alpha = 1$, that is, when $\alpha = 45°$, and we actually observe in experimental specimens slip-planes which make an angle not far different from 45° with the stress P. Although the shearing force τ may have its maximum value on a 45° plane the resistance of the rock to shearing may not be equal in this plane to that in any other plane; indeed experiments have shown that it varies with the normal stress σ on the plane. Therefore

$$\tau_{\max} = f(\sigma)$$

so that one must investigate the relation between τ and σ on different planes. This has been done by Mohr (1914) in his diagram representing the three principal stresses in their proper relation.

When we consider the plane in which P_1 and P_3 are situated, and measure their values on the abcis to the right of the zero value when

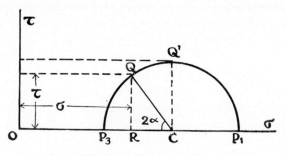

Fig. 10. Mohr circles.

positive and to the left when negative as in Fig. 10, then the normal stress (σ) on a plane which makes an angle α with P_1 is equal to OR and the shearing stress τ is equal to RQ.

This follows since in the figure

$$OC = \frac{P_1 + P_3}{2} \text{ and } CQ = \frac{P_1 - P_3}{2}$$

then

$$OR = OC - CR = \frac{P_1 + P_3}{2} - \frac{P_1 - P_3}{2} \cos 2\alpha = \sigma$$

and

$$RQ = \frac{P_1 - P_3}{2} \sin 2\alpha = \tau$$

When $\alpha = 45°$, Q is situated perpendicularly above C and τ reaches its maximum value. We could have completed the diagram of Mohr by including the intermediate principal stress P_2 as in Fig. 11, which then represents the situation in the three normal planes.

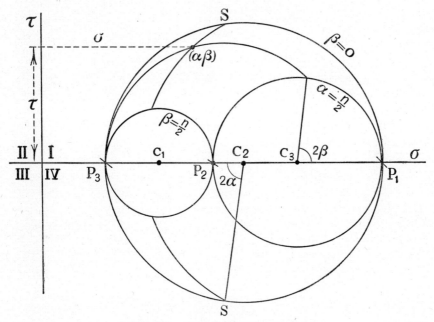

Fig. 11.   Complete Mohr circles.

In this diagram all the poles of planes parallel to P_2 are situated in the outer circle, those of planes parallel to one of the other axes are situated on the appropriate smaller circles, and those on any other

plane in the portion between the main circles. When in Fig. 11 the values
of the three principal stresses approach each other, the circles become
smaller and smaller and when $P_1 = P_2 = P_3$ they have become one point
— under hydrostatic conditions there is no shearing stress and the
normal stress is equal on every plane. The complete diagram of Fig. 11
may be shifted towards the left by subtracting an equal amount from
each principal stress, their differences remaining the same, as in Fig. 12.

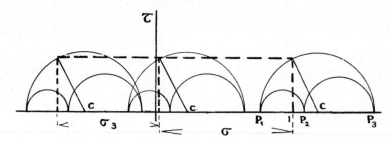

Fig. 12.   Shift of Mohr circles.

The shearing stresses remain unchanged, but the normal stresses differ
appreciably. Hence when the shearing stress at the point of rupture
is dependent on the normal stress on the plane, it then varies with the
absolute values of the largest and smallest principal stresses and their
differences, but is independent of the intermediate principal stress
because $P_1 - P_3$ is always greater than either $P_1 - P_2$ or $P_2 - P_3$. The
relation between the shearing stress and the normal stress on an
arbitrary plane can be represented by

$$\tau_{max} = f(\sigma) = c + \sigma \tan \beta$$

where c is a constant, the threshold value of the shearing strength,
and β the angle of internal friction (Fig. 13). The resistance to shearing
can then be written as:

$$R = c + \left(\frac{P_1 + P_3}{2} - \frac{P_1 - P_3}{2} \cos 2\alpha \right) \tan \beta$$

and the difference between the resistance and shearing stress:

$$R - \tau = \Delta \tau = c + \left(\frac{P_1 + P_3}{2} - \frac{P_1 - P_3}{2} \cos 2\alpha \right) \tan \beta - \frac{P_1 - P_3}{2} \sin 2\alpha$$

On those planes where this difference between the strength and the shear stress becomes minimal the material will rupture, therefore when

$$\frac{d(\Delta\tau)}{d\alpha} = 0 \rightarrow \tan\beta\,(P_1 - P_3)\sin 2\alpha - (P_1 - P_3)\cos 2\alpha = 0$$

or

$$\tan 2\,\alpha = \cot\beta$$

and

$$\alpha = 45° - \frac{\beta}{2} \text{ and } \beta = 90° - 2\alpha$$

According to these considerations the angle between the plane of rupture and the deformative stress will be in general less than 45°.

The shearing plane angle (2α) is dependent on the angle of internal friction (β), a specific property of the material which in itself may vary

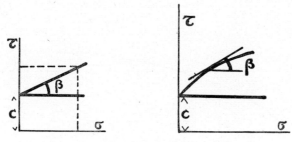

Fig. 13.   Angle of internal friction, β.

with the normal stress. The internal friction is large for sandstones and small for clays; moreover, it increases rapidly with growing confining pressure in sandstones and only little in clays. We can introduce the curve of $\tau_{max} = f(\sigma)$ very easily into Mohr's graphic representation, because both have the shearing stress and the normal stress on the y and x axes (Fig. 14). The largest circle of Mohr can never traverse the

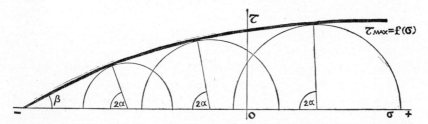

Fig. 14.   Enveloping curve of Mohr circles typical for different rock types.

τ_{max} curve, because there would otherwise be shearing stresses larger than the maximum. The large circles of Mohr will therefore be tangential to the τ_{max} curve and the angle 2α of the tangent point will give the orientation of the shear-plane, as is shown in Fig. 14. In this diagram the value of β is represented by the angle between the x axis and the tangent and is always equal to $90° - 2\alpha$. The τ_{max} curve is always the one which envelops the largest circles of Mohr. So far we have considered only rupture along a shearing-plane due to a compression. A tension stress will cause rupture in the same way. The formulae we have used are not altered when the smallest stress becomes negative, the largest deformative stress still remains $P_3 - (-P_1)$ or $P_3 + P_1$. In Mohr's diagrams a negative value for P_1 means that the P_3/P_1 circle is shifted to the left beyond the zero point of the diagram (Fig. 15). But as the shearing stress needed to cause rupture is decreased with σ, the difference $P_3 - P_1$ also decreases. In other words the largest circle of

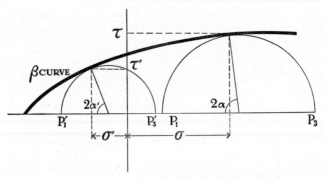

Fig. 15.   Variation of α and β by shift of Mohr circles.

Mohr becomes much smaller when it is shifted towards a negative value of the smallest stress, and while the angle between the largest stress and the shear-plane decreases ($2\alpha > 2\alpha'$ in Fig. 15), the angle of internal friction increases. The larger the angle of internal friction, the more the shearing stress needed for rupture increases with increasing confining pressure. Different materials are therefore characterized by the enveloping β curve (Fig. 16) and the steeper this curve, the more rapidly the difference in shearing strength grows with increasing confining pressure. It follows that the tension strength is smaller than the compression strength. When this difference between tension strength and compression strength for a certain material is large, we call the material brittle, and when the difference is small we call it ductile. With increasing confining pressure the β curve tends to flatten, the shear-plane angle (α) increases, and the difference between ductile and brittle material disappears. Whether the compression strength of rocks is still dependent on the changing confining pressure or not is dependent on where this flattening

SHALE   LIMESTONE   SANDSTONE

Fig. 16. Enveloping curves typical for different rock types.

of the curve sets in, and we may expect that it will be different for various kinds of rocks. As we shall see later, competent (hard or brittle) rocks like sandstone and limestone have a different enveloping curve: the sandstone curve remains steep under increasing confining pressure, whereas that of limestone flattens and clay or shale has always a flat enveloping curve (Fig. 16). In the light of these considerations one can see why brittle materials like rocks under high confining pressure behave as ductile materials, such as copper, under atmospheric pressure. They have not lost their strength and flow does not start under small differential stresses, as Gignoux maintains. Under a differential stress greater than their strength at atmospheric pressure they no longer rupture (in the sense of disintegration), but flow along an infinite number of small shear-planes just as metals do under atmospheric pressure.

When the stress conditions are such that the smallest principal stress is negative, there exists a maximum tension stress in all planes perpendicular to this direction. Instead of rupture along shear-planes the material may be torn asunder along such planes. In that case there is no question of shearing stress, because along that plane the shearing stress is zero; but brittle materials with little internal cohesion may rupture in this way before the stress difference $P_3 - P_1$ has caused a sufficient shearing stress τ along inclined planes. In the light of the foregoing reasoning it is obvious that while tensional rupture plays an important role in near-surface structures, it will not occur at great depth. Tensional cracks are always parallel to the largest principal stress direction.

The strength of a material, as tested in the laboratory, is therefore generally given as three different strengths, the compression strength (K_c), the shearing strength (K_s), and the tension strength (K_t). For rocks under atmospheric pressure the following values are given:

Table II

Rock	K_c in kg/cm^2	K_s in kg/cm^2	K_t in kg/cm^2
Granite	1350	102	48
Sandstone	530	46	27
Limestone	1360	104	64
,,	502	35	15
Dolomite	1300	70	28
,,	790	75	16

The compression strength for these more or less brittle rocks is about thirty times larger than their tension strength.

FLOW OF ROCKS

We have seen that in elastic deformation the strain, γ, is dependent on the rigidity and the shearing stress

$$\tau = \gamma \, G$$

In a viscous fluid, the amount of strain is no longer governed by the rigidity, which is absent but has become a function of time. The strain ratio, D, is now dependent on the shearing stress and the viscosity η

$$\tau = D \, \eta$$

The viscosity is measured in poises: that is to say that when $\tau = 1$ dyne/cm^2, and there is a distance of 1 cm between two surfaces of area 1 cm^2 (which volume is occupied by the viscous fluid), and if the velocity is 1 cm/sec, then the viscosity is 1 poise. The dimension of a viscosity is therefore $[ML^{-1} T^{-1}]$.

The fluids which follow this law of $\tau = D\eta$ are called Newtonian fluids, the relation between D and σ being linear (Fig. 17, curve a). In non-Newtonian fluids the viscosity curve is not straight but curved (Fig. 17, curve b) and is determined by $d\tau/dD$. They have a differential viscosity, which is given at every point by the tangent to the curve. We have assumed that the motion starts at zero, but some viscous materials seem to have a starting point further to the right (Fig. 17, curve c) which means that the fluid (or solid — the distinction is uncertain here) has a certain threshold value below which no viscous flow exists. The threshold value may be called the strength. We might use the presence of a strength as the determining factor between fluids and solids. Many solids do not rupture when loaded above their strength, but start to flow. They have then a stress/strain diagram of the kind of Fig. 18. With increasing the load $\Delta\sigma$, the first part of the strain curve is steep, and then flattens out rather suddenly. The steep part of the curve represents the elastic strain and P the threshold value, the strength; the flat part of the curve the plastic deformation or flow. By unloading the elastic strain (a) is recovered but not the plastic strain (b). Similar curves to these, which are typical of metals, have been obtained with rocks under high confining pressure, as we shall see later. A remarkable feature of these experiments is that although the strength has been surpassed and the material has flowed, it has not lost its elastic properties. It is said that the material has an elastico-viscosity. One might imagine the process as an elastic strain

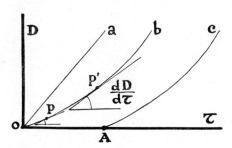

Fig. 17.   Linear a and differential b and c curves of viscosity.

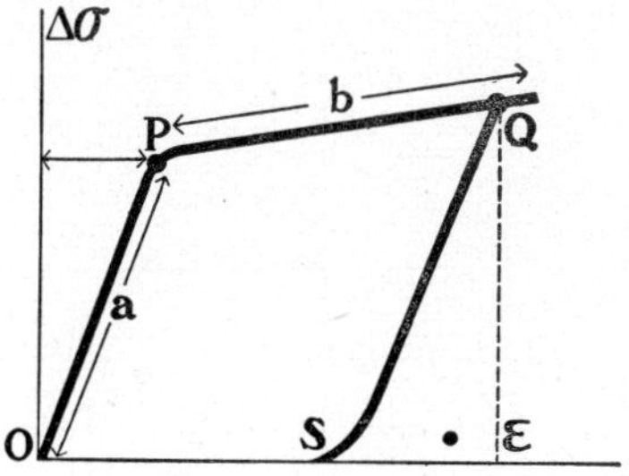

Fig. 18.   Flow of solids in a stress/ strain diagram, with loading and unloading.

which is internally eased by small successive translations of molecules or other small units within the crystal lattice. By such a process of relaxation the elastic strain would disappear after a certain time and be replaced by a permanent strain. By maintaining the load, the double process of elastic strain and relaxation continues and an elastico-viscous flow is the result. This combination of elastic and plastic deformation which we have considered is not the only possible kind of combination. There is a method (Burgers, 1935) which successfully illustrates several varieties of combination: a spiral spring represents an elastic property and a piston in a cylinder represents a plastic flow. The tension of the spring equals αK, when K is the stress and α the elasticity of the spring. The piston will be displaced by the force K with a velocity determined by $dx/dt = \varphi K$ where φ represents the viscous property of the piston cylinder system. In Fig. 19, these two properties are coupled in two different ways, in series and in parallel. In Fig. 19 (a) the total stretch x is the sum of stretch of each element and the force K acts equally on both elements. In Fig. 19 (b) however, the total stretch is equal for both elements. The stretching process can be represented in two

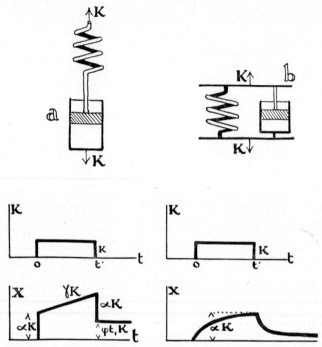

Fig. 19.   Elastic and plastic properties coupled in series a and in parallel connexion b.

diagrams, a strain/time and a force/time diagram, Fig. 19. The corresponding diagrams for the in-series and in-parallel connexions can be found in Fig. 19. In each diagram the force K is active during the time interval t. The strain of the connexion in series starts with an immediate strain of the spring which equals αK, and then begins the slow flow of the piston which equals $\varphi t K$ in the time interval t. On unloading, the strain αK is recovered while the permanent strain remains. This arrangement therefore represents a particular kind of elastic viscosity. When the two elements are coupled in parallel the stretching of the spring is prevented by the slow motion of the piston, and during the motion the force acting on the piston is diminished by the portion absorbed in stretching the spring. Hence the curve is steeper at the start and flattens out to the horizontal. When t is made long enough the total tension equals αK. On unloading, the reverse process takes place. This system represents a strongly retarded elastic strain which is sometimes called elastic flow. The two systems can also be combined in one arrangement. (See Fig. 20 and the accompanying diagrams.) First we notice an immediate strain of $\alpha'K$ in the upper spring, followed by the constant strain velocity of $\varphi_1 K$ per second and by the gradual strain of the spring α_2 retarded by the piston φ_2. The velocity is therefore at the beginning larger than $\varphi_1 K$ and eventually becomes $\varphi_1 K$. On unloading, the permanent strain still equals $\varphi_1 t_1 K$. This combination of pistons and springs gives a picture of the combinations of elastic strain with an elastic-viscous flow, such as we have already described as a typical deformation of ductile materials and rocks under high confining pressure. By adding a new unit representing the strength we should complete the picture. In this way we may illustrate a wide range of possible elastic and plastic behaviour.

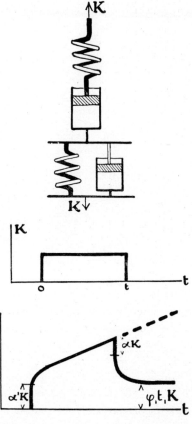

Fig. 20. In series and parallel connexions combined.

We must emphasize, however, that all our deductions from experimental data are extrapolations in time. Neither the absolute value of the strength nor the fact of a constant plastic deformation velocity can be ascertained with enough accuracy in the laboratory. This is due to the fact that the time interval of an experiment, even if it lasts more than a year as has been tried, is too short for the purpose. I shall refer again to this uncertainty when we have examined the experiments themselves.

MECHANICAL PROPERTIES OF UNCONSOLIDATED SEDIMENTS

The physical properties of unconsolidated sediments are rather different from those of ordinary rocks. Since many deformations in surface sediments occur before consolidation, it will certainly be advantageous to understand their peculiarities. During the progress of lithification we might get intermediate stages between soft rock and loose sediments.

The principal difference between unconsolidated sediments and solid rock is that the first are essentially a two-phase aggregate, water and mineral grains. We shall see in the next chapter that the water content of hard rock often plays an important role as well. This is a phenomenon hitherto almost neglected. Nevertheless, it plays a secondary part and not a principal one as it does in loose sediments.

If we consider two sediments, clay and sand, we shall cover more or less the whole range of present-day sediments, since all variations can be classed either with the clays or with the sands, or form a transitional phase. The difference between clays and sands is due principally to two factors: the difference in grain size and the kinds of grain. Sands may be considered as a simple two-phase aggregate of rounded and hard grains resting on one another, with a liquid phase filling the pore space. Clays, on the contrary, have flat, flexible grains surrounded by a water-film and therefore not in contact with each other, the pore space beyond the water-film being also filled with water.

First of all we must give some definition of the terms we shall need in connexion with soils:

1. The ground pressure σ_g at a depth h, is built up from two kinds of pressure, first the weight of the grains, transmitted from grain to grain, σ_K, and the hydrostatic pressure σ_W equal to the weight of a column of water of that height

$$\sigma_g = \sigma_K + \sigma_W$$

2. Colloquially, we distinguish, with increasing average grain size, the following categories:

ultra-clay, clay, loam, silt, sand, coarse sand, pebbles. These names do not of course give us sufficiently detailed knowledge even when exact limits in grain size diameter are allotted to each term, since most sediments contain grains of many different sizes. A much better definition

is obtained by a grain size frequency-diagram of the kind represented
by Fig. 21, where the grain size is noted along the abscissae, using a

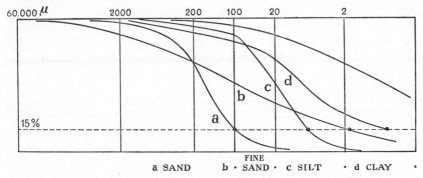

Fig. 21. Grain size frequency-diagram for different soils.

logarithmic scale, and the weight percentage of the grains belonging
to each interval along the ordinates.

A well-sorted sediment such as dune sand (sorted by wind and water),
curve a, or loess (sorted by wind), curve c, has S-shaped curves, the
steep part of the curve indicating its most frequent grain size interval;
and badly sorted sediments, like glacial drift, have a nearly straight
flat curve, curve b.

3. Another important property is the total grain surface, which
increases with decreasing grain size. The *specific* grain surface, U, is
the ratio between the total grain surface of a unit weight of grains and
the surface of a sphere of the same weight. U is therefore always
greater than unity. This specific grain surface can be calculated directly
from the frequency curves of Fig. 21.

Specific grain surfaces of some typical sands are given below:

Table III

Sediment	Specific grain surface
very coarse sand	< 40
coarse sand	$40 - 67$
sand	$67 - 133$
fine sand	$133 - 160$
very fine sand	$160 - 200$
extremely fine sand	> 200

Porosity of Sand and Clays. The character of a sand or clay is not completely defined by its grain size frequency-diagram. The kind of packing of the grains is equally important, and is different for clays and sand. In sand, hard and more or less spherical grains touch each other, whereas in clay the grains are often thin flexible slivers which are separated by water-films. This, more than the actual grain size, is responsible for the great differences in physical behaviour between sands and clays. The structure of sand can be considered to a first approximation as a packing of spheres of the same size. The packing can vary from the loosest form, in which each grain is situated at the corner of a cube, to the densest form, in which the grains are situated at the corners of a tetrahedron, when the porosity varies from about $47\frac{1}{2}\%$ to 26% respectively of the total volume. But since the diameters and shapes of the grains are very variable, these extreme cases are not encountered in nature. We can better describe the packing of grains as:

1. Dense packing of grains touching each other
2. Loose   ,,   ,,   ,,   ,,   ,,
3. Honeycomb texture
4. Flake texture

In the first two subdivisions each grain is a structural unit, in the second two a group of grains is the structural unit. In the honeycomb texture a large pore is surrounded by a group of grains, and in the flake structure the walls of a large pore are built up by a honeycomb texture of small grains. The honeycomb and flake textures can exist only in superficial clays and silts and they cannot stand up to any large load of covering sediments. Nevertheless, in sandstones which are loosely or even densely packed, we find large pores whose walls are formed by many grains. The pore-volume of sands is determined to a very large extent by the manner of sedimentation and it cannot be changed appreciably by subsequent loading. Loose packing may be expected when large volumes of sand are rapidly deposited in water or in wind-blown sand on the surface. Deposition of moist sand in large volumes on the surface invariably results in very loose packing. When on the contrary the sand is laid down gradually in water, as in the ordinary natural process of sedimentation, a dense packing is obtained. Once the sand is deposited as sediment the packing cannot be altered by simple pressure; it remains virtually incompressible. A sand with a wide range in its grain size can clearly attain a much more dense packing than a sand of more uniform grain size.

In order to decide whether a sand has a dense or loose packing one has to determine both its maximum pore-volume n_0 when deposited in a moist state, and also its minimum pore-volume n_{min} when slowly laid down and allowed to settle. The relative density of the sand then follows from a comparison between its actual pore-volume n and its n_0 and n_{min} values. The void ratio is the volume relation between pores and grains:

$$E_n = \frac{n}{1-n}$$

the relative density of the sand is then:

$$D = \frac{E_0 - E_n}{E_0 - E_{min}} \text{ or } \frac{(n_0 - n)(1 - n_{min})}{(n_0 - n_{min})(1 - n)}$$

When we apply a shearing stress to an uncemented sand-layer under normal stress σ, we find in the case of loosely packed sand that a volume decrease occurs when strain takes place; but in the case of densely packed sand we obtain volume increase (Fig. 22).

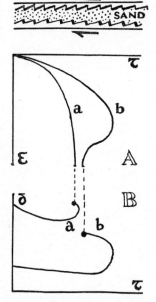

The curve a in Fig. 22 A shows that in the case of the loosely packed sand we need a steady increase of the shearing stress to reach equilibrium with the volume and shearing stress constant. This increase of τ is due to the fact that a small initial movement causes the grains to settle more compactly and therefore an increased deformative stress is necessary (compare curve a in Fig. 22 A). A densely packed sand must first undergo a little loosening, and the shearing stress therefore necessarily increases beyond the equilibrium value. At the same time the density decreases (curve b in Fig. 22 A). Both loose and dense sands reach a constant strain velocity with roughly the same density, and require the same shearing stress after this density has been obtained. This value is called the critical density D_k (Fig. 23). It lies between

Fig. 22. Shearing stress/ strain diagram for loosely and densely packed sand. *(After Keverling Buisman, Grondmechanica, Delft, 1940.)*

D_0 and D_{min}, and is associated with a certain void ratio E_K where

$$E_m < E_K < 0$$

The critical density depends to some extent on the normal pressure σ.

When a loosely packed sand-mass $(D < D_K)$ with water-filled pores is subjected to a shearing stress, the sand will tend to settle in a denser state, but to accomplish this it must get of rid of a certain volume of water. When the water cannot escape immediately the hydrostatic pressure increases and the grain pressure has necessarily to decrease by the same amount. Because of this drop in the grain pressure the sand enters the zone of the critical density (compare Fig. 23, where

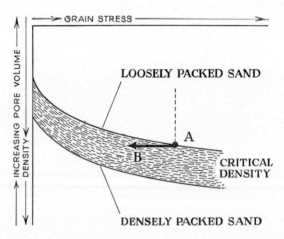

Fig. 23. Critical density field between loosely and densely packed sand.

A moves towards B), where a lower shearing stress suffices for deformation. With the original shearing stress, a lower normal grain stress, and a higher hydrostatic pressure, the motion already started accelerates and sometimes attains catastrophic proportions. There are many examples of such happenings in loosely packed sediments even on a very slight slope — landslides for instance. With a densely packed sand this danger does not exist. The action of a shear stress tends to increase the pore-volume thereby causing a decrease in hydrostatic pressure and an increase in grain pressure. Hence the shearing stress must further increase to make continued movement possible.

The porosity of clay can be much greater than that of sand; this is principally due to the fact that its sliver-like grains do not touch but are surrounded by a water-film.

An increase of the grain pressure σ_K naturally causes an increase of the resistance to shear. In experiments with increasing σ_K we get diagrams like Fig. 24, where

$$S = h + \sigma_K \tan \phi$$

ϕ is the angle of internal friction and has a value varying from $15°$–$32°$. h is the cohesion of the clay, but σ_K is in fact a combination

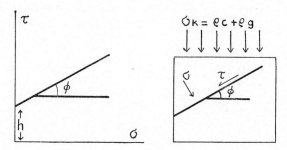

Fig. 24.   Shearing and normal stress on oblique-shear plane.

of two stresses, the capillary tension (ϱ_c is the pore water pressure) and the load ϱ_g; hence:

$$S = h + (\varrho_g + \varrho_c) \tan \phi$$

The same reasoning which we followed in the case of hard rocks can be applied here. The minimum difference between the shearing stress and the resistance to shear will be reached in a plane which makes an angle $\alpha = 45° - \phi/2$ with the largest principal stress. When $\phi = 30°$ α will also equal $30°$.

Most of the intergranular motion in clays is restricted to the films round the grains, the so-called "tough" water. The transition from the "tough" water to the free water of the pore space is gradual. The distance from grain to grain in a typical clay is of the order of 300 Å, and the closer the grain surface is approached the "tougher" becomes the water. It is this "tough" water that gives clays their plasticity. When too much water is added to a clay it starts to flow, too little, and it will break when kneaded. The difference of the volume percentages

of the water which determine these upper and lower limits of the clay
sediments is called its plasticity index.

Table IV

	upper limit or liquid limit	lower limit or plastic limit	plasticity index
fat clay	65.4	27.6	37.8
lean clay	51.7	24.6	27.1
loam	23.3	14.1	9.2
loess	30.4	24.9	5.5

It is obvious that clays, which may contain as much as 80% of
water and in which the grains do not touch, are much more susceptible
to compression than sands. But the compressibility is again a function
of the rate at which the water is disposed of, and therefore of the permeability, which in clays is small. The change in the grain pressure in a
clay after a load has been added is therefore to a large extent dependent
on the time that has elapsed since loading.

The compaction of clay has been studied in great detail by civil
engineers and architects, because building on a clay soil is equivalent
to loading the clay with the weight of the building, and will always
result in compression of the clay. The experimental data are, therefore,
numerous, and observations of settlement over time intervals of tens
and hundreds of years are sometimes available. There is no essential
difference, moreover, between loading with a large building and loading
with more sediments, and so the results of investigations in soil
mechanics are directly applicable to problems of sedimentation. It has
been ascertained that we must make a distinction between two kinds
of compaction:

1. Direct compaction (or primary consolidation)
2. Secular compaction (or secondary consolidation)

The direct compaction is due to the escape of the free water, and the
secular compaction is due to the slow pressing out of the "tough" water.
Both processes are hindered by the low and decreasing permeability
of the clay.

When a clay is loaded with a weight of Pgr/cm^2 the ground pressure at
a depth h will be increased by the same amount. This additional pressure
is initially caused by the pore water (which sets up a hydrodynamic
pressure) rather than by the intergranular pressure. By the gradual
escape of water the load p is slowly transferred from the water to the
grain skeleton; Fig. 25 demonstrates this process. The grain pressure is

hatched, the hydrodynamic pressure is left unhatched. The time t_0 is taken at the moment when, at the depth h, the grain pressure starts

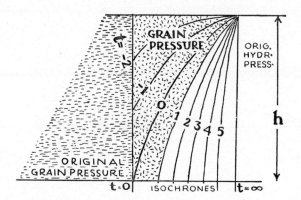

Fig. 25.   Development of 'hydrostatic and grain pressure by loading.   *(After Keverling Buisman, Grondmechanica, Delft, 1940.)*

to increase. The isochrones 1, 2, etc., illustrate the distribution of the ground pressure between the grain and hydrodynamic pressure at the time t_1, t_2 etc. Similarly the isochrones -1, -2, show their distribution before the moment t_0. Complete settling will be reached only after $t = \infty$. The degree of compaction at a particular moment is dependent on both the compressibility and the permeability.

However, it has been demonstrated that after this so called direct compaction, a stable condition has still not been reached. In the compaction diagram of Fig. 26, we do not get the curve a, as should follow from the above mentioned considerations, but the curve b.

It has been proved that after this direct adaptation of the clay to the new load, retarded by the low permeability, the compaction continues, although more slowly. This secular compaction is probably due to the

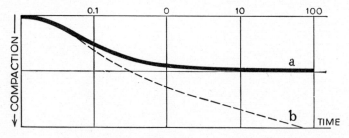

Fig. 26.   Direct a and secular b compaction curves by loading of clay sediment.

pressing out of the "tough" water and is a logarithmic function of the time. The specific secular compaction, of a clay a_S, is the compaction

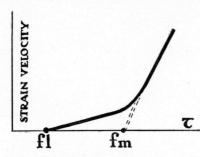

Fig. 27.   Viscosity curve for clay.

per kg/cm² per cm thickness of the clay in the time intervals of 1–10, 10–100, 100–1000 days etc. It varies from 1 to 5%. With a value of $a_s = 3\%$ and a direct settling of 10%, a clay with 30% water would be compressed 25% in three centuries per kg/cm² load. A layer 10 cm thick would be reduced to 7.5 cm. The experiments have always been executed with small loads; there is little doubt that the compaction does not increase linearly with increasing loads, but little is known about this relation.

I shall return to compressibility from the point of view of elastic and permanent deformation when we consider other experiments later, but there is no doubt that a small part of the compaction is elastic.

In experiments on plastic deformation of clay it has been proved that the strain of clay follows the so-called Binghamrmula:

$$D = \frac{1}{\eta}\,(\sigma - \gamma)$$

(and Fig. 27). The viscosity η has a linear relation with the water content, and f_m, the strength, increases with a lower water percentage.

Table V

% of water in clay	η in poises
50.5	0.31
52	0.23
55.5	0.20
55.6	0.16

Beneath the strength there exists a differential viscosity, again with a lower limit (fl in Fig. 27). The threshold value f_m for clay with 50% water lies somewhere between 10 and 15. 10^2 dynes cm⁻².

The experiments with clay give us valuable insight into its behaviour in tectonic processes. Its capacity for flowing under increasing load, explains many features of gliding – and diapiric – tectonics.

Chapter 3

Strain of Rocks in Laboratory Experiments

After the principle of oblique shearing due to a normal stress had been established by Napier (Hartmann), and had been introduced into geology by the experiments of Daubrée (1879), the matter rested there for a long time.

Bucher (1921) applied the principal again and explained joint-systems with it, while Mead (1920) made some very clear experiments in which the relation between folding and faulting direction are admirably expressed; but no fundamentally new material was adduced. Mohr (1914), Anderson (1951), and many others, have pointed out that besides the shearing stress the normal stress on the shearing-plane plays an important role; Anderson and Jeffreys (1936) moreover, drew attention to the fact that a fault is not only a static problem but also a dynamic one, and that the stress conditions are therefore necessarily altered after the birth of a fault (or fold).

Little has been done to apply these shearing principles to folds, apart from the application to a particular fold by H. Cloos (1948).

In the meantime the elastic and plastic behaviour of rock material under stress has been extensively studied by many investigators, among whom special mention should be made of Griggs (1936, 1939) and Goguel (1943).

Thus we see that ever since the beginning of this century laboratory experiments have been made on the behaviour of rock specimens under varying stress conditions. All of them have some bearing on tectonic processes of rock deformation and most of them have been performed with this problem in view.

The imperfection of our knowledge of the mechanism of rock deformation has also been demonstrated by them all. We are at present, nevertheless, in a position to put forward, tentatively at least, a few fundamental properties for several varieties of rock under stress.

The earlier experiments on rock deformation were always performed with a growing stress under high confining pressure. Some of the

43

specimens were wetted, but most of them were dry; sometimes they were jacketed, sometimes they were in direct contact with the high pressure fluid. The results were plotted in a stress/strain diagram and certain features of the curves obtained were regarded as representing fundamental physical properties of the rocks in question. However, as soon as the time element was introduced, it became clear that the rate of increase of stress had an important influence on the measured results, and the earlier type of experiments with a growing stress therefore became valueless as a means of measuring fundamental physical properties in rocks.

This means, unfortunately, that in order to measure one physical property, such as the elasticity limit under a certain pressure, one has to perform a whole series of experiments, each lasting at least a week, instead of one experiment taking a few hours. I do not think that there is any way of overcoming this obstacle to a thorough investigation of rock behaviour under stress.

In addition to that difficulty, to which I shall refer again later, it has become clear that we must not only distinguish between elastic and plastic yield to stress, but must also recognize that there are several modes of both plastic and elastic yield, and even transitory phases where the deformation is both plastic and elastic.

To complicate an already involved matter, the behaviour of rock specimens which are wet is quite different from that of dry ones, and their final rupture may be due to quite different processes, so that even the notion of strength has to be revised.

ELASTIC AND PLASTIC FLOW

In order to be able to discuss these complicated matters we must first define the terms we shall use. Fundamentally, an elastic yield is characterized by complete recovery after unloading. Since hardly any elastic yield is instantaneous but always shows retardation, the recovery is never immediate and one must wait a considerable time after unloading to observe whether any of the deformation is permanent or not. The retardation of recovery is called the hysteresis. When retardation and hysteresis are large it becomes difficult to distinguish between elastic and permanent deformation, but the final criterion is undoubtedly that an elastic strain is related only to the stress, whereas a permanent strain is also related to the time the stress is applied. Therefore in a strain experiment with a constant load, the elastic deformation is characterized by a gradual decrease of the strain velocity leading to a standstill of the process, whilst a permanent (or plastic) deformation goes on indefinitely with a constant strain velocity (Fig. 28).

In curve *A* the strain becomes zero after a certain time, in *B* the strain continues and reaches a constant angle, a constant strain velocity. With higher stresses, curves like *C* have been obtained, in which, after a certain period of constant strain velocity, an increase which eventually resulted in rupture was observed.

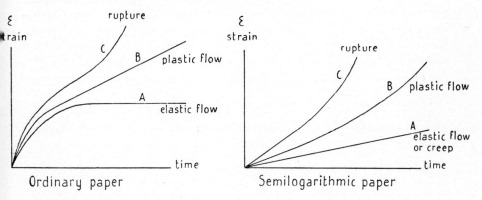

Fig. 28.   Strain/time curves of elastic *A* and plastic *B* deformation, and rupture *C* of a rock specimen by constant load on ordinary and on semilogarithmic paper.

Because the plastic yielding is always accompanied by a permanent rearrangement of particles of the rock, whereas elastic yield means only a temporary rearrangement, the limit between the two modes of deformation is essentially a limit between a non-impaired and an impaired rock and might therefore be called the "strength". I prefer however the term of *elasticity limit* as a less ambiguous term.

Above the elasticity limit, in the plastic field, we must still recognize two different modes of deformation. It is probable that in the lower reaches of the plastic field the elastic properties are not yet lost; the flow is plastic in the sense that the deformation has a permanent character, but elastic in the sense that by release an elastic rebound of the same size as the original elastic strain takes place. This is the elastico-viscous field. Above a certain limit, however, this elastic property may be lost altogether: we are in the truly plastic field. The limit between the two fields might be called the *plasticity limit*. The

field above the plastic field is the fracture field and its lower limit
might be called the *rupture limit*.

Hence when we make a series of experiments under non-variable
conditions of (1) kind of rock (2) environment (3) confining pressure,
and (4) constant stress, our definitions of these terms become as
follows: an *elastic flow* or *creep* is characterized by the fact that the
strain velocity becomes zero (on semilogarithmic paper the curve
becomes a straight line), whereas *plastic flow* or *flow* is characterized
by a constant strain velocity, both after an initial stage of decreasing
strain. Within the field of plastic flow we shall have to distinguish a
lower field where the elastic stress is still an important factor: the
field of elastico-viscous flow, and a higher field where it is of little or
no importance: the field of plastic flow. We shall see that most folding
processes take place in the elastico-viscous flow-field.

The elastic limit is the highest stress with which a zero strain
velocity can be maintained after an initial elastic flow. Rupture
indicates distintegration of the specimen. It occurs above the rupture
limit of stress and is initiated in the experiments by an increasing
strain velocity. The different fields and their limits are schematically
shown in Fig. 29.

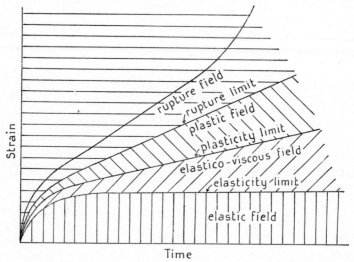

Fig. 29.   Schematic strain/time diagram showing different fields of deformation.

STRENGTH

Originally, the strength of a material was defined as the load under which the material cracked and disintegrated. This definition had been borrowed from the engineers concerned with testing building material. The experimental definition of strength was determined by increasing the load (or the tensile stress) and observing the point at which the first crack appeared. In this way a "crushing-strength" and a "tensile strength" were determined.

It is obvious that such criteria cannot be applied to a piece of rock which is completely surrounded by other rock at depth in the earth's crust. Even when its crushing strength is surpassed, nothing may happen because there is no space around it to be occupied by the crushed rock fragments. Even in a geological experiment where the rock specimen is surrounded by a fluid under high pressure, the circumstances are not quite comparable to those inside the earth's crust. Both Griggs (1936) and Goguel (1943) soon found that the specimen ought first of all to be surrounded by an impermeable jacket of rubber or copper, otherwise the fluid penetrates into the rock specimen and explodes it.

A much better criterion of strength is given by the shape of the strain/time curve. When the velocity of strain increases in the plastic field instead of remaining constant, the inevitable result is that the specimen will finally rupture, as in the curve *C* of Fig. 28.

On the other hand we shall see later that a very common mode of plastic flow is due to intergranular slip-planes, which also certainly represent a kind of rupture. The concept of strength therefore loses much of its interest as a limit between two modes of deformation, and has nothing at all to do with a limit between folding and faulting as has sometimes been suggested. The limit between elastic and plastic flow, commonly called the elasticity limit, may be the passage from elastic flow to intergranular slip; but it might just as well be the passage from intracrystalline to intergranular slip. It seems better to avoid the term strength altogether, and to distinguish only between elastic, elastico-viscous, and plastic flow and rupture. Rate of strain and viscosity of rocks will be considered after we have examined the results of certain relevant experiments.

THE TIME FACTOR INTRODUCED INTO THE EXPERIMENTS

In the classic experiments performed by Adams (1901, 1912) von Kármán (1911), Böker (1915), and later by Griggs (1936), a rock specimen under varying confining pressures was submitted to an

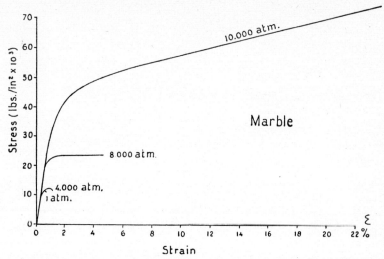

Fig. 30.   Stress/strain diagram of a series of experiments on marble with increasing confining pressure.   *(By Griggs.   Reproduced from Griggs, Deformation of Rocks under High Confining Pressures, Journal of Geology, vol. 44, 1936, by permission of the University of Chicago Press.)*

increasing stress; the moment when the initial small elastic strain changed into a larger plastic strain was found by constructing stress/strain diagrams (Fig. 30).

Invariably the experimenter had to raise the confining pressure to a certain limit to prevent rupture, this adjustment causing a higher

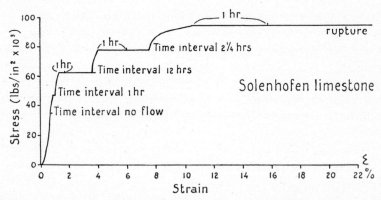

Fig. 31.   Stress/strain diagram of experiment on Solenhofen limestone with pauses in increase of stress.   *(By Griggs.   Reproduced from Griggs, Deformation of Rocks under High Confining Pressures, Journal of Geology, vol. 44, 1936, by permission of the University of Chicago Press.)*

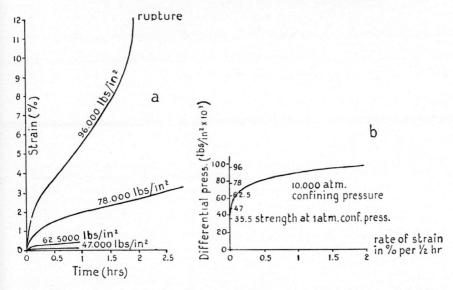

Fig. 32. *a* strain/time diagram and *b* stress/rate of strain diagram derived from Fig. 30.

yield point. This yield point was called the elasticity limit. However, when Griggs repeated an experiment with limestone but introduced pauses in the rise of the stress, he found that during these pauses, and long before the original elasticity-limit was reached, small permanent deformations took place (Fig. 31). Evidently this gradual flow had been masked in the earlier experiment by the rapid increase of stress and its elastic strain. This experiment clearly showed that the rate of strain became greater for each successive pause at a higher stress level. From the stress/strain curve given by this experiment a strain/time curve and a stress/strain velocity diagram (Fig. 32) can be derived. Fig. 32 shows that with stresses of 47,000, 62,500 and 78,000 lbs/in², a constant velocity was attained and that the highest stress of 96,000 lbs/in² led to rupture. The stress/rate of the strain curve shows that the relation between stress and strain velocity is not a straight line but is governed by a differential viscosity, where the viscosity increases when the stress diminishes. The velocity curve apparently reaches a zero value at approximately the rupture point of 1 atm. confining pressure; but the experiment was obviously not sufficiently detailed, the earlier pauses being too short, to be sure about this point. Neither does the viscosity curve tell us much about the velocity of strain and the viscosity at higher levels of stress, the duration of the pauses being too short and the increments in stress being too large. It aeppars probable however that the curve will eventually become a straight line with a small constant angle, or in other words, that above a certain stress the viscosity will no longer be of a differential character.

The field where the viscosity is still differential is no doubt the field of elastico-viscous deformation, where both elastic and plastic deformation are active, in the sense that Burgers (1935) gave to it, i.e. an elastic strain which is taken over by atom or molecule translations and thus eventually transformed into a permanent deformation. We may expect that the elastic deformation is no longer possible above a certain stress limit, and all deformation is directly of a permanent or plastic character, characterized by a constant viscosity. This field where the strain velocity curve has become a straight line, can be termed the plastic field, and its lower limit the plasticity limit (see Fig. 29).

MODES OF DEFORMATION

Even the first series of experiments, those of Adams and Nicholson in 1901, showed that there are two quite different ways in which limestone yields to stress, one by *intergranular* slip-planes with shattering of the crystal edges along those planes, and the other an *intracrystalline* failure, the calcite crystals showing intensive poly-synthetic twinning. They found that intergranular motion prevailed in quick-loading experiments, whereas a very slow increase of load facilitated the twinning mechanism, particularly in the presence of water. Later on von Kármán (1911) showed that low confining pressure favoured intergranular motion and high confining pressure intra-crystalline slip. These results were confirmed by Griggs in 1938 when he showed that a single calcite crystal showed much less strain than either limestone or marble under the same conditions of rather rapid loading under high confining pressure. Apparently under these condi-tions much of the yield in limestone had an intergranular character, whereas the calcite crystal showed only twinning and translation alono intracrystalline slip-planes.

Intergranular slip is a kind of rupture under a confining pressure which is such that recementation along the slip-planes can take place. When once the internal cohesion between the grains has been exceeded by the shearing stress along the planes of maximum shear, the process can continue almost indefinitely as far as the circumstances of the experiment (the length of specimen, the size of pressure chamber, etc.) permit. One will no doubt obtain a certain constant strain velocity for a constant load; this might, however, be modified by rounding off the grain edges and other similar happenings. The process of intergranular slip will be a plastic flow, often followed by rupture of the specimen.

The intracrystalline movement has quite another character. We might expect two different modes of slip, namely *twinning* and *translation*.

Once a polysynthetic twinning plane has been formed the movement on this plane has reached its end. The whole process consists of small incremental movements on successive planes which become more and more unfavourably situated, and it therefore has a definite limit. In this case the strain/time curve should become horizontal. Therefore, although the polysynthetic twinning is certainly a permanent deformation, the movement will still have the characteristics of elastic flow, as was demonstrated by Griggs' 1938 experiment on a single calcite crystal.

Translations on crystal planes, on the contrary, may be infinite. The atoms jump successively from one position of equilibrium to another, and there is no reason why the motion should stop as long as the load remains. The strain/time curve will reach a constant velocity typical of plastic or elastico-viscous flow.

In crystal aggregates with random orientation of the crystals, another factor will become apparent. When the load is applied, the first planes along which either twinning or translation will take place will be those most favourably orientated in relation to the stress direction. Afterwards, even those with a less favourable orientation will successively become involved, but a certain limit will be reached depending on the stress. A higher load will create more slip-planes. The strain/time curves for experiments on single crystals and on crystal aggregates, and even those on aggregates of large and of small crystals, must therefore differ, even when there is only intracrystalline motion.

In addition to the intracrystalline and intergranular motion, it has been demonstrated that *solution* and *recrystallization* on intergranular slip-planes are an important factor in the deformation of soluble substances such as gypsum and salt, and probably limestone as well. Griggs (1940) performed experiments using alabaster with a load of $205/cm^2$, first in a dry state, later in water, and finally in a HCl solution

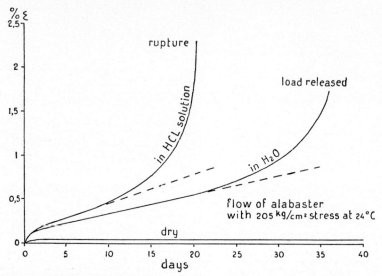

Fig. 33. Strain/time diagram of experiment on alabaster, wetted specimen, with 205 kg/cm² stress at 1 atm. confining pressure. *(After Griggs, 1940. Published by permission of the Geological Society of America.)*

(Fig. 33). The dry specimen very soon reached its maximum strain; whereas with the water-jacketed specimen the rate of strain, which after the first few days had been constant, accelerated again after twenty days and 0.6% strain. The HCl solution favoured an even more rapid strain, 0.5% in ten days, after which a quick acceleration leading to rupture took place. Solution evidently occurs on slip-planes by the heat developed by the shearing stress. When this stress is raised, solution increases and recrystallization may not be able to keep up with the solution. As a result, the strain velocity increases and rupture follows. The minimum stress under which solution and recrystallization occur, will be when the two processes are exactly balanced, and a constant strain velocity will then develop. This is demonstrated by a series of experiments by Griggs (1940) on water-jacketed alabaster specimens with loads increasing from 100 kg/cm² to 300 kg/cm²; and also by one experiment lasting 550 days with a load of 103 kg/cm², in which a constant strain velocity of $7 \times 10^{-6}\%$ per day at 1 atm. was determined (Fig. 34).

Griggs (1940) showed that even quartz in suitable circumstances (solution, temperature, etc.) could be made to flow.

Systematic experiments with wetted specimens have never been made. It seems probable however that in some instances the solution-and-

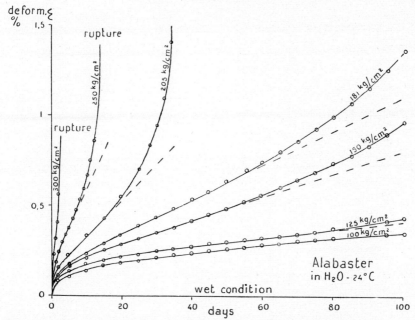

Fig. 34. Strain/time diagram of experiments on alabaster, wetted specimen, with varying load at 1 atm. confining pressure, plastic flow and rupture. *(After Griggs, 1940. Published by permission of the Geological Society of America.)*

recrystallization type of strain becomes a factor of some importance. Goguel (1943), for instance, demonstrated that a gypsum aggregate specimen showed irregular motion along 45% slip-planes, which were recemented during the experiment. The experiment was made with a confining pressure increasing from 100–500 kg/cm², and a stress above 500 kg/cm² for the plastic flow experiment (Fig. 35).

Griggs (1939) completed his original series of deformation experiments on Solenhofen limestone with one on a wetted specimen. First he made

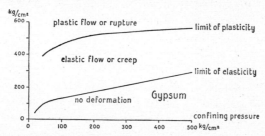

Fig. 35. Stress/confining pressure diagram of stress experiments on gypsum. *(After Goguel. Published by permission of Service de la Carte Géologique.)*

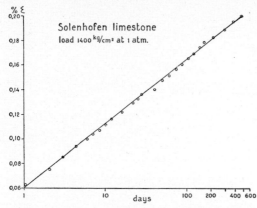

Fig. 36.   Strain/time diagram of stress experiment on Solenhofen limestone, load 1400 kg/cm², confining pressure 1 atm.   *(After Griggs, Creep of Rocks, Journal of Geology, vol. 47, 1939. Published by permission of the University of Chicago Press.)*

an experiment lasting 550 days on a dry specimen with a constant stress of 1,400 kg/cm² and no extra confining pressure. He obtained a perfect elastic flow for the whole of the 550 days (Fig. 36).

He then subjected the same Solenhofen limestone, which showed intense twinning on the $(10\bar{1}2)$ plane when shortened under 10,000 atm. pressure in dry condition, to a stress of 1,500 kg/cm² (as compared to 8,100 kg/cm² in a former experiment) and the same confining pressure of 10,000 atm. This caused only very slight development of twinning with a 40% shortening.

Another experiment by Griggs on a single calcite crystal showed a plastic flow (load 62 kg/cm² at a 1 atm. pressure for fifty days), so that either translation or solution evidently took place (Fig. 37).

There is still another kind of deformation which has to be taken into account, namely compression. Goguel (1943) made several experiments in which the strain was undoubtedly mostly due to simple compression, that is to the elimination of the pores. He even demonstrated that sedimentary rocks not previously subjected to tectonic stress showed a much greater compressibility than those taken from a folded region.

Compression is always a finite motion, and will therefore always show a strain/time curve of the character of an elastic flow, even

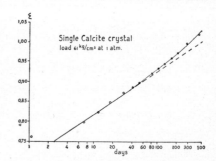

Fig. 37.   Strain/time diagram on single calcite crystal load 61 kg/cm² at 1 atm. confining pressure by Griggs. Elastico-viscous flow by twinning. *(After Griggs, Creep of Rocks, Journal of Geology, vol. 47, 1939.   Published by permission of the University of Chicago Press.)*

when the process in itself is plastic. Goguel (1943) made an experiment on a soft homogenous Miocene marl which showed such a curve (Fig. 38).

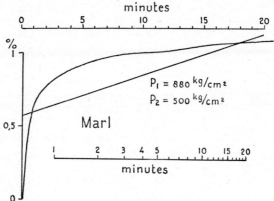

Fig. 38. Strain/time diagram of experiment on marl, with a load of 380 kg/cm² and 500 kg/cm² confining pressure. (*After Goguel. Published by permission of Service de la Carte Géologique.*)

The strain was mostly due to the confining pressure which equalled 500 kg/cm². An Eocene limestone experiment by the same author showed the transition from compression to shear. Up to about 12% the strain was chiefly due to compression. After that critical value had

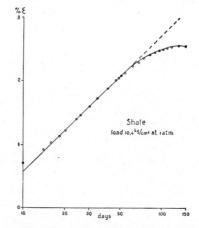

Fig. 39. Strain/time diagram of experiment on an Eocene marly limestone. (*After Goguel. Published by permission of Service de la Carte Géologique.*)

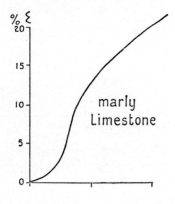

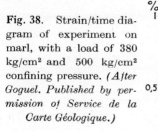

Fig. 40. Strain/time diagram of experiment on Conchas shale, load 10.4 kg/cm², confining pressure 1 atm. showing compression only. (*After Griggs. Creep of Rocks. Journal of Geology, vol. 47, 1939. Published by permission of the University of Chicago Press.*)

been passed owing to a higher load, slip-planes were formed and finally resulted in rupture (Fig. 39).

Griggs performed an experiment on mudstone in which the limit of compressibility was reached with a $2^1/_2\%$ strain for 144 days. Up to about 2% strain the specimen showed a logarithmic elastic flow curve but then slowed down very rapidly to zero between $2^1/_4$ and $2^1/_2\%$ strain (Fig. 40).

THE INFLUENCE OF THE CONFINING PRESSURE

Although it is very difficult to get comparable data on experiments under high, low. or no confining pressure, some pertinent conclusions can still be made.

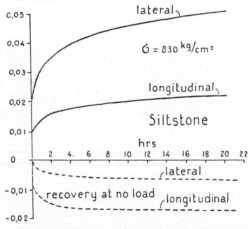

Fig. 41   Strain/time diagram of experiment on siltstone load 830 kg/cm². confining pressure 1 atm. elastic strain. *(After Philips, Contribution to the Symposium on Rock Pressure. Geol. en Mijnb., n.s. jrg.* 10. 1948.)

Philips (1948) performed a few experiments with constant load at 1 atm. pressure in Carboniferous rocks and probably obtained elastic strain alone, obviously with very small strain velocities. Two examples, one on siltstone, the other on shale, both show a strong retardation of the elastic strain and an almost perfect recovery (Figs. 41 and 42).

In a tension experiment of eight days' duration on a marble beam, Philips obtained a rather irregular strain/time curve, the irregularities being possibly due to the development of successive slip-planes and permanent motion along them. The load was rather small. We may conclude that these rocks, with a load below 1,000 kg/cm², did not show an appreciable permanent deformation and that all the strain (max. 0.05%) was due to elastic flow (Fig. 43).

The same is true for the experiments by Griggs under 1 atm. con-

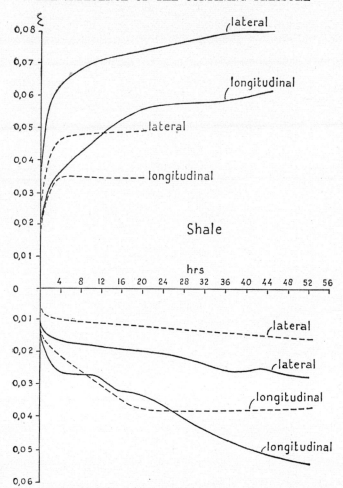

Fig. 42. Strain/time diagram of experiment on shale, elastic strain, small stress, 1 atm. confining pressure. *(After Philips, Contribution to the Symposium on Rock Pressure, Geol. en Mijnb., n.s. jrg. 10, 1948.)*

fining pressure with dry specimens. Limestone under a load of 1,400 kg/cm² showed a purely elastic flow strain/time curve for 500 days (0.02% strain), as did alabaster under 420 kg/cm² for eighty days (0.07% strain). The wetted specimen of alabaster, on the contrary, showed a plastic flow (Fig. 44 and Fig. 45).

A small confining pressure up to 500 kg/cm² used by Goguel was sufficient to allow a wider range of motion. For gypsum he found an elastic-flow field below a curve which, with 50 kg/cm² confining pressure,

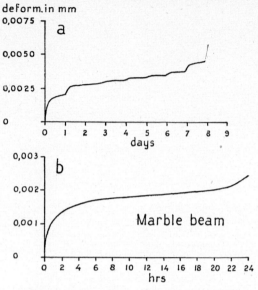

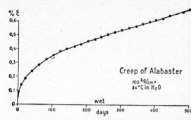

Fig. 45. Strain/time diagram of experiment on wetted specimen of alabaster, with 103 kg/cm² stress and 1 atm. confining pressure. *(After Griggs, 1940. Published by permission of the Geological Society of America.)*

Fig. 43. Strain/time diagrams of bending experiment on marble beam at 1 atm. confining pressure, permanent strain by Philips, *b* enlargement of first day of the experiment elastico-viscous flow. jumps in the strain curve are probably due to formation of slip-planes or other translation surfaces. *(After Philips, Contribution to the Symposium on Rock Pressure. Geol. en Mijnb., n.s. jrg. 10, 1948.)*

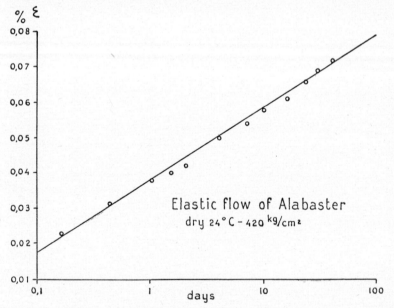

Fig. 44. Strain/time diagram of experiment on dry alabaster specimen with 420 kg/cm² stress at 1 atm. elastic flow. *(After Griggs, 1940. Published by permission of the Geological Society of America.)*

was at 400 kg/cm² stress, and with 500 kg/cm² at almost 600 kg/cm² stress.

Increase of confining pressure from 50 to 600 kg/cm² apparently raised the elasticity limit from 400 to 500 kg/cm². For limestone the confining pressure had to be raised to about 100 kg/cm² in order to cause plastic flow, and with higher confining pressure the elasticity limit was also raised:

Table VI   Elasticity limit with a load of ... kg/cm²

Conf. press. in kg/cm²	Limestone	Carrara marble	Argillaceous sst.
100	1,000	500	200
500	1,600	1,000	1,500

Experiments on sandstone proved that the influence of the confining pressure on this rock was considerably greater. Whereas with small confining pressure the plastic flow or rupture was obtained with a load of 200 kg/cm², it had to be raised to 1,500 kg/cm² to obtain plastic flow when a confining pressure of 500 kg/cm² was applied (Fig. 46). Evidently the confining pressure has a much greater influence on the rough slip-plane surfaces of sandstone than on those of gypsum or limestone (or talc). (Fig. 47.)

For a wetted specimen of alabaster we have a rather contradictory result. The strain velocities are higher for higher confining pressure (the viscosity lower), as was shown by Griggs (Fig. 48).

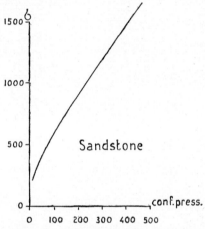

Fig. 46.   Stress/confining pressure diagram of experiments on soft friable sandstone. *(After Goguel. Published by permission of Service de la Carte Géologique.)*

Table VII   Strain velocity in 10⁻⁶ % per day

Load	1 atm. conf. press.	1,000 atm. conf. press.
300	2,000	13,600
250	440	2,650
200	219	390

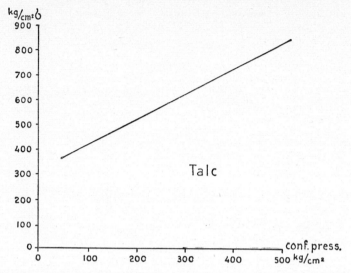

Fig. 47.   Stress/confining pressure diagram of experiments on talc.
(After Goguel.   Published by permission of Service de la Carte Géologique.)

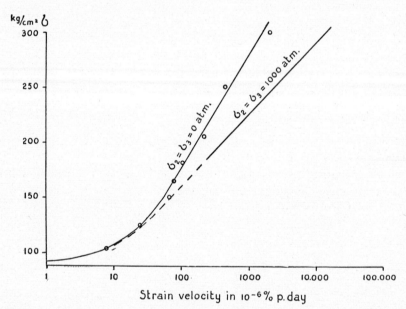

Fig. 48.   Stress/strain velocity diagram of experiments on wetted specimen of
alabaster.   *(After Griggs, 1940.   Published by permission of the Geological Society
of America.)*

This apparent anomaly is present, however, only because with the dry specimen there was little or no solution-recrystallization, whereas with the wetted specimen most of the motion was due to this phenomenon.

In general, we may say that the experiments with constant loads show that the elasticity limit of motion along shear-planes is raised by increasing the confining pressure, a result which is in perfect accordance with the results of older experiments where the load was not constant but gradually increased.

We know that higher confining pressures increase the rate of movement due to solution and recrystallization. Whether the elasticity limit is also lowered is unknown.

Experimental investigation into the behaviour of rock in a stress-field has taught us many important principles but also leaves us with many queries.

We may assume that in tectonic processes in general the stress only slightly exceeds the threshold value of the resistance, and since the longest of our experiments lasted less than two years, there can be little doubt that all the experiments have failed to approach dynamic similarity with natural processes. The numerical values obtained in the experiments are, therefore, probably valueless, but nevertheless the principles which they established may be applicable to a large degree. The most important feature is doubtless the necessity to distinguish between finite processes such as compression and elastic flow, and permanent processes such as elastico-viscous flow and plastic flow. For the present it is almost impossible to distinguish between the last two processes because they give the same kind of deformation curve.

Although the modes of deformation have been studied only superficially, different cases have been recognized. But we do not yet know which of the observed modes is typical for each process — elastic, elastico-viscous, or plastic. In the next chapter we shall see that the results of the experiments cannot as yet be applied with any certainty to explain the characteristics of different fold or fault types. There is still a wide gap between our experimental and field experience, which we can bridge only with hypotheses.

Chapter 4

Experimental Tectonics

In Chapter 3 we made the acquaintance of a set of experiments which investigated certain physical properties of rocks but did not try to imitate actual tectonic processes. This latter kind of experiment has often been performed ever since the beginning of the 19th century (James Hall, 1813). In most cases the experiments tried to imitate the final shape of tectonic disturbances such as a fold, fault, or joint-pattern, and sometimes deductions were made on the history of the event. Their contribution to our tectonic knowledge is very real, although, as we shall learn when we analyse their results, it is decidedly limited in its scope.

THEORY AND PRACTICE OF THE TECTONIC EXPERIMENT

Tectonic experiments, like all other kinds of scale model experiments, are beset from every side by pitfalls and obstacles which prevent a close resemblance to natural processes.

Most experiments on folding have been made in rectangular boxes with one of the shorter sides acting as a moving block and the opposite one acting as a buttress. When pressure is applied by the moving block, the contents are pushed a certain distance towards the stationary end. Both the sides and the bottom, however, exert a friction on the moving material, causing a decrease of stress away from the moving block. The obvious result is that in all these experiments the folding is initiated next to the moving block, and only after this first fold has been strongly compressed does further buckling take place (Fig. 49). In nature, of course, with a much larger lateral extension of the fold, this frictional influence is much smaller or practically non-existent, and a belt of folds develops simultaneously. Lubricating the bottom and walls of the box helps somewhat but does not eliminate the fundamental error.

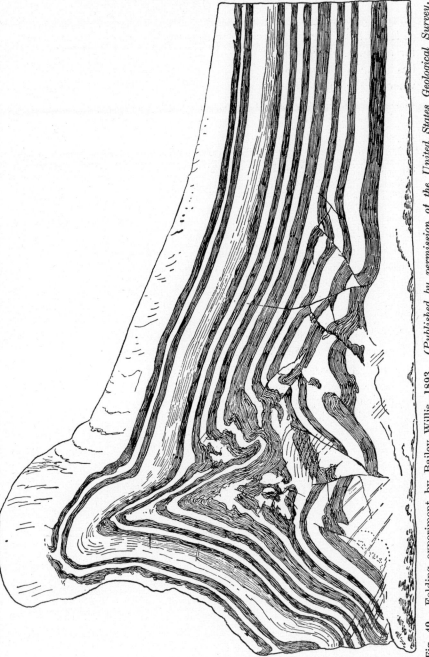

Fig. 49. Folding experiment by Bailey Willis, 1893. (Published by permission of the United States Geological Survey.)

Another difficulty is the confining pressure. The initial fold tends to rise vertically much higher than natural folds, and various expedients have been invented to imitate a load: Bailey Willis (1893), for instance, charged his test-material with lead shot. The difficulty lies in the fact that gravity is as strong in the experiment as in nature, whereas the mass of the scale model is so much less. Loading with heavy material is only a very poor substitute.

The main obstacle however, is the extreme difficulty — if not the impossibility — of achieving dynamic similarity in the scale model.

Most of the theoretical subject matter of scale models has been treated adequately by King Hubbert (1937) whom we will follow here.

Theory of the Mechanical Scale Model. To imitate in the laboratory a fold or fault as observed in nature we must necessarily reduce its scale both in time and in size. Since our purpose is to learn something about the forces that produced the structure, we are not content with a simple model; we wish to reproduce its development, from a supposed initial form, usually a horizontal layered sequence, to the observed distorted shape. We know that we cannot use common rock material for this purpose because when we try to deform it within a reasonable time it will be shattered or broken by the stress we are forced to apply. It is, therefore, necessary to use some material other than rock in order to reproduce a fold or even a fault. The reduction of the time-scale, and perhaps of size as well, necessitates the use of material with "reduced" physical properties. The relation of the reduction factors for each of these properties has been worked out theoretically, and every scale model ought to comply with the theory; otherwise it is impossible to draw conclusions from the results. This principle is much used in hydrodynamic and aerodynamic laboratories, where scale models are constructed and the effects observed.

The basic theory can be formulated thus: The reduction factor of every material property of the scale model is prescribed by the dimensional formula of their mechanical quantities.

Every property such as length, strength, force, etc., is measured by appropriate combinations of three fundamental units: mass (M), length (L), and time (T), and their "dimensional formula" represents this combination. Thus a velocity is represented by ($L T^{-1}$) which means a length divided by time, and a force by ($M L T^{-2}$) which means a mass multiplied by a length and divided twice by time and so on. From the fundamental reduction factors, or model ratios (l for length, m for mass, and t for time), the reduction factors for every mechanical quantity can be deduced by using them in the same combination in which they occur in the dimensional formula of that quantity. Thus in the scale model the velocity must be $l\,t^{-1}$ times the original velocity, and the force must be $m\,l\,t^{-2}$ times the original force. This law enables us to deduce the strength which the material of a certain construction ought to have from the support we had to give it in the scale model in order for it to withstand a measured stress, provided that all the mechanical properties of the model were correct.

In making models to imitate tectonic processes we are, as yet, not so much concerned with measuring mechanical properties, as with simply understanding how each process works, and we can therefore be content with certain approximations. But the fundamental principles must be obeyed; otherwise we should not have the slightest guarantee that a real similarity has been achieved.

In Table VIII, second column, the most important mechanical properties have been assembled; but instead of the model ratio m for mass, we have introduced the model ratio for density d, with the formula

$$D = M\,L^{-3} \text{ (mass/volume) or } d = m\,l^{-3}$$

Table VIII

quantity	model ratio	model ratio disregarding inertia	model ratio $d = 1$
length	l	l	l
time	t	t	t
density	d	d	1
area	l^2	l^2	l^2
volume	l^3	l^3	l^3
velocity	lt^{-1}	lt^{-1}	lt^{-1}
acceleration	lt^{-2}	lt^{-2}	lt^{-2}
force	$dl^4\,t^{-2}$	dl^3	l^3
strength, stress	$dl^2\,t^{-2}$	dl	l
strain, angle	1	1	1
elastic modulus	$dl^2\,t^{-2}$	dl	l
viscosity	$dl^2\,t^{-1}$	dlt	lt

In the first column of this table we have assumed that the similarity as regards the forces is satisfied by the forces due to inertia, MLT^{-2} $(= DL^4\,T^{-2})$, but all scale models are also subject to gravity, and therefore acceleration (LT^{-2}) must equal unity. Hence L and T would no

longer be independent ratios. When, however, our scale model is not
concerned with high velocities, but is a slow-working process, inertia
may be disregarded, and then we may factor out $l\ t^{-2}$ from all the
general model ratios of stress, strength etc. (second column of table).

In scale models of tectonic features the reductions in length and
time are important, while those in density are unimportant because
we can hardly find a material that weighs less than $^1/_3$ of rock; hence
we may take d as equalling 1 and the ratios we then have to comply
with are listed in the third column of the table. By this process of
elimination of factors which are unimportant in our kind of scale
models, we have arrived at the simple condition that all such static
material properties as strength and elasticity must be reduced with
the length reduction factor; the stress we have to apply ought then
to be about l times smaller than the stress in nature. As soon as the
model is slowly deformed, however, we have to take into account
the time factor, and in order to maintain mechanical similarity the
viscosity must be reduced with the factor $l\ t$.

Let us demonstrate this with an example: a scale model of a fold
of the whole crust of the earth is desired,

strength of the crust $= 10^6$ gr/cm^2
thickness of the crust $= 3.10^6$ cm
viscosity of the crust $= 10^{22}$ poises

the reduction factors l and t for an orogenic process would be $l = 10^{-6}$
and $t = 10^{-9}$, if we assume that a cake of 30 cm thickness, deformed
in a few hours, can represent an orogenic process lasting a million years.
The mechanical properties of the material we want to find must
therefore be:

strength $10^6 \times 10^{-5} = 10$ gr/cm^2
viscosity $10^{22} \times 10^{-6} \times 10^{-9} = 10^7$ poises

which would mean the strength of a very soft material like butter
with a viscosity of that of pitch at 20° C, a combination which is
perhaps difficult to find. When the same experiment represented the
folding of a limestone bed of 3 m thickness, strength 10^5 gr/cm^2, and
viscosity 10^{21} poises, the material ought to have had, assuming that
the folding of the limestone bed took 100,000 years, the following
properties:

strength $10^5 \times 10^{-1} = 10^4$ gr/cm^2
viscosity $10^{21} \times 10^{-1} \times 10^{-8} = 10^{12}$ poises

This is even more difficult to match with a well-known material.

When we want to create faults, and are interested only in the kind of fault and its position, the scale model becomes static. We are then much less concerned with its viscosity, and the choice of material becomes much easier. This is one reason why most fault experiments are better imitations than fold models.

With fold imitations there is another difficulty: the shape of a natural anticline is certainly influenced by gravity, which prevents its upward growth. When the reduction-factor is correct the fold in the experiment will also collapse when it grows too high. But since none of the fold scale models have taken into account the reduction of viscosity, the deformative stress and gravity are no longer in the right relation, so that gravity does not control the experiment in the same way that it controls the development of the natural fold. For instance there are many fold-imitations where a void developed naturally in the core of the anticline, an impossibility in nature. But when the material used was weak enough to prevent this void at the bottom of the cake, it would not form a fold, but was compressed without folding.

There are obviously other unavoidable difficulties. For instance the size of the sand grain or clay mineral cannot be reduced in the same way as the length of the scale model, nor can the different modes of deformation which I have distinguished in Chapter 3, be introduced in the model material. There are clearly many more discrepancies which cannot be avoided.

Nevertheless, there are several reasons why the general dissimilarity of the imitation experiments is less serious than would appear from the paragraphs above.

First of all, in any experiment where the purpose is the generation of a set of faults or shear-planes, it is obvious that once these planes have been created any succeeding movement will take place along those planes (see Fig. 96). Therefore the important moment of the experiment occurs when the shear-plane is generated and not the subsequent movement. Hence the viscosity does not enter into the problem. Only the strength and the elastic stress-field are determining factors and a material of about the right strength, such as soft clay, will suffice for this kind of experiment notwithstanding the fact that its viscosity has an incorrect value. Secondly, we have at our disposal a means of studying the relation of the scale model to the large structure in the quite common occurrence in nature of microstructures, a means which has seldom been fully utilized.

Relation of Microstructures to the Tectonic Experiment. We have an enormous mass of facts, from observed microstructures, folds and faults in rocks, which prove that reduction in size does not influence the shape of a fold at all. Any geologist will know, from his own experience, exposures which show microstructures which are exact replicas, including many details, of major structures (compare, for instance, Figs. 62 and 237). In these folds or faults nature performed the experiment with the same material and in the same time interval but on a very much smaller scale, and achieved perfect similarity, infinitely better than any clay cake could ever yield. Evidently size reduction does not play the predominant role which the scale model theory prescribes. There are two reasons for this apparent contradiction.

Firstly, the shape of a fold or the orientation of a fault is purely a matter of relative lengths, or in other words a matter of angles and not of lengths themselves. The relative proportion of lengths, a strain, and an angle, are all dimensionless, and therefore independent of any reduction factors.

Secondly, any later movement will naturally follow the shear-planes; and therefore the final shape of the structure of a rift valley, for instance, is wholly determined by the orientation of the original fault-planes.

The fact that the similarity between microfolds and macrofolds is so striking is now clear: the shape is independent of the size. Because the microfolds were reproduced under the same confining pressure as the major folds, the material had the same state of ductility and therefore the same relation between strength and viscosity, and between tensile and compressive strength; and therefore the same shape. Not only does the contradiction between theory and observed facts disappear, but in the clear similarity we find a proof that the shapes of both microstructures and macrostructures originate in the same combination of elastic and permanent deformation. In the large fold and the small one, the shape is governed by an elastically bent layer, whose thickness is measured in tens of metres in the case of the large fold and in tens of millimetres in the case of the microfold; and the same is true for fault structures.

In the case of a permanent deformation the scale model is concerned with the relation between strength and viscosity or with compressive and tensile strength, and that can be achieved either by raising the confining pressure, which, as we have seen in Chapter 3, changes a brittle material into a ductile one, or by lowering the strength and viscosity of the material. In the imitative experiment the second course is followed, in the microstructures, the first.

It clearly follows that the precaution taken by the experimenters of applying a length reduction factor to the stress, strength, or elastic properties of the material was unnecessary; the natural microstructures confirm this. Still, if the experimenter had taken a slab of rock and tried to fold it as he folded his clay cake, it would have been fractured and not folded. The error he made is that he tried to compensate for reduced time by applying the rule of length reduction factor (into which the time does not enter). It is notable however, that he more or less succeeded in confounding the theory and obtained a considerable degree of similarity in shape, because shape is independent of both time and length reductions.

Notwithstanding all this, such experiments fail completely in dynamic similarity because in nature the deformative stress in most cases exceeds the strength by only very little, so that deformation is extremely slow. In other words the relation between stress and strength differs very little from one in nature, but in the experiments it is much larger, since the experimenter wants to see the result himself. He will never be able to overcome the difficulty that the scale model can never realize, within the span of a life-time, a similarity to the natural relation of stress/strength, or stress/rigidity, or any other elastic property. What the experimenter can do, and what he succeeded in doing, is to achieve a similarity in shape or orientation of shear — or fracture planes — by just guessing the physical properties of his scale model material. The complete lack of dynamic similarity prevents any but superficial deductions from the experiments. A good proof of this conclusion is the fact that not one single experiment has ever succeeded in imitating similar folding with the development of cleavage. The successful tectonic imitative experiment has a great value as illustrative material and might elucidate something about the probable succession of different movements, but it never can teach us anything new.

THE EXPERIMENTS THEMSELVES

To review all the more important experiments would lead us too far, and they will, moreover, be more appropriately described together with the tectonic phenomena they illustrate. I will mention here only those types of structure which have been illustrated experimentally and the degree of success achieved.

Fault Structures. They have been imitated very successfully by a number of experimenters among whom H. Cloos (1930, 1932) has been the most prominent. In several series of experiments with clay cakes he obtained exact replicas of the Rhine Valley rift, with its set of normal and antithetic faults (cf. Fig. 96). His best experiments were made with soft clay mounted on a rubber sheet which could be stretched. By introducing non-homogeneities into the clay cake, i.e. more solid parts with less water flanked by soft parts with more water, he succeeded in locating the normal faults in the softer portions, thus indicating that the location of a rift valley might be influenced by non-homogeneities in the earth's crust, such as granite bodies.

Wrench faults have been successfully imitated by H. Cloos (1929–30) and Riedel (1929) (Fig. 119). Both experimenters succeeded in showing the formation of tension cracks oblique to the vertical shear-plane.

Thrust-faults are less satisfactorily imitated. Many folding experiments have shown a development of thrusts in the later stages of experiment; but the usual low-angle thrust-fault of an asymmetric anticline has never been convincingly imitated. This failure is probably due to the fact that gravity plays an important role in nature, but not in the experiment because deformation is too rapid in the latter (Lohest, 1913; B. Willis, 1893; Kuenen and de Sitter, 1938).

Fold Structures. They have been imitated by numerous experimenters with varying success. Many experiments illustrate, with rubber plates, a pile of paper, and some soft plastic matter, different kinds of deformation (see Figs. 121, 122, and 123). All of these illustrate some characteristics of folding, but none of course shows the combination of the different types which is typical of a normal folding process in nature. Moreover, neither cleavage, nor schistosity parallel to the axial plane (a common characteristic of natural folds), nor joints, have ever been imitated successfully in a fold. Also the spontaneous concentric shear-planes in a non-orientated medium (unstratified) which are a predominant feature in almost all folds of non-metamorphic rocks, have been reproduced only once, by Kuenen and de Sitter (1938, see Fig. 124). The folding experiments in general are therefore rather unsatisfactory, and can be used only by isolating certain characteristics as illustrative material. The reason for this relative failure of folding experiments must be sought in the impossibility of achieving the right relation between deformative stress and the elastic properties or the strength of the material, as has been explained in the foregoing pages. Further experiments should concentrate upon cleavage and on concentric folding of unstratified material.

Diapiric Structures and Disharmonic Folds. The experimental imitation of salt domes has been very successful. Escher and Kuenen (1929), Nettleton (1943), and many others have succeeded in creating typical diapiric structures, always accompanied by flow-structures in the extrusive mass. The success is no doubt due to the fact that in this kind of structure in nature the stress also greatly exceeds the resistance of the material. Disharmonic structures, on the contrary, are apparently very difficult to imitate, although their mechanism is closely related to diapirism. We may presume that this is again due to the impossibility of retaining the right relation in the experiment between the stress and the strength and most of all the viscosity. Perhaps very slow experiments, lasting months or years could succeed.

Joint Patterns (cf. Chapter 9) have been successfully imitated by a great number of experimenters, beginning with Daubrée (1879). They conform to natural patterns to a high degree, although they are not as diversified. The success is without doubt due to the fact that the only requirement for the scale model is to imitate an orientation, which is of course a dimensionless thing. Unfortunately they have been often used in interpretations of folds and other phenomena with which they have little in common.

Chapter 5

Rock Behaviour in Tectonic Processes

COMPETENT AND INCOMPETENT ROCKS

The terms "rigidity" and "brittleness" have been much used, as antitheses of "plasticity", to designate certain physical properties of rocks and in discussion of rock deformation. We have seen in the foregoing paragraphs that the complexity of the physical properties of rocks is far too great for such a simple terminology, and that some rigid or competent rocks become plastic under relatively low confining pressure and stress.

"Hardness" and "softness" are terms indicating the resistance of rocks to weathering. But the two sets of terms are sometimes unconsciously regarded as synonyms. This is unjustified. Goguel (1943), for instance, has shown that marly limestone has a stronger resistance to deformation than pure limestone, whereas it weathers away more easily.

Still, there is undoubtedly a great difference in behaviour in tectonic processes, between the competent type of rock and the plastic or incompetent type. This is particularly noticeable in disharmonic folding.

When rocks are distorted into any new shape, they are either compressed in a single direction and dilated in one or two directions perpendicular to the first; or compressed in two directions and dilated in one direction perpendicular to the two. The distortion may produce great folds, anticlines and synclines, secondary microfolds, cleavage or schistosity, or any other structure. There is in every case thickening in the vertical sense and consequent thinning in a horizontal direction. It is to be expected that the stratification of a rock sequence or the orientation of the clay or mica mineral flakes will induce a preference for certain shear directions.

72

The anisotropy of the rock, however, is not the only, or even the most important, factor which will decide the orientation of shear-planes. On the contrary the orientation of the stress-field is more important. The yield to the stress-field may either be of an elastico-viscous nature or of a semi-plastic character, and the shear-planes will be differently orientated in the two cases.

Hence the distortion of rock under deformative stress is determined by two factors, namely:

1. its anisotropy
2. its elastic or plastic state

Either of the two factors may be dominant, or they may be combined in a certain pattern.

All sedimentary rocks are built of layers of different physical properties. Rigid rock-types alternate with plastic ones. As the tectonic stress grows it reaches an intensity below the elasticity limit of the rigid rocks, but is beyond that of the weaker plastic rocks. At this stage the rigid rocks may have yielded elastically a little under the stress; the plastic rocks are kept in place by the strong adjacent beds. As the stress increases further, it reaches eventually the elastic limit of the rigid layers. The latter will already have been folded into purely elastic waves. At this point the stress is, of course, far above the elasticity limit of the plastic layers.

When deformation of the rigid rock sets in it is therefore entirely governed by the elastic stresses which still exist in the folded sheet. The weaker rocks follow the shape taken by their sturdier neighbours, and their own elastic stresses have no appreciable effect.

Before discussing why a certain rock type has become deformed in a certain way, we shall have to relate the experimental data concerning stress, strain, and viscosity to the types of deformation that we observe in the field or under the microscope.

We have seen that experimental data on rock distortion indicate that we must distinguish between five main modes of deformation:

1. compression into a smaller volume, a finite process
2. creep or elastic flow, a deformation with a logarithmic time/strain curve, which therefore becomes infinitely small for long periods
3. elastico-viscous flow, where the elastic strain is gradually taken over by permanent deformation
4. plastic flow, with a more or less constant but slow strain velocity for a minimum stress

5. rupture, with at the beginning a constant strain velocity which eventually increases and leads to fracture of the specimen

The mechanism of deformation in these five modes is not yet well understood, but we know that certain mechanisms are typical for certain modes. Solution and recrystallization, for instance, is certainly a flow phenomenon.

In fold and fault tectonics it is obvious that compression can play a part in the initial stage only. It may perhaps determine the location of a future fault or of the crest of a fold, but during the actual process of folding, compression ceases to operate.

Nor can elastic flow, since it is a finite process and therefore of strictly limited extension, be an important factor in folding. It is possible of course that in well-stratified rocks, where each member can be folded elastically and independently of its neighbours, the curvature of the folds can reach measurable dimensions, but in general we can assume that the stress will rise beyond the elasticity limit and that the field of pure elasticity will be passed.

We then enter into the elastico-viscous flow field, where the elastic strain is slowly and continuously replaced by plastic strain.

The elastic stresses in an elastically folded sheet are parallel to its surface—tensional at the outer arc, and compressional in the inner arc of the fold. Inside the sheet these stresses result in shearing stress parallel to the surface which causes shear-planes to develop on the flanks of the fold (Fig. 50).

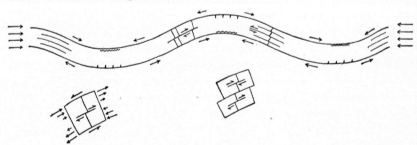

Fig. 50.   Elastic stress in bent sheet leads to concentric shear-planes.

As soon as one of these shear-planes has been formed the original sheet is divided into two elastically folded sheets. During further folding the process repeats itself continuously, so that the elastic state of the rigid rock is never lost. This process of splitting up the original layer into more and more independent arcs allows continuous further bending without increasing the stress. This process of elastico-viscous flow assumes that on the concentric shear-planes the shearing stress rises beyond the limit set for flows and causes rupture.

In the weaker rocks between the rigid layers this process does not take place in the same way, since the stress is well above the elasticity

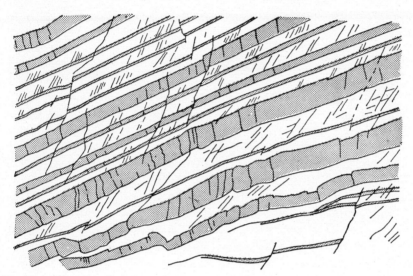

Fig. 51.   Fracture-cleavage in shale, rotational joints in sandstone, drawn from photograph of Ordovician rocks near Aberystwyth, Wales.

limit of the weaker rocks. In these rocks extension in a vertical direction is of a much more uniform character. This dilatation is accompanied by the formation of shear-planes, probably because it is still an elastic effect. The shear-planes are parallel to the axial plane and perpendicular to the principal (lateral) stress-direction as in slaty- and fracture-cleavage. In thick marl or shale beds or in thin competent beds between incompetent beds with slaty-cleavage, one can observe interesting oblique shear-planes. Figure 51 gives an example of cleavage in shale, combined with perpendicular joints in the quartzite layers in a folded series. There is no parallel cleavage in the rigid rock; instead, there are rotational joints. These joints, perpendicular to the stratification, are evidence of the elastic state during folding of the quartzite beds (cf. Chapter 15).

From the foregoing reasoning it follows that in folding processes it is not the absolute value of the elasticity limit of the whole complex which is the most important factor, but the relative competency of the different rock types and the highest elasticity limit of the most competent rock. There are other factors, however, which certainly operate as well.

In the first place it is quite possible that the rate of increase of the deformative stress is important. If this rate is small the relaxation of the elastic deformation soon absorbs its acceleration, and the stress remains constant as soon as it has reached a value only a little above the elasticity limit. When, on the other hand, the rate of increase is greater, this value of constant stress will not be reached until the stress has risen somewhat higher above the elasticity limit of the most competent rock, and the deformation may then be of a different character altogether. If we assume that concentric folding corresponds to a minimum interval between stress and elasticity limit, and that planar-shear corresponds to a somewhat larger difference, then slaty-cleavage could simply indicate a higher acceleration in the rate of increase of the deformative stress.

Secondly, the influence of the depth of burial of the rocks (i.e. the confining pressure) is certainly an important factor. It raises the elasticity limit, changes some rigid rocks into ductile rocks, and thus influences the competency-relation of the different rock types.

Thirdly, temperature, and in particular thermal action by intrusive rocks, may change the whole picture. As we have very little factual data about the manner in which thermal and dynamic metamorphism act, it would perhaps be better to state simply that contemporaneous emplacement of intrusive rocks fundamentally changes the rock reaction under stress. It has, in general, the function of weakening the resistance of the rock material and, perhaps more important, of mobilizing it to a considerable extent.

Finally, the fluid content of the rock, already proved important in the experimental work, also makes itself felt in nature. The fluid content may be either the original connate water in the sedimentary rocks, or an addition through magmatic activity at depth. In many metamorphic processes this original water content is thought to play a decisive role in activating the recrystallization of new minerals (scapolite in limestone metamorphism by means of salt water, for instance) and Griggs (1940) showed in his experiments that water, and an acid solution in an even higher degree, accelerate recrystallization in limestone. In addition to these functions, the fluid might simply act as a lubricator.

Summarizing, we can state that the factors that determine the reaction of rock to stress depend on:

1. its anisotropy
2. the relative competency of its component members
3. the elasticity limit of the most competent rock
4. the rate of increase of the deformative stress
5. the confining pressure
6. intrusive action at depth, both by its thermal influence and its intrusive character
7. fluid content, either connate or intrusive

We are now confronted with the difficult task of relating these different influences to actual observed rock textures. The observations on the rock specimens of the experiments are not a good guide, because we can rest assured that in our haste to achieve a result in the laboratory we always let the stress climb far too high above the resistance limit, even when we wait five years, as Griggs did in some experiments. They served us very well in establishing the principles which are involved, but are certainly not representative of natural circumstances.

From general considerations we can, however, infer some roads along which our thoughts may travel. First of all it seems extremely probable

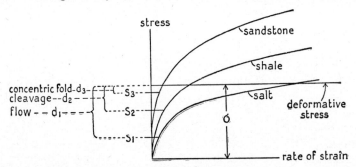

Fig. 52. A deformative stress acts on three different rocks, salt, shale, and sandstone, at the same time. They have their elasticity limits respectively at s_1, s_2, and s_3; d_1, d_2 and d_3 represent the distances between the stress and the elasticity limits; the rocks flow, cleave, or fold in that succession.

that concentric folding, with its elastically induced shear-planes parallel to the bedding, and its tension cracks on the anticlinal hinges, is typical of the smallest possible difference between elasticity limit and deformative stress. On the other hand we can reasonably suppose that flow-structures like those of salt in salt-domes, or marble flow structures in metamorphic limestone, and even flow-structures in gneisses, are typical of the largest separation between resistance and stress, accompanied by large scale recrystallization induced either by the presence of water or by thermal and intrusive action.

Hence it seems reasonable to suppose that planar-shear deformation, like cleavage, is an intermediate stage with an intermediate interval between resistance and stress — that it is more plastic in character but is still influenced by elastic stress. Figure 52 represents this reasoning in a diagram.

This view is confirmed by the fact that, in an alternation of rigid competent rocks and ductile incompetent rocks, rigid rocks such as sandstone fold concentrically, and incompetent shales show fracture-cleavage. And in diapiric structures the very incompetent gypsum, anhydrite, or salt, together with shales and marls, flow through cracks in the concentrically folded upper layers.

Summarizing our experience of fold-mechanics we may construct the following table. In this table the sequence of deformation from top to bottom indicates either a sequence of rocks with decreasing elasticity limit deformed by the same stress, or a sequence of the same rock deformed by an increasing stress (or in other words an increase of the interval between the stress and the elasticity limit), but with the proviso that many kinds of schistosity (and flow in metamorphic rocks) require a rise of temperature:

compression	finite process	no folding
elastic bending	finite process	slight folding
elastico-viscous		
folding	continuous process	concentric folding
plastic folding	continuous process	cleavage and schistosity
flow	continuous process	flow structures

INFLUENCE OF CONFINING PRESSURE ON DIFFERENT ROCK TYPES

Unfortunately we have very little comparative data on the influence of an increase of confining pressure on different rock-types such as limestone, sandstone, shale, siltstone, etc.

As well as experiments on limestone and marble, Griggs (1939, 1940) made extensive tests on alabaster, but apart from this only Goguel (1943) has tried systematically to get comparative data on different rock-types. And he succeeded only partially, because so many other factors became involved.

The most important result without doubt is that Goguel clearly distinguishes between the behaviour of three rock types:

1. Gypsum and salt, which are apt to show considerable solution-recrystallization, even when the samples are comparatively dry.

2. Limestones, in which the motion is apparently mostly due to intergranular shearing with solution-recrystallization, but which have a much higher elasticity limit and smaller velocity (higher viscosity) than gypsum and salt. With high confining pressure we may expect intracrystalline slip.

3. Sandstone, which is characterized by the fact that the internal angle of friction and intergranular slip are important factors. The strain velocity and the elasticity limit are strongly influenced by the confining pressure.

The fact that an increase of confining pressure has a different influence on different kinds of rocks, indicates that the relative competency of rocks changes with depth.

	Shallow depth up to 2 km	Great depth below 2 km
Competent	impure limestone	sandstone
	pure limestone	impure limestone
	sandstone	marl
	marl	pure limestone
	clay-shale	clay-shale
Incompetent	salt-gypsum	salt-gypsum

Furthermore, because the elasticity limit is widely different for different kinds of rocks, we may expect a purely elastic strain in one rock, a limestone for instance, when the next layer of shale is already in the field of plastic yield. With a compressive stress of 600 kg/cm^2 at a shallow depth of 1 km, for example, we may expect plastic flow in shales and salts, but only elastico-viscous flow in limestones and sandstones.

It is desirable to define the relative competency of rocks in terms of physical properties. Goguel (1943) has shown that to a large degree the incompetent rocks have a lower elasticity limit and a lower viscosity for a given stress, but it is impossible to assign to each rock type a numerical value of its physical properties for different depths.

STRENGTH OF ROCKS

There remains one question to which we must now return, after our consideration of rock behaviour in natural folds.

The experimental data could not definitely indicate whether a rock really has a lower limit of strength, beneath which no other deformation than elastic bending is possible, or whether this limit is only apparent and created by the increasing value of the viscosity with low stress. The question has some importance; for flow experiments of long duration using relatively low stresses, showed that the strength of rocks had originally been assessed far too high. Some geologists (notably Gignoux and van Bemmelen) have assumed that at great depth rocks would flow under any stress condition. Others, like Goguel and myself, insist that a real strength is much more probable because we know that large mountain masses do stand up for a considerable time; more important, because longer time and larger masses are concerned, is the fact that the continental platforms can stand stress on their edges for hundreds of millions of years. Hence we may conclude that even the differential viscosity of rocks has a real zero point, a threshold value, which we may call the strength or elasticity limit.

For a folding process the question is not very important, because with a rising stress even an apparent strength would have the same effect as a real threshold value. The author's explanation of the alternation of epeirogenic periods and orogenic periods (Chapter 34), depends to a large degree, however, on the assumption that a real strength does exist.

Chapter 6

Rock Fracturing and Distortion

Under this heading are assembled a number of phenomena produced by rock-deformation which are visible to the unaided eye. They fall into two classes: (1) rock-distortion and (2) rock-fracturing.

In rock-distortion, certain components of the rock, of which the original shape is known either beforehand or by reconstruction, are distorted by minute shear-planes without losing all relation to their original shape. Fossil distortion and distortion of ooliths and pebbles fall in this class.

In rock-fracturing, the production of angular rock-fragments, sometimes accompanied by recrystallization or by development of schistosity, provides evidence of the great stress to which certain zones of the rock mass were submitted.

ROCK DISTORTION

Pebbles and Boulders. The pebbles in conglomerate beds which have suffered the effects of an orogenic phase often show clearly how they have been deformed. They may be flattened by a multitude of minute shear-planes or along a few cracks, and in both cases give us valuable information about the direction of stress in that locality. The flattening is often parallel to the bedding-plane but in other cases it is oblique or perpendicular to it. If we assumed that the original shape of the pebbles was a sphere we could establish their average flattening and its orientation. This assumption is never quite warranted, however, since non-distorted pebbles are almost invariably triaxial ellipsoids, deposited in a position in which the shortest ellipsoid axis is perpendicular to the bedding. The measured relation is therefore almost certainly a maximum when the flattening lies in the bedding-plane, and a minimum when it lies perpendicular to that plane. Moreover,

81

the pebble very often represents a piece of hard rock embedded in a softer medium, and therefore reacts differently to the stress-field

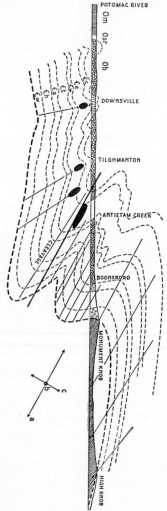

from its matter. The flattening of the pebbles may, therefore, not be representative of the distortion of the whole conglomerate bed. For instance, the pebbles may have been pressed together first before their own flattening took place. Although the actual amount of flattening is therefore only a rough approximation of that of the whole bed, the orientation in space of the plane of maximum shortening is always an important fact, and worth recording.

Ooliths. In the case of the distortion of ooliths, the objections against the exactness of measurements of pebbles disappear. A limestone oolith has almost the same composition as its matrix, the limestone itself, and in addition it is a sphere. An oolitic limestone is therefore an ideal subject for the study of internal deformation. A very complete study of distorted oolitic limestones has been made by E. Cloos (1947b). The South Mountain section of the Appalachian orogeny, which Cloos analysed, is reproduced in Fig. 53. The most striking of his conclusions is that the average elongation axes of the ooliths, measured in many hundreds of slides, are parallel to the axial plane of the recumbent folds and the cleavage; their disposition changes with that of these latter planar features, from a SE dip to a vertical position, going from SE to NW. It would carry us too far to follow Cloos exhaustively; I shall

Fig. 53. Section of South Mountain folds with direction of oolite flattening. *(After E. Cloos. Published by permission of the Geological Society of America.)*

point out only some of the most important details of his methods and results.

The cleavage is well developed in the stronger deformed portions of the structure (above 20% distortion as measured on the ooliths) and shows a clear lineation in the direction of movement. The a and b axes are, therefore, clearly defined. In order to measure the exact distortion of the ooliths two slides of an orientated sample specimen have to be made, one in the ac plane and one in the ab plane. When r is the radius of the original sphere and $a, b,$ and c the three axes of the ellipsoid, and assuming that the volume has not changed by distortion:

$$4/3\ \pi r^3 = 4/3\ \pi abc \quad \text{or} \quad r = \sqrt[3]{abc}$$

from this formula first r and then the extension of a and b and the reduction of the c axis can be calculated.

For explanation of the terms a, b, and c axes, see Chapter 7, p. 106 b is in general the fold axis, a the direction of slip. a is $\perp$ b and c is $\perp$ to the ab plane.

The average extension in b, measured in 124 specimens, was less

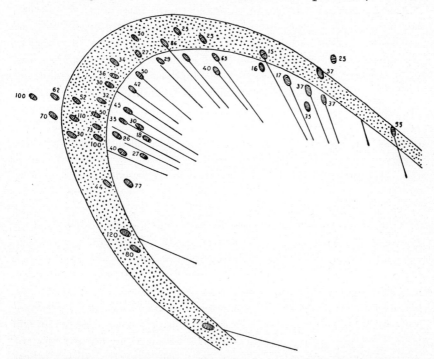

Fig. 54. Recumbent fold with oolite flattening and thickening in the anticlinal hinge. The numbers indicate the flattening in percentages.
(After E. Cloos. Published by permission of the Geological Society of America.)

than 8%. There were occasional high values of b extension; but the low average was judged to justify making slides in only the ac plane and assuming the b extension to be zero in order to save time.

By measuring the orientation of the a direction in relation to the bedding-plane, the thickening of the strata can be deduced from the extension in a throughout the fold. The results indicated that the standard section of the Cambrian of this region, measuring almost 12,000 feet in thickness, has to be reduced to less than 6,000 feet.

Both cleavage and extension showed a fan-like arrangement in all the folds (Fig. 54), opening towards the anticlinal hinge. In the upper limb of a recumbent fold the degree of extension is usually less than in the lower limb.

Conclusions of a more general nature will be made in Chapter 7, but it can be seen that this study of a distortion of a rock constituent of which the original shape was known beforehand is of the utmost importance.

Fossil distortion offers the same possibilities as oolith distortion, but is much more difficult to measure because of the more irregular shape of fossils. The only common fossil remains which might serve the purpose well are crinoid stems. The distortion of fossils has long been recorded but almost exclusively in Palaeozoic rocks (Haughton, 1856; Rutsch, 1948, with extensive literature). This is due to the fact that most Tertiary folding is of the concentric type, in which all movement is parallel to the bedding-plane and mostly concentrated on shaly or marly intercalations. In fact it is astonishing how fossils involved in concentric folding can escape all distortion. Even in strongly folded sedimentary sequences in a vertical position one can find perfectly well-preserved upper bedding-planes of limestones full of undistorted fossils.

Apparently the concentric shear leaves such surfaces alone, and is concentrated within the shale or marl beds.

On the other hand the paucity of fossils in many Palaeozoic rocks is often due to the intense cleavage. It is not only that the rock no longer splits along the bedding-plane on which the fossils lie; the fossils themselves are also often totally destroyed. This is particularly true for fragile fossil remains such as graptolites. A typical example of this influence of cleavage on fossil content is found in the Palaeozoic chain of the Pyrenees: fossils occur only in the northern and southern marginal zones where the folding is of the concentric type; the axial zone, where cleavage folding predominates, is completely barren.

ROCK FRACTURING

Rock fracturing by tectonic processes can simply be called "mylonitization" and the shattered rocks called mylonites. But if the fracturing is not accompanied by slickensiding or intense cleavage or recrystallization, the term "brecciation" is generally preferable, and the shattered rocks are termed tectonic breccias.

Mylonites in the strict sense are rocks which show strong lamination, and in which the original constituent particles have been pulverized

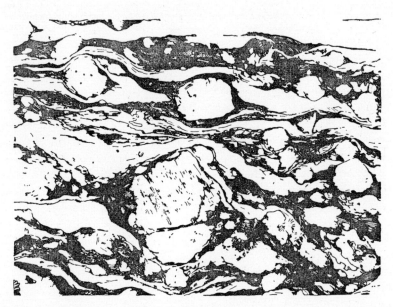

Fig. 55. Mylonite in tonalite Adamello Massif, Carisolo, Northern Italy. White patches are felspars, white zones are quartz, dark zones consist of dark minerals (biotite, etc.) *(After Malaroda, 1946. Published by permission of Istituto di Geologia, University of Padua.)*

and have then disappeared in the general crushing of the rocks. When this process of crushing advances still further there is recrystallization or a kind of fusion. The rocks are then termed "ultra-mylonites".

The particular type of brecciation or mylonitization which is developed is, of course, greatly dependent on the nature of the rock, the depth below the surface, and the stress-field. In crystalline rocks, fracture planes will immediately show lamination, since the shearing motion will take advantage of the mica-flakes and curve round the quartz and felspar crystal. To rupture the rock, the shearing stress must be much greater than the stress which will rupture sedimentary rocks. Rock-fracturing in granites and other massive crystalline rocks will, therefore, always take the form of mylonitization. The superficial mylonites of crystalline rocks show strong lamination and chloritization of all dark minerals. The rock can become so soft that one can crush it with the fingers. Going down into the earth's crust the mylonitization will be accompanied by more and more pulverization. The quartz and felspar minerals will be gradually crushed and appear as a vitreous matrix in which their uncrushed fragments appear as porphyroclastic elements on a dark background (Fig. 55). The extreme form of ultra-mylonitization has been reached when the matrix appears as a glass-like substance and the porphyroclasts have diminished to a diameter less than 0.02 mm (Staub, 1928). The ultramylonite material may be injected into tension cracks. When the injections attain considerable dimensions, they are termed "mylonite dikes" or "pseudo-tachylite" (Shand, 1916; Hall, A. L. and Molengraaff, G. A. F., 1925; Bearth, 1933). Another development of mylonitization is the mechanical gneissification of igneous rocks, of which "Augen-gneiss" is the most typical representative. This happens when the shear is not concentrated on a few very limited surfaces but becomes general, and when recrystallization in preferred directions predominates.

The development in sedimentary rocks is analogous. The most superficial fracturing is described as tectonic brecciation. In all classifications of breccias, these tectonic breccias are distinguished from sedimentary breccias (cf. Reynolds, 1928; Norton, 1917; Leuchs, 1933), but their field characteristics are very similar. Breccias of this kind are frequent in limestones, which are brittle rocks when near the surface. The result is a zone full of angular limestone fragments in a finer limestone matrix very like a primary sedimentary breccia. When the intensity of movement and the depth increase, the limestone becomes more and more plastic, and the final stage is a marble mylonite such as is found, for instance, at the base of thrust sheets. When the movement is no longer concentrated on limited surfaces but becomes general, we find that the whole limestone has been marmorized.

In shaly rocks, crush zones are often developed as clay streaks, and when shales or marls alternate with limestones the clay may lubricate the fault-plane even where it crosses the limestone. At the surface such clay streaks can seldom be found, but in artificial exposures in mines or tunnels they are frequently encountered. Mylonitic and fracture zones in both igneous and sedimentary rocks are great sources of danger in tunnelling. They are very often water conduits, and the whole crushed rock may start to flow into the tunnel if precautions are not taken immediately.

Mylonitic zones in igneous and metamorphic rocks have a far greater importance than in unmetamorphosed sedimentary rocks, for they are often the only traces that the tectonic stress has left. They are difficult to trace, however, because erosion has often taken advantage of the disintegration of the rock along the mylonitic zones, and river courses mask their presence.

BOUDINAGE, MULLION, AND ROD STRUCTURES

Peculiar shapes of a sausage-like appearance in sandstone and limestone beds, always parallel to the b (fold) axis, have been called "boudins", and the phenomenon "boudinage" (Lohest, 1909). These structures are typical of competent bands interbedded with incompetent rocks and represent rounded segments (Fig. 56) of the rigid bed. The

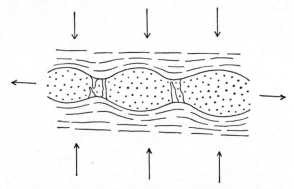

Fig. 56. Boudinage in a sandstone bed between slates. The cracks between the boudins are filled with recrystallized quartz.

pinched intersections between the segments almost invariably show recrystallization of the rock material — quartz when the competent bed is a sandstone, calcite when it is limestone. In one instance I have even noticed that a boudinaged limestone with chert layers showed recrystallized calcite opposite the limestone and recrystallized quartz opposite the chert bands (Fig. 57). There can be no doubt, therefore, that the intersections represent zones of tension, and consequently that the whole phenomenon is attributable to stretching of the competent bed in the direction of the dip; or conversely, to compression of the bed perpendicular to the bedding. The fact that boudinage occurs only in strongly compressed areas of isoclinal folds supports this view.

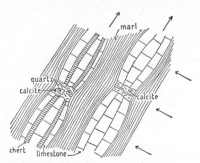

Fig. 57. Boudinage in limestone with chert beds. Opposite the chert beds the filling of the cracks between the boudins consists of quartz.

Boudinage is not restricted to sedimentary beds but also occurs in quartz veins (Lohest, 1909) and dikes (Holmquist, 1931).

The boudins themselves have also often been fractured by shear-planes oblique to the bedding. In an advanced stage of boudinage the elongated segments may be separated completely and linked only by thin streaks of their recrystallized components (see, for instance, E. Cloos, 1947a, with many illustrations and bibliography).

The usual first stage of boudinage is presumably the development of jointing of the ordinary kind perpendicular to the bedding, but it can also begin as shear-joints oblique to the bedding (Fig. 58). In the Pyrenees I have found a rather exceptional kind of stretching in the direction of the bedding: the shape of the segmented rock does not resemble the classical boudins, never-

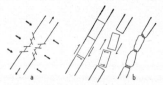

Fig. 58. Development of boudinage from oblique shear-joints due to stretching *a*, or from rotational joints due to concentric shear *b*.

theless it has the same origin. In the isoclinal folds of Devonian limestones with shale streaks which occur in the axial zone of the central Pyrenees, the limestone has become incompetent in relation to the intercalated thin shale beds, perhaps through the influence of nearby granite intrusions. The shale beds have been broken and one can see (Fig. 74) that the limestone has flowed into the cracks. The same phenomenon is seen in the drawing of microfolds, Fig. 237, where the limestone flows into cracks in the intercalated chert beds and calcite even recrystallizes in the cracks. The shale fragments in Fig. 74 become smaller when the shale beds become thinner; and when the rock becomes thoroughly tectonized, one sees only dark shale lenses in the white limestone.

Mullion structures are closely related to boudinage but have a some-what different origin. Wilson (1953) firstly distinguishes mullion structures from rodding, mullions being formed from the normal country rock, and rods from quartz that has been introduced into or has segregated in the rocks. Among these mullions he then distinguishes (1) bedding mullions or fold mullions, (2) cleavage mullions, and (3) irregular mullions. I should like to add (4) boudinage mullions (Fig. 59). Fold mullions are formed by small folds, with curvatures up to say three feet, and are therefore always parallel to the *b* axis of the general structure. They are not complete cylinders; they generally

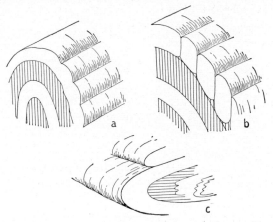

Fig. 59. Mullion structures. *a* boudinage mullions, *b* cleavage mullions, *c* fold mul-lions. (*b and c after Wilson, Proceedings of the Geological Association, vol.* 64, 1953.)

have the form of a semi-cylinder or of a lesser segment. The surface may be lineated, either by the intersections of cleavage and folded bedding-planes or by folded bedding-planes with different curvature; such lineations will lie in the *b* axis. Or it may be lineated by striation in the direction of movement, lying in the *ac* plane.

Cleavage mullions are due to the intersection of cleavage-planes and bedding-planes. In cross section they may be either angular, or rounded off like fold mullions. They lie in the *b* axis of the folds. Some mullions described by Wilson have very irregular cylindrical surfaces, and are coated, as are the other types, by a thin micaceous veneer. Their origin remains obscure.

Quartz rods are frequent in severely crumpled metamorphic rocks. As soon as quartz veins have developed (mainly by segregation from the

country rock in zones of minimum tension, but also by recrystallization on cleavage-planes), subsequent internal movement may crumple
them and form cylindroidal quartz rods. They occur more frequently
in the incompetent rocks between competent beds, since internal
movement is concentrated in these more plastic intercalations. They
do not occur in pure cleavage folding, where crumpling is rare; but
they are frequent in the intermediate stages of concentric and fracture-
cleavage folding. In minute folding of the pinched type they can form
as saddle reefs in the anticlinal hinges.

PTYGMATIC STRUCTURES

This term, coined by Sederholm (1913), connotes contorted veins
which show a meander-like pattern. They occur most frequently as

 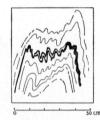

pegmatitic veins in either migmatites
or in gneisses, but occasionally consist of other material. Their most
distinctive feature is their apparent
independence of the texture of their
host rock; in particular, the schistosity planes of the country rock do not
cross the ptygmas. Nevertheless, the
numerous illustrations given by Sederholm (1913), Milch (1900), Read
(1928), Kuenen (1938), and Wilson
(1952) contain quite a few examples
in which the folding process of the

Fig. 60. Ptygmatic veins from
Finland with deformation concordant with that of country rock.
*(After Kuenen.   Published by
permission of the Geological Society
of Finland.)*

ptygma is obviously due to the same process of deformation along
planar shear-planes which prevails in the country rock. Such ptygmas
show attenuated limbs and thickened hinges, and their axial plane is
parallel to the prevailing schistosity. Only the foliation of the host rock
is missing (Fig. 60). Kuenen (1938) has illustrated by experiment the
possibility of the development of this type of ptygma by deformation of
a planar vein during deformation of the country rock around it. The lack
of foliation in the vein is doubtless due to some difference in physical
properties such as a slightly greater rigidity. These concordant ptygmas
are not, however, the most typical kind. Wilson quotes several instances
(his Figures 1, 3, 7, 8, and 9; the last is reproduced here as Fig. 61) in
which the country rock either shows no regular foliation at all or has
foliation which is deflected along the margins of the ptygma. In the

non-foliated migmatites of the first type a texture parallel to the ptygma is visible, as is shown in Fig. 61. Wilson concludes from this evidence that the vein material was injected in the fashion of putty injected into a jelly, and that it attained its tortuous shape when an obstacle prevented its further forward advance; he illustrates his thesis with experiments. According to this view the ptygma is a primary structure injected at a stage when the texture of the host rock had

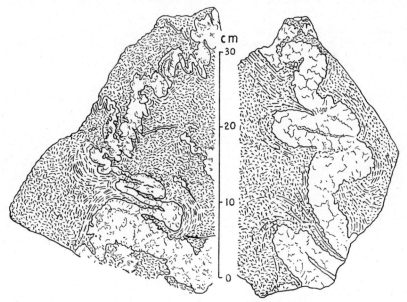

Fig. 61. Ptygmatic veins from Finland with deformation independent of that of country rock (migmatite). *(After Wilson, Geological Magazine, vol. 89, 1952. Published by permission of the Editor.)*

already been fixed. The contortions are thought to be due to plastic buckling of a material slightly more rigid than the host rock, injected by means of magmatic pressure. Apart from the difficulty of imagining a migmatite or a gneiss of such jelly-like substance, the main argument in favour of such a process — the local parallel texture of the host rock — is certainly not convincing.

On the contrary, it is clear that the cause of the peculiarity of every ptygmatic structure lies in a difference in physical properties between the vein and host rock material. They react differently in the stress-field. Their differential response to the strain of the whole rock-mass will necessarily cause slipping and drag on the boundary planes. If the host rock is a migmatite without foliation this does not mean that it has not been tectonized, but only that its internal deformation has not been orientated – or not visibly orientated. Many of the ptygmatic veins are probably segregation veins which originated during the migmatization or granitization process; they do not represent a faithful recording of the strain of the whole rock mass, because there is no reason to expect segregation to take place along planar surfaces only.

Chapter 7

Structural Petrology, Cleavage, and Schistosity

In concentric folding most of the slip is concentrated along the bedding-planes, although some movement also takes place along a number of concentric slip-planes inside a particular bed. In planar-shear, however, the bedding-plane plays a much less prominent role, and the deformation is often mainly, and sometimes wholly, expressed by a multitude of internal planar shear-planes.

Fig. 62. Fracture-cleavage in slate-sandstone alternation in anticlinal hinge of Ordovician fold, Rio Lladorre, Spanish Pyrenees.

93

This type of deformation merits our special attention because it requires special methods of study. The study of concentric folding or faulting is based principally on the outward shape of the distortions as defined by curved or broken bedding-planes. In planar-shear the bedding is as often as not partially or completely destroyed. The subject must consequently be studied by other means.

CLEAVAGE

We shall start with a description of a few rock samples.

The first is a slab of rock consisting of a rapid alternation of sandstone and slate, from the Ordovician in the Rio Lladorre of the Spanish

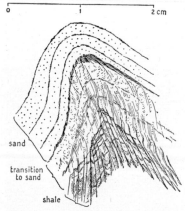

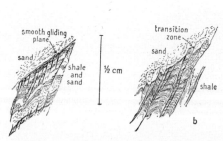

Fig. 63. Detail of microfold of specimen of Fig. 62, showing concentric folding in sandstone, fracture-cleavage in slate.

Fig. 64. Details of same specimen of Fig. 62; a, smooth gliding plane along abrupt bedding-plane, b, transition from cleavage to concentric folding when there is a transition from sand to slate.

Pyrenees (Fig. 62). The Ordovician series there is very thick, comprising several thousand metres of slates, sandstones, and grits. Although it is pretty certain that anticlinal and synclinal hinges exist, it is almost impossible to observe these folds directly in the isoclinal sequence. The series has a general dip of 60–80° North and an E–W strike. On the road along the Rio Lladorre, one of the very few known hinges can be observed, and the present specimen, Fig. 62, shows the crumpled condition of the strata on the top of the anticlinal hinge.

Comparing details of thicknesses at the hinge and on the flanks of the folds, it is clear that the slate layers thin out on the flanks to a much greater extent than the sand-layers. The figure reveals that this thinning in the slate is due to a multitude of small parallel shear-planes, oblique to the stratification in the flanks and perpendicular to it in the hinges. These shear-planes are lacking in the sand-layers. In some instances, as in Fig. 63, we can see that the sand-layers are deformed by concentric shearing parallel to the bedding — we can discern a concentric pattern due to very thin shale films, within the sand, along which the movement has taken place. This is confirmed by the fact that the upper limit of this sand describes a much broader arc, and is thus concentric with its steeply pinched lower boundary. When the shale sand limit is sharp we see that the sand-layer has moved along the boundary plane, sharply cutting off the parallel shear-planes within the shale (Fig. 64a). When on the other hand there is a gradual transition from shale to sand, the parallel shear-planes continue into the sand, and are only gradually replaced by a concentric shear (as in Fig. 64b).

The co-existence in the same minute fold of concentric shear and cleavage is therefore clearly demonstrated. Concentric shear in the competent, hard, and brittle sandstone layers, and cleavage in the incompetent, soft, and ductile shale layers, occur quite independently of the stratification, which is much better developed in the shales than in the sands.

Let us consider the cleavage in some greater detail. The frequency of cleavage-planes in the shale layers of the present specimen is about 5 per mm in the flanks of folds, and about $3^1/_2$ per mm on the hinges. Moreover, the frequency is to some extent dependent on the sand content: a sandy shale layer has only half the number of shear-planes. In one instance the top of the shale layer contains less sand and about twice as many shear-planes as the bottom.

The sand-layers are concentrically folded to maximum compression within the geometrical limits of this kind of folding. This necessitates the accommodation of the shaly parts to the spaces left between the folds of sandstone; this is chiefly accomplished by cleavage.

A particularly clear instance illustrating the different roles of the sandstone and shale layers is provided by another Ordovician specimen from a different locality (Barradós Valley, Val d'Aran, Spanish Pyrenees), reproduced in Fig. 65. Here the space left between the double anticlinal hinge at the bottom and the single syncline at the top is filled by a sheared sandy-shale bed (now a biotite schist). The shear-planes

Fig. 65.   Sandstone-sandy-slate alternation in specimen from Ordovician of Río Barradós, Spanish Pyrenees.   By fracture-cleavage the slate adapts itself to the space left between sandstone folds.

are not clear cut; the mica schists are crumpled, and in the shear zones, which divide the rock into compartments, the mica flakes have a steeper inclination (Fig. 66). Sometimes both zones are about equal in width, 0.5 to 0.3 mm, and equal in angle of inclination; both are then about equally sheared. It is clear that the compression perpendicular to the major stress and the extension parallel to the smallest stress are mainly effected by a concertina-like movement. This mode of extension and compression is no way different from that of our first specimen. The two specimens differ only in the arrangement of the mica flakes.

In the Barradós specimen (Fig. 65) we have a particularly clear demonstration of the fact that cleavage is roughly parallel to the axial planes of the folds, except on the actual hinges where it deviates slightly. In none of the samples examined is there any trace of intersecting shear-planes. Whether the fold is steep or flat, the shear-planes are parallel. From this fact we can draw three conclusions:

1. Since the axial plane of any fold is always perpendicular to the direction of greatest stress, and since this kind of fracture-cleavage is parallel to the axial plane, it has been generated by the same stress.

2. Cleavage is therefore independent of the bedding-plane and of the lithology of the rock. We have also learned earlier that the cleavage-

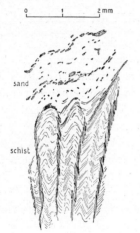

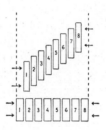

Fig. 66. Detail of fracture-cleavage in slate of Fig. 65.

Fig. 67. Lateral compression and vertical extension combined with shear.

planes are closely connected with crumpling; and crumpling involves dilatation in the plane perpendicular to the stress and compression in the stress direction. Our third conclusion can therefore be formulated as follows:

3. The cleavage-planes enclose narrow slices which have been compressed between them and have extended parallel to them. We shall call these minute slices "microlithons".

The process of the folding of a shale layer between two concentrically folded sandstone layers can be visualized in the manner of Fig. 67. If we imagine a row of clay bricks which are still plastic and which have slipped one over another, becoming flattened at the same time, we have an adequate analogy of the mechanism of cleavage. This kind of deformation is apparently quite compatible with concentric shear. Our examples have shown several kinds of transition from one mechanism to the other.

The cleavage in the shales can, of course, extend itself suddenly or gradually through the whole series, simply by cutting through the intervening sandstone layers. I think we are justified in regarding our Ordovician specimens as a transition phase between ordinary concentric folding and slaty-cleavage — the Rio Lladorre samples being nearer to ordinary folding, and the Barradós sample being further on the way to schistosity deformation.

SLATY OR TRUE CLEAVAGE, FLOW CLEAVAGE, AND FRACTURE-CLEAVAGE

In the foregoing description of Pyrenean Palaeozoic samples we have learned to distinguish the kind of cleavage which is usually called "fracture-cleavage". We concluded that it could develop into a general cleavage. Such a general cleavage is termed "slaty-cleavage" when recrystallization on the cleavage-planes is small. When other minerals, in addition to mica, become involved in the process of recrystallization (with the result that the original bedding disappears or is recognizable only as a faint relic texture) it is termed "flow cleavage".

On the other hand cleavage sometimes assumes a much coarser texture than is seen in our slightly metamorphic samples. In the same axial zone of the Pyrenees, for instance, there are Devonian limestones alternating with shales and sandstones, which are always sharply folded — isoclinally folded in the most strongly compressed zones — with strongly developed cleavage. The cleavage-planes often cut through the whole series, but the distance between the cleavage-planes can be measured in millimetres or even in centimetres instead of in tenths of millimetres. The whole folding mechanism of this series is based on this cleavage system. In other outcrops a fracture-cleavage in the shales is very pronounced, but cuts through the sandstones and limestones only in the anticlinal or synclinal hinges.

The explanation of fracture-cleavage in incompetent beds which one often encounters in textbooks, refers to the drag exercised on the incompetent beds by the slip of the competent beds above and below (cf. Wilson, 1946) as in Fig. 68a. The expression "drag" is not very satisfactory because the cleavage is not restricted to the flanks. It is equally well developed on the hinges, even when they are broad crestal zones where the dragging effect of the competent beds is surely absent.

Nor can this kind of fracture-cleavage be due to oblique-shear, for in that case we ought to find intersecting fracture-cleavage due to the rotation of the beds in relation to the deformation stress (Fig. 69).

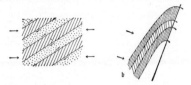

Fig. 68.   Fracture-cleavage; *a* seen as originated by drag of competent beds on shale. *b* in competent bed between slates with slaty-cleavage.

Sometimes we do find intersecting shear-planes in shale beds; the so-called "pencil shales", in which the rock breaks up into irregular elongated angular chips, may be an example. This kind of fracturing occurs in thick shale beds which have been rotated, by the bending of under-

Fig. 69.   Fracture-cleavage seen as oblique-shear in shale bed between competent beds.

lying or overlying competent beds, during the development of the shear-planes (cf. Fig. 70).

Another kind of fracture-cleavage is sometimes found in the competent beds of a severely compressed sequence; it must be seen as

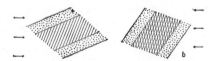

Fig. 70.   Intersecting oblique-shear generated in thick shale bed.

shear-planes oblique to the stress and the angle they make with the stress direction is dependent on the lithology of the rock (Fig. 68b).

My general experience, however, is that slaty-cleavage and fracture-cleavage are both roughly parallel to the axial plane, fracture-cleavage converging upwards towards the top of an anticline, true cleavage converging downwards to the anticlinal core as in Fig. 71.

In addition to slaty-cleavage, there are several other kinds of fracture planes, such as joints of various types, and also slickensiding.

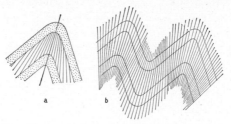

Fig. 71.   Fracture-cleavage *a* and slaty-cleavage *b*.

A shale bed between competent beds such as coal-seams is often slickensided parallel to the bedding. This slickensiding is an immediate result of the slipping of the competent beds along the bedding-planes and may be contemporaneous with the development of fracture-cleavage in the shales. Simultaneously, joints will be formed in the competent beds. I shall refer more extensively to joints in Chapter 9, but here it is worth noting that in a folded competent bed we can expect many types of joint. Three types are illustrated in Fig. 72:

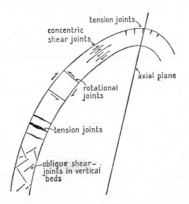

Fig. 72.   Joints in concentrically bent competent bed.

tension-joints develop in the regions of greatest curvature as a result of relaxation of the elastic bending; *rotational joints* are due to a couple, perpendicular to the bedding-plane and generated by the slip in opposite directions along the top and bottom of the competently folded bed. Finally, ordinary *shear-joints*, sometimes developed as fracture-cleavage as in Fig. 68b, can develop in the steep flank of a fold when further lateral shortening by folding becomes impossible. Such shear-planes may even be curved within one bed when the lithology changes, e.g. in a graded sandstone bed. We must remember, however, that an exposure of a fold shows us the final stage of a long history during which the beds have changed from one position to the next in space and in relation to the principal stress, in a continuous process; they carry all the scars inflicted upon them during that process. Moreover, a type of fracture belonging to an early stage may grade into another belonging to a later stage: Fig. 73, part of a close isoclinal fold in the

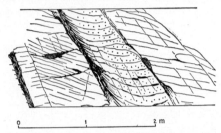

Fig. 73. Curved joints in graded sandstone, Devonian, of axial zone of the Pyrenees.

Central Pyrenees, represents a series of vertical beds of Devonian sand-stone of varying composition. The sandstone to the left shows only rotational joints; the next shows oblique-shear joints; and the one to the right, which is a graded sandstone, shows curved joints, curving from a perpendicular rotational joint position to an oblique-shear joint position, then to cleavage, and finally to slickensiding.

Resuming our discussion of the origin of slaty-cleavage, fracture-cleavage, and flow-cleavage, we must conclude from the field evidence that none of these can be due to oblique-shear; they must arise from simple flattening of the rock in a direction parallel to the largest principal stress, accompanied by differential movement along planes perpendicular to this stress. Such shear-planes have never been repro-duced in experiments, probably because laboratory experiments never reproduce this kind of elastico-viscous flow.

SCHISTOSITY

Following this reasoning, schistosity is merely a cleavage with clearly recrystallized micas on the cleavage-planes. In the sample of the Rio Lladorre, which we examined, the recrystallization is very slight or non-existent on the cleavage-planes, but quite marked on the bedding-planes at the top and bottom of the sand-layers. The rock still parts easily along these planes. It seems that it is the mica flakes bending from the cleavage-planes to the bedding-plane (see Fig. 66) which give this appearance of recrystallization on the bedding-plane. No wonder that field geologists often report that the schistosity coincides with bedding.

In true schistosity the cleavage-planes extend through all the layers that build up the rock. The bedding becomes largely or entirely obscured. The trained eye is often still able to discern its traces, however, by faint markings on the weathered surface.

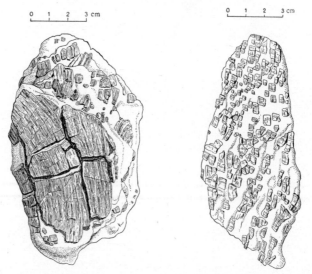

Fig. 74.   Two samples of fractured thin slate bed in limestone.

In an advanced state of schistosity, where the finer bedding has been totally obliterated by recrystallization of quartz as well as mica, the only indication of the original bedding may be coarser white bands in the dark coloured rock, oblique to the schistosity. Usually this strong recrystallization is partly due to thermal action by syntectonic intrusions or other magmatic activity, but it is the dynamic action which determines the texture. The importance of this dynamic action in the formation of schistose rocks is demonstrated by Fig. 74, which represents two specimens of limestone with thin shale beds. The folds that have been formed in this rock are isoclinal and almost vertical;

the limestone (white in the drawing) is extensively recrystallized. The thin shale beds, heavily slickensided, were not able to undergo the extreme stretching to which the limestone was subjected and broke up into small angular patches. The thicker the shale streaks, the larger the patches. The cracks between the patches were filled with calcite which has been weathered away again in our outcrop specimen. As the limestone underwent more and more deformation, the sharp edges of the shale patches were rounded off, and the final result is a marble with thin shale lenses. The whole process is of a mechanical nature, the formation of chlorite in the shale and the recrystallization of calcite in the limestone being of minor importance. The appearance of the final product of this process seen in a cross section is very similar to that of an "Augen-gneiss". There can be little doubt that such gneissic structure is mostly due to a similar process of deformation, helped of course by recrystallization.

We have already seen that in certain circumstances recrystallization also takes place on slip-planes which follow the bedding. We may therefore expect that bedding-planes can also become schistosity-planes or give rise to comparable metamorphic rock textures. They will differ from the ordinary schistosity described above in their lower dip. We do, in fact, encounter many descriptions of low-angle schistosity. At one time this was referred to as "load-schistosity", in particular by Daly, who thought the flattening in the sub-horizontal plane was mainly due to the load of the overlying rocks. Daly presumed that this recrystallization could develop at a depth of some 6-7 km, simply as a result of vertical pressure, or perhaps with the aid of a rise in temperature due to invading granites. There are strong reasons, however, for doubting the reality of this process. Sub-horizontal schistosity is typical of the Archean rocks of Scandinavia and Canada and Pennine nappes of the Alps. All these regions have been submitted to considerable lateral stress, causing enormous mass translations, and it is therefore highly probable that the sub-horizontal schistosity is also due to this lateral stress.

Turner, also, gives several reasons for doubting Daly's view (Turner and Verhoogen, 1951, pp. 574–5). He points out, for instance, that despite subjection to the requisite influences of pressure and temperature, hornfelses and other deeply buried silicate rocks have often no schistosity at all, particularly if they have not been involved in a major orogeny.

Indeed, it seems much more probable that the sub-horizontal

schistosity is due to recrystallization of the kind which develops on slip-planes in concentric folding, augmented by syntectonic intrusions. As we have seen earlier, those concentric slip-planes are due to original elastic bending or doming which occurs when the deformative stress has only just exceeded the strength.

Unfortunately we are not yet in a position to understand why in one case slaty-cleavage develops, in another fracture-cleavage, and again in others sub-vertical schistosity or sub-horizontal schistosity. No doubt variations in the combination of confining pressure, deformative stress, and temperature are the determining factors, but how the system works cannot yet be defined.

STRUCTURAL PETROLOGY

In order to assess the exact relation between known rock textures and the stress-field, the science of structural petrology has been developed. Although the work of Sander goes back to 1911, and his new textbook of 1950 lists some 350 studies on this subject, the influence of the methods of structural petrology on structural geology is still comparatively small.

The basic concept of the whole science is that by measuring statistically the preferred orientation of minerals in deformed rocks in relation to cleavage, fold axes, and other structural lines, it is possible to find a simple relation between stress and strain. This object has certainly not yet been realized. That there is some relation nobody doubts, but extensive research has shown that it is very complex. Statistical measurements show that the simple theoretical background of strain phenomena is inadequate to explain the observed orientations; they demonstrate emphatically that the reaction of the mineral grains to strain varies greatly. The systematic orientation of rock particles can frequently be measured without the help of the microscope, and one often gets a much clearer picture from megascopic study than from microscopic analysis. It should also be remarked that in many cases in which microscopic analysis gives a clear picture, simple observation of the rock exposure *in situ* would have also given the desired information, though not in the same detail since the orientation of the quartz or calcite grains remains hidden.

Notwithstanding the practical shortcomings of petrofabric methods, our knowledge of the variety of preferred orientation has been much advanced, its terminology has entered in our vocabulary, and some of its results have deepened our insight considerably. Here we can treat the subject only in a very superficial and inadequate way, since it needs a full textbook to explain its methods and results. (For fuller information see the textbooks of Sander, 1930 and 1950; Knopf and Ingerson, 1938; Fairbairn, 1942; Turner, 1948.)

The Theoretical Background of structural petrology is the same as that for the deformation of all solids, as treated in the foregoing chapters. Deformations are termed "affine" when they result from movement on a single set of parallel planes with equal direction and equal differential velocity on thin parallel layers of equal thickness. "Non-affine" movement occurs when the direction and velocity of movement is unequal and the parallel layers are of unequal thickness. Non-affine movements are much the most common, and create folds; affine movements are typical of the flanks of accordion folds. Both are generally described in textbooks on structural petrology as movements along shear-planes oblique to the deformative stress. We have seen, however, that this kind of shear-plane is rather rare in naturally deformed rocks; neither the concentric shear-planes, nor the slaty-cleavage shear-planes, nor the planar-shears of accordion folding, belong to this class. But in experiments, oblique-shear is very common.

The textbook explanation of oblique-shear leading to ordinary slaty-cleavage or schistosity points out that the two original sets of intersecting rupture shear-planes rotate as the flattening of rock proceeds; that when they finally arrive at a dead point not far away from a position perpendicular to the stress a new set is formed, and that this will rotate in turn. The observed single set of shear-planes is represented as a kind of accumulation of dead oblique shear-planes all rotated towards the 90° position. Other explanations for the preferred slip on one plane have been advanced, but none of them gives an adequate explanation of the great preponderance of only one schistosity- or cleavage-plane in non-metamorphic and in metamorphic rocks. Our assumption of an elastico-viscous flow and consequent elastically defined slip-planes in one set only, provides a more logical relation between stress and deformation. This does not mean that oblique-shear along two sets cannot occur; many metamorphic schists show them clearly and the common type of "Augen-gneiss" is certainly one of the rock types which is generated by this type of shearing. Besides the slip on one set of shear-planes, or on an intersecting set of slip-planes, with its accompanying lineation in the slip-direction (the a axis) one can expect rotational movement around axes perpendicular to the slip movement. All kinds of microfolds with accompanying mullion or rod structures can be formed, with a common orientation parallel to the fold axis (*b* axis). This is particularly true of rocks in which the original bedding or stratification remains a prominent factor during the process of tectonic deformation; in rocks with fracture-cleavage for instance.

The preferred orientation may be due to two different processes: on the one hand to tectonic deformation or reorientation of the minerals, and on the other to secondary growth of new minerals or extension of old minerals in preferred directions of minimum resistance. It will often be impossible to distinguish the two phenomena in thin sections.

The Petrofabric Methods. They are based on comparison of the megascopic data of the structure and the microscopic data of the

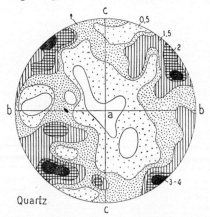

Fig. 75. Incomplete preferred reorientation of quartz optical axes, rhombic symmetry. *(After Niggli, Gesteine und Minerallagerstätten, vol. 1. Published by permission of Birkhauser A.G., Basel.)*

mineral orientation. Amongst the megascopic data the so-called *s* surfaces, which are any planes of slip (cleavage, bedding, or fractures), lineations on the *s* surfaces, and joints, are important. They are plotted on an equal area spherical projection, a Schmidt net. The direction of tectonic transport is called the *a* axis, which coincides with the slip-direction on an *s* surface, or with maximum elongation of particular rock particles (ooliths, for instance). Perpendicular to it one can distinguish the *b* axis, which is the axis of internal or external rotation or the intersection of bedding- and slip-planes. In general it will coincide with the fold axis. The *c* axis is perpendicular to *a* and *b*. All the movement usually takes place within the *ac* plane. As the determination of the *a* and *b* axes can often be done only after extensive microscopical study with the universal stage, a tentative scheme is established first and this may later be rotated until the desired coincidence between mineral orientation and elongation and the supposed tectonic directions has been established. There is no doubt that this procedure may be misleading, for the relation one is looking for may thus have been introduced into it beforehand.

Once the tectonic axes have been provisionally fixed, the orientations of the crsytallographic properties of the minerals are measured – the optical axes, cleavage, twin lamellae, etc., separately for each mineral – and are plotted on the equal area net, in which the a, b, and c axes are taken as co-ordinates. In order to bring out the pattern of preferred orientation the axes and poles of crystallographic orientation are counted within circles of 1% standard area, covering the whole net. With the help of density contours and by shading areas of equal density, the maxima are made easily legible (Fig. 75).

Symmetry of Preferred Orientation Pattern. The link between the observed pattern of the preferred orientation and the mechanics of deformation is forged by the symmetry of the pattern, which has proved to be a reflection of the internal tectonic movement. The kinematic interpretation may be wrong in many cases, because our theoretical and practical knowledge of what really happens is certainly inadequate, but nevertheless the identification of symmetry remains a fact.

Three kinds of symmetry are observed in the orientation patterns:

1. Triclinic symmetry, or absence of any plane of symmetry. It is typical of flow-structures without preferred direction of internal movement, or of two succeeding deformation phases which were not parallel.

2. Monoclinic symmetry, with one plane of symmetry, which in most cases can be identified with the plane of schistosity or cleavage.

3. Orthorhombic symmetry, with three mutually perpendicular planes of symmetry, which is in agreement with oblique-shear.

The measurements are carrried out on a variety of minerals, mainly mica, quartz, felspars, hornblende, and calcite, and on easily recognizable crystallographic properties such as the cleavage of micas, the optical axes of quartz and hornblende, and the twinning planes of felspars and of calcite. Often the orientation diagrams of different minerals in the same slide have different symmetries; for instance mica flakes are generally more or less parallel to the main slip-plane (s plane) of schistosity showing a monoclinic symmetry, but the quartz grains are inclined to this plane, showing an orthorhombic symmetry. The explanation is often difficult and sometimes very dubious. It is generally believed that quartz is the most mobile of all the minerals, and the most apt to be reorientated. The fact that the mica and quartz diagrams have different symmetries is therefore

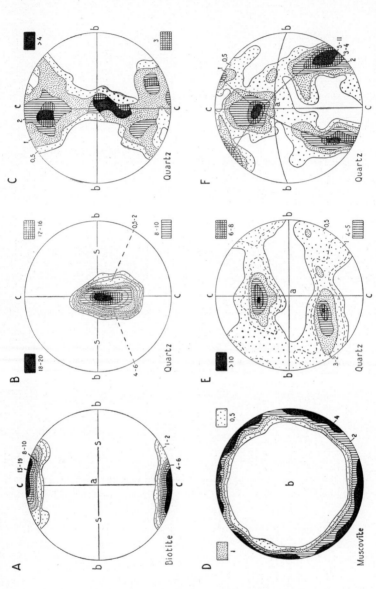

Fig. 76. Different patterns of preferred orientation. A. Biotite axes maximum vertical to schistosity plane. Garnet schist from S. Valpurga d'Ultimo. B. Quartz axes maximum parallel to an axis in granite mylonite, Odenwald. C. Girdle of quartz axes in a-c plane. Quartzite from East Alps. D. Girdle in a-c plane of muscovite cleavage. Mica schist from Schimborn. E. Two small girdles of quartz optical axes. Granulite from Saxony. F. Two crossing girdles of quartz optical axes. Granulite from Finland.   *(After Niggli, Gesteine und Minerallagerstätten, vol. 1.   Published by permission of Birkhäuser A.G., Basel.)*

often ascribed to a later reorientation of the quartz. Another solution of the contradictory symmetries of these two minerals can be drawn from our experience of microfolds, in which we often notice that several kinds of deformation can co-exist in the same microstructure. In Chapter 22, Fig. 237 I give a clear example of this. Oblique-shear, flow-cleavage, drag-folds, and concentric folding, and still other types of internal deformation are clearly shown to have acted simultaneously in the same fold, doubtless because most of the internal deformation was influenced both by an elastic stress-field and by a permanent stress-field. Or, if objections are raised to the complete simultaneity of the different modes of distortion, it would not invalidate our assumption of coexistence if these modes followed one another in a quick succession within the same folding process. Both assumptions, simultaneity and quick succession, have the same result — different modes of deformation coexisting in the same fold and due to only one folding process. We therefore consider it quite possible that one mineral reacts to the flattening and another to the rotational or oblique-shear, both in the course of the same process of distortion.

The preferred orientation minerals can assume either of two patterns — maxima (m) or girdles (g). There may be several maxima in one section; several girdles are much less common. The maxima are often enclosed in a girdle pattern (Fig. 76).

Significance of Preferred Orientation Patterns. Turner (1948) gives a very useful compilation of the significance of the orientation patterns in terms of tectonic or growth structures, which I shall follow here in a slightly modified form (Fig. 77):

I. A concentration of poles in one maximum m.

    a. presence of a single set of s planes, the pole of which coincides with m, commonly shown by (001) of mica either due to growth in a plane of least resistance or to mechanical reasons; common for (001) in mica and ($01\overline{1}2$) of calcite (IA).

    b. presence of a single set of s planes within which m coincides with direction of slip. Very common in quartz (0001) (IB).

    c. presence of a b axis whose pole coincides with m, either by mechanical reasons or due to fabric growth of prismatic crystals in that direction; (001) in hornblende, for instance (IC).

II. An arcuate girdle of concentration in a great circle. The measured optical directions tend to fall within a plane surface.

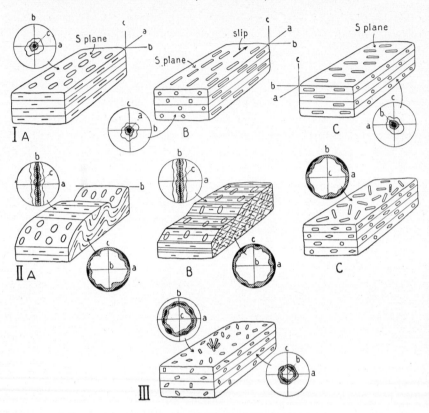

Fig. 77.   Preferred orientation patterns of different structural features.   For
explanation see text.

a. The same case as in IA, but the single set of s planes has been
    folded; the fold-axis is then the axis of the girdle (001) in mica
    and chlorite, (01$\bar{1}$2) in calcite, (0001) in quartz (fig. IIA).
b. Intersection of several sets of s planes in a line coinciding
    with the axis of the girdle (b axis); (001) in mica and chlorite,
    (01$\bar{1}$2) in calcite, (0001) in quartz (IIB).
c. The same case as in IA or IB but the faces or cleavage parallel
    to the axes of the prismatic minerals, and not the axes them-
    selves.
d. Growth of elongated crystals with their longest dimension
    (e.g. 001 in hornblende) orientated at random in a plane
    of minimum resistance to growth, which coincides with the
    plane of the girdle (IIc).

III. A girdle which is *not* a great circle but a small circle of the sphere of projection. The measured optical lines thus tend to lie on the surface of a cone (Fig. III).

    a. The measured optical direction makes an angle with the crystal face orientated in *s*. This is essentially the same case as IA except that some optical angle and not the crystal faces is measured; as for instance the (0001) axis of calcite which is orientated in the *s* plane according to its (01$\bar{1}$2) faces. The diameter of the ring is then 52°.

    b. The *b* axis is an axis of rotation, the pole of which coincides with the centre of the ring. Quartz diagrams very often show this arrangement.

With all these possible orientation diagrams in mind it is usual to distinguish, in accordance with Sander, between *S*-tectonites and *B*-tectonites.

S-tectonites are those in which a single well-developed planar schistosity is characterized by lack of any pronounced lineation. Elongated crystals are absent or are inconspicuous. In consequence the preferred orientation diagrams are mostly of the type of IA, a single maximum, or sometimes of the type of III, a single "cleft girdle". The rocks which have been marked by a single slip movement or are flattened without prominent lineation belong to this *S* category.

B-tectonites are those rocks whose fabric is characterized by a linear parallelism of elements to the *b* axis. There is generally some external evidence of rotation of individual crystals or layers, as in the types IC and IIA; *a c* girdles are typical of the *B*-tectonites. When the rotation is clearly indicated they are sometimes classified as *R*-tectonites, to distinguish them from *B*-tectonites which are due to intersection of *s* planes (type IIB). A *B*-tectonite is, then, the result of intersecting oblique-shear. Notwithstanding the very detailed method of analysis of preferred orientation in metamorphic rocks, of which only the broadest outlines have been sketched in the foregoing pages, the interpretative value is still doubtful. We shall learn in the course of our descriptions of structures that hardly any deformation of rocks in slightly metamorphosed zones (epi- and mesozones) is simple. In an accordion-fold, for instance, the flanks form *s* planes parallel to the bedding, but in the axial planes we find flexural slip combined with planar slip and recrystallization along the *B* axis. In the examples of fracture-cleavage in Figs. 68 and 71, we find a combination of *s* planes parallel to the axial plane and flexural slip along the bedding-planes. It is possible that in deeper metamorphic zones the orientation pattern becomes more simple through the preponderance of flow-cleavage, but in this case we might also expect to get more lineation in the b axis and even undirectional flow. The method has one great advantage over any megascopic measurements in that it reveals the orientation of quartz, calcite, and felspar, which is not observable without the use of the universal stage. A great disadvantage from which the whole petrofabric method has suffered is the fact that it has been first applied to structural problems which could not be solved otherwise. The interpretation of its results could therefore not be tested or checked against other tectonic data.

In my opinion the interpretational problems can be solved only by careful fabric studies of structures whose major features and micro-structures are both well known beforehand. The tendency to depend on deformation experiments in the laboratory in order to find the solution is to my mind a wrong road; we have, for the same reason that megascopic imitation experiments will always fail in dynamic similarity, not the slightest guarantee that the experiment arrives at an identical structure by the same path as in nature.

Part Two

Comparative Structural Geology

Introduction

When we leave the theoretical and experimental study of the deformation of rocks and direct our attention to the facts observed in nature, we meet with great difficulty in applying our former findings to our later observations.

This discrepancy is due to a different approach to the subject matter. The experimental study was mostly concerned with the mechanics of inner deformation, on the scale of the rock-grain, whereas ordinary tectonic study in the field is mostly concerned with the shape of a structure on the scale of major folds or faults, the latter scale being at least 100,000 times the former. No wonder that a chasm exists between the two points of view.

This chasm has been bridged to a certain extent by the imitative experiments whose important results we have already indicated, and by the science of structural petrology. This latter subject, however, cannot reveal any tectonic feature unless a reorientation of the grains has taken place, and in most unmetamorphosed rocks there has been no reorientation. Nevertheless, the methods of structural petrology have been applied with considerable success to megascopic features of rock distortion.

This difference in approach to the study of the tectonics of metamorphic rocks and of the non-metamorphic sedimentary cover, reflects a fundamental difference in the way the rocks yielded to the stress-condition, in the "basement" and in the "sedimentary blanket". Each division has its own structural characteristics, due in the first place to an increase of temperature and hydrostatic pressure downwards. Hence we must distinguish between "basement tectonics" and "sedimentary-cover tectonics". Obviously there must exist a roughly horizontal plane or a transition zone between the two modes of deformation, separating the basement from its sedimentary cover. When this plane coincides with a pronounced break in the nature of the rocks, such as the break between the folded Hercynian basement and its Mesozoic cover in most Tertiary mountain systems in Europe, this feature then becomes by far the most important structural factor. Often, however, the division plane is not provided with such a prominent and predestined horizon, and a transition zone is developed. In the first case, that of a clear-cut boundary plane, we find totally different tectonic shapes above the plane and below; such superficial structures have been called "plis de couverture" (superficial folds) by Argand (1916) (or epidermic folds by Escher). It is with these superficial folds in sedimentary rocks that we shall be mainly occupied in the next chapters. Other structures reach much deeper, and their forms do not differ materially from those of their upper reaches except in size. This deep-reaching kind of structure has been called a "plis de fond" (deep-seated) by Argand (derma fold by Escher). The structural features in its lowest reaches comprise the structural features of metamorphic rocks.

The plane which separates the superficial fold from its basement is the plane of "décollement", which we can translate as a basal shearing-plane or plane of detachment. The production of this phenomenon is not only due to the difference in the mode of rock-yield to stress with increasing depth, but is also inherent in all concentric folding processes, independent of depth or temperature. It is an essential consequence of the geometry of the superficial concentric fold, as we shall explain later. Minor basal shearing-planes do, therefore, almost invariably develop in the vertical range of superficial folds. There are, then, three factors which tend to separate the upper sedimentary cover from a differently folded substratum. First, the increase of hydrostatic pressure and temperature; secondly, the nature of the rocks; and thirdly, the geometry of the concentric fold. In the case of the European example already quoted, a Mesozoic cover on a Hercynian basement, the effects of the three factors often more or less coincide on a single level, but elsewhere there is frequently no such coincidence and less obvious structural features develop.

Structural geology describes the deformations which result from the action of stress conditions in the earth's crust, as we can observe them at the surface and at depth. Our depth of penetration below the surface is not very large, since the deepest mines reach only some 2,000 m and the deepest boreholes useful for structural purposes do not generally reach more than twice that depth. On the other hand, the greatly variable depth of erosion due to uplift of portions of the earth's crust gives us opportunity to look at structures which were originally buried beneath great masses of other rocks.

It is obviously impossible for one geologist to see and judge with his own eyes a sufficient number of typical structures, and he is obliged to draw heavily upon published reports. But in the majority of cases the published sections and maps are interpreted representations of observed facts and not the facts themselves, and are therefore strongly charged with the subjective views of the observer. By using these data indiscriminately we should probably arrive at a classification of different schools of thought instead of a systematic classification of structural features. Hence it is most important to use only those sections which are fully factual; those in which subjective interpretation plays a minor role.

We can find the kind of data we need in the deep ravines of mountain systems; and also in artificial exposures produced by mining.

We shall start our survey with faults of different kinds, since they represent the less complicated features of deformation, and proceed to simple folds in which we shall again observe many different kinds of faults. Finally, we shall try to penetrate somewhat deeper into the relation between sedimentary history and structural features, and into the relation between structures of different classes.

Chapter 8

Origin of Faults

Faults are an extremely common feature in all deformed strata; and even in unfolded strata, if we regard joints as very small faults. In our theoretical and experimental studies we found that nearly all deformation can be considered as movement along shearing-planes; that its effects may be either invisible or healed by recrystallization, or visible as planes along which either small or comparatively large translations have taken place. In the majority of cases, faults are simply such shearing-planes along which a great deal of deformation has been concentrated. The total slip along hundreds of thousands of small closely packed shearing-planes can alternatively be concentrated on one plane, parallel to the small ones, with a hundred- or thousand-fold larger motion and with the same overall result. When the shear-planes are small and numerous we speak of plastic deformation, and "folding" or "flexuring"; when there are a few large shearing-planes we call the deformation "rupture" and speak of faults. There is no fundamental difference however between "rupture" and "plastic" deformation, between "faulting" and "folding". In the next chapter, where I compare faults with joints, we shall see that all transitions between folding and faulting do actually exist in nature.

Why then do the deformations in one case occur along numerous small shearing-planes and in another along a few large planes? There is no one simple answer to this question. Sometimes there is simply no place for further folding. Sometimes a secondary tension causes faults. In many cases we do not know the answer.

CLASSIFICATION OF FAULTS

According to Anderson (1951), the three main types of faults — (1) normal or tension-faults, (2) thrust-faults, and (3) tear- or wrench-faults — differ only in the varying orientation of the three principal stresses in relation to the earth's surface.

118

All three are shear-planes of which the acute angle is intersected by the largest principal stress, and which are parallel to the median principal stress. When the median principal stress lies in the horizontal plane we get either thrust planes, when the largest stress is also in the horizontal plane (Fig. 78B), or normal faults, when the largest stress is vertical (Fig. 78A). When the median stress is vertical we get wrench-faults (Fig. 78C). In general a stress condition in the upper part of the earth's crust will be a tangential pressure or tension. A tensional stress in a horizontal direction will represent the smallest principal stress, and the largest stress will result from the weight of the rock acting in a vertical direction. The result will be a normal fault. In the case of a horizontal tangential pressure we can find either wrench-faults, which result in an extension in the horizontal plane, or thrust-faults, which mean an extension in a vertical sense. Hence, according to this simplified reasoning, we might expect thrust-faults near the surface and wrench-faults at depth. So far this reasoning does not indicate why in one case we find folds and in another case thrust- or wrench-faults, and why normal faults have no apparent counterpart in fold tectonics. The latter query is easiest to answer. When a tensional stress in a horizontal direction is applied, the confining pressure is also lowered, and we have seen already that rupture in the sense of movement along a single plane is more easily performed with low confining pressure. We have seen that this is due to the fact that the normal stress on the shearing-plane is decreased to such an extent that the cohesion of the grains is completely lost as soon as the motion starts. A tension stress will, therefore, nearly always produce a normal fault or tension crack and very rarely anything else.

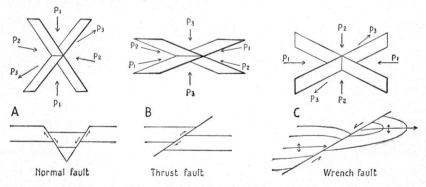

Fig. 78. The origin of faults. P_1 = largest, P_2 = median, and P_3 = smallest principal stress.

It is more difficult to understand which factors determine the preference for a fold, a thrusted structure, or wrench-faulting. First of all, the three modes of deformation are often mixed up in nature. When there is thrust-faulting in the superficial layer, there is usually folding as well, inseparably associated. Wrench-faulting and folding are often similarly associated. In general we find that really big wrench-faults and some thrust-faults originate in the basement and are features which penetrate deep into the earth's crust, whereas smaller faults of both kinds are closely connected with folding in the sedimentary blanket. There are, however, wrench-fault patterns which are more or less independent of folding, and we may presume that in those cases there actually existed a tensional stress in the horizontal plane. Yielding in a horizontal direction thus replaces ordinary folding by wrench-faulting. Folding along vertical axes might be produced instead of wrench-faulting in such circumstances, but it appears to be extremely rare in the superficial sedimentary layers. It may play a much larger role in the dynamo-metamorphic field.

There is a fourth kind of fault, unconnected with oblique-shear, and parallel to the cleavage-plane. It often occurs in microstructures, but is very difficult to map in megastructures. Some of the upthrusts and some of the mylonite zones in metamorphic or crystalline massifs probably belong to this category.

In order to relate, as far as possible, our theoretical reasoning and observed phenomena in our study of faults, we shall first discuss the joint and fault patterns which have been observed, and then proceed to normal faulting and wrench-faulting. Thrust-faulting will be treated in a separate chapter after we have considered fold mechanics.

THE STRAIN ELLIPSOID

Rock deformation has often been described both by the deformation of a unit square and by that of a unit circle. By inserting the circle in the square, as in Fig. 79, we get both of them at the same time. The kind of deformation indicated in Fig. 79A is then called "pure shear" and that of Fig. 79B "simple shear". The ellipses are congruent in both cases, which shows that the final shape cannot indicate the kind of deformation which actually took place. Because the simple shear is accompanied by a rotational movement of the strain ellipsoid it is also called simple rotational shear. In Fig. 79C the identity of the different modes of deformation has been illustrated so far as the resulting shapes are concerned.

A normal stress will always create a shearing stress, and whether the actual deformation takes place by pure or simple shear, the shape of the deformed object is identical. The rotation in Fig. 79B is an apparent one, a displacement of the unit in space only, and has nothing to do with the internal deformation of the rock, nor with any peculiarity of the stress-field. The strain ellipsoid is nothing but a simple graphic way of demonstrating the geometric consequence of a deformation and has no physical sense.

All this does not mean that there is no difference between simple and pure shear, but only that the final shape of any unit particle of

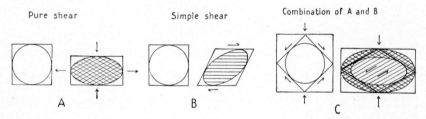

Fig. 79. The strain ellipsoid, A-pure shear, B-simple shear, C-combination of A and B.

rock cannot inform us about the mode of deformation. Pure and simple shear have no definite significance concerning the mode of deformation; they may mean, for instance, only that in pure shear both possible shear-planes have been active, and in simple shear only one set. On the other hand pure shear might mean a fluid or a purely plastic deformation involving extension in only one direction and compression in the others, without any shear-planes.

Hence the use of the strain ellipsoid in structural problems is often misleading, even in structural petrology where the shear-planes are visibly planes of movement, since we still do not know the real function of such a shear-plane.

Chapter 9

Joint-Patterns and Fault Patterns

The relation between joint-patterns and stress-direction has often been investigated, but that between joints and faults has received much less attention. It has nevertheless been assumed in general that there exists a certain relationship.

Both joints and faults are believed to have a common origin in deformative stress acting during a folding phase, and must therefore be closely related. The nature of this relation, however, has seldom been ascertained. In general the belief prevails that there exists a gradual transition from joints with no motion along their faces, through joints with a small motion, to small faults, and then to large faults.

THE RELATION BETWEEN JOINT AND FAULT PATTERNS

The Heidelberg school of joint investigation,* for instance, tried originally to prove the compressive origin of the great Upper Rhine rift valley by extensive joint surveys on both its sides. It failed completely in its purpose but gave us valuable general data. In the later surveys of this group the original purpose was abandoned. Most of the joints proved to be vertical, one group with horizontal and another with vertical striation, but there were none consistently dipping away from the rift and showing dip-striation. This extensive survey, therefore, more or less proved that there is no relation between the great rift faults, which have since been proved to be normal faults heading towards the rift valley, and the joints on both sides of the trough.

Another instance in which this relation was the subject of a survey is work by Kwantes (in Sax, 1946), in the South Limburg coalfield of the Netherlands.

* Salomon, 1911, 1925, 1927; Dinu, 1912; Engstler, 1913; Hillebrand, 1934; Lind, 1910; Pfannenstiel, 1927; Roehrer, 1916, 1922; Voelcker, 1927.

This report tells us that the NW direction of the major post-Carboniferous faults (Fig. 101) is *not* represented in the joint diagrams of the Carboniferous rocks, and that several maxima of the tension-joints diagrams, in particular the E–W one, are *not* represented in the fault pattern (Fig. 80). Other directions, noticeably of N60° W and N55° E, are maxima in both the fault and shear-joint patterns. The survey was extremely extensive. The faults were measured from the colliery production maps and the joint survey was carried out in several mines by trained geologists. We may conclude that the shear-joints and the majority of the fault-directions are both due to the folding-stress of late Carboniferous origin. Some tension-joint directions, probably of the same age, are not duplicated by a corresponding set of faults, however, and the Mesozoic stress or tension, causing the major NW–SE trending faults, although active at several distinct periods from the Triassic onward to recent times, did not cause a joint-pattern in the older rocks. This result accords with the negative result of the Heidelberg survey.

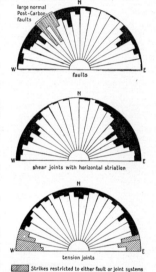

Fig. 80. Strike frequency diagrams of faults and joints in the South Limburg Coalfield. *(After Sax. Published by permission of Geologisch Bureau voor het Mijngebied, Heerlen.)*

Another set of observations may contribute to the solution of our problem. In vertical aerial photographs of an adjoining anticline and syncline in eastern Algeria, a pattern of very small faults, which can be compared to a joint-pattern, can be observed in two limestones which respectively form the axial arc of two adjacent and parallel structures. The synclinal limestone is obviously much younger (Eocene in fact) than the anticlinal limestone, which is of a Middle-Cretaceous age. In the syncline the foraminiferal limestones form the top of a table in a reversed relief; in the anticline a hard limestone crops out. Their stratigraphical distance is some 1,500 m (Fig. 81). The most striking feature of the fault patterns is that both show a double maximum, with an intervening angle of 20° in the anticline and 35° in the syncline, but orientated differently in relation to the axis.

From these examples of fault and joint-patterns it follows that, on

the one hand, small faults discernible in favourable circumstances
on aerial photographs are almost certainly orientated in some way in
relation to the direction of the principle folding-stresses; and, on the
other hand, that not all deformative stresses result in joint systems or
even in fault systems.

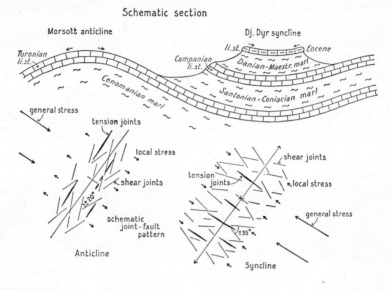

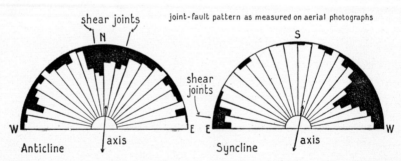

Fig. 81. Origin of fault patterns in adjoining anticline and syncline adopted
from aerial photographs of adjacent structures in south-east Algeria with fault
strike frequency diagrams.

According to the theory of Mohr and Anderson, shearing-planes,
either faults or joints, may develop in planes parallel to the median
stress-direction and making an acute angle bisected by the largest
stress-direction, whereas tension-joints or fissures will be orientated

parallel to this largest stress and perpendicular to the smallest stress.

This theory gives us a ready answer to the question of why sets of differently orientated small faults developed in the anticline and syncline mentioned above. In the anticlinal arch of a competent limestone layer we may expect a local tensional stress in the outer arc perpendicular to the axis. This would therefore be the direction of smallest stress, with the overburden constituting the median stress, and the largest stress parallel to the axis (Fig. 81). In the syncline we may expect, on the contrary, a local compression in the direction perpendicular to the axis. In both cases a set of shear-joints develops, at an acute angle bisected by the largest stress, but differently orientated

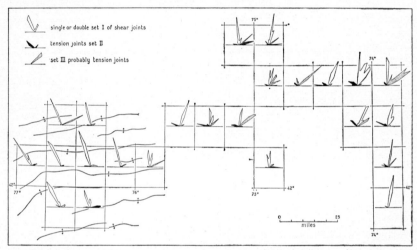

Fig. 82.   Map of strike frequency of joints in central and north New York and north Pennsylvania.   *(After Parker.   Published by permission of the Geological Society of America.)*

in relation to the axis direction. In this very simple case in Algeria we found remarkably good agreement between theory and practice, but in general the agreement is much less obvious and the joint-pattern or fault pattern much more complicated. Joint surveys from tectonically complicated areas are mostly far too complex to allow any trustworthy interpretation, although this has often been attempted. But when we consider regions which are almost unfolded, the patterns are much more simple and show obvious relations to known tectonic features. The survey by Parker (1942) in central and northern New York and northern Pennsylvania (Fig. 82), shows a very marked consistency of pattern, slowly swinging from the NNW in the central portion of the surveyed area to the NNE in the eastern portion, in close relation with the bend of the Appalachian fold axes but independent of local variations in the individual folds. Parker distinguishes three sets of joints, all of them perpendicular to the bedding plane. Set I is a double set with an average intervening angle of 19° (varying from 13° to 26°) swinging round from N 30° W in the west to N 10° E in the East. Set II is somewhat less regular, but perpendicular to the median line of Set I. Set III seems to be independent of the other two as it does not follow the swinging motion clearly exhibited by Sets I and II, and it has an average direction of N 60° E with a very small deviation of the median value. (It varies only from N 50° to 65° E.) The joints of the compound Set I are remarkably plane; they slice clearly through hard concretions in weak strata, and pass without deviation through extreme cross-bedding etc. They are obviously shear-joints.

The surfaces of the joints of Set II are, on the contrary, curved and irregular with a rough, torn appearance, and must be regarded as tension-joints.

Tentatively, I would explain the compound Set I of shear-joints as normal shears caused by the main stress-direction which bisects the very small angle of 20° between the two components. Set II, being perpendicular to this stress-direction, cannot be a normal set of tension-joints (which ought to be parallel to the main stress-direction), but may perhaps be regarded as due to tensional stress produced by an elastic release of the compression. Set III may be due to a later (or earlier) stress-direction of unknown quality. The main conclusions which may be drawn from this survey are:

1. the angle between the two components of a compound set of shear-joints may be very small (20°) and is intersected by the main stress-direction.

2. a set of tension-joints perpendicular to the main stress may develop as an effect of elastic release of the compression.

In the survey by Wager (1931) on the Great Scar limestone of Craven, we have another valuable contribution to our knowledge of the relation between regular joint-patterns and tectonic features. The limestone is cut by two sets of joints which are nearly at right angles to each other; one of them is parallel to lead-veins, which are common in this region. The sets of joints again perform a swinging motion in the field of observation (Fig. 83). The frequency diagrams of different parts of the region all show the same two perpendicular sets. In some places the joints, which are generally straight and perpendicular to the bedding-plane, are joined by "en échelon" gash (tension) joints, filled by calcite. The gash-joints make an angle of 45° with the main joint sets. The whole area is limited in the south by the North Craven fault and in the west by the Dent fault, the latter being a thrust. The compressional stress direction of N 55° W is fixed by this Dent fault thrust. This direction bisects one of the angles between the joints,

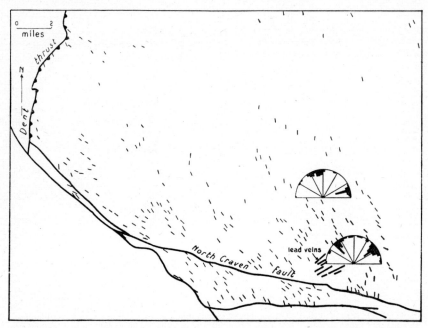

Fig. 83.   Joint patterns in the Great Scar limestone.   *(After Wager, Q.J.G.S., vol. 87, 1931.   Published by permission of the Geological Society of London.)*

which can therefore be regarded as normal shear-joints. The western portion of the North Craven fault, parallel to one of the joint-sets, is most probably a tear-fault.

In this example of joint-pattern we again find a close relation between compressional stress and shear-joint direction, but we notice a rigorously perpendicular system of two sets and not the acute angle found in many other instances.

A joint survey of the lignite field of Cologne by Wölk (1937), gives quite another picture (Fig. 84). The Miocene lignite layer, more than 30 m in thickness, is exploited in open-cast pits and shows excellently

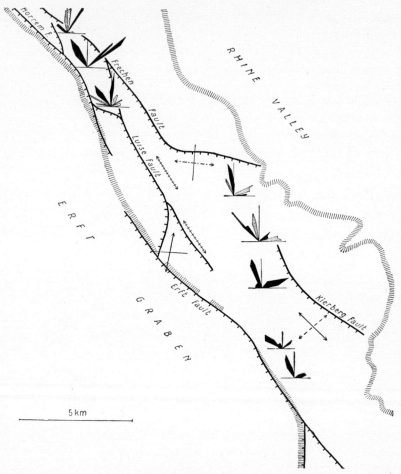

Fig. 84. Joints parallel to normal faults in Miocene lignite of the Ville lignite field near Cologne. *(After Wölk, Zeitschrift der Deutschen Geologischen Gesellschaft, vol. 91/1, 1937.)*

developed and very long joints in regular sets. The general geology is very well known, thanks to the numerous bore holes and open workings of the lignite, and shows a pattern of normal faults which have a general NW–SE trend but often deviate from this direction, thus joining and then separating again. The general result of the survey showed that the joints are very consistently parallel to the nearest normal fault whatever its strike may be. When the field of observation is situated between two main faults of different direction, both directions are represented in the joint-pattern. The joint surfaces are plane, and cut through irregularities of the strata. Their hade is steep and they usually occur in two perpendicular sets of which one is predominant and parallel to the nearest fault. It is a curious fact that the number of joints does not increase near the fault.

There can be no doubt about the conclusion that the joints are due to the same stress conditions as the normal faults. During the faulting the lignite layer carried very little overburden and this fact may possibly explain the steep dip of the joints. The other member of the conjugate set, perpendicular to the joints parallel to the faults, indicates that a tensional stress parallel to the faults also existed. As the joint frequency is independent of the faulting it seems probable that the joints were formed at the very beginning of the stress condition.

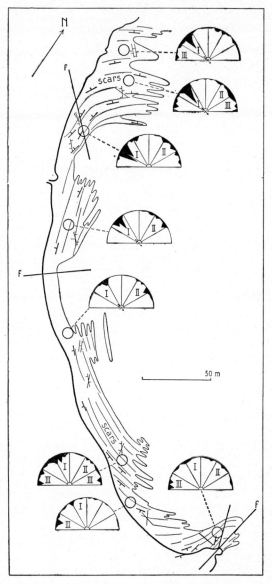

Fig. 85. Joint frequency in Robin Hood's Bay. *(After Zwart, "Breuken en Diaklazen in Robin Hood's Bay", Geol. en Mijnbouw, 1951.)*

The outcome of this survey is in direct contradiction to that of

the South Limburg coalfield, where no joints are related to the
normal faults. This is most probably due to the fact that the
Carboniferous rocks were already folded, cemented, and generally
lithified before the faulting started, whereas the Miocene lignite was
still a very soft rock.

A last example I should like to quote is that of the very gently
folded anticline of Robin Hood's Bay described by Zwart (1951).
Figure 85 gives the joint direction frequency diagrams for different
places on the western flank of this gentle structure. We find a well-
developed, sometimes double, set of shear-joints (set I) making the
very sharp angle of 15°, the median line of which is parallel to the
anticlinal axis. Another set (II) are by their appearance clearly tension-
joints, being orientated perpendicular to the axis, and were cut off
by the shear-joints. There is a third group (III) of EW direction,
restricted mainly to the anticlinal plunges. The compound set is
contradictory to that we found on the Morsott anticline in East Algeria,
but the two anticlines have in common the set of tension-joints

Fig. 86.   Shear-joints and tension-joints   Fig. 87.   Shear-joints due to
       in an unfolded sheet of rock.   elastic bending of a sheet of rock.

perpendicular to the axis. The tension-joints are due to the tension
parallel to the folding-stress, whereas the shear-joints are due to the
local tension caused by the arching on the outer arc of the anticline.
Set III is characteristic of the plunge, and is therefore due to a local
stress condition.

I will try to summarize the results of these joint surveys on very
gently folded competent layers which we have reviewed.

In the first place we must distinguish between shear-joints and tension-joints; each type can be recognized in the field by its special
characteristics. Further, we have found that there are shear-joints
due to a general stress-direction; and others which are due to local
stress conditions, as in the anticlinal and synclinal axial regions. The
intervening angle between two sets of shear-joints may vary widely;
the minimum we found was 15°, the maximum almost 90°. The
difference may simply be due to differences in rock properties or to
the weight of the overburden; but on the other hand it may merely

indicate that two quite different kinds of shear-joints exist. Tension-joints may develop either parallel to the compressive stress or as an elastic release perpendicular to it. Here also we must distinguish between local and general stress-direction.

THE RELATION BETWEEN JOINT AND
FAULT PATTERNS AND STRESS

As we have seen in Chapter 8, Anderson (1951) distinguishes three main types of faults: normal or tension-faults, thrust-faults, and tear- or wrench-faults, which differ only in their different orientation in relation to the horizontal plane. The same classification can be applied to joints, with the important addition of tension-joints, which would find their equivalent in the fault system as fissures or gash-fractures. All three kinds of faults mentioned by Anderson are shear-faults making an angle varying from 15° to 45° with the largest principal stress; the tension-joints or gash-fractures which we encountered in several examples are parallel to the largest principal stress. Because they have no motion along their faces they are generally not considered as faults, but they are frequent in joint diagrams and play an important role in ore deposits.

Let us consider what kind of joints (and faults) we might expect in a moderately folded limestone.

At first the sheet of rock is in the simple stress condition of Fig. 86. We find *shear-joints* making an acute angle with the deformative stress, and *tension-joints* parallel to this stress.

In the next stage we might expect the *secondary stress condition*, caused by elastic bending of the sheet as described earlier, which will cause a set of shear-joints with their acute angle bisected by the anticlinal axis, and tension-joints parallel to the axis (Fig. 81).

Besides these secondary shear- and tension-joints the elastic state of stress in the bent sheet is apt to create still another system. When we consider a block on the flank of a bent sheet we find opposite stress-directions on the upper and lower surfaces, necessarily compensated by a couple on the other faces to compensate the rotational effect of the first couple, as sketched in Fig. 87. These frictional shear-joints are parallel to the anticlinal (or synclinal) axis.

Finally, we might perhaps expect *release tension-joints* after the stress has vanished, as was suggested by the tension-joints in the Parker survey in New York. They will be either parallel or perpendicular to the axis, depending on whether they release the main or the secondary stress. We have not yet considered the possible shear-joints or faults which make an acute angle with the stratification plane. Since the main stress is always directed parallel to the bedding-plane in an elastically bent sheet, they might cause thrusts or normal shear-joints making an angle of more or less than 45° with the bedding-plane.

If all these possible joints or small faults were formed in one and the same structure, they would appear diagrammatically as shown in Fig. 88 where the normals to the joint planes have been plotted in a stereographic projection instead of in a frequency diagram. If the

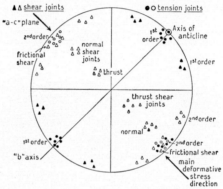

Fig. 88. Stereographic representation of possible joints in an anticlinal structure.

anticlinal axis had a distinct plunge and the survey had been made on the longitudinal curvature of the crest, the picture would have been much more complicated; even in this rather simple case, the distribution of the joint planes becomes so general that a slight deviation of the shear angle from 30° would result in a continuous girdle around the circumference, and another one perpendicular to the first. It would then be obviously impossible to distinguish between the joints by means of their position. In nature we seldom find all kinds of joints in the same outcrop; but as soon as we combine too many outcrops in one diagram, the fact that we are apt to find continuous girdles can be explained by the multitude of possible joints, and need not be due to a varying stress-direction. Difference of joint-patterns from one outcrop to the next may also be due simply to a difference in the lithology of the rocks, one lithology being preferred by one kind of joint, the other by another. As I have mentioned before, only very simple cases, where elastic bending has not played a preponderant role, give reliable results.

Many investigators, including Deenen (1942), who made a very extensive and detailed survey of jointing in a coal mine, have concluded, from the fact that all joints are orientated to the plane of stratification instead of to the horizontal plane, that the joints were originated before the folding. In other words, they found that their picture of the joint-, or fault-frequency became intelligible only if the strata were rotated to their original horizontal position. In my exposition I have presumed, on the contrary, that many of the joints are due to the folding itself and hence are formed continuously during the folding. This difference arises because Deenen, and those who share his view, assume that the deformative stress is invariable in direction and always in the horizontal plane only; whereas there is ample evidence in favour of the view that during folding there are elastic stresses always necessarily orientated to the upper and lower limit of the deformed sheet or mass of rock, independent of its position in space.

In order to check this assumption we made a joint survey of the well known "Sleek Stone", an asymmetric anticline (one flank dipping at 90°, the other at 25°) exposed in the coastal cliffs of western Pembrokeshire, near Broad Haven. This anticline has the great advantage of showing excellent jointing on the surface of one and the same bed, from one flank into the other.

The net result of the survey was that:

1. the joint system is very much dependent on the lithological character of the rock; a massive sandstone, a grauwacke, and a sandy shale each have their own type of jointing with characteristic frequency and direction. They have some major directions in common but in general the angle of intersection of a conjugate set is different for different kinds of rocks.

2. Some joint directions are early features in the structure; this is proved by the fact that in the sharp anticlinal hinge they show curved faces, obviously bent along with the bed that contains them.

3. Some joint directions which occur near the axis do not occur in the gentle flank.

4. The simple relations between joints and stress which we could discern in some of the examples quoted earlier, cannot be established in this strongly folded structure.

5. Although in limited areas of a few square metres the joint systems are very regular, this regularity disappears as soon as the area under consideration is enlarged to a 100 or 200 square metres.

From these points, which roughly summarize our results, we can conclude that the jointing is certainly partly contemporaneous with the folding. Further, that both the lithological character of the rock and relative position in relation to the fold structure determine the joint orientation; and finally, that in a fold like Sleek Stone, the elastically induced local stress-fields are so variable that they escape our analysis.

EXTENSION AND RELEASE FRACTURES, DIKES, VEINS, AND SILLS

All the fault types and most of the joint types which we have considered up to now have been shear-faults. Normal, wrench-, and thrust-faults differ only in their orientation to the horizontal plane or their relative movement. There exists, however, a distinct group of faults and joints which are characterized by the fact that their origin is not a shearing movement but the widening of a tension crack, parallel to the largest principal stress and normal to the smallest principal stress.

We have already made their acquaintance in our survey of joints, where we distinguished shear-joints from tension-joints. A wide-open tension crack can hardly exist at depth, and is always infilled with some material — either an intruded foreign rock, or a recrystallized component of the surrounding rock. The widening movement is relatively small. The two walls commonly move no more than some tens of metres from one another at most; some dikes, however, have thicknesses measured in hundreds of metres.

The origin of tension cracks can be twofold. They may be a direct consequence of the deformation in the form of a dilatation parallel to the largest principal stress; or a secondary consequence of the deformation, through an elastic dilatation in a plane perpendicular to the principal stress. It is only rarely that these two modes of origin can be distinguished, and elastic dilatation has rarely been mentioned as even a possible explanation. Some of the joint-patterns we examined strongly suggest, however, that it is much more frequent than was originally supposed. Personally, I feel inclined to accept this explanation, particularly for parallel dike swarms.

Dike Swarms. E. M. Anderson (1951) discusses the problem at great length. To establish the right kind of stress-field with a minimum stress-direction in the horizontal plane, in order to get vertical tension fissures, he presumes a radial vertical stress exerted by a rising magma. His most convincing example is the Tertiary Mull Swarm (Fig. 89), which spreads from a centre which is occupied by ring-dikes on the Island of Mull, and extends into the Southern Uplands to the south and into the Hebrides in the north. About the origin of the ring-dikes themselves there can be little doubt. Their concentric arrangement makes a definite *centre of stress* an almost essential assumption. That this can be due only to a push from below by a rising magma in a kind of volcanic vent is equally likely. The arrangement of the dike swarms, originating from the Mull and Skye centres, is a very convincing argument for the close relationship between the ring-dike and dike swarm phenomena. The very fact, however, that ring-dikes and dike swarms differ in their outer shape suggests that they originate in different kinds of stress-fields, though these must obviously be closely related. It is true, as Anderson pointed out, that it is more probable that the filling of these long cracks, sometimes 400 km in length, with igneous rock did not take place from below, upwards, but by lateral filling from the centre outwards. Perhaps the simplest way of conceiving the ring-dike system and the dike swarm in one stress-field would be to presume a lateral tension in the WSW–ENE direction, with points of incipient failure at various places of which the upwelling magma immediately took advantage, producing first the ring-dikes and, immediately afterwards, a parallel fissure system perpendicular to the general tension. The ring-dikes are then the expression of a secondary and momentary stress-field, touched off by the rupture of the crust just as the weight of a single person on an ice-covered lake can touch off the cracking of the ice in long and almost straight cracks running from shore to shore.

The Tertiary dike swarms of Scotland are not the only evidence of cracking of the crust. The Caledonian orogenic belt of this country runs from NE–SW, with the Moine thrust as its most striking structural feature. The Caledonian dike system runs parallel to the main folding axis. This direction suggests that the dike formation is due to an elastic release of the NW–SE compression.

The Hercynian (Armorican) stress finds its most spectacular expression in the great wrench-faults, with a NE–SW trend: the Great Glen fault, the Highland Boundary fault, and the Southern Upland fault.

Fig. 89. Tertiary dike swarms in Scotland. *(After Richey, Trans. Edin. Geol. Soc., vol. 13/4, 1939. Published by permission of Messrs Oliver & Boyd, Limited.)*

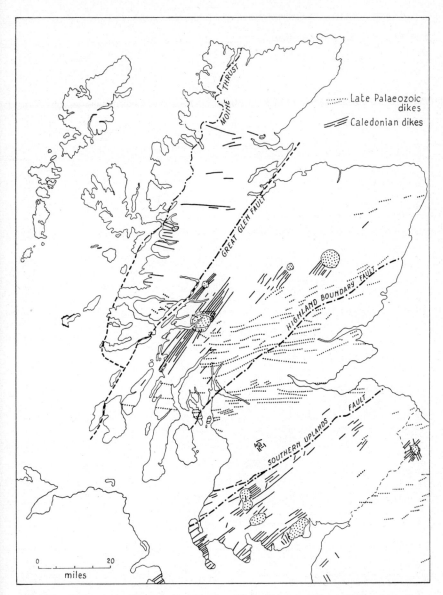

Fig. 90.   Palaeozoic dikes in Scotland.   *(After Richey, Trans. Edin. Geol. Soc.,*
vol. 13/4, 1939.   Published by permission of Messrs Oliver & Boyd, Limited.)

The direction of these wrench-faults and other structural evidence from the Upper Palaeozoic strongly suggests that this folding phase was due to a NS compression. The Hercynian dikes trend EW, perpendicular to compressive stress, again suggesting that they are due to an elastic release of the compression (Fig. 90).

In view of these conclusions on the orientation of the dikes in relation to the Caledonian and Hercynian stress-fields, a similar relation suggests itself for the NNW–SSE Tertiary dike swarm, e.g. a tension in a perpendicular direction due to elastic release of an ENE–WSW compression.

Apart from dike swarms, nearly all intrusive granites – in particular those of the late orogenic type – are accompanied by dike intrusions, showing a much less regular pattern, although preferred directions are generally noticeable. The cracks they fill are most probably due to the pushing of the granite itself, and very often a detailed scrutiny of the walls of the dikes can prove that they have simply moved apart. Small notches or other specific rock characteristics can sometimes be matched in the opposite walls. This was demonstrated very convincingly by E. Niggli (1953), who cut out a dike shown on a photograph and joined the fragments of the host rock again in their original position (Fig. 91).

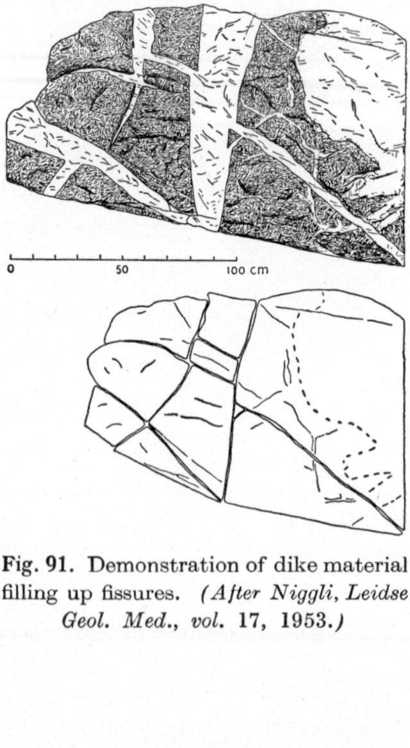

Fig. 91. Demonstration of dike material filling up fissures. *(After Niggli, Leidse Geol. Med., vol. 17, 1953.)*

There are many other examples where dike intrusion can be directly related to a tension field, without the mechanism of elastic release. A particularly convincing instance has been given by Wager (1938, 1947) from East Greenland. A basalt blanket covers a metamorphic series and is bent in a flexure along the coast, along a stretch many hundreds of kilometres in length. The axis of the flexure lies along a smooth curve which follows the run of the coast. This flexure is accompanied by a dike swarm which is most intimately connected with it (Fig. 92). Not only does it follow the flexure most faithfully but it is also restricted to the convex bend of the flexure and absent in the concave part. There is, moreover, a direct relation between the frequency of the dikes and the maximum curvature in the flexure. When the dip is 55°, more than 100 dikes per mile across the structure are found; when the dip is only 12° the swarm contains only some twenty dikes per mile; and where the dip decreases to 7° only a few

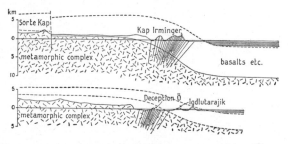

Fig. 92.   Dike swarms from East Greenland coast.   *(After Wager, Meddelelser om Grønland, vol. 134/5, 1938.)*

dikes are observed. The dikes themselves dip approximately perpendicular to the lavas. The position of the dike swarm in relation to the flexure strongly suggests that the dikes fill tension-fissures due to bending of the earth's crust along the coast. The flexure causes a maximum structural difference in level of at least 8 km.

Sills. A sill is a sheet of igneous rock injected parallel to the bedding. All the great sill complexes of the world consist of basaltic rocks, dolerites, etc. An interesting system occurs in the Anti-Atlas, where its close relation with a dolerite dike 120 km long is clearly established. The intrusion of the dike and sills is earlier than the slightly folded margin of the Sahara craton, and can be dated as very early in the Upper Carboniferous. Sills occur at different horizons ranging from the Cambrian to the Devonian. Because of the lack of vegetation and deep erosion of the country, it is sometimes possible to see, in a single outcrop, the transition from dike to sill. On the southern slope of the Djebel (mountain) Saghro, in the eastern part of the Anti-Atlas, for instance, one can follow the dike intrusion in the Lower Cambrian, rising and causing considerable and violent disturbance in the otherwise extremely even bedding just before it turns into the sill. From the moment the sheet assumes a quasi-horizontal position between the thick sandbeds, all evidence of disturbances disappears. Apparently the vertical crack which was followed by the dolerite magma did not extend through the whole series towards the surface; the ascent was stopped, but the intrusive mass possessed sufficient momentum to cause violent disturbances before it found its way between the sandstone.

That the transgression of a sill can take advantage of existing faults is proved by the Stirling dolerite sill (Macgregor, 1943) of the Midland Valley, Scotland (Fig. 93). In the mine workings the sill repeatedly changes its stratigraphical position by following some of the normal faults of this coalfield.

The preference of a dike intrusion for either a sub-vertical or a sub-horizontal extension is evidently due to a particular property of the post-orogenic stress-field. Dolerite dikes are always characteristic

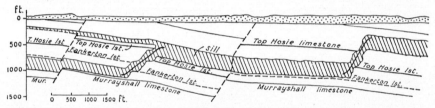

Fig. 93.   Stirling dolerite sill.   *(After Macgregor, "British Regional Geology: The Midland Valley of Scotland". Published by permission of Her Majesty's Stationery Office.)*

of non-orogenic or specifically cratonic conditions (the Karroo formation in South Africa for instance), where epeirogenic lateral tension is a frequent occurrence (rift valleys). During its ascent the dike meets less and less vertical stress, and at a certain stage its own upsurge may turn the scales so that the median and smallest principal stresses, which hitherto were orientated respectively in the vertical and horizontal sense, change places. It will then make a sharp bend from the vertical to the horizontal, and intrude itself between the layered beds at the appropriate horizon.

Veins. They differ from dikes in that their emplacement is certainly a long and complicated process. It is true that in dikes also, a succeeding series of intrusions can sometimes be observed, proving that the same stress-field reigned for a long time, but more generally only one kind of rock is intruded, probably in one single process. In metalliferous veins, where the filling has a hydrothermal character, successive phases can almost invariably be deduced from the mineralogical sequence, by the evidence of one kind of mineral systematically corroding another. Evidently such processes are comparatively slow.

This is a warning that faults, which in a tectonic sense are often regarded as sudden occurrences, may also in fact be the result of slow processes. The complete integration of faults in the folding movement, which we shall consider later on, leads to the same conclusion. Veins, in common with dikes, are often orientated

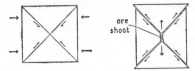

Fig. 94.   Ore shoot on the intersection of shear-planes.

perpendicular to the smallest stress-direction. In other instances, however, veins obviously follow oblique shear-planes, even intersecting shears, and ore-shoots on the intersecting lines of shear-planes are a frequent and well-known phenomenon. This latter fact can readily be understood, for even when the movement of the blocks separated by the intersecting shear-planes is small, there will always be a zone of crushing and tension on the intersecting line (Fig. 94), and this will be favourable for hydrothermal intrusion or recrystallization. Veins on the shear-planes themselves are less easily understood, but unless the shear is very regular and planar, every irregularity will cause a certain crushing and widening of the fracture. Moreover the vein emplacement is often not only the filling of a void but also a replacement by metasomatism, facilitated by the crushing of the host rock.

This explanation, however, is not entirely satisfactory in view of the great frequency of veins along oblique-shear. The problem is presented in a more trenchant form by the pattern of clastic dikes of the Big Bad Lands of South Dakota (Smith, 1952, Fig. 95). According to Smith's description, there can be no doubt that the filling of the cracks with volcanic ash, sand, silt, and clay proceeded from above

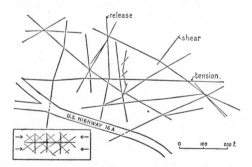

Fig. 95.   Clastic dikes of the Big Bad Lands of South Dakota.   *(After Smith, Transactions of the American Geophysical Union, vol. 33/6, 1952.)*

and not from below. Hence they must have presented open fissures at some time or other. The pattern clearly represents a conjugate set of shear-planes, intersected by a main tension phase parallel to the stress, and other tension-joints perpendicular to this stress. The main tension-joint bisects the acute angle of the intersecting shear-joints very accurately. All of the planes are filled with clastic material. From this picture it is obvious that the fissure system is due to a uniform stress-field and its elastic release. The elastic release not only originated the secondary set of tension cracks perpendicular to the original stress, but also opened up the shear-joints. This mechanism of elastic release explains satisfactorily the filling up with vein material of shear-joints or fractures, and makes intelligible the fact that very often only one direction of a conjugate set is favoured by metalliferous ore deposition.

Chapter 10

Normal Faults*

THE ORIGIN AND CHARACTERISTIC FEATURES OF LARGE FAULT TROUGHS

The simplest structural feature is without doubt a normal fault in an unfolded region. It is simple in the sense that it is unaffected or hardly affected by other structural features. In the earth's crust we find large and very long zones which have repeatedly been disturbed by large-scale normal faulting alone, forming horsts and rift valleys. The most famous example is the African rift zone, extending 6,000 km from south to north and accompanied by volcanoes, which reaches the Red Sea graben and is continued in Palestine and the Lebanon. A second, with the same direction, is the upper Rhine graben, which with a detour round the Alps reaches the Rhone graben and can be followed northwards until it is lost in the Roer Valley rift, in the Westphalen Ruhr coal-basin † faults, and in the Hessische Graben. The latter is often thought to extend below the North German plain into the Oslo Rift. In the West American Cordilleras also we find extensive normal faulting—in the Basin and Range province, for instance. Besides the major fault zones, innumerable smaller normal faults occur all over the world. All of them are regarded in general as the outcome of tension stress in the earth's crust. It is true that compressive stress has been proposed for the African fault zone, the Upper Rhine rift, and the Basin and Range province, but these views have never gained much support, and their arguments have been proved insufficient, particularly the gravimetrical argument of Bullard (1936). In every instance in which sufficient data were available, it has been proved that the faults hade towards the down-thrown block, and the mechanism

*) Synonyms: gravity-faults, tension-faults, dip-slip faults.

†) The Roer Valley rift and the Ruhr coalfield are named after two different rivers although pronounced exactly alike in Dutch and German, the Roer being an affluent of the Meuse, the Ruhr of the Rhine.

therefore represents a broadening or a stretching of the surface and not a compression. The problem of the origin of the rift has been illustrated by H. Cloos (1929, 1930, 1931, 1932) by a series of experiments with clay cakes, and very convincing imitations of a rift valley were obtained. Cloos carried out several experiments: firstly with a clay cake mounted on two boards which were drawn apart; secondly with an inflated rubber balloon at the base of the clay cake; and finally with a rubber plate which was stretched (Fig. 96). The balloon best imitated his theory that the rift valley was due to an arching of the Rhine shield, while the other two experiments simply illustrated a stretching mechanism.

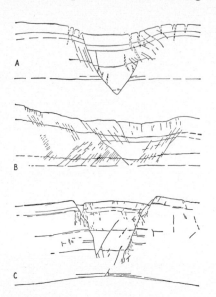

Fig. 96. Three experiments imitating normal faulting. A — clay cake mounted on two boards; B — clay cake mounted on stretched rubber plate; C — clay cake mounted on inflated rubber balloon. *(After H. Cloos, Natur und Museum, H. 6, 1930, and Die Naturwissenschaften, 18e Jahrg., H. 34, 1930.)*

With the rubber balloon the upper layer of the clay cake is stretched much further than the bottom. In all three instances we find a very good imitation of rift valleys in general, with their limiting step-faults and other peculiarities. Very often the lips of the rifts are raised, and this is certainly true, as Cloos pointed out, for the Upper Rhine Valley and the Red Sea. This fact was the basis of Cloos theory connecting the rift with the arching of the Rhine shield. The same observation led Taber (1927), and, in the beginning, also Cloos (1929), independently to the theory that the inward sloping normal faults of a rift are the boundaries of a trapezium-shaped block of the earth's crust, which by virtue of its shape will become depressed into the heavier substratum in which it floats (Fig. 97), whereas the borders

Fig. 97. Experiment demonstrating tilting of floating blocks. *(After Taber, Fault Troughs. Journal of Geology, vol. 35, 1927.)*

of the trough will rise on account of their shape. The hypothesis is very attractive, but has the disadvantage that the mechanism can be applied only to major fault troughs where the faults are sufficiently far apart to reach this substratum. With a width of 30 km the limiting faults could just reach the substratum, but smaller troughs and horsts would not come into contact with it. The Lower Rhine fault system, for instance, consists in part of a close succession of much narrower alternating horsts and rifts (Fig. 101), all of which have exactly the same character as the larger ones. To make a distinction between the larger and the smaller rifts would be illogical. Moreover, the raising of the lips of the rifts is definitely *not* a feature typical of the Lower Rhine faulting. Other great rifts such as the Upper Rhine Valley rift

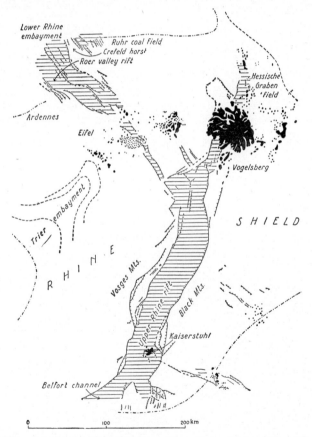

Fig. 98. Rhine shield with Upper Rhine rift valley. *(After Cloos, Einführung in die Geologie, Borntraeger, Berlin, 1936.)*

or the Red Sea rift approximate much better to this outline. The two
theories, arching and hydrostatic equilibrium, are not however
mutually exclusive. When the doming effect is too small for the faults
to reach the substratum, the hydrostatic readjustment is impossible.
When on the contrary the substratum is reached, an extra amount of
sinking may occur in the trough and the lips of the bordering high
will be warped up. In that case the formation of the trough might be
accompanied by volcanic activity along its boundaries. In a later
paper, Cloos (1932) has given a very convincing analysis of the doming
of the Rhine shield (Fig. 98). He regards the arching of the shield as the
direct cause of the down-faulting of the Upper Rhine graben. He
considers that the stretching of the upper arc of the dome, and, indeed,
the filling up of the rift structure, started in the Oligocene, contem-
poraneously with a major diastrophism in the Alps. He agrees that in
detail there may seem to be many anomalies and difficulties, but points
out that the intricate older structure of the shield must have interfered
with the regularity of the phenomenon. The main objection against
his conception is that in the Lower Rhine fault region the Upper
Cretaceous uplift is distinctly prior to the Miocene down-faulting. This
may be answered by assuming that there was no faulting during the
first stages of doming — but that the fault-troughs were formed only
in the later stages, when the crust finally gave way. Another objection
to Cloos' theory is the fact that the Upper Rhine rift does not end
against the Jura Mountains near Basle, but sends out a branch which
connects it with the Rhone Valley rift by way of the Belfort channel
(de Sitter, 1939b). The doming is therefore partly a circum-Alpine
phenomenon, partly a NS directed dome perpendicular to the Alpine
folding, and partly a posthumous Variscean doming. As far as the Lower
Rhine embayment is concerned, we can say that it is due to a tension
force, following a compressive doming effect, acting on the NW flank
of the uplifted Variscean orogenic belt, which is crossed by an approximately NS secondary axis of positive movement.

CHARACTERISTICS OF NORMAL FAULTS

The hade of the major faults is an extremely important factor for
the collieries of the South Limburg coalfield, since these faults form the
boundaries of the individual fields of exploitation. In addition, the
probable position of the fault at depth is a matter of considerable
anxiety to the mining engineer, since serious water trouble may be

expected in its vicinity. Hence a trustworthy prognosis of the positions of the fault-planes with increasing depth is, apart from its theoretical interest, a matter of considerable eco-
nomic value. In textbooks, the dip of large normal faults belonging to rifts are stated to vary from 45° to 90°, but values between 65° and 70° are most frequent. The only dip actually measured that Cloos mentions in his textbook is one of 55° (1936, p. 407), observed in the Loretto tunnel near Freiburg i. Br. (cf. Brill, R., 1933). Elsewhere Cloos (1936, p. 274) remarks,

Fig. 99. Normal faults in South Limburg coalfield exposed at different levels. *(After Dik- kers, Geol. & Mijnbouw, 6 Jaarg. N.S., 1944.)*

concerning this same measurement: "Von diesem einzigartigen Querschnitt wird jede künftige Diskussion des Rheingrabens, ja der groszen Brüche der Erde überhaupt auszugehen haben". I quite agree with Cloos that such artificial outcrops in tunnels, borings, mines, etc. are more valuable to our problem than surface outcrops in general, since the latter are mostly too small in the vertical sense to yield satisfactory and trustworthy measurements of the general dip of the

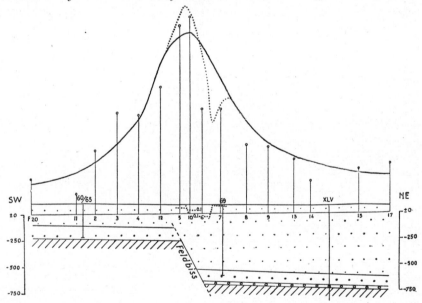

Fig. 100. Torsion-balance section across normal fault (Feldbiss) in South Limburg coalfield. *(After Zijlstra, Geol. & Mijnbouw, 6 Jaarg. N.S., 1944.)*

fault. Even better than the measurements in the Loretto tunnel are
those of some sections published by Dikkers and Patijn (1944) (Fig. 99)
and Rutten (1943), all on the limiting step-faults of the Roer Valley
rift in the South Limburg collieries. Rutten measured in the Coal
Measures in one section a hade of 60° and in another one of 50°.
Dikkers measured in four of his sections angles of 50°, 60°, 57°, and 65°.

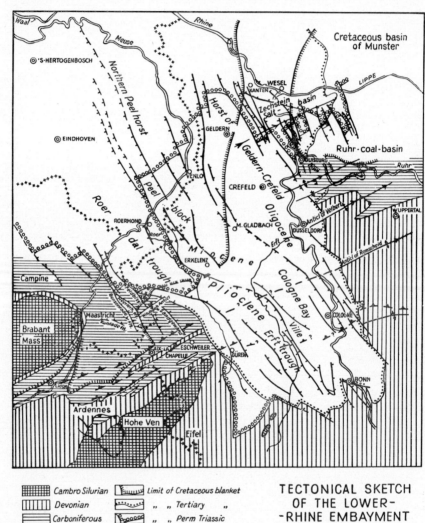

**TECTONICAL SKETCH
OF THE LOWER-
-RHINE EMBAYMENT**

Fig. 101. Fault pattern of Lower Rhine embayment. *(After de Sitter, Med.
Geol. Stichting, Serie C 1--3, no. 1, 1949.)*

These important measurements are very accurate, as all of them are founded on two or more determinations of the fault-plane, in drifts or in underground boreholes, at least 100 m apart in vertical distance.

The torsion-balance survey of the great faults of the Roer Valley rift revealed that flat dips predominate, particularly when the throw is large (de Sitter, 1947b) (Fig. 100). Let us consider this particular rift in more detail. The Roer Valley rift is the deepest rift belonging to the extensive system of NW–SE faults which reaches from the Belgian Campine in the west far into the Ruhr coalfield in the east (Fig. 101), and from Bonn on the Rhine to s'-Hertogenbosch in the north of the province of N. Brabant of the Netherlands. Its continuation further northwards is surmised, but has not been ascertained. The fault system probably originated at the end of the Permian, and had a maximum period of activity on the late-Cimerian phase of Stille, between the Lower Jurassic and the Cretaceous, and another period of activity in the younger Tertiary. A detailed description of the gravimetric survey can be found in de Sitter (1947b), the tectonic structure of the South Limburg coalfield in Sax (1946), that of the Ruhr coalfield in Kukuk (1938). Together these give a complete bibliography of the whole area. The faulting is due to lateral tension, and must be connected with the Upper Rhine Valley rift. Locally, it is closely connected with the repeated uplift of the older ENE–WSW Variscean orogenic belt of the Armorican mountains, of which the Ardennes form a portion, cutting it almost perpendicularly. The maximum total throw of the Roer Valley rift is perhaps some 2,000 m, and it is filled with some 900 m thick series of Triassic and Lower Lias, perhaps 200 m of Upper Cretaceous, some 300 m of Lower Tertiary, and 600 m of Upper Tertiary (depending of course where these thicknesses are measured, since the throw of the fault decreases in a southern direction). These numerical values of the thicknesses are somewhat conjectural, however, as no drill-hole in the rift has penetrated much beyond the younger Tertiary. The data are derived from drill-holes on the fault-steps along the border of the fault-troughs, from quantitative calculations of numerous gravimetrical sections and from general geological considerations. All the fault-dip measurements which could be made arrived at the same result, i.e. of dips less than 70° and more than 40°. Kukuk (1938, p. 337) reports that the normal faults of the Ruhr coalfield have a hade of 50–70°, but that the flatter dips are to be found in the less folded regions to the north, and the steeper dips in the zone of the steep anticlines and synclines in the south, where the throw is, moreover, much smaller, i.e. the dips decrease from north to south. The same is true for the South Limburg coalfield where it was observed that the larger the throw the flatter the dip. I do not think that Carboniferous folding has anything to do with the dip of these normal faults (as Kukuk suggested) but believe instead that the dip simply decreases with increasing throw from both extremities towards the centre of a normal fault.

For this aspect we shall review a region in southern Arkansas where the extremities of the fault are better known than in the Ruhr district.

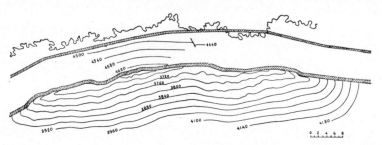

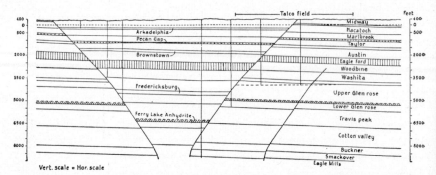

Fig. 102. Talco oilfield, Texas, map and section. *(After Shelby, University of Texas Publications no. 5116, 1951. Published by permission of the University of Texas.)*

We find here several oilfields which show an oil accumulation against a normal fault, e.g. the Fouke, Nick Springs, Stamps-Lewisville, and Fray oilfields. Each of them shows a doming effect against the normal fault, which has a dip of 45–55°. The same feature of a half-dome limited at one side by a normal fault can be observed in nearly all the fields of the Mexia fault-zone, to which I shall refer further on. Perhaps the best developed half-dome of this type is the Talco oilfield in Texas

(Fig. 102) (Shelby, 1951). I do not think that the doming ought to be regarded as a folding phenomenon due to a compressive stress separate from the faulting. On the contrary the two features belong to one and the same tensional stress-field. The development of even a normal fault is not due to a static stress condition; it is a dynamic process during which the stress conditions necessarily change in consequence of the very effect they produce. We may expect the initial stress condition to be more or less homogeneous along a certain horizontal distance (Fig. 103a). For some reason or other the shearing process starts at one point (P in Fig. 103a), and soon a small normal fault has developed. It has been shown by E. M. Anderson (1951) that the shearing stress is variable along the shearing-plane, being maximal at its edges and minimal at the starting point P.

In order to allow the fault to develop, either both lips of the fault must move, one upwards the other downwards, or one is stationary

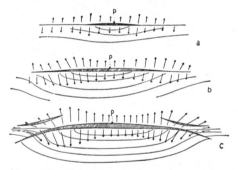

Fig. 103.   Development of normal fault.

and the other moves. The result is half a dome as figured by the contour lines in Fig. 103b and c. I have represented the process in a horizontal plane, but if we regard it as we ought to do as a three-dimensional process, we should probably see that the stress condition at the edges no longer conforms to the original condition, but that horizontal stresses along the fault-planes have developed as a result of the doming effect at the centre. It therefore seems very probable that the edge conditions may cause both a steepening of the original 45°–70° dip of the normal fault-plane and its splitting up into several divergent smaller faults—so called "splays". These splays are very frequent at the extremities of large rifts as Cloos has pointed out (Fig. 98).

A very thoroughly explored fault-zone is the Mexia group of faults (Fig. 104) in Central Texas, against which, in a number of formerly

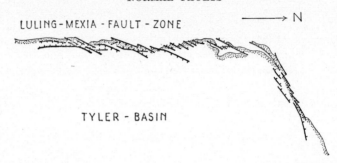

LULING - MEXIA - FAULT - ZONE

TYLER - BASIN

Fig. 104. Mexia fault-zone from tectonic map of U.S.A. *(From tectonic map of U.S.A. Published by permission of the United States Geological Survey.)*

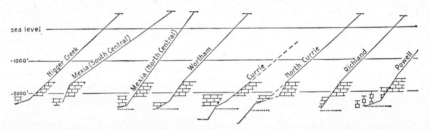

Fig. 105. The hade of the Mexia faults. *(After Lahee. Published by permission of the American Association of Petroleum Geologists.)*

important fields, oil has accumulated. The dip of the main fault-planes can be measured very accurately by joining the surface outcrop of the fault with the numerous points at which the fault has been crossed by the drill-holes (Lahee, 1929). In his paper, Lahee assembles the dips of fault-planes of eight oilfields (Fig. 105); they vary from 35°–53°, with an average of 45° (Table IX).

Table IX
Dip of the Mexia faults in eight oilfields

Oilfield	Dip of Fault Plane	Maximum Displacement
Nigger Creek	43°	500′
Mexia (South Central)	35° ⎫	550′
Mexia (North Central)	53° ⎭	
Wortham	46°	600′–650′
North Currie	42°	395′
Richland	45°	450 –500′
Powell.	51°	650′
Average	45°	

Actually, the dip of the faults varies from the extremes of 16° to 63°, being steeper in the brittle Austin chalk, less steep in the soft Eagle Ford shale, and steeper again in the Woodbine sandstone. In Fig. 106, a typical section through one of the oilfields, these particular features are evident. The nature of the rock has apparently a great influence on the hade of a normal fault, and we may imagine that in a

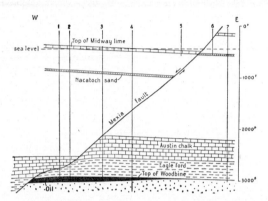

Fig. 106.   Section through Mexia fault.   *(After Lahee. Published by permission of the American Association of Petroleum Geologists.)*

particular incompetent layer of sufficient thickness at greater depth, the fault will be lost altogether when the tension diminishes downwards or is replaced by another stress condition. This is in perfect accordance with the experimental evidence, by which we learned that the angle between the shear-plane and the largest stress direction depends on the nature of the rock and the hydrostatic pressure. Near the surface we may expect higher dips than at depth.

TILTING OF STEP BLOCKS AND ANTITHETIC FAULTS

Large normal faults are often accompanied by so-called antithetic faults, which hade towards the main fault and therefore away from the main rift valley. They appear clearly in some of Cloos' experiments (see Fig. 96) and are particularly well developed along the Rhine rift. They have been explored in great detail in the Pechelbronn oilfield. The average dip measured on three sections by Haas and Hoffmann (1928), containing some 15 faults (one section is represented by Fig. 107) is 49°, varying from 43–57°. On a more recent map by

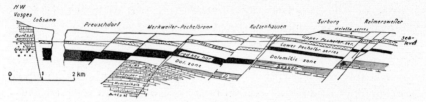

Fig. 107. Section through Pechelbronn oilfield, with faults antithetic to main rift fault *(After Schnaebele, C.R. Congr. Mond. Pétr., Paris, 1937.)*

Schnaebele (1937), dips of 40–60° appear. This author says: "Leur inclinaison est en général de l'ordre de 50°, mais peut varier de 40 à 65°'".

Sometimes the whole graben structure is more like one major fault with one or two accompanying antithetic faults, as in the Hessische Graben belonging to the Saxonic faulted area, which has been treated extensively by H. Stille and Fr. Lotze and their students in the series of "Geotektonische Forschungen". I reproduce here the schematic section of the Egge rift from a paper by Martini (1937), Fig. 108. In

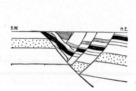

Fig. 108. Section through Egge rift, showing small antithetic faults. *(After Martini, Geotektonische Forschungen, H. 2, 1937.)*

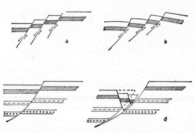

Fig. 109. Tilting of blocks: *a* planar step-faults, no tilting; *b* curved step-faults with tilting; *c* development of antithetic faults due to curved shape of main fault.

many outcrops faults with hades of 50° and less were measured (cf. Lemke, 1937, pp. 39, 40). These narrow rifts, often not more than 1 km wide, are not supposed to be formed by two equivalent faults but by one major fault with a rather flat hade and one or more antithetic secondary faults, as in Fig. 108.

In the Pechelbronn section, the tilting of the blocks is well demonstrated. This feature is very common, and is regarded as quite a normal phenomenon accompanying step-faults. But it does not occur on the steps of the Roer Valley rift. The tilting is easily understood when we realize that a block is limited by two faults, and that its relative movement along these two faults is contradictory. The two shearing stresses together form a couple which will give a rotational motion to the block. Whether the couple succeeds in tilting the blocks or not will be on the one hand a matter of fortuity and depend largely on the nature of the rocks involved (incompetent rocks will allow more scope to this motion than will competent rocks), and on the other hand a question of the shape of the fault (a downward flattening of the fault will facilitate the rotation better than will a straight and invariable dip). (Fig. 109a.)

Goguel pointed out that the antithetic faults accompanying a single normal fault-plane are a result of the somewhat curved shape of the main fault — because further slipping down of one block would result in a gap at the surface and this is filled up by antithetic blocks (Fig. 109a). We might conclude that the forming of antithetic blocks and tilted step-blocks are alternative solutions of the same problem of tectonic forces: both indicate a flattening of the hade of the main fault with increasing depth.

FAULTS OF THE BASIN AND RANGE FAULT SYSTEM

Tilting is very pronounced in the faulted Basin and Range system of the Great Basin of the Rocky Mountains. In central Utah the Wasatch Mountains and the Oquirrh Range have been faulted after folding. The faults are true gravity-faults limiting tilted blocks. Their dips can be measured with some accuracy in this bare hill-country. The Oquirrh Range has been mapped by Gilluly (1932), and I quote from his paper: "An additional point of interest in connection with the frontal faulting of the Oquirrh Mountains is the prevailing steep dips of the fault-planes. Fourteen measurements of dip were made, either on bedrock fault surfaces or by the 3 point method, in places where the topographic relief of the country traversed by the faults was sufficient. The measurements range from 40°–64° and average 57°. The West Mercur fault changes in dip from 40°–60° within a mile. . ."

The Wasatch Range has been mapped by Eardley (1933), and is also a tilted fault-block. The net slip on the major fault-planes ranges from 2,200 m to 2,600 m. Two dip observations indicated a dip of 50° W.

I quote from Eardley's paper:

"Two parallel faults of the Basin and Range orogeny cross the mouth of North Canyon. An old prospect hole follows down a silver gouge on the eastern of these two faults, just north of the canyon. The footwall is the fault-plane. The dip, definitely defined, is 50° W. At the mouth of Santaquin canyon the trace of the main fault is seen in the south wall and, if the writer's interpretation is correct, measures about 50° W. . . . which facts add additional weight to the conclusion (of Gilluly) that the main faults of the Basin and Range orogeny in the vicinity of the Wasatch Mountains dip about 50°–55°''.

A general review of the Basin and Range faults has been given by Nolan (1943). The eastern limit of the faulted part of the Great Basin is formed by the Wasatch fault. Further west we find the faulted Oquirrh Range, the Stansbury Range, and the Cedar Range, each of them another tilted fault-block of some 20 miles breadth. The western limit is the great normal fault which limits the tilted Sierra Nevada block to the west. A typical range in the north-central part of the province is the Ruby and Thumboldt Mountain Range (R. P. Sharp, 1939). All these faults have undergone recurrent motion, usually in the same sense. In the Basin range one can distinguish five periods between the first (Late Middle Miocene) and the last (Late Pleistocene to Recent) phases, a recurrence which is very similar to the recurrent motion on the Roer Valley rift faults. In the case of the Roer Valley rift there are several periods in the Permian and Triassic followed by opposite thrusting movements during the Upper Cretaceous, and then normal movement again at several times from the Miocene to the Recent.

Without doubt, the best exposed normal fault faces which have become known are the Earth Valley and Panamint faults in Southern California. Noble (1925) gives a vivid description of these huge fault scarps. The two faults are so very similar that they may be regarded as twin features with a common origin. They form two escarpments some 60 km long and 40 km apart, and are roughly parallel. I quote from Noble's paper:

"The escarpments are exceedingly rugged, bare, sloping rock-surfaces that rise abruptly from the valley floor. At most places the profile of this rock-surface exhibits three elements, at the base a small vertical cliff or set of cliffs at some places over 30 m high, at other places absent. This cliff marks a recent vertical fault. . Above the small vertical cliff the escarpment rises several thousand feet in an extra-ordinary huge sloping surface whose angle of slope averages 35°. This surface is scored by innumerable parallel ravines which run straight down it to the valley. These gullies are deep, straight and acutely V-shaped. One would like to call it a fault face. Above the gullied surface the slope of the escarpment becomes much gentler changing to about 25°. Wide valleys with broad mouths open out at the top of the 35° slope, and the topographic forms become relatively subdued and rounded. The relatively mature topography above this rock face is then the pre-fault topography".

The rocks which compose the rock-faces are chiefly Pre-Cambrian gneisses and schists, crushed and sheared to a virtual fault gouge. The shearing-planes in this crushed material are parallel to the slant of the rock-face. The date of the normal faulting is probably early Quaternary. The trace of the faults on the map is exceedingly irregular in detail and their escarpments have a roughly zigzag pattern.

I shall try to summarize our experience of normal block-faults.

A normal fault can have a slip from a few centimetres up to some 3,000 m. There is some evidence that the dip near the surface may be greater than at greater depth. In general it varies from 45°–70°, but in some instances dips of even less than 45° have been ascertained. Normal faults are always due to a tensional stress and they represent a shearing-plane parallel to the medium principal stress, which is situated in the horizontal plane, and make an acute angle with the largest principal stress, that of gravity, the least principal stress direction being the direction of tension. The nature of the rocks also influences the dip, which is flatter in soft incompetent layers than in brittle competent horizons. There seems to be a correlation between the maximum slip and the dip of the fault, the dip being flatter at the maximum, and steeper near the edges of the fault, where the dip-slip is probably partly replaced by strike-slip. Normal faulting often shows an en échelon arrangement, which may be due either to the overlapping of different faults of the same origin and direction, or to a surface expression of a deep-seated shearing movement, making an acute angle with the normal fault direction. The width of the blocks between the steps varies greatly, and may be anything from a few metres up to scores of kilometres. There is no apparent correlation between the amount of slip and the width of the steps or any other feature. Both tilting of the steps and antithetic faulting are probably due to the flattening of the fault-face downwards. The origin of tensional stress may vary greatly; we know of long tension zones, local tension zones, tension zones oblique to shearing, and many other types of origin. Individual normal faults have the same characteristics, whatever their cause. Step-faults are very common and antithetic faults are often observed.

There are many normal faults, closely connected with individual folds, which have nevertheless the same characteristics as the block-faults, but these will be described in connexion with folding. On the other hand there is generally no direct connexion between belts of folding and normal faulting; this is logical since the stresses which might be expected to produce them are diametrically different.

Chapter II

Wrench-Faults

Different terms have been applied to these faults; in American usage we find "rifts" and "strike-slip faults" denoting the larger ones; and "tear-faults" used perhaps more often for the smaller ones. In English terminology "wrench-faults" is the common term; transcurrent faults was proposed by Anderson (1942) in the first edition of his book, but in the second edition (1951) this author reverted to preference for the term wrench-faults.

The wrench-fault is a shearing movement along a vertical plane. We can distinguish between sinistral and dextral faults; when the observer views a fault-plane, motion on the distant side will appear either towards the left (sinistral) or towards the right (dextral).

In considering the phenomenon of wrench-faulting we enter a domain in which many more complications arise, and in which the pattern of the faults is much less simple and comprehensible than in that of normal faulting.

We shall find, however, the same general occurrences, e.g. very large faults, fault-belts, and small faults of different kinds, many of them connected with folding.

Wrench-faults are definitely due to a compressive stress. They are vertical, and hence we may presume that the median principal stress is vertical, the largest and smallest stresses lying in the horizontal plane. It is logical to presume that wrench-faults belong essentially to the unflexible portion of the earth's crust, the so-called crystalline basement, for instance. They are certainly not restricted to these portions of the earth's crust, however, since we also find them in highly mobile belts where individual blocks have moved in relation to one another.

As regards the larger wrench-faults, it is for several reasons extremely difficult to prove anything except their strike; and relatively few are definitively determined as wrench-faults. First of all, they often change laterally into thrust-faults; since both thrusts and wrench-faults are due to lateral compression, this would be expected. Secondly, their outcrops are often deeply weathered and therefore covered by alluvial deposits, even when the slip is comparatively small. Very often they have been regarded, and perhaps still are, as normal gravity-faults, for a vertical component of the motion is never altogether absent and is often locally important. Moreover, it is often almost impossible to decide whether the shift of homologous elements on both sides of the fault, when such can be recognized, is due to vertical or horizontal motion or both. Hence it is understandable that wrench-faults have been treated rather briefly in most general handbooks on structural geology, and this fact, in its turn, has not stimulated the study of this important style of dislocation of the earth's crust.

We shall study wrench-faults by means of some well-known examples.

EXAMPLES OF WRENCH-FAULTING

The Great Glen Fault of Scotland. In my description of the Great Glen wrench-fault, I shall follow the recent paper by W. Q. Kennedy (1946), who made a special study of this fault.

The Great Glen fault intersects Scotland from coast to coast with a singular straightness, and has a major effect on the topography of the region; there is a string of lakes along its eroded outcrop. Wherever this outcrop can be studied, the line of disruption is marked by a broad belt of crushed, sheared, and mylonitized rock up to 1·5 km in width. The ultimate products of the dislocation metamorphism are flinty-crush rocks and true ultramylonites.

The deep erosion along the fault, the true depth of which is masked by a filling of glacial sediments (sometimes more than 100 m) and by water (depth of Loch Ness 50 m), is doubtless due to this shatter-belt. Although circumstances nowhere permit a factual measurement of the dip, it is obvious from the rectilinear character of the fault that it cannot deviate much from the vertical. Moreover, many subsidiary fractures, branching out from the main fault-zone, are definitely vertical; some of these have however been proved to be steep thrust-faults.

Kennedy advances very convincing arguments for a horizontal displacement along the fault of more than 100 km; the argument is chiefly based on the correlation of corresponding geological structures on either side of the fault.

The Moine schists on both sides of the fault show a central zone of migmatite in whose centre we find intrusive granites, the Strontian granite on the NW side of the fault, and the Foyers granite on the SE side. When the north-west block is shifted 107 km to the north-east along the fault-plane (as in Fig. 110), the two granite masses become one mass, the migmatite zones correspond neatly, and the different metamorphic zones of the Moine schists, the kyanite and sillimanite zones principally, form continuous belts. In addition, the characteristics of the two granite masses are very similar, each being a half-dome truncated by the fault. Together they would form a typical granite stock with an outer tonalite

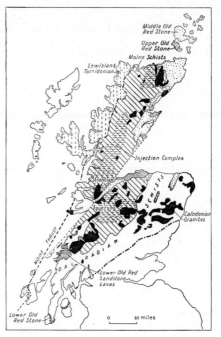

Fig. 110. The displacement along the Great Glen fault in northern Scotland. *(After Kennedy, Q.J.G.S., vol. 102, 1946. Published by permission of the Geological Society of London.)*

Fig. 111. The Strontian and Foyers granites joined. *(After Kennedy, Q.J.G.S., vol. 102, 1946. Published by permission of the Geological Society of London.)*

zone round a centre of porphyritic granodiorite, penetrated by a somewhat later intrusion of a fine-grained biotite-granite with typical structural features which would join admirably (Fig. 111).

By shifting the north-west block to its original position we can even find the continuation of the famous Moine thrust plane, south-east of the fault in a thrust plane on the island of Islay. Finally, there are many parallel wrench-faults north and south of the Great Glen fault, several of which have been proved to possess slips of 3 to 5 km in the same sinistral sense as the main fault.

The age of the main lateral movement

falls in the Upper Old Red sandstone or Lower Carboniferous period.

The main characteristics of this great wrench-fault are its strictly rectilinear character, its wide shatter-belt, containing true mylonites, its vertical position, parallel wrench-faults of much smaller slip, and oblique thrust-faults merging into the lateral shearing on approaching it. Although its age is Upper Palaeozoic, seismic disturbances along its course still occur quite frequently.

The Great Glen fault was most certainly due to a north-south lateral compressive stress at the beginning of the Hercynian folding, and runs parallel to the grain of the Caledonian structure; this latter perhaps provided a zone of weakness of which the fault took advantage.

The San Andreas Wrench-Fault, California. The fact that the San Andreas fault of California is such a widely known structural feature is no doubt mainly due to the great earthquake of 18th April, 1906. It also has a great influence on the topography of the region, which is marked by the very recent movements along its face.

We possess in an article by Taliaferro (1943) an excellent study of the San Andreas fault which is based on intimate knowledge of the field characteristics along 80 km of its length and of the earlier literature. I shall mainly follow this author in his exposition of the known facts of its northern half.

Figure 112 presents the main faults of this region. The San Andreas fault can be traced for more than 800 km. At both ends it branches into two splays (the Hayward fault of San Francisco and the San Jacinto fault in the Peninsular Range). Such "splays" are a common feature of the extremities of all kind of faults, not of wrench-faults alone.

The fault may be divided into two portions, a northern one with a NNW direction from the Tejon Pass northwards, belonging to the structural field of the coast ranges, and a southern portion striking south-east of the Tejon Pass. The southern part is a structural feature of the Basin and Range province. At the junction of the north and south branches of the fault, the Garlock fault branches off from the San Andreas fault.

Although the two portions are certainly one fault now, their earlier history may have been quite different; they may only recently have been united into one fault-zone. The northern branch has been studied most closely. It runs parallel with the western limit of the San Joaquin Valley basin, but is itself not the limit. As Taliaferro describes it, it is very close to the large Eocene normal fault which really limits this

EXAMPLES OF WRENCH-FAULTING   163

basin, but seldom coincides with it. This earlier fault is always the boundary between crystalline Basement Complex and Mesozoic sediments, whereas the San Andreas is either wholly within the crystalline rocks or in the Mesozoic rocks, except where it cuts through younger

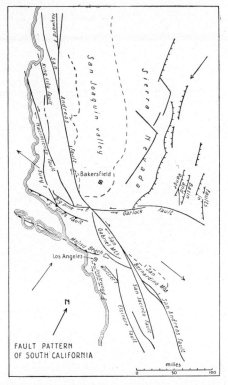

Fig. 112.   The fault pattern of Southern California with the San Andreas fault.

Tertiary formations. There is no doubt that its present major features were formed by Plio-Pleistocene disturbances. It cuts the late mid-Pleistocene thrusts and other tectonic features, which can actually be traced at the other side of the fault. Nearly everywhere along the San Andreas fault there are attendant physiographic evidences of recent shift, such as true sag-ponds, offset ridge and drainage lines, etc. For example the Caste Mountain thrust, 15 km east of Parkfield, which brings Franciscan (Jurassic) rocks above overturned Miocene and Pliocene, can be traced northwards until it becomes entangled with the San Andreas, 20 km NW of Parkfield, and for about 5–6 km the two cannot be separated because of the very acute angle of intersection. However, 25 km NW of Parkfield the thrust is found back to the west of the San Andreas fault and can be followed for another 25 km before it is lost. There is abundant evidence of recent movement along the thrust in the section where it intermingles with the San Andreas. Taliaferro mentions several similar mid-Pleistocene structural features which are traversed by the San Andreas fault. Nowhere is its dextral horizontal slip larger than some 3,000 feet — as measured by the offsetting of drainage lines and such recent features.

The degree of movement during the April, 1906 earthquake amounted to some 4 m through a distance of 435 km along the strike. The time occupied by the movement was but a few seconds.

The Pleistocene San Andreas rift, therefore, may be a very prominent and long feature but it is certainly not a large one. According to Taliaferro, the supposed branches or "barbs" are actually earlier faults formed by a different type of movement, with the probable exception of the Hayward fault. This is certainly true for the San Andreas fault movement as compared to earlier Tertiary tectonics; but whether or not it already existed in the Jurassic is more difficult to prove.

Bailey Willis (1938) succeeded in finding an independent proof of the orientation of the main stress-direction that caused the fault In a quarry in the Logan granite near the fault trace he made a careful analysis of the joints, and concluded that they were caused by a stress direction of N 15° E. Bucher arrived independently at the same conclusion in a study of the same quarry.

The southerly branch of the San Andreas rift, in particular where it traverses the San Gabriel granite basement, is less well known. It has been described chiefly by Noble (1926), Bailey Willis (1938), Nolan (1943), and Wallace (1949). We find the same features as in the northern portion — a remarkable straight fault-line, numerous offsets of topographical features, evidence of uplift rapidly varying from one side of the fault to the other, and repeated evidence of upwarped blocks in the fault-zone itself; but unfortunately no definite proof of large-scale strike-slip by homologous elements on both sides of the fault. The shift of stream channels amounted to 25 km, that of terrace deposits possibly to as much as 10 km.

The problem of the total strike-slip of the San Andreas fault has been taken up recently by Hill and Dibblee (1953). These authors consider the possibility of a pre-Cretaceous age for the fault and of recurrent movements in the same sense at different periods up to the present.

The cumulative effect would amount to a 580 km offset. The older phases are obviously difficult to prove, but the younger ones seem very probable. They conclude a displacement of 16 km since the Pleistocene, on the ground of an offset of a particularly Pleistocene facies, and of 370 km since late Eocene time.

For several wrench-faults the actual displacement caused by seismic shock has been measured. In the case of the April, 1906, San Andreas earthquake, the maximum displacement was 6 m, and not more than 450 km of its total length of 850 km is believed to have been in motion.

In 1857 displacements of over 10 m took place in the Tejon Pass region along a distance of 330 km. During the earthquake of 1868 in the San Francisco area, strike-slip displacements reached 3–4 m, and in the recent earthquake of 1940 in the Imperial Valley, displacements averaged about 1 m over a length of 70 km.

The Tarma fault in Japan (Otuka, 1933), 26 km in length, showed a displacement of 2.7 m. during the earthquake in 1930.

There would obviously have to be very many such earthquakes to obtain the great displacements which have been inferred from geological evidence. The Great Glen fault would have needed some 20,000 earthquakes within a relatively short period to reach its present displacement. This is not unreasonable in view of the present frequency of earthquakes in active seismic zones.

When we have learned more about the characteristics of faults we shall try to analyse the stress system which caused the Andreas wrench-fault, in connexion with the rest of the major tectonic features of the California region.

Many of the best known wrench-faults are a direct consequence of folding, and interfere with the fold-structures. In so far as they form an integral part of one fold, they will be described after I have described the folds themselves, but at present I shall mention some wrench-faults which cut through several folds in the Jura and Säntis Mountains, and one in the southern Alps which shows the main characteristics of this kind of faulting in a very simple way.

The Valganna Fault (between the lakes of Lugano and Maggiore). We find here an elongated dome with a steep overthrust north flank striking NE and a much flatter south flank. In the centre of the dome the crystalline schists of the basement rock and overlying Permian volcanics are exposed, the flanks being formed mostly by Triassic limestone (Fig. 113).

The fault-line itself has again given rise to a deeply eroded valley

dividing the core of the dome into two portions. The stress-direction
is given by the straight line of the steep north flank which has a strike
of N 60° E. The main stress had therefore a direction of N 30° W. The
Valganna fault, with a strike of N 3° W, makes an angle of 27° with
the main stress-direction. The fault increases very rapidly in importance
from north to south. The main result of the strike movement is that
east of the fault-line the south flank of the dome is somewhat steeper
than on the west of the fault, and consequently, although the move-

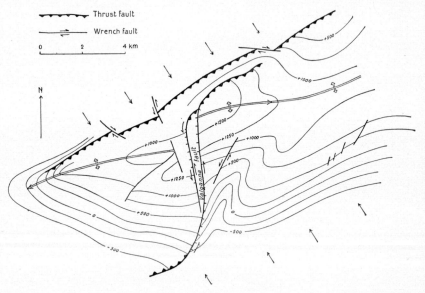

Fig. 113.   The Valganna fault of the Lombardy Alps. *(After de Sitter, Leidsche
Geol. Med., vol.* 11. 1939c.)

ment was originally a strike-slip, the net observable movement is
largely vertical, increasing rapidly southwards. At its southern
extremity the fault curves sharply to the west, where the Triassic
limestone is thrust over the Cretaceous.

The opposite extremity also curves into a steep thrust, and the
crystalline basement is pushed upon the Permian extrusive rock. The
fault is most probably accompanied by another parallel one which
runs in the valley floor, for the offsetting of the northern thrust-fault
is much bigger than the visible offset on the eastern slope of the valley.
As a result of the two thrusts at its extremities the fault is given an
S-shape — which we often observe elsewhere, and which always has

the same origin, a combination of thrusting and a wrench-movement.

The fault demonstrates very clearly the close connexion between the production of a wrench-fault origin, vertical movements, and thrusting and folding.

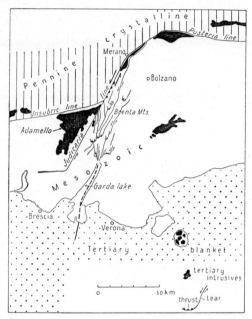

Fig. 114. Map of the Brenta faults in the Lombardy Alps. *(After Trevisan. Published by permission of Istituto di Geologia, University of Padua.)*

Although its origin is certainly typical of that of a vertical shear-fault with a horizontal slip, most of the actual motion is vertical. The Valganna fault represents a type of wrench-fault which is often referred to as a basculating- or torsion-fault, and its origin can easily be misunderstood when only a portion of the fault is open to accurate mapping, or when its dip cannot be ascertained.

The Brenta Mountains Set of Wrench-Faults (in the western Trentino district of the Lombardy Alps). This very interesting set has been described by Trevisan (1939).

The Lombardy Alps are separated from the vertical root-zone of the Penninic nappes by the well-known Insubric or Tonale line, an EW fault-zone of a character which I shall describe further on. In the eastern part of the Lombardy Alps we find the Tertiary batholith of the Adamello Mountains, bounded at its northern limit by this Insubric

Fig. 115. Diagram explaining
the origin of the Brenta faults.
*(After Trevisan. Published by
permission of Istituto di Geologia, University of Padua.)*

line and at its eastern limit by another
large fault-line, the Judicaria line, which
is itself a wrench-fault that shifts the
Insubric line in a NE direction (Fig. 114).
The continuation of the Insubric line in
an eastern direction along the slip is
called the Pusteria line. No detailed data
have as yet been assembled about the
major wrench-fault, the Judicaria line,
but a set of nearly parallel faults east of
this line in the Brenta Mountains has

received more attention. The principle of the movements was very
clearly demonstrated by Trevisan (Fig. 115). Again, as in the case
of the Valganna fault, we find the remarkably close connexion and
transition between overthrusting and wrench-faulting, here accompanied by an en échelon arrangement of the latter. Some of the
wrench-faults are vertical, but many are inclined to the west; this
is probably due to the fact that some of their movements still had a

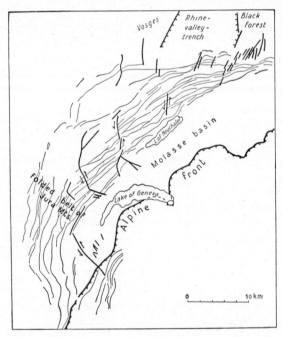

Fig. 116.   The Jura folds with their wrench-faults.   *(After Heim, Geologie der
Schweiz, I.B., III Hauptteil, 1921.)*

thrust character, although the striation on their faces was always horizontal. In this case it is impossible to deduce the direction of the largest principal stress from the accompanying fold-strikes. Firstly there is not much folding in the very strong limestone blocks; and secondly, the tectonic history is so complex that one well-determined folding-stress cannot be defined.

The Jura Mountains Set of Wrench-Faults. Perhaps the most famous set, traversing the numerous folds of the Jura Mountains (Heim, Alb. 1919). The four largest are tabulated here:

Table X

	Strike direction	Angle with fold	Angle with stress direction	Max. net length of slip
Salève fault	N 40° W	70°	20°	1 km 50 km
Dôle-Champagnole fault . .	N 20° W	60°	30°	1–1·5 km 40 km
Vallorbe-Pontarlier fault . .	N 9° W	55°	35°	10 km 45 km
Montruz fault	N 10° E	50°	40°	0.5 km 1.5 km

Together with many smaller ones (see Fig. 116), they form an outstanding example of a regular and constant tectonic feature. Their strike swings from N 40° W to N 10° E together with the arc of the Jura folds; but their swing is rather greater than that of the arc because the intersecting angle diminishes towards the east together with the decrease of the thickness of the strata involved in the folding, and consequently the depth of the basement. The same stress-direction which caused the folds obviously caused the wrench-faults. Why this angle increases from 20° to 40°, from west to east, is not yet quite clear. At their extremities the wrench-faults either disappear in one of the longitudinal thrust-faults of the folds, or branch off in several splays. They originated, without any doubt, during the folding process, for left and right of the fault the folding is not quite the same. A fold may be much more accentuated and steeper at one side than at the other, or there may be two folds instead of one with similar differences.

Although these wrench-faults can be adequately explained as a consequence of the folding-stress, it is equally true, as Heim (1919) pointed out, that the original arc of the whole Jura belt of folds would promote lengthening of the arc as folding proceeded, and lengthening would be facilitated by the formation of the diagonal wrench-faults. Relatively speaking, the theory advanced by Kraus (1951), that the folding movement was not an outwards-directed motion from the

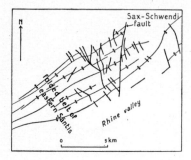

Fig. 117. The Sax-Schwendi fault system in the Säntis Mountains.

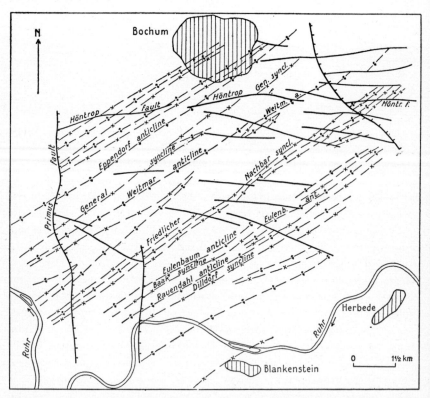

Fig. 118. The wrench-faults of the Bochum area of the Ruhr coalfield. *(After Kukuk, Geologie der Niederrheinisch-Westfälischen Steinkohlengebiete. Published by permission of Springer-Verlag, Berlin.)*

upper crust, but an inward motion of the basement, a kind of underflow, expresses exactly the same thought; there is no fundamental difference between the two concepts.

The Sax-Schwendi Fault (in the Swiss Säntis Mountains) is certainly one of the most famous wrench-faults in a folded belt. The Säntis belt is in itself a strongly folded flat-lying overthrust mass which has probably glided down for some of its way; but the folding- and fault-tectonics are in all appearances perfectly similar to ordinary folding and faulting.

The eastern portion of the Säntis Mountains has been particularly disturbed by a set of diagonal wrench-faults; of these the largest is the Sax-Schwendi fault (Fig. 117). It is most spectacular in its appearance. Where it cuts the steep anticlinal limestone ridges its brecciated fault-zone has given rise to depressions; the anticline has been shifted in front of a syncline and is mirrored in the lake which it formed. The brecciated fault-zone is sometimes very narrow, less than 1 m, and at other places some tens of metres. It is 8 km long and the sinistral strike-slip varies from 500–800 m. The numerous striations on the fault-faces have a dip of 12°–15° N, roughly parallel to the dip of the gliding plane.

To the west of the Sax-Schwendi fault we notice a swarm of similar but much smaller faults, which together occupy a triangle with its base to the north and apex to the south. The apical angle is about 50° and the bisectrix, the assumed stress-direction, runs N 21° W, whereas the strike of the folded belt is N 123° W. The wrench-fault group originated in a very late phase of the folding, for the homologous folds on either side of the faults are in general of the same structure, but not of the same intensity, except in the northern anticlines. It is quite possible that during the gliding an obstruction in the substratum caused a slight deviation of some 10° in the general stress-direction, and hence in that of the wrench-faults themselves.

The Ruhr Coal Basin Wrench-Faults. Very similar to the Sax-Schwendi fault are the wrench-faults in the strongly faulted Ruhr coal basin south of Bochum (Fig. 118). Here, however, only one set of faults is developed, whilst in the Säntis Mountains, both sets are present. The faults belong, again, to a very late phase of the folding-stress, or are simply post-folding.

It would be wrong not to mention one of the greatest wrench-faults which have so far been suggested. For western New Zealand, Wellman, in Hill and Diblee (1949) suggests a 300-mile displacement

along an Alpine fault parallel to and to the west of the New Zealand
Alps, on the evidence of similar structures and rocks on different sides
of the fault in the northern and southern extremities of South Island.
Considerable work will obviously have to be done before the suggestion
becomes an established fact, but it is a fascinating concept. Such
large wrench-faults as the San Andreas, the Great Glen, and the
New Zealand faults are not far removed from the great fundamental
faults which I cover in Chapter 12.

CONCLUSIONS AND EXPERIMENTAL DATA

Experiments on wrench-faulting have revealed some interesting facts
which may quite well have a certain bearing on natural belts of faults.

The clay-cake experiments by Riedel (1929) (Fig. 119) showed that
in a plastic medium such as wet clay a shearing motion originating
at the bottom had a tendency to propagate itself upwards, in a wedge-
shaped zone widening towards the surface. The first cracks that were

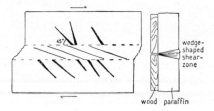

Fig. 119.   Diagram explaining Riedel's experiment.

observed made a 45°–47° angle with the shear-plane and were obviously
tension cracks (gash-fractures) which rotated during the movement,
the angle increasing to 50° or 60°. New cracks with a 45° angle were
then formed, and these in their turn rotated in accordance with the
shearing movement.

The tension cracks were parallel to the principal normal stress that
can be derived from the applied shearing stress.

During the process there developed at the surface a zone of shear,
containing vertical shearing-planes making an acute angle of 10° to
15° with the shearing stress. The reason for the origin of these shear-
planes is not at first apparent. However, since they did not develop
immediately, but only when a distinct shear-zone in the plastic
material had developed, the shear-planes must belong to the dynamic

process. It seems probable that in a less incompetent medium a clear-cut shear-plane would have developed; and in a still less viscous medium, a broader zone of flowage. The observed wedge of shearing with diagonal shear-planes is an intermediate stage between very incompetent flow and very incompetent shear.

R. W. Brown (1928) performed a series of experiments on wrench-faulting by mounting a block of paraffin-vaseline mixture on two wooden bases which were moved horizontally in opposite directions. When the paraffin blocks had a uniform composition the tear-fault between the wooden blocks simply expanded through the paraffin block to the top, but when several paraffin layers were applied, some less competent than the others, it happened that the tear-fault did not penetrate a particular incompetent layer—this was simply contorted, and the higher competent layers showed a complicated set of wrench-, normal, and thrust-faults combined with folds.

One case in which deep-seated wrench-faulting has been assumed to explain another kind of faulting at the surface is that of the belts of en échelon normal faults in Osage and Creek counties, Oklahoma (Fath, 1920). The normal faults have the same function and direction as the gash-fractures of Riedel's experiment. It is true that Fath's explanation has not been accepted either by Sherrill (1929), or by Melton (1929). Melton found that the strike of normal en échelon faults coincides with a very constant shear-joint strike, but since the latter is vertical and normal faults have a dip of 50° to 65°, they cannot have the same origin. Nevertheless, it is quite true that the kind of torsional motion due to unequal vertical movements of the basement which was suggested by Sherrill could explain the normal faults as well, and is actually less hypothetical than a deep-seated wrench-fault. It is equally true that the typical alignment of the faults in narrow NS striking belts may be due to the fact that the faults are observed or developed only in particularly brittle strata which outcrop in the belts. Still, the Fath hypothesis has not lost its originality and appeal, and I should also like to apply it to the set of normal faults which are together called the Mexia fault-belt, in Texas. (See Fig. 104.)

When taken together the seven instances of wrench-faults I have selected give a fairly complete picture of the characteristics of this kind of faulting; for convenience these characteristics are repeated below:

1. The fault outcrop is usually remarkably rectilinear
2. The dip differs little from the vertical

3. There is apt to be a fault-breccia, mylonite or even ultra-mylonite along the fault-line

4. In general their topographic expression is excellent even when the shift is small

5. The shift along the fault may vary from a few centimetres to hundreds of kilometres

6. When the main stress-direction is known from an independent source (e.g. fold direction), the angle is normally less than 45°

7. The length may vary, from very small faults to faults many hundreds of kilometres long

8. Very often they merge either into thrust-faults, making oblique angle with their own strike at their extremities, or thrust-faults merge into the wrench-fault along their course

9. At the extremities, splays which differ little from the main strike are often formed

10. The wrench-faulting generally belongs to a later phase of a folding process

11. The vertical throw along the fault varies very much, either because synclines abut upon anticlines and vice-versa, or because some independent vertical warping occurred

12. There is no preference for sinistral or dextral faults

13. An en échelon arrangement is not common, but in general the wrench-faults are accompanied by many smaller parallel faults of the same character.

Chapter 12

Great Fundamental Faults

Besides the normal faults and wrench-faults described in the foregoing chapters, and the thrust-faults, which will be described in Chapter 17 after we have considered folding, there are certain great fault-lines which do not fall clearly into any of the classes mentioned above. They represent great cracks in the earth's crust; and either the multiple movements which have occurred along them have obliterated their original character, or they never had the characteristics of one of the distinct classes.

Some of these fault-lines, all belonging to major mountain chains, have been investigated in fairly great detail. As typical examples we shall consider the Insubric-Tonale-Pusteria fault-zone of the Alps, and the North Pyrenean fault-zone of south-western France.

The North Pyrenean Fault-zone. Let us first consider the simpler North Pyrenean fault-line (de Sitter, 1954, Fig. 120.) It runs roughly WNW–ESE, and separates the axial zone of Palaeozoic rocks, intruded by granites, from the North Pyrenean zone where Mesozoic rocks, often surrounding secondary Palaeozoic domes, are predominant. The fault-zone obviously separates a downwarped northern zone from an uplifted central zone south of it. The fault-zone itself is almost everywhere marked by Mesozoic rocks dipping at 90° — limestones and pellites, often highly metamorphic and accompanied by intrusions of basic and ultrabasic rocks. When the fault-zone runs between a Palaeozoic dome like that of the St Barthélemy or of the Trois Seigneurs massifs and the axial zone, it invariably consists of crushed, vertical Mesozoic strata. There can be no doubt that the zone was already formed at an early phase of the Alpine folding process, for the non-metamorphic Upper Cretaceous rests unconformably on the crushed metamorphic rocks of the Lower Cretaceous. But the history of this fault goes back further than the phase of post-Lower Cretaceous folding. Along the tear-fault line from Foix to Tarascon, the St Barthélemy massif was shifted some 7 km to the south, and thrust over the plunging nose of the Trois Seigneurs massif, the latter being shifted, at the same time, some 9 km to the west. This double shift produced a basin-like depression, round Tarascon, in which the Trias has a much more pronounced evaporite facies than it has elsewhere (Zwart, 1954). This

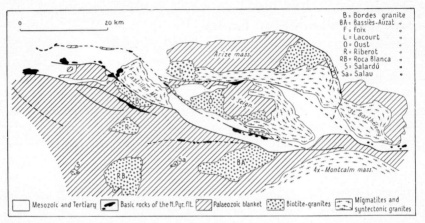

Fig. 120. The fault pattern along the North Pyrenean fault-zone in the Central Pyrenees.

proves that here, at least, fault-movements were already active at the beginning of the Mesozoic. The slow transgression of the Mesozoic on the tilted block of the St Barthélemy massif confirms this hypothesis (de Sitter, 1954). On the other hand, the fault-line from Auzat to Biella and further west, cuts obliquely through the late-Palaeozoic structures. Hence the horizontal movements to which I referred must belong to a late tectonic phase of the Hercynian orogenies, post-Westphalian but pre-Triassic.

We can follow the history of the fault-line still further back in history. At present it separates the integrated Hercynian axial zone from the dissected North Pyrenean zone (see Fig. 258). It also forms a line separating a North Pyrenean differentiated facies of the Devonian from an axial non-differentiated facies. It is even possible that it acted as a facies boundary line in the Ordovician.

Hence we know that since the Upper Palaeozoic, and perhaps earlier, there was in existence a narrow mobile zone of the earth's crust which became a distinct fault-line at the end of the Hercynian folding, and was rejuvenated in the first phase of Laramide folding.

Its horizontal extension is probably much greater than the present

Pyrenees. It probably extends westward into the Asturian-Cantabric mountains, and to the east it possibly links up with the Insubric line of the Alps.

The metamorphism of the Lower Cretaceous and Jurassic rocks is of a peculiar kind—the limestones have been scapolitized—and it is accompanied by the intrusion of numerous small stocks ranging from ultrabasic peridotites to gabbros (ophites) (Zwart, 1953b). These basic magmas cannot be regarded as an initial magmatic phase in the development of the Pyrenean geosyncline, since we cannot call the Lower Mesozoic of the Pyrenees a geosyncline; but they certainly indicate that the fault penetrated very deep into the crust, and reached the basic substratum. We are justified in calling the fault-zone a fundamental feature because of its great lateral and vertical extensions and its long history of activity.

The Insubric Line of The Alps. The next compressive zone to which I should like to call attention is the Insubric-Pusteria line (Cornelius, 1930). This line of dislocation is one of the major features of Alpine structure, and one of its most enigmatic ones, as demonstrated by the fact that different authors have ascribed to it most diverse inter-pretations. It has been described as a normal gravity-fault, sometimes with the northern limb, and sometimes with the southern limb warped down, as a thrust-fault, and even as a "Verschluckungszone" a zone in which by a process of "downward-sucking" a large slice of surface rocks has disappeared, as a "Narbe" (i.e. a deep scar) of some unknown orogenic origin, and as a wrench-fault.

Structurally it is a most important line (see Fig. 262). In the terminology of Staub (1924) and many others, it represents the boundary between the "Dinarides" and the "Alpides" which are sometimes translated by "Africa" and "Europe", a rather fanciful terminology which teaches us very little about its function (de Sitter, 1947a).

Along its most prominent portion, the stretch between Lake Como and the Tonale Pass, it actually constitutes the boundary between the vertical roots of the lower and middle East-Alpine thrust-sheets in the north, and the crystalline Orobic mass in the south (Cornelius, 1930). The latter is simply a block of the basement rock of the southern Alps, with a few remnants of its Permian cover in a more or less horizontal position (see Fig. 177). The rocks on each side of the line of dislocation are crystalline schists, but in the Tonale zone to the north of the fault the metamorphism is of a much higher order than that south of the fault. Along the fault-line we can recognize long narrow slivers of Triassic and Permian rocks, and the fault-plane itself is characterized by strong crushing and mylonitization. It is followed by the great valley of the Valtellina, and hence is usually covered by alluvial deposits. Both north and south of the fault there appear large granite intrusions, the Adamello in the south-east and the Bergello granite in the north-west. They were intruded, to all appearances, after the dislocation came into existence, and they do not cross it.

The main feature of the Insubric dislocation-line is therefore its extremely fundamental character from a structural point of view. It certainly penetrates very deeply into the earth's crust, and has given access for granites and probably for basic rocks (Ivrea zone) to reach the surface, but it certainly is not a normal gravity-fault, although large vertical movements have taken place along its plane.

Towards the east, it is displaced northwards by a great tear-fault, the Judicaria line (de Sitter, 1947a), and it continues much further eastwards as the Tonale-Pusteria line. Towards the west, it first curves southwards and then disappears beneath the Tertiary sediments of the Po plain. Whether it reaches the Mediterranean, and whether it links up with the North Pyrenean fault are matters of conjecture. In its known and exposed course it is not generally accompanied by intrusions of basic rock, unless, as is quite possible, one regards the thick basic rock-mass of the Ivrea zone as an Alpine intrusion (E. Niggli in Cadisch, 1953). Like the North Pyrenean fault-zone, it is marked geophysically by a pronounced gravimetric maximum, perhaps indicating a basic rock-mass of considerable width intruded into the sialic crust.

It is difficult to find equally well-known examples of similar dislocation lines which separate two structurally different units over long distances within the same mountain system. With some hesitancy I quote the serpentine belt along the western border of the Piedmont system of the Appalachians, and the line separating the western gneisses from the eastern granites in Scandinavia (Fig. 287). The latter is also accompanied by a long belt of basic rocks, the hyperite belt. The last two fundamental faults are both characterized by the fact that they separate two units with a difference in metamorphic state: in the Appalachians, highly metamorphic schists are separated from recognizable Palaeozoic strata, and in Sweden, kata-zone gneisses from granites. The same is true for the Insubric line but less obvious for the North Pyrenean dislocation. All four show an accompanying belt of ultrabasic rocks. The two last zones, characterized by serpentine belts, have also been regarded as compressed geosynclinal belts with an initial magmatic phase. In our present state of knowledge it is impossible to decide whether they really represent such a geosynclinal belt, or whether they are comparable with the Pyrenean and Insubric lines.

Another very important fault-line of fundamental significance is, for instance, the line which separates the Sahara craton from the Atlas mountain chains along its northern border (Fig. 299). It is characterized by big facies differences on each side, by enormous movements, by great unconformities, and even occasionally by rather modern volcanoes.

There evidently exist in the earth's crust long fundamental cracks which are characterized by frequent movements along their contiguous faces, and by the fact that they penetrate the whole solid crust and occasionally constitute a way of access to the surface for basic or granite magma. Their particular tectonic function at a particular moment in geological history entirely depends upon the stress-field which prevails at that moment. They may facilitate radial displacements, they may act as wrench-faults, or as great zones of compression, as the stress-field dictates. They often accompany the great orogenic belts of the earth, and are always parallel to the grain of the mountain chains to which they belong.

Chapter 13

Principles of Folding

FOLDING AS A SHEARING PHENOMENON

Geological experience has taught us that folding is the most common form of distortion of the earth's crust. But whereas faulting is easily understood from a mechanical point of view, folding of such brittle material as rocks is a baffling problem which has occupied the minds of geologists since the earliest observations. One of the means of approach to this problem has been experimental investigation. Kuenen and de Sitter (1938) for instance, made a series of folding experiments with different materials to show different possibilities of deforming solid or half-solid cakes into folded structures.

The purely elastic fold is illustrated by the bending of a squared rubber plate, Fig. 121. The internal deformation of the material can be

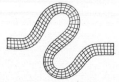

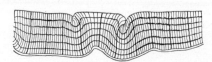

Fig. 121. Folded rubber plate. Deformation of original squares indicate their elastic deformation.

Fig. 122. Thickened and folded weak paraffin cake floating on water.

(Both after Kuenen and de Sitter, Leidsche Geol. Med., vol. 10, 1938.)

judged by the distortion of the squares, showing flattening parallel and perpendicular to the bedding-plane. We tried to illustrate the purely plastic fold with a weak paraffin cake floating on warm water (Fig. 122). The incipient deformation was a simple thickening of the cake, which would certainly have continued without folding if we had not added an irregularity to the structure by a small load of vaseline. Folds developed on both sides of this small irregularity. Folding began earlier when the compression was accelerated, but again the initial process was a simple thickening. The distortion of the squares indicates that the more rapid deformation caused some elastic resistance, since the squares then show the same stretching and compression pattern as in the rubber plate. No shear-planes could in any way be produced in this kind of material. Finally, to illustrate the concentric folding of layered sediments, a pack of paper sheets was folded (Fig. 123).

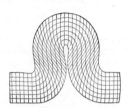

Fig. 123. Folded pack of paper   Fig. 124. Folded unstratified clay
sheets, illustrating pure concentric   cake with spontaneous concentric
folding.   shear.

(Both after Kuenen and de Sitter, Leidsche Geol. Med., vol. 10, 1938.)

The distortion of the squares was now quite different. As I was personally convinced that this concentric folding is also the predominating principle, even when stratification does not predispose the material to this mechanism of folding, Kuenen tried different materials and other conditions, and finally succeeded in folding an unstratified clay cake in this way (Fig. 124). Concentric shear-planes, parallel to the bottom and top of the cake, were spontaneously formed. The conclusions from this series of experiments will be drawn further on, but one conclusion is obvious: that except for the last experiment with spontaneous concentric shear, none of the experiments show any convincing analogies with natural folds in rocks so far as their internal mechanism is concerned — for under the microscope or to the naked eye, shear-planes are almost invariably visible in natural folds of rocks.

Concentric and Planar-Shear in Folding. From microtectonic and theoretical considerations we can conclude that there exist only three fundamental modes of folding:

1. Concentric folding
2. Cleavage
3. Flow

All the endless variation of tectonic features and shapes can be explained by different combinations of these three processes.

Concentric Folding means that all internal movement is parallel to the bedding-plane. It is fundamentally an elastic bending of an originally horizontal sheet, with development of parallel concentric shear-planes in the flanks of the folds. It belongs to the elastico-viscous field of deformation, and is typical of the upper part of the earth's crust but by no means restricted to this part only (Fig. 125a). Concentric folding is also called parallel folding or distance-true folding, because the thickness of any concentrically folded bed remains unchanged.

Cleavage is a process by which all internal movement is along shear-planes which do not change their position during the process of folding. Normally they are perpendicular to the deformative stress, and therefore sub-vertical. The process is fundamentally a dilatation in a vertical sense and a compression in a lateral sense. It presumably also takes place in the elastico-viscous field of deformation, where

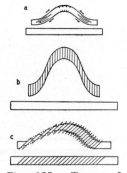

the elastic properties have not yet lost their influence, but is probably quite near to the plastic field. Cleavage or similar folding is typical of the lower regions of orogenic belts, but is by no means restricted to them (Fig. 125b).

Cleavage is the basis of all similar folding.

Another kind of planar-shear takes place along planes oblique to the deformative stress. It accompanies both the fundamental modes mentioned above, chiefly by replacing fault-planes (either as wrench-faults, thrust-faults, or normal faults) and always by means of internal readjustment along multiple planes, as in cleavage (Fig. 125c).

Fig. 125. Types of folding processes:
a. concentric fold,
b. cleavage folds,
c. oblique shear-fold.

Flow, finally, is a kind of distortion in which a fixed orientation of shear-planes to a stress-direction is lost. The internal movement itself is no longer orientated but can take any direction, with the result that it can no longer be represented adequately in a section. It is typical of very weak rocks like salt, or of very high confining pressures or high temperatures, and is the only true plastic deformation of rocks.

The old classification of van Hise into parallel and similar folds still holds good, since parallel folding is synonymous with pure concentric folding and similar folding always shows some influence on cleavage folding.

Combinations of cleavage and concentric folding are very common, which shows that the two main kinds of folding are not very far removed from one another in a mechanical sense.

Every kind of folding is, moreover, accompanied by faulting, demonstrating that even folding and faulting are not widely separated processes. In particular, oblique-shear must be very near to faulting since we often see transitions from the one to the other. A flexure, for instance, becomes a fault, or a steep flank becomes an overthrust.

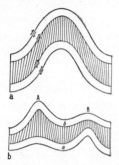

Fig. 126.   Fracture-cleavage: *a* similar fold, *b* disharmonic fold.

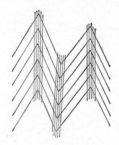

Fig. 127.   Accordion-folding due to cleavage zones in axial zones.

Fig. 128.   Oblique shear- or chevron-fold.

By studying planar shear-folding and concentric shear-folding and their different kinds of combinations, one arrives at the following classification:

1. Concentric folding
2. Similar folding
    a. slaty-cleavage folding
    b. fracture-cleavage folding
    c. accordion-folding
    d. chevron-folding or oblique shear-folding
3. Flow

Concentric shear, and its origin in an elastically curved sheet, have already been explained in Chapter 7. The assumption that cleavage is also a result of elastic stresses set up in a thickening sheet of solid material has been advanced in the same chapter. This view is supported by the fact that in a very plastic material, such as the heated paraffin of the experiment illustrated in Fig. 122, folding is favoured by raising the stress. We also saw that it is the more incompetent rock which shows the kind of fracture-cleavage which occurs between concentrically folded competent beds. We are, therefore, perhaps justified in assuming that, with cleavage, there is in general a rather greater separation between stress and strength than there is in the case of concentric folding.

The combination of concentric shear and cleavage gives, in the first place, similar folds with fracture-cleavage in the more incompetent layers (Fig. 126a), as illustrated in Chapter 7. Fracture-cleavage also allows, of course, the production of non-similar folding of the kind we call disharmonic folding (Fig. 126b), but I shall refer to this phenomenon again in Chapter 16. Another form is reached when slaty-cleavage is confined to certain zones which become the anticlinal and synclinal axes, and all internal movement between these axes is restricted to the unbent but tilted bedding-plane. The result is a type of sharp fold which can best be described by the term accordion-fold (Fig. 127). In connexion with low-angle thrusts we often find a type of folding which is very like these accordion-folds, but which has a peculiarity — one flank is formed by planar-shear cutting obliquely through the bedding, and the other by planar-shear in the bedding. The result is a series of straight-legged folds of which one limb is often somewhat irregular (Fig. 128). It is frequently a source of disharmony between the lower and higher parts of a fold.

In the following table some of the characteristics of these types of folds have been listed. (Table XI.)

A very important consequence of concentric folding, in contrast with all similar folding, is that a concentric fold cannot continue downwards indefinitely. The further down we go within the concentric fold, the narrower becomes its core, and finally something else must replace the purely concentric fold. A similar fold, on the contrary, has no geometrical boundary.

Another peculiarity of concentric folding is its close relation to the original sedimentary structure of the beds involved in the folding. This property is the consequence of its origin in the elastic bending of horizontal sheets, the sheets being the competent members of the sedimentary sequence.

Both these characteristics tend in the same direction so that the shapes of concentric folding are more diverse and show more variety than those of cleavage folding. In the following paragraphs some general aspects of folding will be described, but they belong almost exclusively to concentric folds.

Table XI

Kind of fold / Characteristics	Concentric	Fracture- and Slaty-Cleavage	Chevron- and Accordion-folding	Flow
Synonyms	Parallel or distance-true	Similar		
Position of shear-planes	curved and concentric, parallel to bedding	planar, parallel to axial plane of fold	planar in axial plane and parallel to bedding planes	random
Position in earth's crust	superficial	superficial and deeper levels	superficial and deeper levels	deeper levels
Competent or incompetent	competent	Incompetent and competent		incompetent
State of metamorphism	non-metamorphic rocks	Metamorphic and non-metamorphic rocks		
Elastic or plastic	elastico-viscous	elastico-viscous { Accordion-folds are related to cleavage / Chevron-folds are related to oblique-shear }		plastic
Accompanying faults	many, in varying directions, but always in relation to the folding	perhaps fewer mostly parallel to fold axis or oblique shear-planes, either thrust-faults or wrench-faults		rare and then independent of folding

DIFFERENT KINDS AND MECHANISMS OF FOLDING

The question of which circumstances determine the kind of folding that will be followed by the rocks is impossible to answer adequately before we know more about the incipient stages of folding. The study of E. Cloos on the oolite deformation, to which I have already referred in Chapter 7, showed that slaty-cleavage becomes visible only after an initial deformation in the same sense of up to 20%. In other words, the principle of cleavage-deformation along planar shear-planes parallel to the axial planes, was already active before the cleavage-planes became visible in the rock. Consequently the incipient folding had exactly the same character as the later intensification, and we can rest assured that in this case no concentric folding preceded the cleavage folding. Although we know of other cases where it seems probable that the deformation started as concentric folding in the

competent rocks and as fracture-cleavage in the incompetent rocks
(as we have seen in Chapter 7) and later changed into a general slaty-
cleavage of the whole rock sequence, the former example shows that
this is not the only way to arrive at pure cleavage folding.

The shapes of accordion-folds also suggest that this kind of folding
was never preceded by any other kind; otherwise we should find relics
of it in the present folds, as curved forms in the flanks. Nor could
cleavage have been obliterated by later planar-shear. Hence it seems
most probable that preference for a certain type of folding was established early in the process of deformation. An exception to this rule
can be made for flow, in which traces of other original kinds of folding
could certainly have been obliterated later.

The mode of folding is, consequently, somehow inherent to the rock
in its unfolded state, related either to its individual lithological
properties or to the stress-field. It is improbable that lithology is an
important determining factor. It is true that similar folds, of both
the cleavage type and the accordion type, are typical of Palaeozoic
folding although not restricted to it, and that concentric folding is
typical of the younger periods of folding, although it occurs also in
Hercynian orogenies. It is, moreover, very improbable that the
Palaeozoic strata at their time of folding differed in some fundamental
way from the Mesozoic or Tertiary rocks. The sandstones, quartzites,
shales, and slates of the Upper Carboniferous were sand and clays at the
time of the Asturian folding, completely similar to the Tertiary sands
and clays that were folded in the Miocene. Still, parts of the Ruhr and
the Belgian coal districts are characterized by accordion- and chevron-
folding which are almost, or altogether, unknown in Tertiary basins.
The Devonian of the axial zone of the Pyrenees, folded by cleavage into
isoclinal folds, did not differ at the time of its late Carboniferous
folding from the Cretaceous limestones of the Pre-Pyreneic zone folded
in post-Eocene time. Neither can the depth of burial be the only, or
most important, factor, although it is certainly true that the deeper we
look into the earth's crust the more frequently do we meet cleavage
folding and schistosity (and flow).

I shall refer to this question again when, in Chapter 32, the difference
in character of Pre-Cambrian, Palaeozoic, and Tertiary orogenies are
described. But one of the main factors is probably the fact that
orthotectogenesis is characterized by cleavage and schistosity-folding,
and paratectogenesis by concentric folding. Most Tertiary orogenies
have a paratectonic character, and in those that possess a good

development of magmatic phases cleavage folding does occur, as in the Pennine zone of the Alps.

In view of the facts that concentric and planar shear-folding often alternate in the same structure, and that the lithology of the rock is apparently only a secondary factor, it seems probable that difference in kind of folding is mainly dependent on the intensity of the deformative stress in relation to the elastic limit of the rocks.

DETACHMENT ALONG A BASAL SHEARING-PLANE (DÉCOLLEMENT)

Without doubt, the concept of the basal shearing-plane has been one of the most fruitful thoughts in the realm of comparative tectonics. It teaches us that a superficial cover may have been deformed, for one reason or another, independently of its substratum. Argand distinguished clearly between "plis de couverture", folds belonging exclusively to the superficial cover, and "plis de fond", where the substratum took part in the folding process. Since Buxtorf advocated the thesis that the folds in the Mesozoic rocks of the Jura were folded independently of their crystalline basement, and glided on the very incompetent anhydrite layers of the Triassic, this concept has gained in weight, and

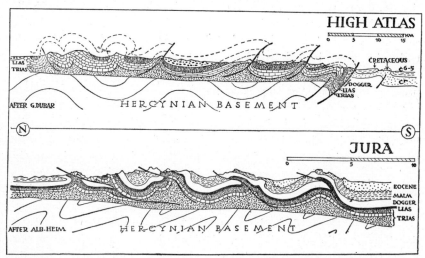

Fig. 129. Décollement or detachment along basal shear-plane. Jurassic folds in Jura Mountains and in High Atlas. *(After Heim, Geologie der Schweiz, I.B., III Hauptteil, 1921, and Dubar, Monographies Régionales, 3e série, Maroc, no. 3, 1952, Pl. V.)*

superficial folds have been called simply "Jurassic" folds (Fig. 129). The process of "décollement", which means the detachment of the upper cover from its substratum, is the fundamental concept which lies at the base of all thrusting, gliding, and diapiric structures, and is equally important for the understanding of most of the tectonics of superficial folding.

It would be erroneous, however, to presume that the phenomenon of detachment is necessarily or even ordinarily restricted to one surface. On the contrary, we may safely assume that in a thick stratigraphical column several horizons are very often prospective horizons of detachment, and it depends largely on the relative incompetency of the several lithological units, which build up a sedimentary cover, as to whether one or more will act as detachment layers or not. It is obvious, for instance, that the extreme incompetency of the salt-bearing clays of the upper Triassic in Europe and North Africa has determined the tectonic style in several independent fold-systems, since it has repeatedly acted as the preferred detachment horizon. But as soon as another propitious incompetent layer is present, as for instance the Lower-Malm clays of the Western Pre-Alps, this plays locally an equally important or even a predominant role.

The effect of the detachment is such that the series of rocks above the detachment layer moves and takes its shape more or less independently of the underlying series. In the case of gravity-gliding tectonics, for instance, the underlying series is not deformed at all. Only the cover has glided down and has been eventually, but not necessarily, folded under its own weight on arrival at the base of the pre-existing slope. On the other hand the presence of a detachment layer may mean only that the shortening is concentrated in a fold at one position in the series above the layer, rather than in the series below it. Or in other circumstances it may facilitate deviations from pure concentric folding, as for instance when lack of space due to the high curvature in the core necessitates the crumpling of either an anticline or syncline. In the selection of the detachment surface it is relative incompetency which is important, not an absolute incompetency. Locally, a shale between thick limestones (and at greater depth even a limestone between thick sandstones series) may act as a detachment-plane. Nevertheless, we mostly find that one special horizon such as the gypsiferous marls and the cavernous dolomites of the Lower Triassic of the Southern Alps, covered by thousands of metres of Lower, Middle, and Upper Triassic limestones, acts as a

basal shearing-plane over a large area. It is adopted both by gravitational gliding sheets moving from north to south, and by ordinary
thrust sheets moving from south to north. And even when no percep-
tible displacement can be ascertained, the same horizon of cavernous
dolomite has been strongly brecciated, again demonstrating some
movement along this plane.

THE SIZE OF A FOLD

I have enlarged somewhat on the function of the basal shearing-
plane because it is a fairly universal factor in folding processes, not
restricted to concentric folding. In concentric folding, however, a
basal detachment is more common, and its presence also determines
the size of the fold. In its most simple shape the concentric fold consists
of one regular arc with its centre in the core of the fold, flanked at both
sides by two similar synclinal arcs, with centres above the surface,
as in Fig. 130.

It is obvious that below the centre O the principle of concentricity
can no longer be sustained; nevertheless the volume of the triangle
below the last concentrically folded bed is still the same as in its

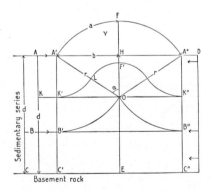

Fig. 130. Simple concentric fold; for explanation see text.

unfolded shape. We may assume that the strata in this triangle have
been shortened by cleavage, but faulting or crumpling of the strata
may equally well have occurred. The lower, straight boundary of the
fold is the basal detachment plane of the fold. Referring to Fig. 130, we
see that the breadth of the fold is then determined, from the very
beginning, by the thickness of the sedimentary blanket. As no appre-

ciable compression of the rock into a smaller volume is possible. the volume of rock above the surface, $A'HA''$, must equal the total volume of the shortening in a horizontal direction, viz: $2 \times ACC'A'$ or

$$\text{surface } A'A''F = 2 \times \text{surface } CC'A' \text{ or}$$
$$\text{surface } A'A''F = d \times 2 \times AA' \text{ or}$$
$$\text{surface } A'A''F = d \times (AD - A'A'')$$
$$\text{surface } KK''F' = 2 \times \text{surface } KCC'K'$$
$$KK''F' = d' \times (AD - AA'')$$

This is equally true for any other concentrically folded bedding-plane of the same fold.

The amplitude of the fold-length AD at any stage of the folding is therefore dependent only on the thickness of strata involved in the folding, e.g. the folding depth d or d'. Thus we see that the position of the particular incompetent layer determines the size of the fold. This gives us the possibility of calculating the depth of the detachment surface. The elevation above the surface and the shortening can be measured on a section, and the depth is their quotient. The theory can

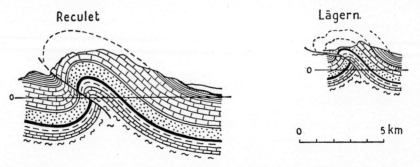

Fig. 131. Comparison of Reculet and Lägern folds, both from Jura Mountains.

be checked by measuring different adjacent sections, in the Jura Mountains for instance, and the result is surprisingly good, the differences in the calculated depth of the basement being only about 6%.

The relation between thickness and size of folds is also very well illustrated by Fig. 131, where two very similar overthrust folds from the western and eastern Jura Mountains are drawn on the same scale; in the Reculet section the same strata are considerably thicker, and hence the fold amplitude is larger than in the Lägern section.

LOCATION OF FOLDS

Because the distance from one crest to the next is determined beforehand by the thickness of the strata, the initial location of one crest can determine a whole belt of folds. The location of the first fold is still arbitrary, however.

R. W. Brown (1928) has shown experimentally that the location of folds in younger unconformably overlapping rocks is strongly influenced by the structure in older strata. In his experiments, renewed compression in the same direction, after deposition of the younger unconformable strata, resulted every time in a fold in the younger strata directly overlying the older structure. This conclusion, moreover, is in agreement with the observation that, during the same cycle of sedimentation, recurrent folding accentuates almost without exception the first formed structures, and seldom creates new ones in other positions.

This principle cannot be applied, however, when a complete detachment of the basement takes place. In that case it is principally sedimentary features which predispose some regions as the sites of the first folds. In particular, the edges of competent strata determine the location of the anticlinal axes, as is shown by many parts of over-thrust-faults where we find this kind of wedge exposed (cf. Fig. 132 and Figs. 181, 187). It is evident that other kinds of prominent irregularities, lenses for instance, will have the same capacity of locating a fold.

THE DIRECTION OF FOLDING STRESS

A process of geological deformation is no laboratory experiment, and we can try to read the direction of the deformative stress only from the orientation of fold or fault structures. From a general point of view the problem is not difficult to solve. One of the principle stresses is always assumed to be necessarily vertical, because the surface of the earth with gravity perpendicular to it is by far the most important plane of discontinuity that enters into the stress-field. In the horizontal plane, we can determine the largest principle stress as either bisecting the acute angle of a set of tear-faults, or, better still, as perpendicular to the longer axis of folding or to the strike of the thrust planes.

It is, of course, inconceivable that a fold making an oblique angle with the major stress should be formed, unless some local factor of disturbance is present and makes the major stress deviate from its regional direction. This factor of disturbance must be determined before the deviation can be assessed.

Since this process of determining the direction of the main stress is simple, controversies seldom arise, except on minor points, or if the evidence is contradictory.

Great difficulties and long discussions have, however, arisen from a very simple misconception: that a stress-field can be divided into an active one in one direction and a passive one in the opposite direction. All discussions, and they are very numerous, as to whether the "push" is from the north or from the south, whether there is an underthrust or an overthrust, whether there is a buttress or an active moving block, are irrelevant. Each and every observed displacement is relative to

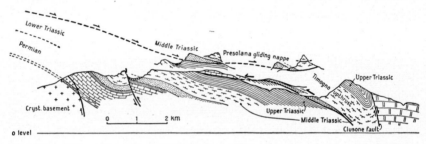

Fig. 132.   NS section through Bergamasc Alps, showing combination of N to S and S to N movement.   *(After de Sitter, Leidse Geol. Med., vol.* 14B, 1949.*)*

the next block only, and never absolute in relation to the centre of the earth. We have no means whatsoever of determining which part has actually moved in relation to the earth's centre and which has remained stationary. This applies only to tangential movement; in all radial movements we might expect some evidence of the actual sense of movement because the sea-level may sometimes be expected to remain stationary, or at any rate to have a limited radius of action, and gravity necessarily acts only downwards in the vertical. Colloquially we may talk of an "over" thrust, and may imagine the upper flank to have been "pushed" over the lower flank; but exactly the same structure would have been formed if the lower flank had been pushed under and the upper flank had been stationary. This applies just as well to a simple thrust anticline as to the whole Alpine structure. When Ernst Kraus (1951a) advocated an underthrust from north to south of the foreland below and towards the centre of the Alpine chain, as compared with the classical way of expression, by which the Alps advanced from south to north over and on their foreland, he merely used different words to say exactly the same thing. In order to illustrate this fact we can advance several examples where the sense of movement in the upper and lower portions of a structure in the same section is opposite. In a section of the Bergamasc Alps (Fig. 132) we see an "upthrust" from south to north, and an overthrust, cutting it off at the top, directed from north to south. In this case it is true that some of the north to south movement is probably due to gravitational gliding.

The Tarra structure, south-west of Lake Maracaibo, offers another very clear example. In its northern portion the anticline has a steep largely overthrust eastern flank, but in the south it is the west flank which is considerably steeper than the east flank. It is quite possible that in the lower levels (Fig. 187) below the eastward-thrust structure we still may find a westward-thrust structure.

This is not true only when we think of an asymmetry in a cross-section, but also on the map. An island arc is no proof of an active push against the concave side and a buttress on the convex one, neither has a wedge "penetrated" as an "active" block in resistant medium.

Even in structures due to gravity gliding it is immaterial whether we think of a sedimentary cover gliding down or a rising block.

Once this has been clearly understood we may revert to the classical expressions — overthrusting, or pushing folds against buttresses, or letting one portion of the crust advance, or any unidirectional term.

DEPTH OF EROSION

In the following chapters I shall describe many different shapes of fold-structure and shall try to classify them according to their peculiarities. All our information about their shape is, however, derived from a relatively thin section of the crust, in the first place that which is exposed on the surface, and secondly the knowledge which the drill or tunnelling has brought us. But a large portion of the fold seen in a section is interpretative — either in the air, representing the upper portion carried away by erosion, or in the subsurface, below the reach of the artificial exposures. The manner in which the section is completed is largely a matter of the experience of the geologist concerned, and he prefers to take his examples from the surrounding structures on the just assumption that they will have a similar structural history and similar physical properties. He will be confronted immediately,

however, with the difficulty that all the structures in the neighbourhood
are laid bare by erosion to about the same level and thus give him
little information about either the deeper or the higher structural
levels. He will have to look elsewhere for information, but then he
will perceive that in a more deeply eroded country the structures do
not resemble his original ones, and he will not know how to conjoin
higher structural features with deeper ones. When we think, for
instance, of the complicated superficial structures in the Lower-Fars
series in Iran (Fig. 133) we see that it would be quite impossible
to construct the structure of the Asmari limestone from the surface

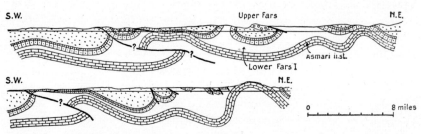

Fig. 133. Section through Iranian oilfields. (After Lees, "Science of Petroleum",
vol. 6, 1953. Published by permission of the Oxford University Press.)

data alone. Here the interference of a basal shearing-plane at the top
of the limestone makes construction impossible.

In Fig. 134 we can compare an ordinary section through a Jura
fold with one north of Thüringen. In the Jura the folds appear as a
series of broad anticlines in upper Jurassic limestones with relatively
narrow synclines, whereas in Thüringen we find narrow compressed
anticlines with broad sweeping synclines. The comparison suggests
that the lower part of the section of the Jura anticline may be completed
by taking account of the data from Thüringen, and vice versa.

When we think of an overthrust anticline where the upper flank is
still well preserved, as for instance in the Tarra folds (Venezuela), or
the Turner Valley structure (Canada) (Figs. 187, 190), we can understand
that it would be difficult for any tectonician to draw this kind of
structure if erosion had carved away the structure to a level $1^1/_2$ km
deeper. We should have found at the surface a relatively broad belt
of vertical strata, certainly faulted since several members of the
stratigraphical sequence were missing, but there would be no indication that there had originally been a large overthrust.

Consequently we often find apparently different kinds of folding described as separate types although in reality they merely represent different levels of the same type of folding. Only very wide experience can in some degree guard us from this fallacy.

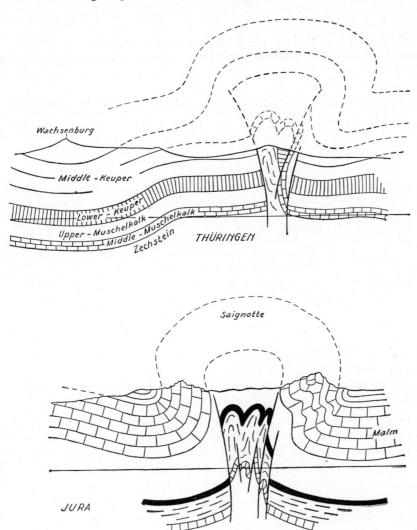

Fig. 134. Comparison of Jura section with Thüringen section.

Chapter 14

Concentric Folds and Associated Faults

In the previous chapter I explained that concentric folding is one of the leading principles in folding processes because incipient folding usually involves the elastic deformation of the most resistant and rigid rocks. I shall dwell at some length on the development of concentric folds, because other types of fold can often be regarded as derivatives from the fundamental concentric principle.

THE DEVELOPMENT OF A CONCENTRIC FOLD

The birth of a simple fold can be imagined as taking place at a single point, which later becomes the culmination of the fold in both the cross-section and longitudinal section. The axis of such a fold may be horizontal for some distance but it will always show an axial plunge eventually at each end. Since the compressive force is acting perpendicular to the fold-axis, there will in general be no tensional stress in that direction; but perpendicular to the stress-direction and parallel to the fold, tension due to the arching of the axis may be expected. The size of the fold is determined firstly, by the total thickness of strata involved in the particular fold, and secondly by its rigid, elastically deformed members. Hence the incompetent members simply have to follow the prescribed shape, which they will do passively when no extra stress becomes involved. A consequence of this is that the upper, soft, non-consolidated part of a stratigraphical sequence which has to follow the elastically determined shape of lower strata, may have another stress condition different from that of the intermediate layers, and different again from that of the basal layers.

In Fig. 135 three stages are constructed in the development of the most simple imaginable shape of a concentric fold. This simplification does not, however, invalidate the conclusion for more complex forms.

By drawing lines joining the numbered points on the original

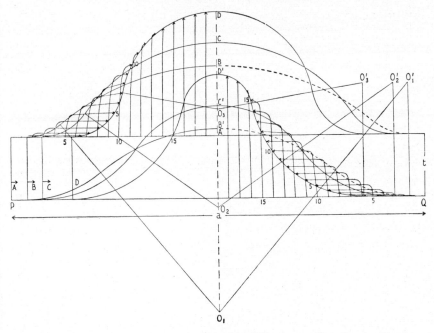

Fig. 135.   Development of a concentric fold; for explanation see text.

horizontal surface and its subsequent positions, we get the trajectories of these points in space. We notice that each point starts with a vertical motion and then suddenly turns to a horizontal direction. Hence at each stage there are in any one anticline two marginal blocks moving inwards and one central block moving upwards (Fig. 136); the latter narrows down to a small wedge in the course of the process. The relative motion of one point to the next on the same bedding surface is therefore practically negligible during almost the whole of the process, except at the precise moment when the upper point is still moving upwards but the lower one turns to its horizontal stage. If we join the points at which this occurs on different surfaces we obtain a line slanting towards the centre of structure. Such a line of turning-points obviously represents a possible break in the smoothness of the motion, and these lines are therefore potential faults (Fig. 136). We find during folding that the centres of the anticlinal curvature (O_1, O_2, O_3 in Fig. 135) move upwards, and those of the synclinal curves move horizontally inwards. In its upward course the anticlinal centre moves much more quickly than the strata themselves, since the radius of curvature is shortened simulta-

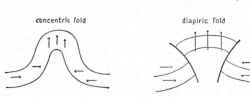

Fig. 136. Horizontal and vertical movement in a concentric fold, leading to diapirism.

Fig. 137. Lack of space in the core of fold.

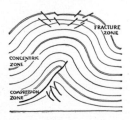

Fig. 138. Zoning on a concentric fold.

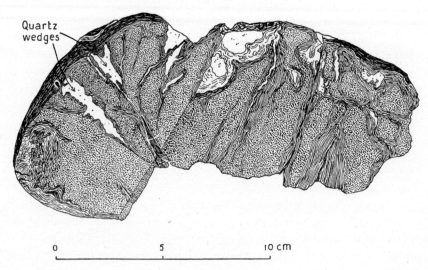

Fig. 139. Crestal tension fractures in a microfold. Carboniferous sandstone shale alternation from East Asturia (Spain).

neously. Hence its position in the stratigraphical succession wanders from one layer to the next. In Fig. 137 we can see that as soon as this centre has passed any particular horizon, the latter surface can no longer fold in the same concentric fashion and maintain its original length; in other words, at the base of each fold with a definite basal shear-plane there is a layer which, because of lack of space, can no longer be folded concentrically. This layer may be expected to thicken in the core of the fold during the folding process. Besides the fact that the increasing curvature cannot be concentrically followed by an increasing thickness of bottom strata, we also find that whatever the exact shape of the fold, the narrowing of the upward moving axial wedge causes an increasing lack of space in the core of the fold.

This lack of space in the core of the anticline creates a tendency to broaden the wedge of upward thrust within the centre of the fold or for a break-through by faulting; both actions involve disturbance of the concentric mechanism. In the second case, where faulting occurs we get complications such as overthrusts or diapiric structures, which will be described later. In the first case we shall find a flat-topped broad anticline with steep flanks, a so-called "boxfold".

At the top of the fold the softest layers are not actively concerned with the folding. They follow the shape prescribed by the more rigid competent beds below. They may, therefore, show all the characteristics of tension, both in cross-section or in longitudinal section. Hence, in an ordinary concentric fold we can distinguish three zones: a lower zone, broken and compressed, a large middle zone which has been folded concentrically, and an upper zone with tension-faults and other adjustments (Fig. 138).

From this standpoint, the supposed tensional stress on the crest of a fold is limited to the most superficial layers, and may even be altogether absent if the stratigraphical sequence has no particular competent series in its middle portion. The relative scarcity of longitudinal tension-faults on the crests of anticlines is thus explained.

Nevertheless, it is undoubtedly true that in an elastically bent sheet the concentric shear-planes are restricted to the flanks — the crest showing tension cracks, and the core crumpling. In Fig. 139 the tension of the zone of maximum curvature has resulted in the filling up of wedge-shaped cracks by recrystallized quartz. It seems logical to suppose that the quartz is not derived from the sandstone next to fractures but from this inner curvature where the pressure is greatest. The fold of Fig. 139 is a microfold; we find the same phenomenon in folds which are some hundred times larger, of the size of a big cliff, as for instance on the South Wales coast (Fig. 140). The tensional cracks and the wedge-shaped recrystallization zone probably originate in most cases during the latest phase of folding, and sometimes actually after the folding, as release tension cracks. It is improbable that

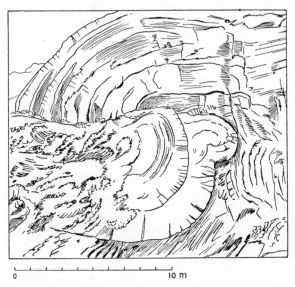

0 _____ 10 m

Fig. 140.   Crestal fractures in minor fold of Carboniferous sandstone, Millstone Grit; cliff near Amroth, South Wales.

folding would continue in the same strictly concentric fashion if the tension fractures existed long before the process stopped; the width of the cracks, moreover, is usually very small in comparison with the total curvature.

We have seen that during the advanced stages of concentric folding an active role is played by the incompetent bottom layers, which have a tendency either to break through the core or to broaden the anticline. In both cases we get a tensional stress even on the crest of the fold. The faults that are characteristic of the upper incompetent top layers may penetrate much deeper in this advanced stage, and interrupt the concentric folding of the intermediate, concentric layer, and may eventually link up with the complications in the core (cf. Figs. 142 and 144). In ground-plan, folds, and concentric folds in particular, have generally an elongated shape, the crest being much longer than it is broad, but the relation of length to width may vary considerably. We find all variations from domes which are nearly round, and short or brachy-anticlines, to very elongated structures. There are many domes which are supposed to have been formed, not by tangential pressure but by radial pressure, caused, for instance, by deep-seated salt-domes, such as those in the Texas embayment. Such an origin has not, however, been postulated for the domes and brachy-anticlines of the Rocky Mountains districts. As far as I know there has never been an adequate answer to the question of why in one case we find a system of parallel elongated anticlines, and in another a group of domes and short anticlines with varying strikes. The explanation might lie in irregularities in the sedimentary pattern or in succeeding folding phases.

The faults which accompany ordinary concentric folding can be divided into two groups, those of the upper zone and those of the lower zone. The group of the lower zone is apt to break through the concentric zone to the surface and give rise to thrust-faulted and diapiric structures, which will be described in their own chapter. Those of the upper zone can be sub-divided into:

1. longitudinal crest-faults
2. cross-faults and flank-faults
3. diagonal tear-faults

which I shall describe when we meet them in the following sequence of examples.

LONGITUDINAL CREST-FAULTS

The Three Kettleman Hill Domes. They are situated near the western border of the San Joaquin Valley basin. Their closure is in the Pliocene San Joaquin shales. The structure is slightly steeper towards the west, in accordance with the general thinning of the strata in that direction towards the basin border. On the map of the central part of the dome, Fig. 141, we notice a whole set of longitudinal normal faults with throws which are seldom more than 100 feet, as shown in the cross-section. The origin of this set of faults is undoubtedly the tension of the outer arc of the fold, typical of the upper portion of the fold.

Because the longitudinal faults converge downwards, embracing small grabens, they cut one another out not far below the present surface. We may surmise that we then enter the better consolidated

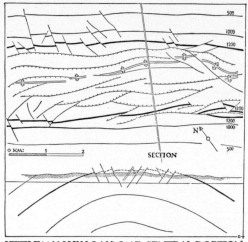

KETTLEMAN HILLS, N-DOME, CENTRAL PORTION

Fig. 141.   Crestal faults in central portion of Kettleman Hills, North Dome, California.   *(After Woodring and Stewart, 1934.   Published by permission of the United States Geological Survey.)*

and therefore concentrically folded part of the fold. Similar longitudinal crest-faults are numerous since they characterize, for instance, several other oilfields: Quitman Oilfield, Wood Cty, Texas; Sand Draw Oilfield, Fremont Cty, Wyoming; La Paz Oilfield, Maracaibo district, Venezuela, and also the large broad Waubach anticline of the South Limburg coalfield.

La Paz. Here the crestal faults (Fig. 142) penetrate very deeply into

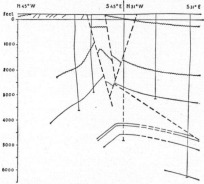

Fig. 142.   Section through La Paz fold, Venezuela.   *(After Caribbean Petroleum Company, 1948.   Published by permission of the American Association of Petroleum Geologists.)*

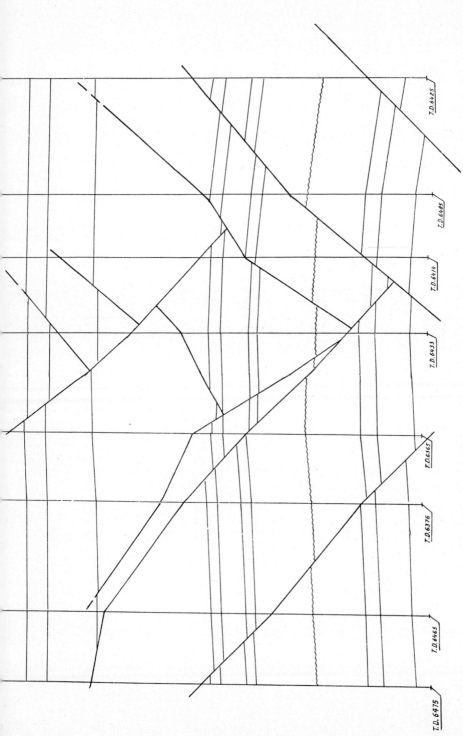

Fig. 143. Quitman Oilfield, Texas; map and section, showing crestal faults. (*After Smith, University of Texas Publications no. 5116, 1951. Published by permission of the University of Texas.*)

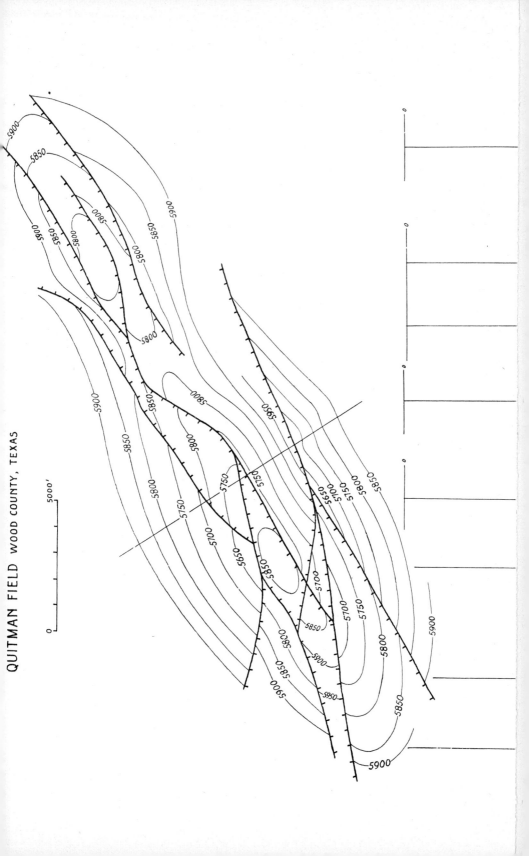

QUITMAN FIELD WOOD COUNTY, TEXAS

the core of the structure, and the original crestal trough has probably been accentuated by thrusting at a later stage.

The Quitman Oilfield. This has an exceptionally well-developed set of normal crestal faults (Fig. 143) dipping at 45–50° and cutting one another out at depth. The Quitman faults also penetrate deeply into the structure — below 6,000 feet — into the Lower Cretaceous. These beds cannot be regarded as the soft passive cover of the fold. The stretching must have another cause and we may presume that there has been upward pressure by the incompetent bottom layers.

This need not surprise us, since the Quitman structure is situated in the same trend as the Opelika and Van Oilfields, both considered to be domes above deep-seated salt plugs. Salt is evidently the best incompetent basal-shearing bed, and is particularly active when it is in a condition of high stress.

The Concepcion Structure of the Maracaibo District, Venezuela (Fig. 144). This provides another curious example of crestal faults, which in this instance curve into diagonal faults. Downwards, the crestal faults merge into the bedding-plane at a depth of about 6,000 feet and produce relative motion along the bedding-planes just the opposite to that which folding would have caused. The folding of Concepcion has been accomplished in two stages, a post-Eocene phase and a post-Miocene phase, with erosion in between, so that the Late Tertiary cover rests on older rocks in the centre of the dome rather than on the flanks. The faults obviously belong to the younger phase. No doubt the crestal region was weakened by the erosion, and it broke through when the second folding created a new anticlinal axis, slightly shifted to the east. The crestal faults are then due in this case to action quite different from ordinary crestal tension. The fact that the northern portion of the field is far more prolific in oil than the southern half, corroborates the hypothesis that after the post-Eocene folding the top of the structure was in the northern area, and that the post-Miocene folding subsequently created the present higher culmination in the south.

The Newport-Inglewood Anticlinal Belt of California. This belt (see Fig. 248) on which numerous oilfields are located, shows a longitudinal crestal fault in its south-eastern fields, i.e. in Seal Beach, Long Beach, and Huntingdon Oilfields. Faulting is often complex, but nevertheless one continuous fault, with a block downthrown to the north-east, is a consistent feature in these structures. The fault is very steep, almost vertical, and the throw increases downwards (Fig. 145). Reviewing the

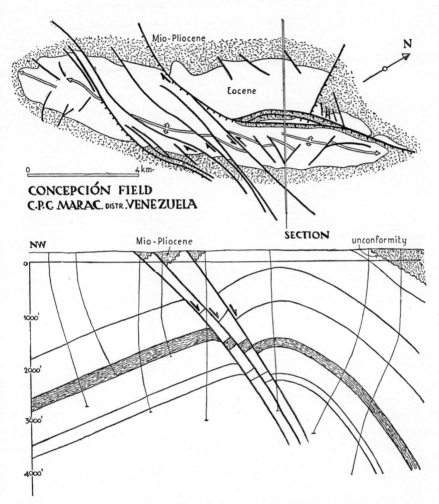

Fig. 144.   Concepcion Oilfield, Venezuela; map and section, with crestal faults.
*(After Caribbean Petroleum Company, 1948.   Published by permission of the
American Association of Petroleum Geologists.)*

literature on the structural features of the Inglewood belt, Reed and Hollister (1936) conclude that the fault-line has probably a deep-seated origin, in the basement, and that motion took place along it at various tectonically active periods during the Tertiary. Either directly or

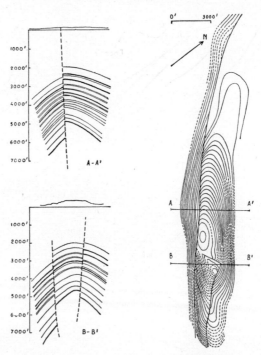

Fig. 145. Crestal faults in Long Beach Oilfield, California. *(After Stolz, 1943. Published by permission of the State Division of Mines, California).*

indirectly the folded structures are supposed to be due to the fault in the basement. It seems probable that the later movements along the fault have been partly horizontal (cf. Chapter 23).

CROSS-FAULTS

Almost every anticlinal structure is accompanied by a host of faults, particularly where the anticlinal axis plunges. All these faults have a common origin in the stretching that results from the three-dimensional shape produced by uplift. The simplest kind of fault is the normal cross-fault, perpendicular to the axis, which results from the

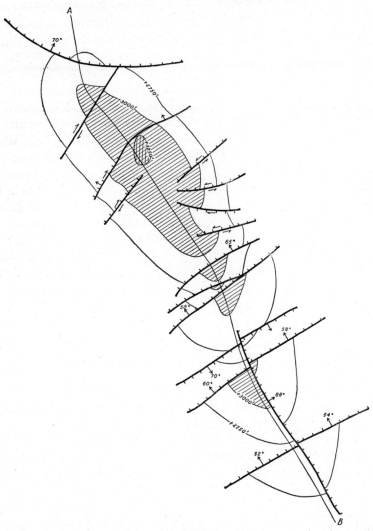

Fig. 146. Elk Basin Oilfield, with cross-faults and diagonal faults. *(After*
Bartram, 1929.   Published by permission of the American Association of
Petroleum Geologists.)

stretching of the longitudinal arch of a culmination in the anticlinal axis. The Elk Basin oilfield (Bartram, 1929) is a classic example

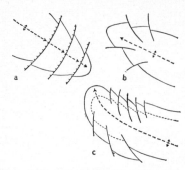

(Fig. 146). The majority of the faults hade towards the culmination point, and their maximum throw is near the crest. They die out in the flanks, where the structure contour lines become parallel, because there the longitudinal tension disappeared.

Usually the cross-faults are accompanied by sets of flank-faults, which die out both towards the crest and

Fig. 147.   Peri-anticlinal faults, *a.* ordinary normal tension-faults; *b.* stretching by shear-faults; *c.* compression shear in convex and stretching shear in concave arc.

further down on the flank. A peculiar set of faults very often occurs in the plunge of an anticline. We might call them peri-anticlinal faults. In general one can distinguish two kinds of

peri-anticlinal faults: those which have the effect of "drawing-out", to lengthen the nose, and those which are connected with a curvature of the peri-anticline (Fig. 147).

The "drawing-out" faults have the same origin as the normal cross-faults. The anticline, which grows during folding from its centre outwards, causes longitudinal stretching which can translate itself by

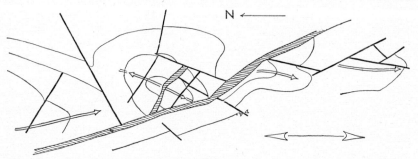

Fig. 148.   Map of Mene Grande Oilfield, Venezuela.   *(After Caribbean Petroleum Company, 1948. Published by permission of the American Association of Petroleum Geologists.)*

shear-faults in the flanks, as sketched in Fig. 147. A very good example may be quoted from the structure of Mene Grande (Fig. 148) in Venezuela and of Lake Bisteneau in Louisiana. The movement along the fault-faces has been partly horizontal and partly vertical, since they were in motion during the folding and not afterwards; they are typically syntectonic, since they merge into the fold by dying out towards its axis. Many anticlines are slightly curved in ground-plan as a result of a slight asymmetry in their cross-section, the curve being convex towards the steep flank. This is easily understood if we again imagine the structure as the result of the dynamic process, starting at the centre, and growing in height and in length at the same time; the culmination will move forward slightly more than the peri-anti-clines.

This curvature in the peri-anticline causes two kinds of faults, one due to compression in the inner curve, the other due to stretching in the outer curve (Fig. 147c). A particularly clear example of this kind of compression faulting can be seen in the southern peri-anticline of the Kettleman Hills Middle Dome where both kinds of faults are repre-sented (Fig. 149). We also find the same kind of faults in the northern peri-anticline of Kettleman Hills North Dome (Fig. 150), where the stretching in the west flank is partly due to "drawing-out" faults and partly to curvature stretching. The eastern peri-anticlinal flank is characterized by curvature-compression faults. The same stretching can also be effected by normal faults alone. This is proved by the plunge of the Wilmington (California) peri-anticline, Fig. 151. The majority of the diagonal flank-faults which we frequently encounter in the flanks of anticlines, even opposite a horizontal portion of the axis, can be considered as older peri-anticlinal faults of the types described above. During the longitudinal growth of the anticline the anticlinal plunge is gradually pushed outwards, leaving its faults to adorn the flanks of the later horizontal axis.

The fact that a peri-anticlinal fault is frequently found to merge into another kind, a normal cross-fault for instance, can easily be understood when we realize that the growth of the structure is a dynam-ic process and not static. The faults as well as the fold grow and extend; faults may meet and merge into one another, especially since during the process their extremities are the scene of maximum stresses. The two stress-fields will merge even before the faults have joined. The normal longitudinal crestal faults are the last to come into existence, because they belong to the anticlinal and not to the peri-anticlinal stage. This is clearly illustrated by the two examples I have given of Kettleman Hills North Dome where crestal faults are lacking in the peri-anticline (Figs. 149 and 150), but are present on the crest (Fig. 141).

If I were to extend this review of the characteristics of concentric

KETTLEMAN HILLS M.DOME

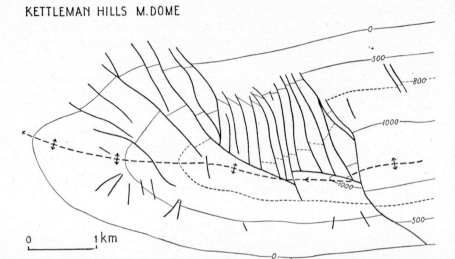

Fig. 149. Peri-anticline of Kettleman Hills, Middle Dome, California. *(After Woodring and Stewart, 1934. Published by permission of the United States Geological Survey.)*

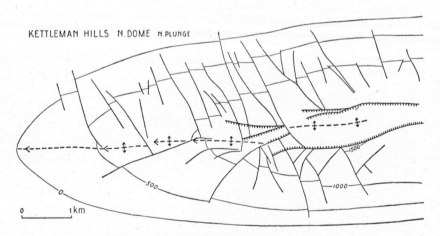

Fig. 150. Peri-anticline of Kettleman Hills, North Dome, California. *(After Woodring and Stewart, 1934. Published by permission of the United States Geological Survey.)*

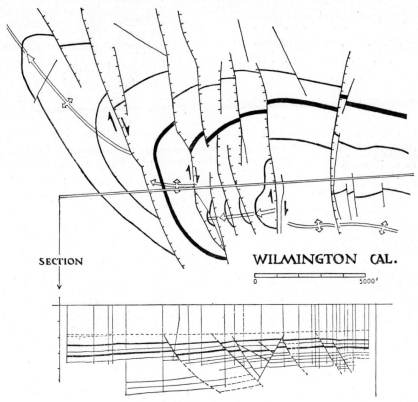

Fig. 151.   Peri-anticline of Wilmington Oilfield, California; map and section.
(After Winterthurn, 1943.   Published by permission of the State Division of Mines, California.)

folds to a further stage we should perceive that all kinds of other complications set in when anticlines become very steep. We should enter the domain of thrust, diapiric, and pinched anticlines. I shall deal with these in separate chapters.

CONCENTRIC FOLDS AND OIL ACCUMULATION

Concentric folds are pre-eminently the realm of oil and gas accumulations. The oil which is driven out of its pellitic mother rock by compaction, as a suspension in water, enters a more permeable psammitic layer and is trapped in it by another overlying pellite. The droplets of oil in the reservoir rock are too large to enter the narrow capillaries of this rock above, and are left behind as the water continues its upward travel. This process implies that the porosity of the rock was not too much impaired by the tectonic processes which tilted the reservoir bed and caused the oil to travel to the highest position it could reach. In this respect it is interesting to remember that Goguel (1943) succeeded in demonstrating in the laboratory that a folded rock has lost a considerable percentage of its porosity by comparison with its unfolded condition. We may expect, therefore, that the liberation of oil from its source rock can take place in two stages. Firstly the compaction stage, which lasts for long periods of continuous loading as sediments accumulate. The compaction drives the connate water and its oil content out of the fine-grained source rock and into the sands or limestones with their larger pores. The original slope of these reservoir rocks towards the centre of the basin will encourage accumulation of oil in the basin-margin, a process facilitated by the fact that the centre of the basin will have a more pellitic facies than its shores. Sand-tongues will reach from the margin towards the basin, and differential compaction will increase the original depositional slopes.

This first period of accumulation will fade out as compaction slows down in the course of time. It will be reactivated, however, if there is subsequent folding which compacts the pellites again, and the whole process of liberation, lateral migration, and accumulation will begin again. It seems improbable that a second folding phase will start a new cycle of accumulation, since the compression of the rocks is certainly a finite process.

The repetition of the process of oil migration and accumulation explains why it is possible to find oil accumulations both in unfolded marginal rocks of a basin, and in folded rocks of the same age in the centre of the basin, as occurs, for instance, in the San Joaquin basin of Southern California. On the other hand a well-known reservoir rock, like the Cretaceous Woodbine sand of the Texas embayment, is often locally barren in structures that can be proved to have belonged to a second folding phase which occurred after the migrating oil had reached the older structures.

Vertical migration of oil is relatively rare, and when it does occur, the much smaller secondary accumulation above the original pool is generally filled with a so-called "freak oil", a much lighter derivate from the original oil, which can apparently pass upwards although heavier oil is trapped. Faults can act as oil conduits, as is proved by oil-filled fault breccias for instance, but they serve much more frequently as oil traps. The peri-anticlinal faults, and particularly those that cross the anticlinal axis, often retain the oil behind them. A well-known and spectacular example of such traps is offered by the Elk Basin Oilfield (Fig. 146) situated in the axis of the Bighorn basin.

Strong folding and even large overthrusting do not prevent the accumulation of oil. Oil accumulations are known in the lower flank of overthrust anticlines such as the Tarra anticline in Venezuela (Fig. 187) and even in nappe-like structures such as the old Borislaw field in Poland. Real Alpine structures, however, are always barren.

In those structures the oil has apparently been driven out through the many fractures that invariably accompany such severe folding.

As soon as the deformation has the character of cleavage folding, oil can no longer be expected, since the compression has been too severe. This is probably one of the major reasons why Palaeozoic oil accumulations are restricted to those regions where there has been no Alpine deformation later.

Any review of the tectonic shapes of oil accumulations would comprise the whole gamut of concentric fold-structures and their faults, besides a number of pure fault structures (see Figs. 102 and 104), and diapiric structures and domes, which latter will be treated in Chapter 18.

Chapter 15

Cleavage and Shear-Folds

ORIGIN OF CLEAVAGE AND SHEAR-FOLDS

We have already referred extensively to the phenomenon of cleavage in Chapter 7, where it has been explained that planar-shear deformation can have two different mechanical backgrounds. One is a dilatation in a sense perpendicular to the deformative stress, accompanied by compression parallel to that stress and by slip-planes in the direction of dilatation; the other is slip along oblique shear-planes (Fig. 152). Both can either cross a complete fold (slaty-cleavage) or be restricted to a single bed (fracture-cleavage). Although the two kinds of shear

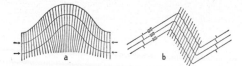

Fig. 152.   Two aspects of cleavage folding: *a* cleavage perpendicular to stress, *b* cleavage oblique to stress.

are quite different in their mechanical aspects, they often occur together, and are, therefore, treated under one general heading. They have in common the outward character of similarity, i.e. of continuing downwards without necessarily changing the shape of the fold, because their shear-planes are independent of the bedding.

The origin of shear-planes during the flattening procedure, although extremely prominent in nature, is not easily understandable from a kinematic point of view, because in kinematics only oblique shear-planes are recognized. The same kind of deformation could have been produced without visible shear-planes and these are absent in imitative experiments. We think that their formation is also due to the influence of elastic strain on the process of plastic deformation.

Instead of an elastic bending of the beds as illustrated in Fig. 50, we may presume an elastic thickening of the whole sequence (Fig. 153), with a slow and gradual transformation of the elastic strain into a permanent strain, along definite slip-planes. These slip-planes are not due to the shear component of the lateral stress, but are parallel to and dependent on the elastic strain, having a similar origin as those of concentric folding which has been demonstrated by the experiment represented in Fig. 124. The fact that the flattening always results in folds and not simply in thickening of the strata forms the basis of our conception of the origin of cleavage phenomena and schistosity.

When the shear-flattening is equally distributed through the whole mass of rock we get typical similar folds with thin limbs and thick hinges, as sketched in various stages of compression in Fig. 154. The amount of compression can be roughly evaluated by comparing the

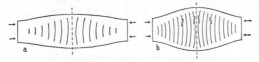

Fig. 153.   Origin of cleavage folding.   Elastic strain determines cleavage perpendicular to stress.

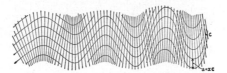

Fig. 154.   Cleavage folding.

thickness of a particular bed in the hinge and in the flank. The hinge-stretching and flank-flattening can be compared to the longest a and shortest c axes of the ellipsoid formed by flattening of a unit sphere. Then the flattening

$$\alpha = \frac{100}{\sqrt{x}} \%$$

when x is the relation between a and c ($a = cx$). This is only an approximation because the shear-planes are never really parallel but are always fanning out towards the convex side of the arc, and extension in the b direction can be a further source of error. E. Cloos (1947) showed in his survey of the oolite flattening in the South Mountain fold that the flattening starts before the cleavage-planes become visible megascopically. From a flattening of 20% onwards the cleavage became increasingly clear. Pure compression without dilatation and the initial elastic deformation are together possibly enough to account for the observed 20 % flattening, but some relaxation and further elastic strain is probable.

One can solve graphically the problem of the relation between amount of dip on the flank and the percentage of shortening perpendicular to the fold axis. Roughly, the minimum values are as follows:

10% equals a dip of 13°, 20% equals 30°, 30% equals 45°, 40% equals 60°, 50% equals 72°, and 60% equals a dip of some 80°.

For some reason or other it often happens, however, that cleavage is much more pronounced in the hinges than in the flanks. The flanks remain straight, and their slip is not along cleavage-planes but along the bedding-plane. It seems reasonable to suppose that this will happen when the bedding is well marked and slips along it more easily. The result then is a series of straight-flanked folds which one may call *accordion-folds* (Fig. 155). Accordion-folds have the same characteristics

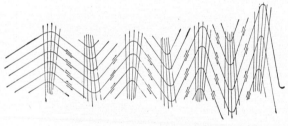

Fig. 155.   Accordion-folding.

as cleavage folds, in that they are *similar*, with thickening in the hinges, but the straight flanks maintain their original thickness. It is obvious that there will be all kinds of transition between the two modes of folding, and the steeper the folds become the more the cleavage will predominate.

From this accordion-folding it is only a small step to "*chevron-folding*" where the shear-planes are oblique shears, without any real internal flattening. In chevron-folding, one flank is sheared obliquely to the principal stress and parallel to the axis; the other flank is simply tilted, with slip along the bedding-planes (Fig. 152b). This is the only example in which the axial plane need not be perpendicular to the folding-stress, but makes the same oblique angle as the cleavage with this stress. The shearing is of quite another kind since there is no actual dilatation in one direction and compression in another; and the sheared flank becomes thicker or thinner according to the angle of shear-plane to bedding and the amount of shearing. This kind of folding is also similar, but cannot go on indefinitely because the bedding slip in steeper folds increases out of all proportion. The same consideration applies to accordion-folding. As we shall see further on, chevron-folding is often connected with thrust planes — if the few examples which are at our disposal are representative.

The difference between accordion-folding and pure cleavage-deformation has one important consequence. In a schematized way we can regard cleavage folding as a series of compressed bricks (microlithons) which have been lifted to form a staircase (Fig. 67) and accordion-folding as two series of flat-lying slabs, tilted and lifted as in Fig. 157.

Cleavage folding will give rise to tensional stress in the microlithons, and either oblique shear, tension cracks, or crumpling can develop (Fig. 156). In the accordion-fold we always find a tensional stress in

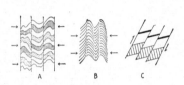

Fig. 156. Different aspects of micro-lithons in cleavage folding.

Fig. 157. Accordion-folding, schematized to show tension in axial zone. B > A.

the axis (length B is longer than length A in Fig. 157). This will invariably result either in all kinds of wrinkles and small disturbances in the axial plane, or in recrystallization of the country rock, filling up the voids. The numerous "saddle reefs", sterile or metalliferous, are doubtless a demonstration of this zone of minimum stress (Fig. 160). This recrystallization is of the same origin as that in the tensional cracks in the anticlinal arch of a concentrically banded sheet, and here, also, we may expect that the recrystallized material can come from quite a distance.

When the two flanks of an accordion-fold do not locally show the same stretching along the axial plane, for instance when the tilting is different, the axial plane will be a fault-line, along which the throw may vary greatly or even be reversed. As a matter of fact the axial plane will always be a "potential" fault-line, and as such it is sometimes occupied by a dike (see Figs. 160 and 161).

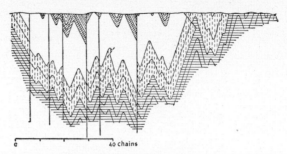

Fig. 158. Bendigo Goldfield. Cleavage folding in Ordovician with faults parallel to cleavage. *(After Herman, 1923. In David, "Structural Geology of the Commonwealth of Australia". Published by permission of Messrs. Edward Arnold (Publishers) Limited.)*

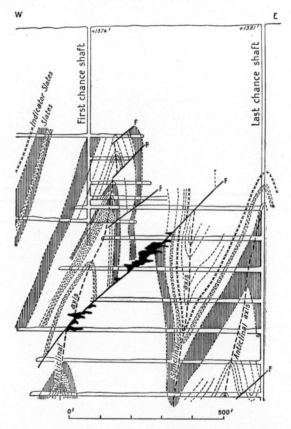

Fig. 159. Section of Ballarat East Goldfield, Victoria. Similar fold with thrust-faults and dilatation in the vertical direction. *(After Baragwanath, 1923. In David, "Structural Geology of the Commonwealth of Australia". Published by permission of Messrs. Edward Arnold (Publishers) Limited.)*

EXAMPLES OF SHEAR-FOLDING

The Ballarat and Bendigo Goldmine Districts, Victoria (Australia). They are particularly good and clear examples of cleavage folding of the accordion type. The Ballarat district contains three separate belts, Ballarat West, Ballarat East, and Little Bendigo. A section through the Bendigo Goldfield (Fig. 158) shows the general structure, consisting of a synclinorium with numerous pinched folds and a few vertical faults parallel to the axial planes and cleavage. The Lower Ordovician rocks consist of fine sandstones and slates, which in places have been much altered.

Detailed sections are available from a number of goldfields. In Fig. 159 the folds are slightly overturned and the steep flank is cut by a series of thrust-faults, which make an angle of 40° to 50° with the axial plane and as such suggest an extension in the vertical axis or a lateral compression. This is confirmed by the shape of the ore-bodies, which show a clear horizontal extension starting from the inclined fault-line. The whole structure seems, therefore, to have resulted from a single deformational episode with a uniform orientation of the stress-field, with the minimum principal stress in the vertical direction and the largest principal stress in a horizontal position.

The saddle reefs of Bendigo (Fig. 160) give a similar picture. As has been explained above it is the anticlinal axial plane which is the main zone of extension in this kind of structure. The monchiquite dike along the axial plane also demonstrates the probability that it is a fault

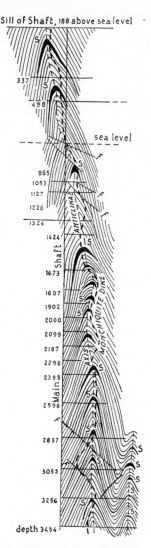

Fig. 160. Bendigo, Victoria. Hustles Shaft showing saddle reefs and dike in axial plane. *(After Herman, 1923. In David, "Structural Geology of the Commonwealth of Australia". Published by permission of Messrs. Edward Arnold (Publishers) Limited.)*

with very little displacement. A few fault-lines, with the same inclination and character as in the former section, demonstrate the close resemblance of the two structures.

In Fig. 161 a combination of saddle reefs (both of the anticlinal and synclinal type), fault reefs, and axial dikes demonstrates the close relationship between these features. A discussion of the origin of the ore should start in this case from the clearly demonstrated fact that structural control is absolute. Both the saddle reefs, anticlinal or synclinal, and the fault reefs occur on planes or zones of minimum

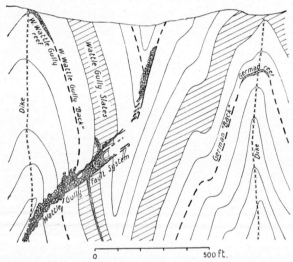

Fig. 161. Wattle Gully Goldmine, Chewton, Victoria, with axial plane dike, thrusts in flank and saddle reefs. *(After Thomas, 1939-1941. In David, "Structural Geology of the Commonwealth of Australia". Published by permission of Messrs. Edward Arnold (Publishers) Limited.)*

stress; or, in other words, are associated with structural features due to extension in a vertical sense and lateral compression. I should like to suggest that all the reefs are due to recrystallization of the country rock itself, with concentration of its most mobile elements, the metals, in the reefs.

Ruhr Coal District. In the Westphalian Ruhr coalfield the folding has a remarkable character—half concentric folding, half cleavage folding. The two styles of folding are not equally distributed through the whole field; similar folding is best seen in the older beds in the south while the concentric habit is better represented by higher beds, and in the north.

In the section in Fig. 162 we recognize the typical features of accordion-folding — straight flanks and narrow and sharp anticlinal hinge. Even the axial fault with very small displacement is present, and in the

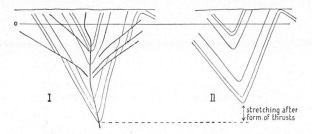

Fig. 162. Ruhr coal district section of Fröhliche Morgensonne, with axial plane fault and thrust-faults in flank. *(After Nehm, 1930. In Kukuk, "Geologie der Niederrheinisch-Westfälischen Steinkohlengebiete". Published by permission of Springer-Verlag, Berlin.)*

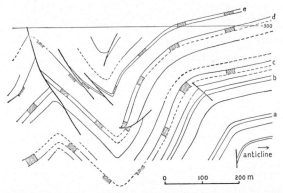

Fig. 163. Section through north flank of Gelsenkirchen anticline; syncline with thrusts in flank. *(After Nehm, 1930. In Kukuk, "Geologie der Niederrheinisch-Westfälischen Steinkohlengebiete". Published by permission of Springer-Verlag, Berlin.)*

flanks we find the same kind of thrust-faults that we noticed before and which emphasize the vertical dilatation. By reconstructing the fold before the thrust planes came into action, one gets an idea of how much they contributed to the dilatation in the vertical.

In the section of Fig. 163 we find the same peculiarities as in the syncline of Fig. 162, except the axial fault. In the middle bed we see a thrust-fault which has movement opposite to the others. The axial fault of the adjoining anticline runs into the flank instead of staying in the axial plane, and through that deflection becomes a thrust-fault of the syncline.

Figure 118 depicts a small portion of the Ruhr coalfield which shows narrow folding and a rapid succession of anticlines and synclines. In this map the numerous wrench-faults which offset the axes are very significant; all make an angle of 40° to 50° with the fold-axis. (The normal faults on the map have a distinctly later origin.) This wrench-fault movement is not post-tectonic but late-tectonic, because in several cases the width between the axes, and even the number of folds, is not the same on both sides of the fault. These wrench-faults have the same inclination to the principal stress as the inclined thrusts which we mentioned before, but they represent an elongation in the b axis, whereas the inclined thrusts represent a stretching in the a axis direction.

Many more examples could be quoted, particularly from ore-mines, but all of them have the same characteristics. In Fig. 282 I give a map and section of the Coniaurum Mine (Canada) which shows a peculiarity often met with in cleavage (schistosity) folding, excessive axial plunge. The map and the section both show the sharp fold, whose plunge is reputed to be locally some 80°.

EXAMPLES OF CHEVRON-FOLDING

The Belgian-Dutch Coal District. From this coal district many good examples of concentric, accordion-, and chevron-folding can be collected. I will mention here two series of chevron-folds. The first is a section from the Domaniale colliery, Fig. 164. The section shows two thrust-planes with a 30° and 35° dip, which seem to be of post-folding origin on first sight because they are independent of the fold-shape and cut from flank into crest. The folds themselves are clearly of chevron type. When we draw the anticlinal and synclinal axes, both straight lines, they enclose the steep flank. The shear makes an angle of 35° or 45° with the bedding, depending on which flank one makes the measurement, and is apparently shear oblique to the lateral stress. When we consider the thrust planes in greater detail, it becomes clear that they cannot be altogether post-folding because their throw is too variable. Along the lowest thrust, for instance, the slip for bed c is some 300 m, whereas for beds a and b the thrust is only some 50 m on both branches of the thrust combined. Apparently some of the folding is taken over by the thrust movement. As both the thrusts and the oblique shear-folding are thus due to the same stress-field, one wonders why they have a different orientation. The next section gives us some insight into this problem.

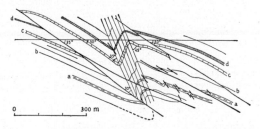

Fig. 164. Section in Domaniale colliery with thrusts and chevron-folding. *(After Sax, 1946. Published by permission of Geologisch Bureau voor het Mijngebied, Heerlen.)*

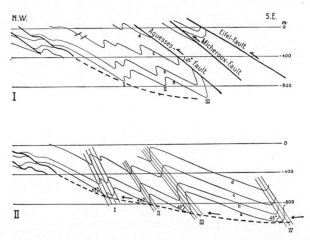

Fig. 165. Section through Liége coal basin: (I) present section, (II) thrust movement reconstituted, showing chevron shearing making 45° angle with curved basal thrust plane. *(After Humblet, Revue Universelle des Mines, 1941, tome 17, 8e série, no. 12. Published by permission of the Editor.)*

The section from the nearby Liége coalfield (Fig. 165 I), after Humblet (1941), also shows chevron-folds and thrusts. A reconstruction of the folds before thrusting is given in Fig. 165 II. When we draw a line tangential to the foot of the synclines we get a slightly flattening curve starting from a very flat thrust in the upper left hand corner. We find then, to our satisfaction, that the oblique shear-folding consistently makes a 45° angle with this lower curve, with the result that the axial shear of the folds becomes steeper towards the left. Apparently a detachment-plane, somewhere below the folds and showing itself as a flat overthrust in the upper left hand corner, locally reorientated the lateral stress, to a position parallel to this plane. This local stress-field caused the shear-folds. At a later moment during the folding the shear-folding stopped, the detachment-plane over which it moved stopped functioning and the temporarily reorientated stress-field returned to its original horizontal position; the thrust steeper than the shear-folding developed again, making a 45° angle with the deformative stress. This example shows very clearly the local variation in the orientation of the stress-field caused by the development of the deformation. In such a simple case, where the relation between slip-direction and stress-orientation in the course of the deformation process can be reconstructed, we get a clear picture; but in most cases the relation is far too complex to be unravelled by such simple methods, and there is then often a certain tendency to postulate several successive phases of folding in order to explain the structural details.

The Pennsylvania Coal Basin. A last example of oblique shear-folding, of a peculiar kind, is given in Fig. 166, a section from the anthracite coal basin of Pennsylvania. The steep but very shallow folds in the coal seams are not easy to understand unless one sees them as shear-folds. By drawing the lines of shear it becomes evident that we have here a conjugate set of shears, which intersect in the centre

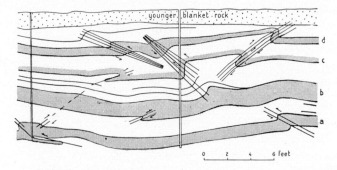

Fig. 166. Section through Kingston colliery, anthracite basin, Pennsylvania, with lines indicating direction of oblique-shear movement. *(After Darton, 1940. Published by permission of the United States Geological Survey.)*

of the section. They make an angle of 25° to 45° with the lateral stress, and cause a pronounced disharmony in the folding picture which is typical for the whole basin. In Chapter 16 we shall see that the combination of concentric folding and shear-folding often leads to disharmonies in the folding picture.

PARTICULAR CHARACTERISTICS OF CLEAVAGE AND SHEAR-FOLDS

When the folds are not very pronounced, and hence the cleavage or shear not well developed, or when one is not familiar with the region by personal observation, the shear-folding and cleavage folding is still distinguishable from concentric folds by the fact that small irregularities on a folded bedding-plane are repeated in other bedding-planes in the direction of the shear, without change in character and with little change in size. In concentric folds the contrary is true: there, a small secondary wrinkle will either grow upwards and die out quickly downwards, or will be replaced by a fault, or disappear

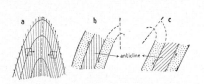

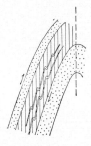

Fig. 167. Cleavage in relation to the
axial plane.

Fig. 168. Drag-folds in relation to
cleavage.

in a secondary detachment-plane. Similar wrinkles in a cleavage or shear-fold will be repeated every time in other bedding-planes, increasing or decreasing somewhat, but retaining their character. In the foregoing examples we saw many instances of such repeated similarity in detail.

The fact that, in cleavage folding, the cleavage is parallel to the axis, gives the field geologist a valuable opportunity of deciding on which side a formation is "younging", and on which side the anticline is situated, even when the fold is overturned. In Fig. 167a a normal anticline is represented; the cleavage will always be steeper than the bedding unless the bedding is near to 90°. As the cleavage gives, approximately, the position in space of the anticline, an outcrop of the size of one of the small squares on the drawing allows one to determine the direction in which the anticline must be sought. This is equally true for fracture-cleavage, as in the outcrops represented in Figs. 167c and 167b. In a recumbent fold the bedding is steeper than the cleavage. Theoretically it ought to be possible to locate all anticlines and synclines in a certain region by measuring the cleavage and bedding without seeing a single hinge. In practice, however, the outcrops are seldom sufficiently numerous to allow a trustworthy result.

The peculiar phenomenon of "drag-folds", i.e. small asymmetrical folds in a cleaved bed, as in Fig. 168, demonstrates irregular slip along the cleavage-planes. The name drag-fold is not very satisfactory as it again introduces the concept of drag by the competent beds on the incompetent bed, as with fracture-cleavage. As we have argued already, fracture-cleavage is not a drag phenomenon due to friction on the walls of the shale layer; nor are drag-folds influenced by this friction.

As we shall see in Fig. 282 the peri-anticlines of accordion-folds figure on the map with the same sharp hinges as in the section. The width of a fold on the map depends, of course, on the plunge of the axis; and it is a remarkable fact that the alternation of anticlines and synclines in cleavage or accordion-folding is much greater than in concentric folding. This is due to the much greater plunge of fold-axes in cleavage folding. As the transverse curvature of the fold is not a matter of bending, but is dependent only on a variation of vertical shear, there is no kinematic limit to the ordinary plunge of the fold-axis. We also notice that in cleavage folding an anticlinal fold can find its birth in the centre of a syncline, or two anticlinal axes can converge into a single axis, whereas in concentric folds a new fold almost invariably originates in a wrinkle on the flank of another anticline. Cleavage folds are, therefore, much less predictable than concentric folds.

The faults which characterize concentric folds are invariably due to secondary elastic stress-fields set up by doming and curving of the axes. These faults are completely absent in all cleavage folding. They are replaced in some measure by concentration of slip on one of the shear-planes, parallel to the axis, as in Fig. 158; these are very difficult to locate, however, in mapping practice. Further, shear-faults, either vertical and oblique to the axes, or parallel to the fold-axis but inclined to the axial plane, are quite common. They are represented on several of the sections and maps in the foregoing paragraphs. Whether these faults are always late-tectonic or even post-tectonic, as is often stated, seems doubtful. They certainly belong to the same stress-field, and will be confined to the later periods of compression when further cleavage, shear and slip, in the bedding-plane became difficult; but there is no reason to think that they are due to a late phase of folding. The same is true for other irregularities in steep cleavage folds. When the flanks have reached an almost vertical position, further slip on the bedding-plane becomes impossible and the only way of achieving further compression lies in further flattening along the cleavage-planes. As competent beds, such as quartzites, are not easily sheared and flattened in that way, they are often deformed by oblique-shearing, causing boudinage or fracture-cleavage (Fig. 169b). In other cases, inclined shear-planes are developed which allow the formation of one

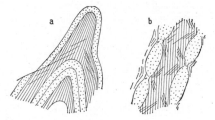

Fig. 169.   Oblique-shear intersecting cleavage; *a* due to a pinched anticlinal top, *b* due to boudinage.

pinched fold on top of another, as sketched in Fig. 169a. This is also clearly visible in the microfold of Fig. 237. Again, every other kind of irregularity in the steep flanks will always be accompanied by new shear-planes, either of slickenside type or of the oblique-shear type. All these later slip movements will cut the original cleavage and disturb it. Nevertheless, they do not indicate that another phase of folding has superseded the first, even when they are widely observed; and certainly they do not warrant this assumption if they are seen in only a few limited outcrops. A close scrutiny of the microfold of Fig. 237 teaches us that the same stress-field can and does generate a multitude of different kinds of shear-planes, intersecting one another, disturbing one another, but all belonging to the same compression.

We have already referred in Chapter 6 to different kinds of distortion of fractional parts of rock, rock beds, fossils, oolites, etc. The same distortion will affect all other sedimentary structures, such as cross-bedding, slumping, load castings, etc., often to such a degree that they are no longer recognizable. In that case they may easily be mistaken for divergent slip-planes, and wrong conclusions drawn. In general, I should like to warn against conclusions of the existence of a second (or third) orogenic phase on the flimsy grounds of disturbed cleavage.

Chapter 16

Disharmonic Folds

General Characteristics. Disharmonic folding is a general term, giving expression to the observation that the continuation of a fold downwards is often neither concentric nor similar. Its most extreme form is found when a fold dies out downwards very quickly and thus forms a "wrinkle" above an undisturbed flat surface. In such a case we clearly have a detachment horizon; the beds above the undisturbed horizon have been folded independently of their basement. Between this extreme case of disharmony and the case of a fold in which only a slight difference in shape can be noticed between two overlying beds, all transitions exist. In the course of our descriptions we have already met with quite a few instances of disharmony.

The bed in which the disharmony between the overlying and underlying bed has been effected is always an incompetent member in relation to its wall and roof. In this incompetent bed the mechanism of folding is different from that in the competent members — flow in the case of salt-bearing beds, cleavage folding with faulting in the case of ordinary shales or clays.

The lateral shortening of the underlying less-disturbed bed must necessarily be more or less equal to that of the overlying sequence of beds. It may either be folded more intensely elsewhere, or it may be folded along cleavage-planes and thus compressed in another way within the same section. Lack of sufficient exposures usually makes it difficult to decide between these possibilities.

We have already seen, in Chapter 14, that concentric folding inevitably leads to detachment, and therefore to disharmonic folding. And as the erosion has to cut deep down into the structures in order to reveal its disharmonic nature, the Hercynian folds, being more deeply eroded, show disharmony more often than do Tertiary structures.

The Ruhr Coal District. Disharmonic folding is often developed on the flank of a concentric structure. In Fig. 170, a thrust on the flank of a concentric anticline, the Wattenscheider structure, has its origin in

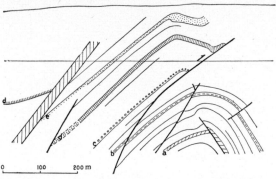

Fig. 170. Thrust in flank of Wattenscheider anticline, Ruhr coal district. *(After Kukuk, 1938. "Geologie der Niederrheinisch-Westfälischen Steinkohlengebiete". Published by permission of Springer-Verlag, Berlin.)*

one of a set of oblique shear-planes which developed at a late stage in the folding process. Where this thrust plane cuts the Hugo and Robert seams at the top of the anticline, we perceive an extra wrinkle which preceded the thrust (beds b and c in Fig. 170). The thrust plane cuts very obliquely through the left hand flank. In other instances it often stays in one particular bed and thus takes part in the concentric folding in the flank. In such cases one can say that the direction of slip along the bedding in the flank, due to concentric folding, cuts through the anticline instead of following its curvature. This will happen when the folding has advanced so far that the flank has a dip equal to or higher than 45°, and the bedding slip-planes in the flank happen to coincide with the potential oblique-shear direction, oblique to the general lateral stress. In this way a small disharmonic fold appears, for instance at the apex of a major fold (Figs. 170, 171, and 172), or even sometimes on the flank (Fig. 173).

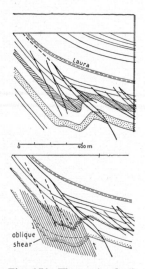

Fig. 171. Thrust in flank of syncline, Gelsenkirchen syncline, Ruhr coal district. *(After Böttcher, 1925. In Kukuk, "Geologie der Niederrheinisch - Westfälischen Steinkohlengebiete". Published by permission of Springer-Verlag, Berlin.)*

A perfectly analogous case is represented by the section in Fig. 171, where the same kind of structure is found in a syncline. The disharmony is somewhat more pronounced

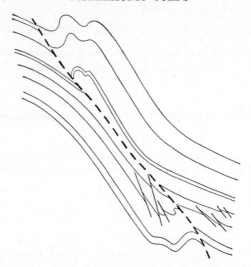

Fig. 172. Hypothetic upwards completion of synclinal thrust of Gelsen-kirchen syncline.

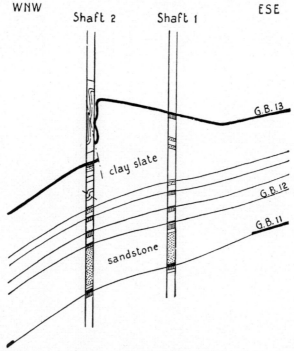

Fig. 173. Disharmonic fold exposed in shafts of Willem-Sophy Colliery, South Limburg coalfield. *(After Sax, 1946. Published by permission of Geologisch Bureau voor het Mijngebied, Heerlen.)*

than in Fig. 170. The numerous oblique fault-planes of this section
are parallel to a set of minute shear-planes which are oblique to the
detachment-plane of the disharmonic fold; the latter coincides wiht
the bedding-plane of the upper structure. The thickening of the
strata on the crest of the disharmonic fold is of the oblique-cleavage
type which we called chevron-folding. With the flattening of the dip
towards the synclinal axis, the position of the oblique shear-faults
also becomes flatter. This is the same phenomenon we found in
Chapter 15, Fig. 165, where the formation of a basal shear-plane as
a thrust plane causes a reorientation of the stress-direction, parallel
to this plane, which in its turn causes shear oblique to the thrust plane.
In this case the several thrust planes actually disappear in the shale
beds below the Katharina seam. This structure has given rise to a
supposition that the folding of the lower series, below the Katharina
seam, took place before the deposition of the upper beds and that
the upper beds are unconformable on the lower beds. The fact — that
no such unconformity exists elsewhere — supports the view that the
section shows only a particular kind of disharmonic folding, and no
unconformity.

The necessary shortening in the upper beds, Laura-Zollverein, could
have taken place by disharmonic folding on top of a thrust plane in

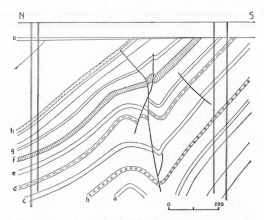

Fig. 174.   Disharmonic fold in Grubenfeld, Holland, Ruhr coal district.   *(After
Bötjcher, 1925.   In Kukuk, "Geologie der Niederrheinisch-Westfälischen Steinkohlengebiete".   Published by permission of Springer-Verlag, Berlin.)*

the same stratigraphic position, but higher up the structure. The
thrust movement would be concentrated, for both structures, on the

same thrust plane, and the two disharmonic folds would compensate one another as sketched in Fig. 172.

A very similar disharmonic fold, exposed in the shafts of one of the Dutch collieries (Fig. 173), shows the development on the gentle flank of an anticline.

In Fig. 174 another kind of disharmony is represented, arising not by the prolongation of slip along the bedding beyond its proper place, but by the formation of an accordion synclinal fold, dying out upwards against a gentle flank. The axial plane of this fold is accentuated by an axial fault-plane of the kind that we have already encountered (Fig. 162), and the mechanism by which it dies out is clearly demonstrated by the presence of secondary faults. We can regard this fold as an example of one of the many means by which the lack of space in the core of an anticline is solved — the anticline in question being a much larger structure situated further to the south.

The Anthracite Coal Basin of North Pennsylvania. All the detailed sections of this basin give numerous instances of disharmonic folding. In the section in Fig. 175 we observe that the beds, b, c, and d have

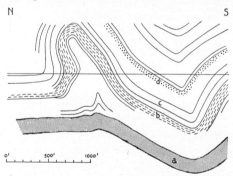

Fig. 175. Disharmonic folding in anthracite basin of Pennsylvania. Upper beds in extra disharmonic fold. *(After Darton, 1940. Published by permission of the United States Geological Survey.)*

been folded independently of bed a, which reflects the sharp anticline of the upper beds only very faintly. The shales between beds a and b have acted as a detachment horizon, and have thus given the upper beds the opportunity of folding independently of the lower beds.

On the other hand, compression in the upper beds must be compensated elsewhere by an equal compression in the lower beds. This is illustrated by Fig. 176, in which the same detachment horizon has allowed the lower bed a to make a much sharper fold than have the higher beds. Without detailed field observations it is impossible to decide what kind of shearing took place in the intervening shale bed; but in the anticlinal and synclinal folds, concentric folding has been preserved to some extent.

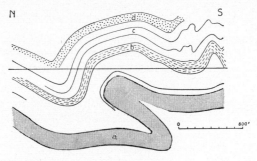

Fig. 176. Disharmonic folding in anthracite basin of Pennsylvania. Lower beds in extra disharmonic fold. *(After Darton, 1940. Published by permission of the United States Geological Survey.)*

In general, disharmonic folding represents a possibility of transition from one kind of folding to another, and from one fold shape to another. It is very difficult to predict from surface observations whether disharmony can be expected or not, but one can safely assume that in a concentric structure either faulting or disharmony will set in at a certain depth. Whether the disharmony will be distributed over several incompetent layers or be concentrated on a single one is unpredictable, unless one has information from adjacent structures. Although disharmony is not restricted to concentric folding, it occurs much more frequently in this kind of folding than in similar folding.

Chapter 17

Thrust-Faults

Thrust-Faults. Whereas normal faults are typically independent of folding, and wrench-faults show frequent transitions to folding but are still often independent, thrust-faults on the contrary are usually closely connected with the folding process. This difference in the relation between folding and the three best-known classes of large faults is readily understandable when we realize that the orientation of the three principal stresses in thrusting and folding are the same: the plane of the largest and smallest principal stresses being vertical, the plane of the median and largest principal stresses being horizontal. Both folds and thrusts show an expansion in the vertical, and a shortening in the horizontal direction.

Before we treat low-angle thrusts, which form an integral part of asymmetric folding, we shall consider a smaller but important class, the so-called upthrusts, which are features more or less independent of folding.

Upthrusts. The upthrust is a rather steeply dipping reversed fault ($> 60°$) which develops most frequently in massive crystalline rocks of the basement. The same kind of movement in stratified rocks would give rise to flexuring or other kinds of asymmetric folding. Upthrusts are found, therefore, in the stable shields of the continents; but they are also particularly frequent on the borders of the great folded mountain chains where the central part has been pushed over the subsiding marginal troughs. We find, this latter situation, for instance, in the Lombardy section of the Southern Alps (Fig. 177).

The general structure of the Bergamasc Alps (de Sitter, 1949; Dozy, 1935; Zijlstra, 1941) consists of a series of longitudinal blocks, separated by upthrusts, and strongly pressed together along these thrust zones.

To a certain degree each block is characterized by rocks of a particular age; the southern and lowest block by Triassic limestones, the middle block by Permian clastic and volcanic rocks, the northern and highest

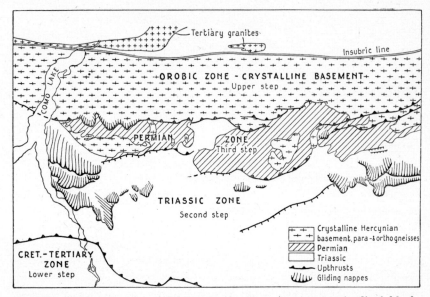

Fig. 177. Schematic map of the Lombardy Alps, showing longitudinal blocks limited by thrust-faults. *(After de Sitter, Leidse Geol. Med., vol. 14B, 1949.)*

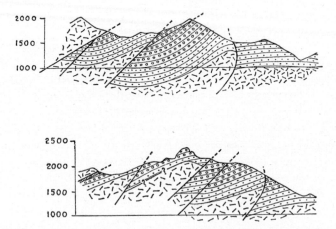

Fig. 178. Two sections through the Orobic zone of the Lombardy Alps showing imbricated structures. *(After Zijlstra, Geol. & Mijnb., 3e Jrg. N.S., 1941.)*

block by crystalline schists, gneisses, and granites. The Orobic fault which separates the northern crystalline block from the Permian zone is one of these big thrust-faults which flattens out towards Lake Como in the west and is accompanied by a whole series of similar thrusts to the south. The two sections of Fig. 178, are taken from the western and eastern parts of the Orobic zone, where the upthrusts are very frequent and form an imbricate structure.

These faults are not particularly straight, their surface outcrop resembles those of normal faults and they often replace one another en échelon. Mylonite zones are frequent and often very thick. Their dip below the higher block can be ascertained only when the topography is sufficiently pronounced.

Very often the nature of upthrusts is masked when sedimentary rocks are involved. On the southern border of the High Atlas, for instance, the Upper Cretaceous presents a series of vertical flexures which limit blocks of almost horizontal strata (Fig. 179), but I think that there can be little doubt that in the basement we should find a series of thrust-faults similar to those in the higher parts of the Bergamasc Alps. The same kind of structure has been described in the Pyrenees (Destombes, 1948; de Sitter, 1949).

Besides thrust-faults of considerable throw, every tectonized region contains numerous small faults (less than 5 feet throw) which cannot be mapped on the usual scale of geological maps and appear only on mining maps. A statistical review of all the small faults in one of the South Limburg coal mines revealed that the average dip of small thrusts is 22° and that of small normal faults 63° (Fig. 180). The average dip of small normal faults is in good agreement with the dip of large normal faults but the thrusts are decidedly of low-angle type, and not of steeper upthrust type.

The average angles that these small faults make with the principal stress (27° for the normal faults with a vertically directed stress and 22° for the thrust-faults with a lateral stress) differ only slightly, and we may presume in this case that the thrusts are due to a tectonic compression and the normal faults to a dilatation of the elastic release type. From this evidence we may perhaps conclude that the steep upthrusts, certainly different in origin from the low-angle thrusts, are not due to a simple lateral compression acting in the horizontal plane, but to a differently orientated stress-field. As we have remarked already, big steep thrusts are characteristic of the marginal areas of mountain chains and the uplifted central massifs of crystalline rocks.

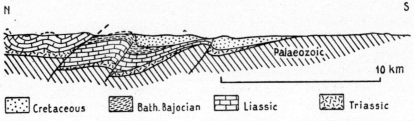

Fig. 179. Section through southern margin of High Atlas in Morocco.

Cretaceous Bath. Bajocian Liassic Triassic

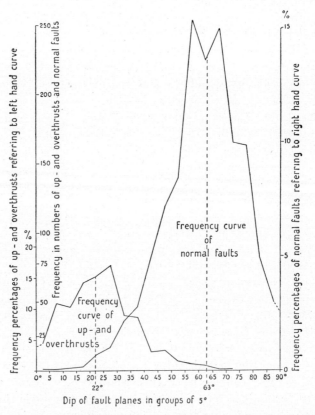

Fig. 180. Statistical frequency curves for small faults in Willem-Sophy Colliery, South Limburg, Netherlands. (*After Sax, 1946. Published by permission of Geologisch Bureau voor het Mijngebied, Heerlen.*)

Evidently this uplift implies in itself a radial force. Thus the imbricate structure of crystalline massifs can be compared to the faulting which is often observed in microstructures of the similar cleavage type. These latter faults are parallel to the cleavage and to the axial planes, and represent a concentration of the usual slip on multiple cleavage-planes into one fault-plane. That they generally hade towards the centre of the massif is in accordance with the fan-like arrangement of cleavage in a fold.

Asymmetric Folds and Low-Angle Thrusts. Asymmetry of folds is a very common feature which always originates because of irregularities in the structure of the basin.

The two irregularities which are the most frequent causes of asymmetry are: (1) wedging-out of the folded series, (2) original differences of altitude between two flanks of the same fold.

When a sedimentary series wedges-out towards the basin border, and later compression originates a concentric fold on this thinning portion of the basin margin, the two flanks of this structure are no

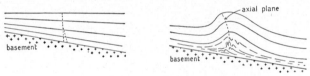

Fig. 181.   Asymmetric fold on basin margin due to thinning of sedimentary series.

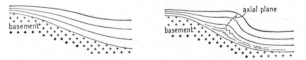

Fig. 182.   Asymmetric fold on basin margin due to higher elevation of basin border.

longer equal; the sedimentary series of the flank nearest to the basin border are thinner than those of the opposite flank. As the radius of curvature is a direct consequence of the thickness of the sedimentary series involved in the folding, the flank facing the border will have a shorter radius and will therefore be steeper than the opposite flank.

In this case we have assumed that the surface was horizontal; but it often happens that in the first stage of compression the basin borders have been elevated, and that a considerable slope towards the basin centre has been established. In that case further lateral compression may result in an asymmetric anticline where the steep flank is facing the basin centre (Fig. 182).

The two examples here advanced are the most simple forms of asymmetric structures, where the whole sedimentary series is folded in one structure and the basement is thought to have been completely passive. It will often occur that a detachment-plane is formed below a conspicuous competent member of the series, and when either the whole series or that particular competent member is wedging-out the same effect will be produced in the upper fold (Fig. 183). What happens to the lower series, below the detachment-plane will remain hidden to the field geologist; in my example of Fig. 183 I presumed it was

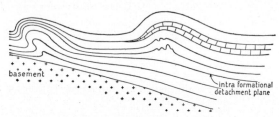

Fig. 183.   Asymmetric fold due to thinning of competent member of sedimentary series and located above its thin wedge.

folded higher up on the basin border. It is often observed that the fold is located on the thin wedge of the competent member; this is probably due to isolation of the topmost series by means of the detachment-plane below this competent member.

When the basement itself is involved in the folding, we may get quite different structures, mostly unpredictable and therefore often misinterpreted. The axial plane of a concentric asymmetric anticline necessarily hades away from the steep flank, and the axis of the fold is therefore displaced towards the flatter flank. In drilling for oil this displacement has to be taken into account, and the construction of the section from surface dips assuming pure concentric folding will indicate the displacement (Fig. 184).

Construction along those lines will reveal that at a certain depth pure concentricity is no longer possible unless we suppose that the sediment can be compressed in a smaller volume, which is evidently possible to only a very small extent. The shaded part in layer l_2 of Fig. 184 for instance, represents the volume of that layer which has been omitted in the section-construction. Obviously, this cannot be a true representation of the real fold, and this lack of space due to the geometrical

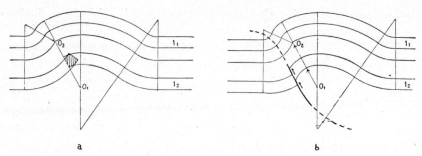

a   b

Fig. 184.   Origin of thrust-fault in asymmetric anticline.

impossibility of maintaining concentricity downwards results in the breaking through of layer l_2 before this stage of folding is reached. In Fig. 184b a much more probable construction has been drawn, showing the origin of a thrust-fault in the steep flank of the asymmetric anticline.

The frequency of asymmetric and overthrust anticlines in folded regions shows that they are closely associated. It can often be observed that the two merge into one another in a lateral sense. We shall find the overthrusts in the structurally highest area of a fold, since it is the most strongly compressed portion. Laterally the slip along the thrust diminishes and finally disappears into a simple steep flank, or splits up into tear-faults which cross the anticline diagonally. The Jura Mountains, for instance, show many examples of the transition of a thrust-faulted anticline into an asymmetric one.

The development of the thrust has been explained by Albert Heim (1921) as due to attenuation of the middle limb of a recumbent fold (Fig. 185). His conception was derived from the tectonic features of the Säntis Mountains. Buxtorf (1916) on the other hand, studying the tectonic conditions of the Jura Mountains, concluded that a flat reversed fault gradually develops into a thrust-faulted anticline. The

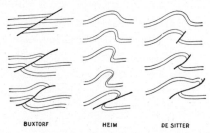

BUXTORF   HEIM   DE SITTER

Fig. 185.   Origin of thrust-faulting according to Buxtorf, Heim, and de Sitter.

same conception of the origin of flat thrusts prevails with the geologists of the Westphalian coal basin (Kukuk 1938, p. 138).

Besides these contradictory conceptions, a third possibility is here presented, i.e. the development of a thrust-fault in a much earlier stage of folding than Heim observed and a much later phase than Buxtorf and Kukuk presume, as explained above.

As we have seen, the first phase of the steep reversed longitudinal fault in an anticline will originate in the core of the structure; its location is solely due to the relative position of the centre of major curvature, and is independent of the actual dip of the flank, but depends on the breadth of the steeper portion of this flank. Figure 186a represents a very flat structure – an oil-bearing anticline in Java, which, however, has at the surface a narrow zone of steeper dips, with

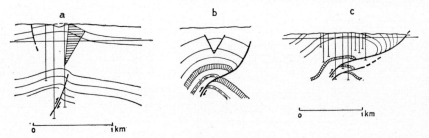

Fig. 186.   Development of a thrust-fault in an asymmetric anticline exemplified by three structures; *a* Nglobo (Java), *b* Lok Batan (Apsheron Peninsula), *c* Kampong Minjak (Sumatra).

a maximum of 26°. This relatively "steep" flank, in a structure with flanks dipping mainly at 3°–6°, develops downwards, as revealed by drilling, into a very steep flank with broken strata etc., as shown in the section. The steep dips are encountered only below the centre of curvature of the steep part of the flank. The formation consists of hard limey sandstones and soft marls and shales, a well-stratified formation.

Figure 186b, a section through the Lok-Batan Oilfield of the Apsheron Peninsula, gives an example of a further stage of a thrust-structure. A really vertical zone is not yet present, neither has the thrust movement become great.

In Fig. 186c, a section through the old Kampong Minjak (oil village) Oilfield of Sumatra, a still further advanced stage of thrusting is revealed. The original S-shaped thrust which provided an obstruction to further movement has been flattened by means of a second lower thrust. We see very clearly the development of a broad apex in the overthrust flank arching over the buried centre of the structure, a feature which we shall also find in much larger overthrusts.

The few examples advanced to illustrate the growth of a thrust plane all depend on the assumption that an overthrust anticline is a typical superficial structure. This assumption is substantiated by the fact that thrust and asymmetrical anticlines are favoured by the existence of a particular incompetent layer at the base, above the basal shearing-plane, in which the thrust plane is lost. When no single outstanding basal shearing-plane exists somewhere at depth, then the amplitude of structures may vary, and each may have taken up a different incompetent layer as its basal shearing-plane; and the thrust planes may run for considerable lengths above one another before they eventually unite at a lower level.

Very much also depends on the distribution of competent layers in a folded sequence of strata. When there is mainly one thick competent layer, it will to a large extent control the amplitude of the folds; and when there are two or more outstanding competent horizons they may each of them have their own influence. In the Tarra anticline (Colon district, Eastern Venezuela) we find two competent horizons. The upper one is a thick, occasionally oil-bearing arkosic sandstone of Eocene age which shows an overthrust to the east (Fig. 187). Below that, the Cretaceous limestones apparently show an overthrust in the opposite direction. This structure is not revealed in one section, but in the prolongation of the anticline towards the south. In Fig. 187 the two phenomena have tentatively been combined.

In this respect it is of interest to recall a structure which Fallot (1949) described, in the western Alps, as a subcutaneous thrust (Fig. 188); in this the independence of the upper and lower parts of a series separated by a thick incompetent bed is clearly demonstrated.

The sequence of Fig. 186a, b, and c illustrates the growth of the overthrust from the inconspicuous original shape to the developed shape of the ordinary overthrust anticline, and the upper part of the Tarra anticline section demonstrates its possible further development.

Thrusting of the type of the Tarra anticline is quite a common kind of structure. We find it for instance in the section of the Sarrebrück anticline (Fig. 189), the upper part of which has been well explored by coal-mining, and in the Turner Valley Oilfield (Fig. 190). The development of the Turner Valley structure as figured by Link (1949) again shows the location of a fold on a wedging-out member of the series, a limestone (Fig. 191). In this kind of thrust-faulted anticline the actual

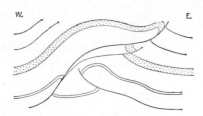

Fig. 187. Overthrust of Tarra anticline, Colon district, Venezuela, completed with deeper structure revealed in southern extension of the same anticline.

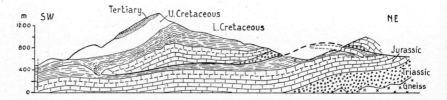

Fig. 188. Intercutaneous thrust in Royce structure, Western Alps. *(After Fallot. Published by permission of the Director, Laboratoire de Géologie de la Sorbonne, Paris.)*

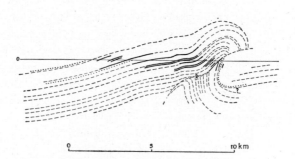

Fig. 189. Sarrebrück anticline with thrust-fault. *(After Pruvost, Description Géologique, Strassbourg, 1934.)*

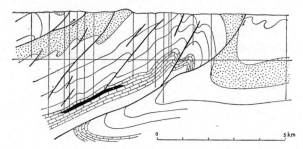

Fig. 190. Turner Valley overthrusted anticline. *(After Link. Published by permission of the American Association of Petroleum Geologists.)*

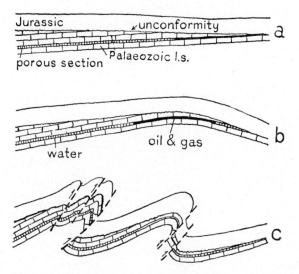

Fig. 191. Development of Turner Valley structure. *(After Link. Published by permission of the American Association of Petroleum Geologists.)*

bending of the strata stops as soon as the thrust plane cuts through them in the course of its extension upwards and downwards during folding. Once it has, in its downward course, reached the basal detachment-plane, the folding stops altogether, and the rest of the compression is wholly taken up by the thrust movement. Extreme cases of such thrust-structures are found in the Valley and Ridge province of the Appalachians. Its best known structure is perhaps the Cumberland thrust, Virginia (Fig. 192) (Miller and Fuller, 1955).

In this section we observe that the Pine Mountain thrust plane reaches its basal detachment-plane just below the Mississippian and stays in the same horizon for 20 miles; it then cuts obliquely down to a lower detachment-plane, a shale in the Cambrian Rome group. It seems probable that it is forced down by the next thrust plane, the Wallen ridge thrust. The structure can be compared to the succession of thrust-faults of the Charleroi coal basin as Kaisin Jr (1947) figured them (Fig. 193) and the incipient stage of the Helvetian thrust sheets was probably similar (cf. Fig. 223).

The S-shape of the thrust plane is prominent only in the first stage of the thrust, when it is still more or less parallel to the curved axial plane of the asymmetric fold. Later thrusting has to obliterate the curve and therefore we often find intermediate blocks and crushed zones along the later thrust plane.

Development as sketched above and illustrated by many examples is not the only possible result of further compression on an asymmetric thrust anticline. When the folds are closely packed, without broad synclines, and when they are well developed before the thrust plane breaks through, the front of the upper thrust-mass soon abuts upon the next fold, and no further thrusting is possible. Further compression is then continued again by folding, the thrust plane being folded together with the original fold. A well-known example of this development is that of the Graitery-Grenchenberg tunnel section in the Swiss Jura Mountains, Fig. 194. The original S-shape of the thrust plane is now more pronounced by further folding.

The same kind of development is found in the Ruhr coalfield, where the famous Sutan thrust has been severely folded in the later stages of compression (Fig. 195), and also in many of the low-angle thrusts of the Liége coal basin.

Flat Planar Thrust Planes. Although the early-stage overthrust has been illustrated by many examples in the preceding paragraphs, we must not forget that Buxtorf's hypothesis, that the overthrust anti-

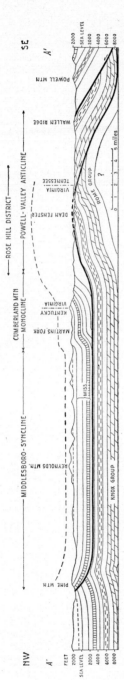

Fig. 192. Cumberland overthrust, Ridge and Valley provinces Appalachians. *(After Miller & Fuller. Published by permission of the United States Geological Survey.)*

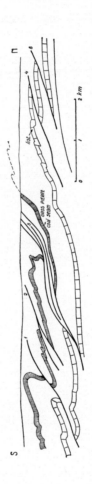

FIG. 193. Charleroi coal basin thrusts. *(After Kaisin Jr., Mém. Inst. Géol. Univ. Louvain, t. 15, 1947.)*

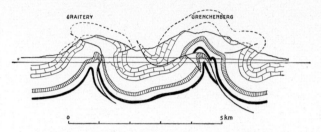

Fig. 194. Graitery-Grenchenberg structure. *(After Buxtorf, in Heim, Geologie der Schweiz, I.B.. III Hauptteil, 1921.)*

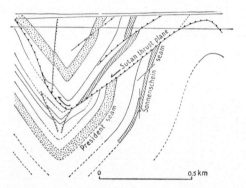

Fig. 195. The folded Sutan overthrust, Ruhr coalfield. *(After Kukuk. 1938, "Geologie der Niederrheinisch-Westfälischen Steinkohlengebiete". Published by permission of Springer-Verlag, Berlin.)*

cline originated in an unfolded flat overthrust, was based on substantial evidence.

Both in the Limburg and in the Liége coalfields, extensive and extremely flat thrusts have been revealed by coal mining. They are in no way connected with any individual folds I know of. The thrust movement can easily disappear from sight by running into a bedding-plane. These very flat thrusts possibly represent nothing more than the prolongation of anticlinal thrusts back from the anticlinal front which have been carried away by erosion, but there is no direct supporting evidence for this hypothesis. They are frequent in the Liége coalfield (Fig. 196) where it is certain that they belong to a very early stage of the folding process, since they have been folded after the thrust movement.

In this respect it is interesting to turn our attention to a feature of faulting in the calcareous Apennine ridges which has

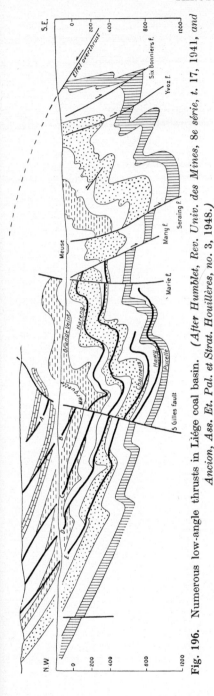

Fig. 196. Numerous low-angle thrusts in Liége coal basin. *(After Humblet, Rev. Univ. des Mines, 8e série, t. 17, 1941, and Ancion, Ass. Et. Pal. et Strat. Houillères, no. 3, 1948.)*

been demonstrated by Beneo and Migliorini (1948). The most typical section is that of the Montagna del Morrone (Fig. 197), and the resulting structure has been called a "composite wedge" by Migliorini. The structure is characterized on one side by low-angle thrusts over a subsided basin; these become steeper towards the centre, and change their character from thrust-faults to normal faults, on the other side of the ridge. Because the thick rigid limestone, never covered by much sediment, was near the surface, it did not fold but became faulted. The schematic section of Fig. 198 shows that the whole structure can be seen as a compression phenomenon due to an inclined stress-field. I would even suggest that the fan-like arrangement of the thrusts is due to a rotation of the original set of shear-planes, their substitution by a new set when the position of the first became too unfavourable, and so on. One could imagine that the departure of the stress from the horizontal by some 30° could be due to loading by a large mass on one side of the basin. This also happens on the internal side of a marginal trough; the Liége coal basin is an example. A simplified section (after Humblet, 1941) corrected for its southern part with the help of Ancion's section (1948), Fig. 196, shows that the structure of this basin is peculiar. In the gentler northern part of the basin, where it rests on the flank of the Brabant massif, we find the succession of six flat thrusts which have been mentioned above; and in the south,

Fig. 197. Triassic to mid-Miocene limestones overlain by Tertiary and Pleistocene clastics (in black). Montagna del Murrone composite wedge. *(After Migliorini. Published by permission of Società Geologica Italiana.)*

in the deepest part of the basin, we find a few normal faults. Still further south, the Eifel fault is a low-angle thrust with a large throw, along which a large overthrust mass passed over the Cointe anticline and onto the southern border of the coal basin in front of it. I think that this conflicting appearance of flat thrusts in the north and steep normal faults in the south can be regarded as analogous to the composite wedges of Migliorini, as a *set* limiting a series of upthrusted central wedges. The tilting of the stress could arise from the extra loading of the thrust-mass above the Eifel fault. It is significant that the axial planes of the sharp folds in the southern part of the basin also indicate that the principal stress had this inclination to the horizontal.

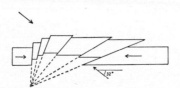

Fig. 198. Composite wedge due to inclined stress-field. *(After Migliorini. Published by permission of Società Geologica Italiana.)*

We should commit a serious error if we imagined the complicated structure of the Liége basin to be the result of one stress-field caused by a lateral stress which originated the Eifel thrust. On the contrary, we must view it as a slowly developing process, in which the stress, moving the advancing main thrust sheet, first caused the flat overthrust in the north; later, when the loading began to make itself seriously felt, the sharp folds; and lastly, near the end of the process, the normal faults in the south. This sequence is proved by the fact that the flat overthrusts are folded, and that the normal faults cut through the folds. Nevertheless, the final configuration of the basin seen as a whole is the result of one stress-field slowly rotating from a slightly inclined to a more strongly inclined position.

Chapter 18

Diapiric and Collapse Structures, Domes, and Cauldrons

In this chapter I propose to describe two opposites: diapiric structures which are formed by pressure acting upwards from below, and collapse structures which are formed by different sorts of caving-in due to voids below the surface. They have one thing in common, however, their circular shape, due to a peculiarity of their stress-field. In this the lateral forces are equal and unvariable, and the active force is vertical and either positive (upwards) or negative (downwards). It is true that many diapiric structures are not circular. This happens when the horizontal stress-field is not homogeneous but has been changed and orientated by a folding-stress. Nevertheless even the oblong diapir is due to a vertical stress.

Because many domes are due to a deep-seated diapir they are described in this chapter. They could, however, have equally well been discussed in connexion with ordinary plunging anticlines, of which they are an extremely short variety.

Collapse structures are either connected with volcanism, as cauldrons of different kinds and crypto-volcanic structures, or are due to solution of salt or limestone at depth. The literature on salt-domes is very extensive but some useful compilations are fortunately available.*

DIAPIRIC STRUCTURES

In Chapter 13 we saw that every concentric fold finds more difficulty in maintaining its concentric habit as folding progresses. There is less and less space left in the core of the fold, occupied by its basal incompetent layers. The solution of the difficulty is either a broadening of

---

* For the United States we have "The Geology of Saltdome Oilfields", 1926 and "Gulf Coast oilfields", 1936, both published by the Am. Ass. of Petroleum Geologists; for Germany "Erdöl und Tektonik in N.W. Deutschland", 1949, published by the "Amt für Bodenforschung Hannover—Celle".

the fold or a break-through in the flanks. Broadening is often checked both by the weight of its own arc and by the proximity of the next fold. The break-through is therefore the normal consequence in advanced folding. The asymmetric break-through is a thrust-fault. In this chapter we shall get to know its symmetrical form, the diapir. The diapiric structure is characterized by the expulsion of the core of the anticline through the crest of the fold, and as such is an example of two horizontally moving flanks in contrast with a vertically moving crestal wedge (cf. Fig. 136). The lines joining the turning points from vertical to horizontal movement turn into fault-planes leading towards the core of the anticline, and the block comprised between these faults is pressed out. This action is realized only in nature when the bottom layers are extremely plastic; this can be understood when we consider that only a fluid or, as in this case, an extremely plastic material, is able directly to transform a lateral stress into hydrostatic pressure.

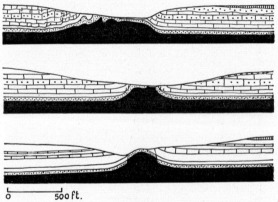

Fig. 199.   Load structures in Northampton Ironstone field.   *(After Holling-worth, Q.J.G.S., vol. 100, 1944.   Published by permission of the Geological Society of London.)*

This mechanism of diapirs due to folding is, however, not the only cause of upwards break-through of plastic material. The other cause is the simple load of sediments overlying the plastic layer; this can cause an upwelling either because the specific density of salt is much smaller than that of ordinary rock material or because a local thinning or removal of the load, by erosion for instance, will allow the plastic material to be pressed out.

It is of course impossible in most cases to judge how much of the

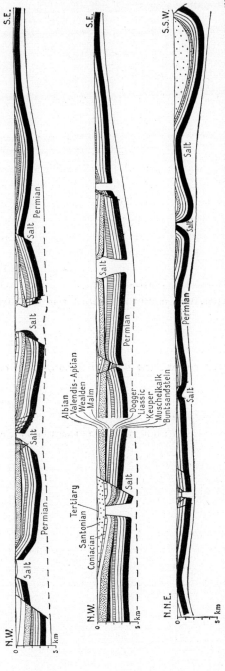

Fig. 200. Three sections through Hannoverian salt-dome region. (*After Roll "Erdöl und Tektonik in Nordwestdeutschland",* 1949.)

movement is due to one or the other factor, whether a slight folding started the movement or whether hydrostatic adjustment was the primary cause. Let it suffice to say that the upwelling of the lower plastic layer can always be connected with both folding and hydrostatic movement.

Hollingworth (1944) described structures in the Northampton Ironstone field, where Middle Lias limestones rest on Upper Lias clays. Valleys have been eroded through the limestones into the underlying plastic beds, with the result that the limestones dip towards the valleys, and that in these, the clays have risen up (Fig. 199). The structures are always narrowly linked to the erosional valleys, and the latter do not show any directional preference. The whole process, which is evidently due to the unevenly distributed load of the limestones on the plastic clays in consequence of erosion, is accompanied by faulting and open fissures in the limestones which have been bent down. In trenches dug in the Lias clay considerable contortion has been noticed. It seems probable that a temporary permafrost condition of the clays and its seasonal surficial melting, as Hollingworth thinks at present (personal communication) was an important factor in the whole process.

The Hannoverian salt-dome region has many analogies with the English example just described. In Fig. 200 (from Roll, 1949) we find the same arrangement resembling floes drifting on a viscous fluid; but on the other hand it is obvious that here tectonic factors of folding and faulting have been much more pronounced. The overlapping of the Cretaceous over the Jurassic proves a folding in a NE–SW direction; later, faulting, which began in the Upper Cretaceous and continued during the Lower Tertiary tensional phase, gave rise to normal faults with NW–SE strike. The two main tectonic directions combined with the hydrostatic rise of the salt created the present complex pattern of salt extrusions of Hannover. The "floes" have also been pushed around on their plastic substratum, so that the structural history of each salt-dome forms a problem in itself.

A clearer insight into the problem of the origin of the diapir can be obtained when the incipient stage of these structures is studied. Some sections from the north-east part of the Netherlands, wholly based on a seismic reflection survey for oil-prospection, are helpful (Fig. 201). Four stages are represented by four different sections. In the first section we perceive hardly any deformation of the horizontal succession of Permian (Zechstein) salt, Jurassic, Cretaceous, and Tertiary rocks.

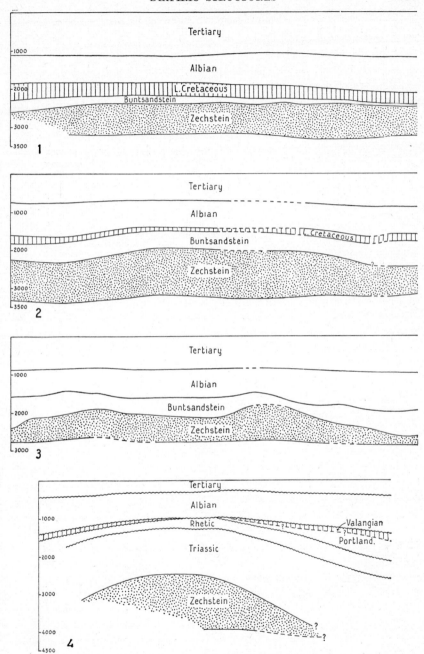

Fig. 201.   Incipient salt-dome structures revealed by seismic exploration in the
north-east Netherlands.   *(Unpublished.   Reproduced by permission of Nederl.
Aardolie Mij., Oldenzaal.)*

In the second section the upper boundary of the salt-bed is distinctly wavy; this is reflected in the base of the Albian (Lower Cretaceous) but not in the base of the Tertiary. It indicates that the movement took place before the deposition of this last formation.

In the third section the structures become more pronounced. In the fourth section a distinct dome has been formed. The base of the Jurassic is slightly unconformable, and so is the base of the Portlandian; the base of the Lower Cretaceous has a stronger unconformity; and the strongest unconformity is found at the base of the Albian. The base of the Tertiary is horizontal. On the flank, the Zechstein salt thins to almost nothing, proving that quite a volume of salt has flowed towards the dome. (The third section shows the beginning of the effect of flow.) The repeated unconformities throughout the Mesozoic prove that the movement was more or less continuous, but with a distinct maximum in the Lower Cretaceous. Once it was initiated at the close of the Trias, probably by a very slight tectonic movement, it continued slowly by itself, and was reactivated by a Pre-Albian folding phase. Some subsequent slight hydrostatic rise is discernible but the movement stopped before the deposition of the Tertiary, probably by the lack of salt within the synclinal regions. It never attained true diapiric character.

A sequence of examples with increasing tectonic intensity is seen in these Dutch salt structures, of which only a few rose towards the surface; in the Hannoverian salt-dome region, where stronger folding and a tensional phase created separated rows of salt structures; and in the Rumanian salt-bearing diapirs.

The section by de Raaf (1953), Fig. 202, gives us a good example of the complicated history of the Rumanian region. In this southern branch of the Carpathian arc a strong pre-Pliocene phase of folding formed many thrust anticlines, in which the salt-bearing Lower Micoene acted as a lubricating horizon for the thrust planes. After

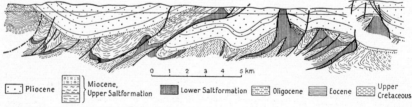

0 1 2 3 4 5 km

[. . .] Pliocene   [≡] Miocene, Upper Saltformation   [▓] Lower Saltformation   [≡≡] Oligocene   [≡] Eocene   [≡≡] Upper Cretaceous

Fig. 202. Section through South Rumanian oilfields. *(After Raaf, Science of Petroleum, vol. 6, 1953. Published by permission of the Oxford University Press.)*

erosion, and deposition of the Pliocene, renewed compression rejuvenated some of these structures with the result that some of the thrusts reached the surface again (Ocnita). These thrusts are always accompanied by Miocene salt. The compression left some of the other structures undisturbed; and in some cases reactivated only the salt diapir itself (Ochiuri Oilfield). In the Gura-Ocnitei Oilfield we find typical normal crest-faults due to a pressing-up of the salt core, the same type which we have already encountered in Concepcion Oilfield, Venezuela (Fig. 144). The whole Rumanian section gives an excellent example of the supple kind of folding which prevails in such flysch sediments in a marginal trough; but in this case the folding is intensified by the presence of salt-bearing beds.

In contrast with the domes of this highly disturbed region, there are many regions, such as the Gulf Coast, which possess numerous salt-domes but show hardly any traces of folding or faulting. Nevertheless, the salt penetrates to the surface. In cross-section there is little difference between a salt-dome of the Hannoverian and the Gulf Coast type, except the slightly more tectonized aspect of the German one. But on the map the alignment of the Hannoverian salt diapirs on anticlinal axes, and their oval shape, are in striking contrast with the circular shape and the haphazard distribution of the Gulf Coast domes.

The Gulf Coast domes are of the static type. It is presumed that at some early stage during one of the many Upper Cretaceous or Tertiary phases, slight folding inaugurated the accumulation of the salt of an underlying salt-bed into anticlinal zones. Another phase with another folding direction possibly accentuated the accumulation of this plastic formation at the points of intersection of the two anticlinal structures. In Chapter 23 a case from the High Atlas will be described in which the Trias diapirs occur at such intersections.

Whatever may be the reason for the inception of the salt structure, as soon as a certain thickening in one place has been accomplished the process of the rise of the salt continues as a result of the unequal static load. The salt flows from the surrounding area towards the salt-stock, which rises vertically. This flow causes a rim syncline encircling the salt-dome, adds to the inequality of load distribution, and extends its area.

An instructive example of rim synclines and their consequences is found in a group of diapiric anticlinal structures in Eastern Algeria, Fig. 203. The Ouenza, Bou Khadra, and Jaber anticlines each possess an extensive diapiric core of gypsum and salt-bearing red shales and

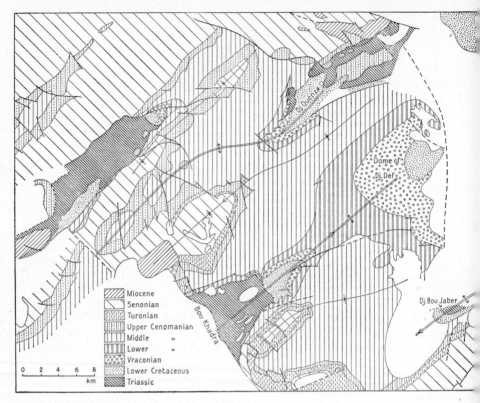

Miocene
Senonian
Turonian
Upper Cenomanian
Middle   „
Lower   „
Vraconian
Lower Cretaceous
Triassic

0 2 4 6 8
km

Fig. 203.   Djebel Def, circular dome structure between diapiric anticlines.   East Algeria

marls. The arrangement of these three anticlines and their plunges leaves a large basin between the Ouenza and Jaber structures. The margins of the anticlines are sharply depressed as a consequence of the salt flow towards the anticline; and the central basin is thus surrounded by a depressed rim and consequently stands out as a circular dome. The dome is totally different in structure from all the other structures in the area. It is characterized by the absence of faults, by gentle dips and by its circular shape and flat crest, whereas the truly anticlinal structures are just the opposite, with steep flanks, diapiric cores, many faults, and elongated shape.

When salt-dome structures of the static type are relatively closely packed, their synclinal rims will also leave a flat, dome-like structure between the domes.

The salt flow towards the dome continues until the salt formation

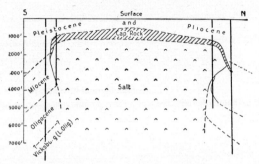

Fig. 204. Barbers Hill salt-dome, Texas, showing overhang of cap-rock. *(After Judson, Murphy, and Stamey. Published by permission of the American Association of Petroleum Geologists.)*

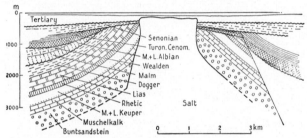

Fig. 205. Stöcken-Lichtenhorst salt-dome. *(After Schlüter, "Erdöl und Tektonik in Nordwestdeutschland", 1949.)*

in the rim is exhausted. On the top of the salt-dome and along its flanks, as far as it rises above the groundwater level, solution of the salt sets in. With solution of the salt, accumulation of insoluble residues commences, and these in their turn are submitted to chemical changes, so that anhydrite, gypsum, limestone, and sulphur form a cap-rock, often showing an overhang (Fig. 204).

Structurally all salt-domes show marked upwards bending of the surrounding beds against the salt-stock, often accompanied by faulting (Fig. 205). In the static type of dome the upward bend and its faults are due to the presence of the salt; in the folded type both the bending and the faulting may be primary.

The beds above the salt-dome, when they are preserved, are domed, and therefore stretched, by the push from below and often show an intricate pattern of normal tension-faults, such as those on the Reitbrook dome, Fig. 206, in Germany. A similar structure is the Hawkins dome in Texas, Fig. 207, where the fault pattern has a more radial arrangement. Both kinds of faults, normal tension-faults and radial

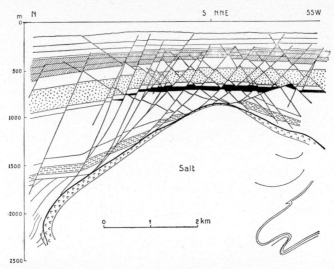

Fig. 206. Reitbrook dome, section. *(After Behrmann, "Erdöl und Tektonik in Nordwestdeutschland", 1949.)*

tear-faults, are typical of this kind of structure, which is directly comparable to that of a plunging anticline. In Chapter 14 these peri-anticline faults have already been explained, and the same explanation is applicable to domes. Normal and radial faults can occur together on both types of structures. They then form intricate patterns and their intersections pose complicated geometrical problems.

Longitudinal crestal faults curving into the flank as shown in Fig. 208 are typical of the peri-anticline of diapiric structures. These faults are almost vertical, and have a vertical throw diminishing towards the plunge and flank. They are due to the uplift caused by the rising salt in the centre of the structure and are neither normal tension-faults nor wrench-faults. They are also present in the plunge of the equally diapiric Ouenza structure shown in Fig. 203.

COLLAPSE STRUCTURES

The largest and most spectacular kind of collapse structures are the calderas or cauldrons. Although the origin of the voids which caused their collapse may differ, the various calderas are all ascribed in some way or other to the formation of an empty space in the centre of a volcanic structure. Williams (1941) distinguishes five types:

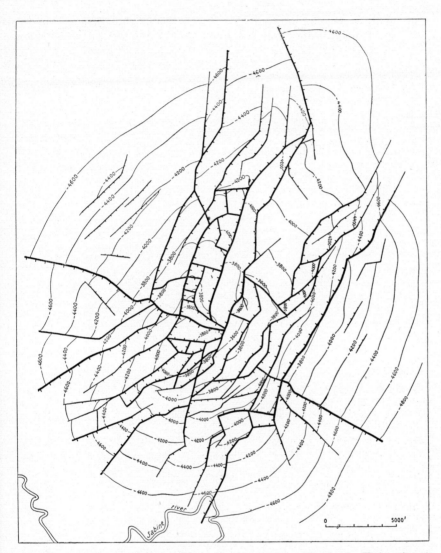

Fig. 207. Hawkins Oilfield, structure map. *(After Wentlandt, University of Texas Publications no. 5116, 1951. Published by permission of the University of Texas.)*

1. Krakatau type, collapse following explosions of pumice and ash
2. Kilauea type, collapse following rapid effusion of lava
3. Katmai type, produced by a combination of internal solution, pumice explosion, and avalanching of crater walls
4. Crypto-volcanic type, subsidence following subterranean explosions with little or no escape of magma at the surface
5. Glencoe type, collapse due to subsidence of magma in magma-chamber

Many calderas are probably due to a combination of several of these mechanisms.

Cauldrons. In the true calderas, types 1–3, the volcano itself is not completely destroyed. The crater walls still form the circumference of the structure. Their history is often very complicated; recurrent explosions, new volcanic vents, etc. abound. The subsidence of the centre is generally depicted in sections by inward-sloping normal

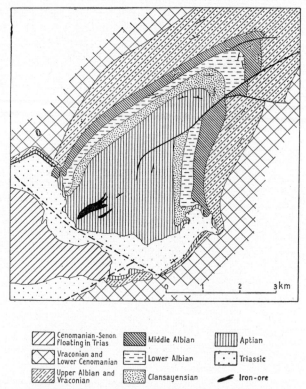

Fig. 208. Peri-anticline of the diapiric Bou Khadra structure.

fault-lines, and since there often is evidence of step-faulting, tilting of the steps seems to be common. Nevertheless, factual evidence about this inward slope is mostly lacking and it seems doubtful, for the smaller calderas at least, that the slope really exists, for it would hinder subsidence in these circular structures.

Crypto-Volcanic Structures. Crypto-volcanic structures are known in many parts of the world. The best-known are without doubt the Rieskessel and the associated Steinheim basin in Germany, both filled with Miocene of fresh water facies. The crypto-volcanic structures are circular, and occur in cratonic regions among flat-lying sediments, or in the crystalline basement. They are related to alkaline gas-rich magma typical of this sort of environment (cf. Chapter 25) and "can be considered as products of abortive attempts to blast diatremes". (Williams, 1941, p. 300). Sometimes the surrounding sediments have been domed before the collapse, as in some of the structures described by Bucher (1933) from the U.S.A. (Fig. 209) and by Monod (1954) from the Sahara. Probably the doming was due to a preliminary rise of the magma along a diatreme, followed by collapse and subsidence.

The crypto-volcanic structures of the Oslo rift, described by Oftedahl (1952, 1953) are characterized by a narrow vertical ring-dike injected along a circular boundary-fault (Fig. 210). As suggested above,

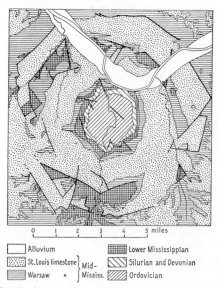

0   1   2   3   4   5 miles

☐ Alluvium   ▦ Lower Mississippian
▦ St. Louis limestone ⎱ Mid-   ◈ Silurian and Devonian
▦ Warsaw ″ ⎰ Mississ. ▨ Ordovician

Fig. 209. Willis Creek basin, Tennessee. *(After Bucher. Published by permission of the Department of Conservation, State of Tennessee.)*

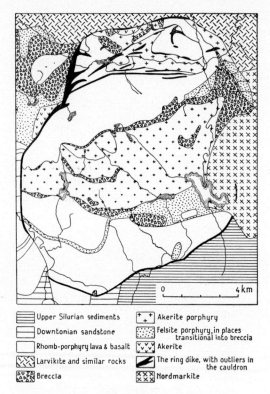

Upper Silurian sediments		Akerite porphyry	
Downtonian sandstone		Felsite porphyry, in places transitional into breccia	
Rhomb-porphyry lava & basalt		Akerite	
Larvikite and similar rocks		The ring dike, with outliers in the cauldron	
Breccia		Nordmarkite	

Fig. 210. Baerum cauldron. *(After Oftedahl, Inter. Geol. Congress. London, 1952, Part XIII.)*

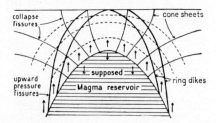

Fig. 211. Ring-dikes and cone sheets. *(After Anderson, Proceedings of the Royal Society of Edinburgh vol. 56, 1936. Published by permission of the Royal Society of Edinburgh.)*

such a vertical position of the boundary-fault seems more logical than an inward slope.

The Scottish ring-dikes and cones have been mentioned already in Chapter 9. Their origin is aptly described by Anderson (1936) and has been sustained by Billings (1943) although some divergence of opinion exists on the mechanism. Anderson presumes that in a magma chamber of circular shape the magma column oscillates in height, pushing upwards and subsiding, and causing tension cracks in the surrounding rock and collapse. The ring-dikes generally dip steeply outwards or are vertical; only a few dip inwards. The cone sheets of the Scottish systems, on the other hand, dip at about 45° inwards, and if projected downwards meet at a focus 4–5 km beneath the present surface. They are much less frequent than ring-dikes. The geometry of the system indicates that the cone sheets originate in the upward push of the magma, and the ring-dikes in the collapse of the cap-rock after its withdrawal (Fig. 211). The exact mechanism seems to be different in various systems, and it remains curious that the faulting of domes, with its radial pattern, is not reproduced in the ring-dike systems. Perhaps the deeper level of erosion of these latter systems can explain this anomaly.

Collapse Structures due to Solution and Mining. Collapse structures are common in all limestone-covered areas, and in those that are underlain by salt-bearing beds. Hundt (1950) devoted a book to the subject. He gives numerous examples of collapse in empty spaces created by solution of limestone, gypsum, and salt. The most interesting examples are perhaps those collapse zones in which swamps came into existence in Tertiary times, creating channel-shaped and round lignite bodies.

In coal mining the collapse above an extracted coal seam, and the damage it causes to buildings, etc. at the surface has led to the development of a special branch of technical science. This has advanced so far that by the regulation of the underground extraction of coal, surface collapse can be kept under control so that buildings are let down gently between regulated shear-zones. This technique is of course highly experimental, and the incipient movements at the surface are detected by repeated, careful, and accurate measurements. Zones of dilatation and compression are mapped to determine where and when collapse can be expected.

Chapter 19

Gravitational Gliding Tectonics

Since the birth of the science of structural geology, geologists describing particular phenomena observed in the field have explained certain structures as the result of gliding down an inclined surface. However, the great impetus that the discovery of large thrust masses gave to structural geology, and the resulting prominence that has been given to lateral compression as the origin of these thrusts, has to a large extent caused structures rightly ascribed to gliding to be overlooked or misinterpreted. Modern thought has taken up the concept of gliding again and has applied it with much success to the great nappes of the Helvetian type in Switzerland and to the flysch nappes of both the western and the central Alps.

At the same time, however, another school of thought has developed which emphasizes the fluidity of rocks under high confining pressure, as observed in laboratory experiments, and the obvious uplift that every mountain system has undergone. It attempts to explain all tectonic features by the influence of gravity on elevated parts of the earth's crust. In this view, the positive and negative vertical movements are caused by hypothetical processes at great depths, and all horizontal movements are due to sliding down hill, even those in the deeper parts of the crust.

Thus there have developed two concepts of gliding, one chiefly concerned with superficial features, the other with deeply buried parts of the earth's crust. Unfortunately, though they originally sprang from widely different considerations, they have mingled when they met at the surface of the crust, and heated arguments have resulted.

They ought to be kept separated, however, and each judged on its own merits. We are here concerned mostly with observable aspects of structural geology and not with theoretical arguments about their deep-seated cause and origin.

I shall not enter into a historical review of the development of thought on gliding tectonics in the last decades. I want to point out,

266

however, that the idea was hatched in Grenoble by Gignoux (1948) and Schneegans (1938), in Lausanne by Lugeon and Gagnebin (1941), and in Rome and Florence by Beneo, Merla (1951), Migliorini (1933, 1936), and others, more or less simultaneously, though it had been present in the mind of many geologists before. Haarman, van Bemmelen, and many others used it extensively but from another point of view, more indiscriminately and as an all-comprehensive theory*.

PRINCIPLES OF GRAVITATIONAL GLIDING TECTONICS

Gravitational gliding tectonics may be understood as embracing all phenomena where gravity has been the cause of movement of relatively large and coherent superficial portions of the earth's crust. In this sense it does not include all such movements as landslides or slumping. Starting from a single pebble rolling down a slope and increasing gradually the mass of the dislocated material gliding down, we would be able to establish a continuous scale ending with nappes of the Helvetian type. We will observe, however, that in this scale the smaller masses have a chaotic aspect, as in landslides, and that the larger the mass the more coherent the structure. Also the larger the mass the smaller the dip of the gliding surface need be.

From a more theoretical point of view we can distinguish in superficial gliding tectonics two extremes, with all transitions between. At one end of the series we may place the gliding of a slab of sedimentary rock on a gliding surface formed most frequently by an exceptionally incompetent member of an otherwise competent series. Hardly any disturbance inside the slab need occur; for example, it may simply glide down an appropriate slope, lubricated at its base by shale containing salt or gypsum. At the other end of the series we may place the gliding of a uniformly ill-stratified mass of highly incompetent strata. The basal shearing-plane would be much less distinctly developed, and most of the movement would occur within the gliding mass, which therefore would possess a more or less chaotic structure. During its downward course the gliding mass may even pick up and incorporate pieces of its substratum, with the result that it might contain much younger constituents than expected.

---

* A survey of the different directions in which such ideas have been tending is provided in: Symposium sur la tectonique d'écoulement par gravité, Geologie en Mijnbouw, 12e Jaargang 1950, pp. 329–65, containing articles by Tercier, Gignoux, Goguel, van Bemmelen, and de Sitter.

All possible transitions between the two extremes can be found. The sedimentary series may possess several incompetent layers, so that the original slab is divided into several slabs moving independently. If these intermediate incompetent layers are relatively thick, the competent layers may be broken up, and distinct secondary folds may develop, separated by internal gliding planes. If the incompetent mass predominates we may find large blocks or folded remnants of the competent layers distributed in an incoherent way throughout the mass. The parautochthonous flysch of the north flanks of the central massifs of the Alps is a good example of this mode of folding and gliding (Fig. 212). Some of the masses of the Argille scagliose in the northern foothills of the northern Apennines give a very good idea of the chaotic

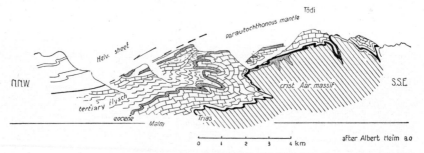

Fig. 212. The cascade folds of the sedimentary mantle of the autochthonous Aar massif, Switzerland, gliding down the northern slope of the massif under the influence of its own weight and that of the overriding Helvetian nappes, also gliding down. *(After Heim, Geologie der Schweiz, I.B., III Hauptteil, 1921.)*

structure of a large incompetent mass of rocks in which there float fragments of the competent members of the original sequence. This so-called "Argille scagliose" is a comprehensive series, ranging from the Malm at least to the Cretaceous, and is so incompetent that it is able to form glacier-like gliding masses originating from a simple outcrop between younger strata, as I had the occasion to observe in the Turinese foothills.

Many good examples of remnants of synclinal and anticlinal folds of older and competent strata embedded in highly incompetent flysch are described by Schneegans (1938) in his thesis on the Ubaye-Embrunais gliding nappe (Fig. 220). The Helvetian nappes, which originally were successive overthrust anticlines, each having its own basal shearing-plane at a different stratigraphical level in the series, illustrate nicely the case of a complicated gliding mass divided by incompetent layers into several independent units (Fig. 222).

The Liassic slabs on the southern border of the High Atlas, and some of the Cretaceous slabs on the southern border of the Pyrenees, are simple undivided masses of competent rocks gliding on a Triassic lubricating plane (Fig. 221).

The size of a gliding mass is probably dependent on several factors. If, as in the case of the Helvetian nappes, a pre-existing thrust plane cuts through the whole series from the basal shearing-plane upwards to the surface and the back portion is then uplifted and tilted, there will be very little or no resistance at the front. As soon as the slope of the thrust plane is sufficient, gliding will start, and it will accelerate as the tilting continues. If, on the other hand, no previous thrust plane has developed, the resistance at the front will in general prevent the gliding of larger masses. As Goguel (1950) has shown, the larger the mass the smaller the slope of the gliding plane need be. But commonly the gliding will not start if the minimum slope for a certain mass has been surpassed because there is not sufficient room in front and at the bottom of the slope, where erosion is less active anyhow. Therefore tilting can continue and nothing will happen until finally a gliding plane having sufficient slope to start the gliding can cut through the strata upwards to the surface. At that moment, however, a much smaller mass can detach itself because the slope has considerably increased.

How far erosion at the bottom of the slope plays an active part in preparing the necessary room in front of the gliding mass by cutting through the competent top layers to the basal shearing-plane is impossible to determine. I do not think erosion is a very important factor, but direct evidence either way is altogether lacking.

EXAMPLES OF GRAVITATIONAL GLIDING

The following examples of gravitational gliding quoted from the literature will give us the opportunity to discuss its particular character.

Bearpaw Mountains, Montana. The simplest case of gliding on a tectonic scale I know is that described by Frank Reeves (1924, 1946).

In the Bearpaw Mountains, Montana, a series of mostly Upper Cretaceous shale and sandstone 4,500 feet thick has been domed, and the top of the arched dome has been eroded. In Tertiary time a great mass of extrusive volcanic rocks, 5,000 feet in maximum thickness, accumulated on top of the dome. The accumulation of this localized mass caused a plainwards sliding of volcanics and sedimentary strata, probably on one or two particularly incompetent bentonite beds in the lower part of the Upper Cretaceous shale. Still later the central portion of the dome caved in along normal faults. The accompanying map and section (Fig. 213) show the thrust-fault pattern and the curious arrangement of broad unfolded belts separated by narrow folded and thrust zones.

On the top of the dome there is a large gap in the volcanic cover, evidently because one half of the cover slid northwards and the other southwards, the only actual example of what we may call "tectonic denudation". The slope never had an angle exceeding 3°, and each whole flank glided down this slope producing thrusts and folding in the untilted horizontal strata of the plain.

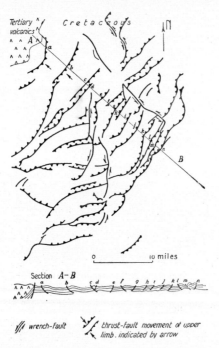

Fig. 213. Gravitational gliding in the Bearpaw Mountains, Montana. *(After Reeves. Published by permission of the Geological Society of America.)*

The thrusts commonly merge laterally into asymmetric folds, the more deeply eroded structures showing thrusting. Probably no thrust plane ever reached the surface. The thrust planes may dip either towards the dome or away from it. Radial tear-faults separate different blocks, with different intensity of thrusting; they have a pronounced tendency to cross the structures diagonally. These tear-faults therefore illustrate the original stress condition, but subsequently they became limits to different "flows", one advancing further than its neighbour.

The mass that slid on the 3° slope had an average thickness of 6,250 feet and a total mass of some 55 million tons.

Tangkuban Prahu and Karangkobar Volcanoes in Java. Very similar to the case described by Reeves are two examples of gliding described by van Bemmelen (1934; 1937; 1949, pp. 610, 641–44). North of the Bandung basin extends the Quaternary volcanic chain of the Tangkuban Prahu, in which we can distinguish an older and a younger volcanic series. At the foot of the volcanoes the volcanic series lie unconformably on folded Upper Miocene marine sediments. The youngest group of volcanoes, of which Tangkuban Prahu is the most western, lie on the axis of an elongated dome (Fig. 214). On the northern flank of the dome a series of arcuate faults were mapped, partly originating in the caldera subsidence of Tangkuban Prahu itself and, judging by their shape, clearly independent of any general tensional

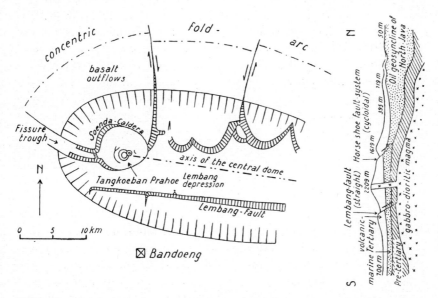

Fig. 214. Map and section of Tangkuban Prahu Volcano, Java. *(After van Bemmelen.)*

faulting. The northern half of the dome is surrounded by the Segalaherang depression and that in turn by a row of hills, the Gunung Tembakan or Damm hills consisting of the older Quaternary volcanic blanket. The flat dips in these foothills, surrounding the Segalaherang depression, are almost exclusively mountainwards (to the south). It seems very probable that the arcuate faults in the volcano mantle and the abnormal dips in the foothills are due to sliding down of portions of the volcanic mantle. We can imagine that similar arcuate faults existed also in the volcanic mantle of the Bearpaw volcano, before erosion obliterated them.

A similar example is cited by van Bemmelen from the Karangkobar volcanic region of central Java. Here the Upper Pliocene uplift reached several thousand metres before the formation of the Pleistocene volcanoes and was accompanied by faulting and tilting of blocks of marine Lower Pliocene. Although some remnants of older volcanic rocks are present, most of the volcanics belong to the Quaternary of the Djembangan Mountain range. In this volcanic mantle arcuate faults have developed, which apparently represent the upper limits of gliding blocks. These Recent faults nowadays form precipitous fault scarps several hundred metres high. In order to check the possibility that these blocks were still moving, the topographical survey triangulated the position of some of the blocks twice, with an interval of 5 years, and noticed a movement of 120 cm, 200 cm, and 200 cm. These displacements are supposed to be much larger than the possible errors of measurements, and should indicate a movement of 24 to 40 cm a year.

Van Bemmelen describes in his work many much larger phenomena, but a careful comparison of his text with the accompanying map and sections allows considerable doubt as to the conclusiveness of the field evidence for ascribing his larger overthrusts to gravitational gliding.

Lobitos Oilfield, Peru. A very uncommon type of gravity gliding is reported from the coastal regions of Peru and Ecuador (Baldry, 1938; Barrington Brown, 1938). The region in question is limited oceanwards by the coastal normal fault, along which movements presumably took place recurrently, and inland by the Amotape metamorphic rocks. The Tertiary rocks deposited in this area measure several tens of thousands of feet in thickness and have been extensively explored for oil in some areas. The strata dip gently oceanwards. According to the authors, slip-planes developed in the gently dipping strata every time a sufficient thickness of rocks had been deposited (Fig. 215). These slip-planes had an original dip of 7° to 10°, and along them are found all kinds of distortion of the beds, often resembling structures due to slumping. Nevertheless the continuous character of the slip-planes, and the regular vertical spacing of 2,000 to 3,000 feet at which they occur make it very improbable that slumping at the time of deposition of the contorted beds is responsible. Along with the brecciated slip zones, sand dikes appear, cutting perpendicularly through the formation.

It seems highly probable that gliding has been favoured by a decrease of grain pressure as the impermeable shales prevented the escape of water expelled from the surrounding sediments by compaction. Any activity along the border fault, increasing the dip of the strata, could set in motion the gliding of the accumulated mass, and before a new slip-plane could be formed a new thick series of sediments had to accumulate in order to establish anew a labile state. The sandstone dikes are formed in general from a normal sandstone, but some

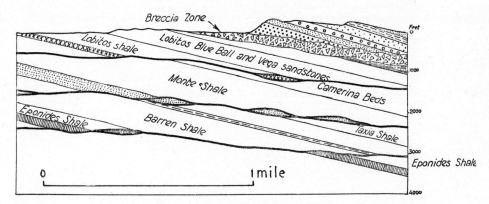

Fig. 215. Schematic section through the Lobitos Oilfield, Peru. (*After Baldry, Q.J.G.S., vol.* 94, 1938. *Published by permission of the Geological Society of London.*)

contain a mixture of shale and limestone fragments. Some of the breccia beds have a peculiar composition described as "clay pebble bed", which consists of highly polished pebbles of all kinds of rocks in a gritty clay matrix that looks like the deposit of a turbulent flow, combined with slumping.

Collapse Structures in Persia. A very interesting phenomenon in which gravity certainly played a prominent role has been described by Harrison and Falcon (1934, 1936).

In the mountainous part of Iran, bordering the Euphrates-Tigris Valley, the structure of the folded strata is extremely well exposed because of the arid climate. The stratigraphic series consists of three thick limestone units, each 1,000 to 3,000 feet in thickness — the highest being the Asmari limestone, famous for its oil-bearing capacity — separated by marls 1,000 to 2,000 feet thick and overlain by 10,000 feet of anhydrite-shale and sandstone, called the Fars series. The incompetent marl series between the limestones have given rise, as is normal, to disharmonic folding, but some of the sections show undoubted gliding phenomena.

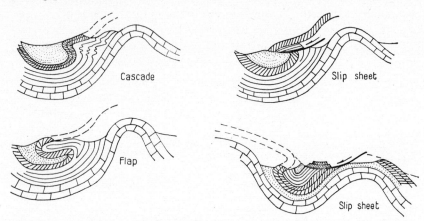

Fig. 216. Examples of collapse structures in Persia. *(After Harrison, Q.J.G.S., vol. 92, 1936. Published by permission of the Geological Society of London.)*

Harrison distinguished several types of structures (Fig. 216): (1) *slip-sheet* structure, (2) *cascade folds*, where the limestone has crumpled up, as it glided downwards, (3) *flap-structure*, undoubtedly the most curious structural feature of the region, where a limestone wall has bent over gradually until a reversed position has been attained.

All these features are explained by Harrison as purely gravitational structures, due to deep erosion in the soft synclinal material of the Fars series and gradual collapse of the vertical limestone flank, which either broke off and glided down the slope in a normal position, or crumpled into cascade folds, or bent over into a recumbent fold.

I am far from convinced that all these structural phenomena ought to be explained by such relatively recent collapse of steep flanks into eroded valleys. The slabs of the normal roofs of the anticline that have glided down in the syncline are doubtless due to gliding only, and some of the cascades probably are also due to these gravitational mechanics, but the most striking "flap" structures can be explained as well by a rather extreme form of disharmonic folding. We know that the folds in the Fars series, the upper incompetent anhydrite, gypsiferous marls, and sandstone overlying the Asmari limestone, are always perfectly independent of the underlying competent limestone in the oil-bearing anticlines of Iran, where no altitude differences are involved. I rather think that most of these structures, which have a distinctly disharmonic character because of the alternation of thick competent and incompetent beds, had already originated in the folding stage and were accentuated later on by gravitational collapse. The overturn is then due mostly to lack of space in the syncline, and it developed because the thick Fars series behaved purely passively and was not a factor in determining the amplitude of the fold at the beginning of folding.

Djebel Friktia, Algeria. A very instructive example of gliding tectonics has been given by van der Fliert (1953), in describing an anticline and syncline in eastern Algeria. The region consists of two anticlinal ridges composed of Lower and Middle Cretaceous limestones, and between them a synclinal region, filled up with Senonian and Eocene marls and shales. The anticlinal ridges received much thinner Upper Cretaceous sediments than the syncline, thus the sedimentation

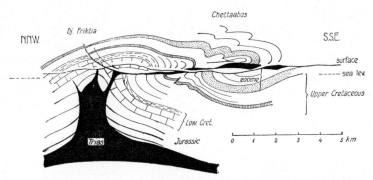

Fig. 217. Cross-section through Djebel Friktia and the Chettabas syncline in Algeria, showing combination of diapiric and gliding structures. *(After van der Fliert, XIXe Congrès Géologique International, Alger, 1952, Compte Rendu, sec. 3, fasc. 3.)*

took place while the basin was sinking much faster than its stable borders. In the whole of eastern Algeria the very plastic Triassic shales and evaporites have acted diapirically, and apparently in the final post-Eocene phases of compression the Triassic was pressed out in the core of the anticline, and the thick Senonian blanket on its flank started gliding down along a slope of 3° to 5°. The top arch of the anticline, loosened from the flanks by the diapir structure, took part in this gliding action, and the gliding plane became lubricated by Triassic shales. The result (Fig. 217) is a rather astounding structure in which Triassic shales cover portions of the Eocene in the syncline while

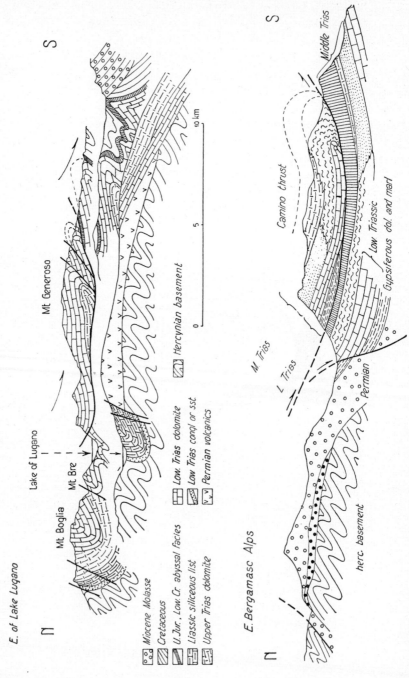

Fig. 218. Two sections showing gliding nappes on the southern slope of the Alps: Mount Generoso east of Lake Lugano, and Pizzo Camino in the eastern Bergamasc Alps. (*After de Sitter, Leidse Geol. Med., vol. 14B, 1949.*)

klippen of Upper Cretaceous rocks and locally even wedges of Lower Cretaceous limestone float on them, and the steep south flank of the anticline shows considerable tectonic thickening. It is quite possible that the pressing out of the Triassic from the syncline to the anticline had already started during the accumulation of thick Upper Cretaceous and Eocene sediments in the synclinal basin, before the folding created the truly diapiric structure of the anticline.

Bergamasc and Luganese Alps. Gliding tectonics can frequently be found on the marginal slopes of the great Tertiary mountain chains. We often find there that the upper surface of the basement is lowered from its lofty position in the axial zone to its deeply buried position in the marginal trough by a series of steps separated by steep zones or faults. The difference of altitude between two steps commonly gives rise to a gravitational gliding of the sedimentary cover along an appropriate horizon on top of the stationary series of the same age belonging to a lower step. Numerous examples of these structures can be quoted from sections in the southern border of the Alps, of which two are reproduced in Fig. 218.

In the section east of Lake Lugano we see a whole mass of Triassic and Liassic limestones gliding down a slope and butting against a solid mass of Miocene Molasse. The cascade folds in front of the gliding mass are typical and illustrate the movement very clearly. The amount of gliding is relatively small, and gliding was probably set in motion by the steep synclinal folding in the Mount Boglia–Mount Bre region, which caused a horizontal push in the upper strata.

The Bergamasc section shows how the Triassic limestones, detached along the gypsiferous dolomites of the Lower Triassic, glided down from a higher step onto a lower one in front. In the frontal portion of the Camino thrust we find exposed the transition zone from a calcareous facies of the Middle Triassic to a marl facies. Evidently the motion again originated in a fold cut by a thrust, located on the wedging edge of this limestone; the thrust plane cut through the Lower Triassic limestones to the incompetent gypsiferous layer. Once started, the structure glided down on the lower step. There can be little doubt that the general compression, which caused steep thrusts in the northern and highest region, and the doming of the basement in the central step were contributing factors as well as the vertical upwarping of the successive steps, which originated the height differences and the resulting slopes.

Southern Border of the Pyrenees. The southern border of the Pyrenees offers many similar gliding nappes, mostly of small dimensions. The best known one is doubtless the cascade folds of Mount Perdu (Fig. 219). The sedimentary cover of the Palaeozoic basement consists here of Senonian and Eocene. In this section we find first of all a sub-horizontal thrust of the basement rock from north to south due

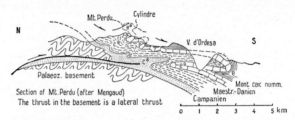

Fig. 219.   Combination of thrust and cascade fold on southern slope of Pyrenees. *(After Mengaud, Bulletin de la Carte Géologique de France, no. 199, 1939.)*

to lateral thrust. Below the thrust mass a thin band of Upper Cretaceous has been preserved. The thrusting movement piled up the upper Senonian and Eocene blanket rocks in front of the nose of the basement thrust, and they started to glide down, forming a cascade of folds, the lowermost one being a large recumbent fold exposed in the Ordesa River. The lateral thrust and the gravitational gliding both operated at the same time, the first causing the second.

A recumbent fold with a complete reversed flank, as encountered in this section, can be considered typical for gliding tectonics under circumstances in which a considerable difference in altitude between the two blocks is most important. A reversed flank which has not been drawn out to the extreme or simply replaced by a thrust-fault, or a combination of these two phenomena, is impossible in an ordinary overthrust anticline, because the result of lateral thrust is to produce a considerable shortening without accumulating too much mass in a vertical direction, gravity preventing a trebling of the load. When on the other hand the sedimentary rock series is gliding down a slope, the result is to fill up a marginal trough with rock masses from a higher altitude; thus gravity is not opposed to a multiplication of the original thickness of the sedimentary strata — on the contrary, gravity will favour it (Fig. 227). Hence when the strata are sufficiently plastic, they may form a cascade of folds in which the larger ones are recumbent folds whose reversed flanks are not attenuated. The recumbent fold of the Grand Morgon (Fig. 220), mapped by Schneegans (1938) is a good example of this kind of structure. In that region we find two incompetent layers along which the higher beds have been detached, the Triassic at the bottom of the section and the Callovian-Oxfordian shales in the middle. In the Grand Morgon area both have been active.

All along the southern border of the Pyrenees we find gliding structures which have been mapped, however, without a view to gliding tectonics, and therefore are sometimes difficult to represent in a section. From Mount Perdu in the west to the "nappes" of Mount

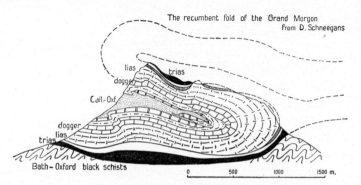

Fig. 220.   Inverted middle limb of recumbent syncline due to gliding, preserved in gliding nappe of Ubaye-Embrunais, French Alps. *(After Schneegans. Published by permission of Service de la Carte Géologique.)*

Grillera in the east, we find these isolated klippen of older formations on the lower Eocene, sometimes doubled, always underlain by a thin slice of Triassic. In Mount Grillera (Fig. 221) we even have three superposed slices, and in the Montsech we find a slice of Palaeozoic rocks on the Triassic.

All those gravitational gliding structures reflect two circumstances, to wit, the presence of an extremely incompetent layer at the base of the Mesozoic mantle — the argillaceous Keuper — and very pronounced post-folding uplift along a narrow zone causing a rather steep slope, locally accompanied by thrusting as in Mount Perdu.

Helvetian Nappes of the Alps. The Helvetian nappes are without doubt the largest coherent gliding masses which have been described as such. In order to understand their mechanism I should like to recall the series of overthrusts exposed in the Charleroi coal basin of the Ardennes (Fig. 193).

We may imagine that subsequent to this folding the rear could have been lifted up to a certain degree, tilting the thrust planes to a horizontal position and even further to a northward slope. If such vertical

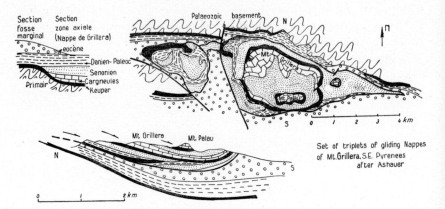

Fig. 221. Set of triplets of small gliding nappes of Mount Grillera, southern slope of Pyrenees; plan, stratigraphic section, and tectonic section. *(After Ashauer, Akad. Wiss. Göttingen. Math.-Phys. Kl., Abh. F. 3, Heft 10. 1934.)*

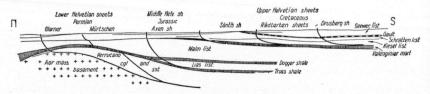

Fig. 222. Reconstruction of the original sedimentary basin of Helvetian nappes between the Aar and Gotthard massifs. Incompetent layers (Valenginian marl, Dogger shale, Triassic shale, and evaporites) alternate with competent layers (Cretaceous limestone, Malm limestone, Liassic limestone, Permian conglomerate, and sandstone). Thinning out of competent layers against basement ridge of Aar massif has caused splitting up of mass by low-angle thrust planes into future Upper. Middle. and Lower Helvetian thrust sheets, which later, after uplift of the Gotthard massif, glided down the northern slope of the Aar massif.

movement had been accompanied by a further slight contraction, the same thrusts would have been reactivated, and in all probability one sheared-off thrust mass after the other would have glided downwards along the slope of their pre-existing thrust planes. Three nappes would result, piled one on the other in the marginal trough farther north which would have originated during the uplift of the central part of the folded basin. As our imagined uplift started somewhere to the rear of the thrust masses it is evident that the southernmost thrust anticline would have started gliding first and successively the other ones would have followed suit as the uplift moved forward. The frontal ones might thus have carried the rear ones forward on their backs.

If we turn now to the Helvetian nappes and first consider their respective position in the still undisturbed position before folding, we find that each of the three principal units, the Upper, Middle, and Lower Helvetian nappes is characterized by its own stratigraphical sequence (Fig. 222). The Upper nappes show a Cretaceous sequence with a thick competent limestone wedging out towards its front, the Middle nappes are characterized by a Liassic limestone also wedging out in the same direction, and finally the Lower nappes consist primarily of Permo-Triassic and are located on wedges of Malm limestone and Verrucano (Permian). The rear of the thrust planes are located respectively in the incompetent Valenginian, Upper Triassic, and basal Permian, the fronts are located on the wedges of competent strata. Each thrust plane forced the next one in front of it down, with the result that in the rear all thrust planes converged on the same basal shearing-plane below the Permian and above the crystalline basement. Wherever a rearward thrust plane cuts obliquely downwards to the same shearing-plane as that of the next thrust plane in front, it first forces the frontal one down to another, lower gliding plane which, however, soon became inactive because it had been cut off from its own rear.

Strong compression narrowed the Helvetian basin between the Aar and Gotthard massifs, and the thrust anticlines were piled one above the other against the south flank of the Aar massif. Subsequent uplift in the rear started them gliding down the northern slope of the Aar massif, accompanied by more chaotic gliding and shearing of the sedimentary cover of this massif (Fig. 212).

We are obviously not able to trace the events in detail but can point out only some general features of the mechanism, in which gliding down is probably continuously or rhythmically accompanied by compression.

When the trough into which the nappes came tumbling down was particularly deep, the frontal noses were partly overturned, as in the section along the Axen road on the Lake of Luzern (Fig. 223). Where

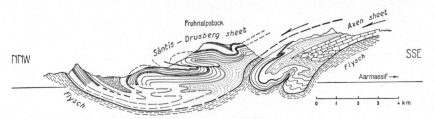

Fig. 223.   The piling up of the Upper and Middle Helvetian sheets in the marginal trough of the Alps, north of the Aar massif. *(After Heim, "Geologie der Schweiz", I. B., III Hauptteil, 1921.)*

thick masses of conglomerates had accumulated already in the Molasse trough, the frontal lobes were arrested sooner than where the late-tectonic molasse sediment was less coarse and less massive.

It is impossible to evaluate the amount of erosion that preceded the gliding mechanism, but I do not think that erosion ever was an important factor because the nappes themselves were never carried away by denudation while at the top of the slope, nor was the autochthonous cover on the northern flank of the Aar massif, and the trough was a place of sedimentation and not of denudation.

Montagne Noire. An instructive case for which gliding tectonics has been proposed is represented by the southern Palaeozoic zone of the Montagne Noire, of which the general geology is described by Gèze (1949) and the gliding tectonics by Trümpy and de Sitter (Gèze, de Sitter, and Trümpy, 1952). The Palaeozoic block of the Montagne Noire in southern France is the south-western prolongation of the Massif Central and is separated only by the small gap of the Corbières from the massif de Mouthoumet, which is considered a part of the Pyrenees.

The Montagne Noire consists of a central massif of gneiss and granite surrounded on all sides by Palaeozoic sediments ranging from Lower Cambrian to Lower Carboniferous (Fig. 224). To the north and south-east the Cambrian and Ordovician, with occasionally some Silurian, is thrust in an imbricated structure against the ancient massif, but to the south of the central massif we find a series of folds

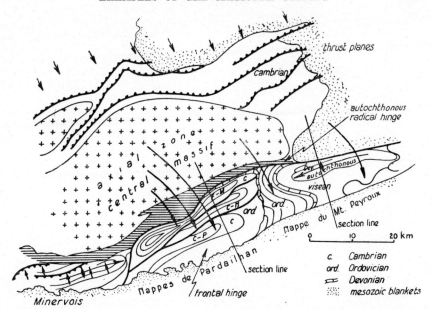

Fig. 224. Tectonic sketch map of Montagne Noire, southern France.
*(After Gèze, de Sitter, and Trümpy, Bulletin de la Société Géologique de France,
sér. 6, t. 11, 1952.)*

which are all, except in the west, characterized by the curious fact
that the whole sequence is reversed. In the core of synclines we find
the Lower Cambrian and the flanks contain Ordovician and further
to the east the Devonian covers the Visean schists. The whole zone
is some 20 km wide and thrice as long (Fig. 225).

The stratigraphic sequence consists of two competent zones, viz.
the Devonian limestones and dolomites, and the Lower and Middle
Cambrian limestones and sandstones, separated, covered, and underlain
by incompetent zones of great thickness, viz: the Visean shales above,
the Ordovician slates and schists in between, and the Lower Cambrian
and Pre-Cambrian schists below. All formations are well dated by a
classical fauna.

Whatever the course of events has been, it is obvious that in order
to overturn completely a thick series of sediments a considerable
trough must have been formed south of the central mass before and
during the folding process, which was subsequently filled by the
overturned folds, of which we now see only the reversed flank.

As explained below, the development of a reversed flank is already
strong evidence for gravity tectonics, and since we see exposed here

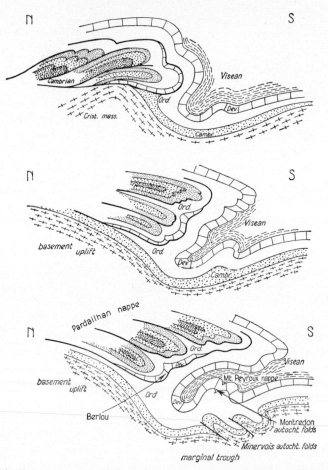

Fig. 225. Development of Montagne Noire gliding nappes according to de Sitter and Trümpy. The three superposed units, Pardailhan nappe, Mount Peyroux nappe, and autochthonous Minervois folds, are, in fact, nowhere present in one section. Hence this section represents a combination of sections along the two lines indicated in Fig. 224.

the inclined gliding surface, I have little doubt that the reversed synclines and anticlines of the southern border of the Montagne Noire are indeed due to a southward gliding of the sedimentary blanket down the south flank of the central massif. To be sure, Gèze originally thought and still thinks that the folds have a southern origin; his view and the alternative here presented are contrasted in a joint paper by Gèze, de Sitter, and Trümpy (1952).

The southern border consists of three units. The western one, the Minervois, consists of normal steeply folded anticlines pressed against the buttress of the central massif; the central one, the Pardailhan nappe, is formed by three longitudinal reversed Cambrian synclines floating in a mass of Ordovician schists, and the eastern one has an autochthonous anticlinal core of Devonian, the Montredon anticline, covered by an arch of Visean shales overlain by Devonian and Ordovician, together called the Mount Peyroux nappe. There is a strong westward plunge so that the Pardailhan nappe covers the Mount Peyroux nappe, the two being separated by a narrow squeezed-out band of Devonian limestone in Ordovician schists.

Evidently the two nappes, which are formed of totally different series of sediments, represent two portions of the same blanket, sheared off in turn from the crest of the central massif. The upper part of the blanket, consisting of Visean and Devonian with a basal shearing-plane in the incompetent Ordovician, forms the Mount Peyroux nappe, and it is covered by the Cambrian core of what was originally the same blanket, now forming the Pardailhan nappe. Most probably the shearing off started as a series of thrust-faults on top of the still submerged central mass, identical with the structures still preserved north and east of the central mass. The basal shearing-plane of the upper nappe cut obliquely through the Devonian with the result that the frontal lobe of the lower nappe still retained a broad wedge of this limestone on top, which now still forms the base of the Pardailhan nappe.

The three Cambrian synclines of the Pardailhan nappe were originally three fronts of thrust-faulted anticlines which slid down one after the other, the originally southernmost one first, being nearest to the edge of the central mass. The frontal nose of the last one is still preserved, and the innermost contact of the whole nappe against the central mass shows all the characteristics of a squeezed-out, stretched, and broken middle limb.

The disharmony between the Devonian-Visean cover and the Cambrian core is emphasized by the fact that the former is now found as one undivided inverted sheet whereas the latter is formed by three separate synclinal folds. It seems probable that this disharmony had already originated in the early phase of folding and thrusting, the Cambrian bed in three separate thrust anticlines penetrating into the Ordovician slates and schists whereas the Devonian limestone with Visean shales on top sheared off in a single large blanket along the top of the Ordovician (Fig. 225). This kind of structure was called an intercutaneous thrust by Fallot (1949). (cf. Fig. 188.)

When the whole structure started gliding down along the newly formed south-facing slope, a large slab of Devonian limestones came into a vertical position, measuring from top to bottom the total height difference between trough and horst. It rested with its back against a Visean syncline and was pushed down and outwards by the advancing Cambrian structures embedded in the Ordovician schists. In this way the mechanism of the nappes can be imagined without having to postulate an unrolling of the Devonian limestone, the width of the Mount Peyroux being about equal to the total subsidence of the marginal trough.

The whole structure resembled very much the plunging fronts of the Axen and Säntis-Drusberg nappes on Lake Luzern (Fig. 223).

Northern Apennines. The most grandiose example of gliding tectonics that has ever been imagined is that of the north Apennines. The geology is extremely difficult to unravel because of the lack of distinctive formations with distinctive fossils, but the effort of three Italian geologists, Trevisan (1950) from Pisa, Merla (1951) and Migliorini from Florence, have finally resulted in a comprehensible general picture, in which gliding tectonics and vertical movements play a dominant role. Long before these geologists formulated their point of view it was known that great portions of both the calcareous core of the northern Apennines, the Apuane Alps, and its extensive northern flank, the northern Apennines, *s. str.*, were overthrusted in an abnormal position. The lubricating formation is the Argille scagliose, or scaly shale, a chaotic shale-marl formation characterized by chunks of greenstones (ophiolites), red radiolarites, jaspers (diaspiri), and limestones. The cover consists of a series of beautifully graded sandstones, the Macigno, and a marl-sandstone sequence, which floats in large masses on the Argille scagliose. As the Macigno-Argille scagliose sequence occurs both west and east of the Apuane Alps, whereas this core itself is free of any ophiolitic intrusion, it has been suggested both by the older school of lateral thrusting and by the modern school of gliding tectonics that the origin of the Argille scagliose sedimentary basin must be sought in the Tyrrhenian Sea between Corsica and Elba. The major objection to a lateral thrust mass of 200 km width is its extreme thinness and its general incompetent character which by no stretch of imagination can be thought able to transmit the stress needed to transport the whole as one coherent mass. The new point of view therefore supposes that the original deep sea basin in which the Argille scagliose accumulated was situated between the islands of Elba and Corsica, and that the shale was pressed out by an east-west lateral thrust, flowing over its borderland far to the east. Afterwards a first zone of upwarping on the eastern border of the original basin, now covered by a thick mass of the Argille scagliose that had been pressed out, made it slide down farther towards the east. This mechanism of upheaval of longitudinal anticlinal ridges was repeated five times, each successive ridge being situated farther to the east. Each time the plastic mass of Argille scagliose glided down the eastern flank of the new ridge and was thus displaced further eastwards. During its repeated movements, its original content of clay, ophiolites, and radiolarites became diluted with strange elements of much younger date, of which the more coherent portions moved as great slabs and the softer formations like shales and marls simply became mixed up with the original shale content. In this way the relative decrease of the ophiolite content of the Argille scagliose in an eastern direction finds a ready explanation.

Several objections against this rather sweeping theory of gliding can be made. First of all, if one abandons the theory of lateral thrust over 200 km and accepts gliding to explain the superposition of the Argille scagliose on younger strata, it seems illogical still to postulate such enormous transportation. Secondly, the whole mechanism of the 200 km transportation would break down if one of the ridges rose before its turn, thus stopping all further eastward transport. Thirdly, the ridges are very different in tectonical style. The first ridge on Western Elba is a Miocene granite intrusion, the second ridge is represented by the insufficiently exposed synclinal structure of Spezia containing Triassic and Liassic, the third ridge is the large arch of the Apuane Alps in which a thrust sheet of non-metamorphic limestones of considerable size overlies highly metamorphic marbles of the same age (Lower Mesozoic) (Fig. 226), the fourth and fifth ridges consist of more or less simply compressed domes in Oligocene strata, locally with Liassic cores, much broken by steep thrusts of the kind called "composite wedges" by Migliorini, (1948) (cf. Fig. 197). Personally I think that the Italian investigators have underrated to some extent the intrusive capacity of such an incompetent formation as the Argille scagliose under lateral compression, producing simple diapiric action. Much of the abnormal position of this formation must certainly be due to gliding down appropriate slopes, but much may be due

Fig. 226. Section through Apuane Alps and Northern Apennines, showing third ridge — Apuane Alps in the core of the Apennines — and the fourth ridge of quite different structure. (After Merla. *Published by permission of Società Geologica Italiana.*)

also to lateral compression, squeezing out, and diapiric intrusions. This implies of course that originally more than one deep sea basin with ophiolite intrusions existed, most probably both east and west of the central core, the Apuane Alps, the latter being free from these ophiolitic intrusions. The intensive mixing of younger and older strata, the gliding down of great slabs, the inserted position of some of these slabs and their frontal noses (which can be ascertained most convincingly by the graded facies of the Macigno sandstones) are facts which very strongly suggest gliding as the origin of many of the structures; on the other hand, the steep thrusts bounding the ridges suggest strong lateral compression through the whole width of the northern Apennines. The combination of the two structural theories evidently leads to the conception that the gliding followed the compression and is due to the upheaval of the longitudinal ridges.

CHARACTERISTICS OF GLIDING STRUCTURES

The main question that arises from our survey of gliding structures is: How can one distinguish between a lateral low-angle thrust and a gliding nappe? As always in geology the answer cannot be conclusive. There is no structural feature that can be decisive in either direction, but the evidence must necessarily be of a circumstantial nature. To my mind the most important evidence consists of:

1. An appropriate slope must be recognizable in the field to account for any gliding. One may of course reason, in case such a slope is absent, that the original slope has been destroyed since the gliding by the sinking of its highest portion, and if such oscillation can be proved by independent evidence, the reasoning may be sound, but in general it can hardly be accepted. For instance, a gravitational gliding of the Jura Mountains towards the north, as suggested by Lugeon and Gagnebin, against its present slope seems highly improbable. Marginal troughs of orogenic belts seem to be the most favourable recipients of gliding nappes.

2. A downward plunge of the basal thrust plane at the rear of the thrust sheet can be regarded as conclusive evidence of its thrust nature.

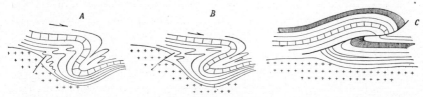

Fig. 227. Contrast between structures produced by gravitational gliding (A, B) and by lateral thrust (C). A middle limb is preserved unthinned in gliding but is absent in thrusting.

The upward curve one would expect in a gliding nappe will seldom be conserved except in small-scale gliding like that of the volcanic mantles described in the foregoing pages. As many gliding structures originated as thrust sheets, a downward curve may be present at the rear even in the case of gliding, but then it can no longer be directly connected with the frontal lobes.

3. An inverted position of a large mass, in particular when it is not laminated or squeezed or otherwise tectonically reduced in thickness, is strong evidence of the gliding nature of the transport mechanism (Fig. 227.) A real thrust sheet has no inverted flank; it is the result of maximum lateral shortening with a minimum of piling up of strata, a compromise between the lateral stress and gravity. Whereas gravity prevents the development of an inverted flank in the case of the thrust sheet, it favours its formation in the case of a gliding nappe because in the latter case the ultimate aim of gliding is the filling up of a pre-existing trough. See Figs. 212, 216, 217, 218, 219, and 223 as compared with Figs. 190, 192, and 193.

4. In general, a chaotic or even a geometrically obscure structure

may be an indication of gliding because each portion of the gliding nappe may move independently of the other, each being under the same gravitational stress as the other. On the other hand, in a thrust sheet the stress must necessarily be conveyed from one end of the sheet to the other by a coherent and competent mass, and any failure would result in the standstill of the portion beyond the failure. Therefore isolated slabs, often anticlinal or synclinal in shape, of competent rocks in an incompetent matrix are valuable indications for later gliding following on former lateral-thrust folding.

5. In the smaller-scale gliding structures the lateral extension of the structure is ordinarily small and has no connexion with its surroundings, whereas in lateral-thrust structures the opposite is true. This is so because the gliding may be due to the hazards of erosion in the lower reaches of the slope or to other irregularities, whereas the thrust structures can move only when a large portion of the crust is in a stressed condition.

From the general outlook on gravitational gliding tectonics we have now gained, there is one fact that emerges clearly, to wit, the close relation between gliding tectonics on a larger scale and lateral compression. In all instances which I quoted, the southern Pyrenees and the southern Alps, the Montagne Noire, the Apennines, and the Helvetian nappes, we found that the structures started as thrust sheets, that the upheaval that caused the slope was probably due to compression, and that the gliding tectonics are only an accompanying feature. The cascade fold of the Mount Perdu is the direct result of a deeper-seated thrust revealed in the same section. The original thrusts on top of the central massif of the Montagne Noire are still preserved on its eastward-plunging nose, and the nappes of the southern Alps override thrust structures abutting against the very thrust faults which limit the upthrusted block from which the nappes glided down. The roofs of the Helvetian nappes compressed between the Aar and Gotthard massifs are as real as the piling up of their frontal noses in the marginal trough, and finally the ridges between the troughs filled with Argille scagliose and Macigno slabs are surely compressional features.

Hence there can be no doubt that the lateral compression is primary, the gliding secondary. This evidence suggests strongly that the vertical movements which give rise to the slope are also due to lateral stress. This close relation between gravitational gliding and tangential compression explains also why there is no clear-cut limit between the two phenomena. In all the larger structures which we described it is very much a question of taste how much one believes should be accounted for by thrusting and how much by gliding. We find this transition not only between thrusting and gliding but also between slumping and gliding. The slip-planes in the non-folded sediments of the Peru oilfield show many characteristics of slumping, and their origin is due to the same kind of circumstances as slumping, viz. a soft formation saturated with water. The difference is not only a question of size and state of consolidation but also of origin of the slope. In slumping no earth movements of structural character are supposed to have created the slope, whereas the blocks in the marginal trough of the Andes in Peru are believed to have been tilted by movements along longitudinal faults.

In the case of gliding in a volcanic mantle there is no longer even any real difference in origin from slumping, for both are due to accumulation of sedimentary materials; their distinguishing feature is only that in one case the process took place under water and in the other not.

Gravity is certainly not a force that plays a role in tectonics only occasionally; it is always present and always influences any structural shape, whether we think of folds, faults, or gliding.

The extent to which the conception of gliding tectonics changes our views on the structural characteristics of mountain chains is rather important in one aspect. Formerly any klippe meant to us that large-scale horizontal thrusting had occurred and therefore that the particular mountain chain had been submitted to important lateral compression. Such a conclusion is no longer warranted. The supposition that the Helvetian nappes and the klippe nappes have gained their present position by gliding certainly means a considerable reduction of the formerly supposed total lateral shortening of the cross-section of the Alps. The same is true for the Argille scagliose gliding nappes of the Apennines and for many other less well-known structures. A klippe is no longer a proof of strong compression.

Chapter 20

Syntectonic and Post-Tectonic Sediments

SYNTECTONIC AND POST-TECTONIC SEDIMENTS

Whereas structural geology is concerned with the forms and history of the deformation of the earth's crust, sedimentology studies the consequences of these deformations. Every disturbance of a hypothetical completely flat earth-surface has its repercussion on sedimentation, by the creation on the one hand of the source of the detritus, and on the other of the depositional environment. Seen from this point of view, every sediment is wholly determined by structural events. But in general we accept the environmental circumstances which determine the facies of a sediment as being static, and determine its structural control as the variations imposed on it by the ever-changing structural conditions. Thus we arrive at a classification of static environmental conditions based on facies characteristics, and try to interpret the variations of the facies in structural terms. The classification of environment is primarily the distinction of continental, littoral, epineritic, infraneritic, bathyal, and abyssal environments; whereas structural control is expressed in terms of stable and unstable shelves, inter-cratonic basins and geosynclinal conditions. From a structural point of view this procedure is not quite satisfactory, because it does not take into consideration the fact that environment is not conditioned only by the negative and positive movements imposed on it by its own structural history, but also by the structural history of the adjoining or surrounding regions. This is true in particular for the orogenic belts, where it makes a great difference whether the sediment is deposited in the early geosynclinal stage, in the late geosynclinal or early orogenic stage, or in the post-orogenic stage. The classification above is valid for the geosynclinal stages of an orthogeosyncline and for inter-cratonic basins, but does not bring into sufficient relief the orogenic and post-orogenic stages of sedimentation, which are of primary importance from a structural point of view.

The main divisions of a structural classification of sediments should read:

1. Orogenic facies:
   a. Syn-orogenic — or grauwacke — flysch facies
   b. Post-orogenic — or molasse facies

2. Epeirogenic facies:
   a. Epicontinental facies
   b. Geosynclinal facies

OROGENIC FACIES

The Syn-Orogenic Facies Type (or Flysch facies, partly due to turbidity currents). Originally the term Flysch indicated only a stratigraphical stage from the Alpine chain, but since it has been proved that the stratigraphical limits of the Flysch as a lithologic unit vary considerably, and that the facies is bound to a certain phase of the Alpine orogeny, it has become increasingly used as a term in the sequence: "Schistes lustrés" (geosynclinal bathyal facies) — Flysch (orogenic facies) — Molasse (post-orogenic facies), (Marcel Bertrand, 1897, Arbenz, 1919). These terms express the close relation between sedimentation and orogenic processes. This has become such a widespread usage that Scandinavian geologists, for instance, discussing Pre-Cambrian geology, try to outline their otherwise undated orogenic periods by establishing the chronological sequence of the flysch and molasse facies. It is therefore of the utmost importance to understand the flysch facies type and its orogenic significance, which has been described by Tercier (Tercier, 1948, p. 166) as "the facies which just precedes the main paroxysmal phase of a mountain chain," in contrast with the molasse facies which "is bound to the terminal phase of mountain building". Because the type locality of the Flysch facies is the Alps, a Tertiary orogeny of the Mediterranean type (see Chapter 26), it has all the local characteristics of this kind of orogeny, and therefore a considerable divergence of this Flysch facies can be expected in other kinds of orogenies. This is particularly true for older orogenies (Hercynian and Pre-Cambrian) and for circum-Pacific orogenies, both having much stronger volcanic phases.

The main characteristic of the Flysch facies is its detrital contents, which largely predominate over organogenic deposits, resulting in an alternation of micaceous sandstones and shales with much rarer marls and limestones. It is essentially a thick formation of purely marine origin, with a facies ranging from neritic to bathyal. The alternation of sandstones and shales, mostly very regular and monotonous, is its most prominent characteristic. The sandstones are micaceous, often arkosic and graded. Cross-bedding and ripple marks are rare. Thick sequences are often almost barren of fossils, and when these are found they are often derived from other formations. Glauconite is frequently found. Conglomerates are scarce but when they occur they replace sandstone zones. They are not restricted to the base of the formation, and are always polygenic. Breccias are sometimes frequent in certain zones and their rock fragments may attain unusually large dimensions. They are derived from cliff erosion, and do not originate in wave-disturbance of a bottom sediment; nor have they the characteristics of transgression breccias. The shaly rocks are often mudstones and always occur in alternation with the sandstones. Although the rocks are in general well bedded, they are badly sorted, because they are derived directly from erosion of a rising cordillera and are not reworked and redeposited by wave-disturbance. Their depth of deposition was below wave or surface current influence except near the steep coastal slope. (For more details I refer the reader to the article by Tercier, 1948.)

The structural environment is perhaps best defined as the paroxysmal phase of the geosynclinal prelude to the orogeny, which at the same time is the incipient phase of the orogenic paroxysm. The orthogeosyncline has been narrowed and split into several geosynclinal basins, between which island arcs and rows are warped up. Erosion of the quickly rising cordilleras is violent; the basins are rapidly subsiding; the littoral facies is deposited next to the bathyal facies without the intervention of a shelf facies. The strikingly regular alternation of micaceous sandstones and shales is at first rather an unexpected feature of a relatively unstable process of sedimentation. The explanation of this feature, which is always combined with grading of the sandstones, has been given by Kuenen and Migliorini (1950) in their work on turbidity currents. Kuenen arrived at his conclusion from experiments with mudflows in the laboratory, Migliorini from observation of the typical Flysch facies of the Macigno in the Northern Apennines. The principle of the origin of turbidity currents is that the rapid accumulation of detrital matter on a continental slope is again and again interrupted by gravitational sliding. Once the labile equilibrium of the thick, water-saturated, and loosely packed sediment is broken, a catastrophic reaction sets in by the sudden decrease of the grain pressure (as explained in Chapter 2), and immense masses become involved in a mudstream flowing downwards towards the basin centre. In this flowing mass of large density, sand and clay are mixed by turbulence until the mass reaches the bottom of the basin. Sedimentation then begins with the deposition of the larger and heavier grains which have accumulated at the nose of the flow, followed by finer material behind the nose, on account of decrease in the velocity of the current. Thus a lateral grading in the turbidity current which develops during its motion downhill results in a vertical grading in the deposited bed. The sorting in the graded bed is poor at every level because of the relatively high percentage of mud which forms an essential constituent of every turbidity current. One of these turbidity currents can cover a large area with a uniformly graded bed several metres thick. The normal sedimentation of clay in the basin centre continues until the next turbidity current caused by further marginal-slope accumulation sets in. The absence of large-scale current-bedding, the grauwacke facies, the absence of ripple marks, and above all the grading, are adequately explained by this process. The turbidity current may not be restricted to the typical Flysch facies; it may occur in the geosynclinal stage.

The concept has revolutionized our ideas about bathyal and neritic facies. According to Haug (1900), the typical bathyal facies was the limestone-marl alternation, and the typical neritic facies the sandstone-shale alternation. It was later realized that limestones are formed primarily on the shelf and indicate an epicontinental neritic facies; the bathyal facies was thus robbed of its most typical constituent. It has now been replaced by the Flysch facies; the filling up of rapidly subsiding basins has become intelligible and the sequence of sedimentation has become much clearer.

The Post-Orogenic or Molasse Facies. An analogue to the development of the term Flysch can be found in the term Molasse, which first meant a definite stratigraphical stage, then a facies of the northern marginal trough of the Alps, and then gradually became used for a general facies type related to the orogenic history of a mountain chain.

In most of its characteristics it is in complete contrast to the Flysch. Irregular bedding, predominance of conglomerates and sandstones, continental or fresh water environment, and frequent cross-bedding and ripple marks are its most prominent properties.

Nevertheless the Alpine Molasse is so closely associated to the Flysch that its lowest member, the Rupelian (Lower Oligocene), shows an almost imperceptible transition into the Rupelian of the top layers of the Flysch. It definitely belongs to the last phase of the orogeny, characterized by the upheaval of the central geosynclinal basin and accompanied by formation of a marginal trough. Gradually, the area of sedimentation was shifted from the centre to the margin, a process which continued to act throughout the sedimentary phase of the marginal trough. The last sediment of the central basin is therefore the same as the first sediment of the marginal trough.

A marginal trough is a decidedly asymmetric basin during its whole history. The *internal* margin, i.e. *facing* the original central portion of the geosyncline, is always sinking more rapidly than the external margin, which merges with the continental platform (see Fig. 303). Hence its external margin has many characteristics in common with the margins of inter-cratonic or geosynclinal basins, but its opposite border, the *internal* margin, is quite different and typical of the Molasse facies.

A prominent property of the Molasse facies is therefore its rapid facies change in a direction perpendicular to the basin axis. On the *internal* margin we find enormous accumulations of conglomerates, often interstratified with sands, sometimes with lignites and fresh water deposits of small dimensions. They rapidly change, however, into thick, often red-coloured sands and shales with evaporites (gypsum, anhydrite, salt, etc.), becoming more fine grained further away from the central chain. The conglomerates contain a considerable proportion. of crystalline rocks furnished by the erosion of the deeper migmatic horizons of the central chain.

The facies change parallel to the basin axis is also very marked. In the Alps the internal margin of the Molasse basin is characterized by a string of conglomeratic deltas, each marking a depression, or saddle, in the axial chain structure. In the same way the red-coloured Devonian delta representing the post-Caledonian Molasse of the Appalachian mountain chain marks the axial depression between the maritime provinces and the Appalachians proper. As most of these sediments are transported and deposited by rapidly flowing streams, they show strong current-bedding and frequent ripple marking. The Molasse, in contrast to the Flysch, shows massive sedimentation of particular types of rock, conglomerates on the internal margin, sandstones in the centre. The Molasse and the Flysch have in common the fact that enormous thicknesses have been deposited in a restricted time interval, in contrast to the pre-orogenic facies which is equally thick or thicker but needs a much longer time for its accumulation.

The Molasse facies of the Hercynian orogenies, the Permian, is characterized by a strongly developed volcanic component. The same is true for the circum-Pacific chains; there also the Flysch facies has a pronounced volcanic aspect. In Part III this fundamental difference in the character of the orogenies of the Mediterranean and the circum-Pacific belt will be further worked out. In the Pre-Cambrian orogenies the dominance of magmatic and volcanic phases during the whole history of their structural development tends to obliterate the facies differences between the geosynclinal — Flysch — and Molasse phases; there is continuous preponderance of arkosic rocks, in all three phases.

EPEIROGENIC AND GEOSYNCLINAL FACIES

The two types of structural basin, on the one hand geosynclines and on the other inter-cratonic basins, have much in common. As I shall explain later, in Chapter 24, the real orthogeosyncline differs from the "basin" principally in the fact that the first has been submitted to a later orogenic deformation and the second has not. Obviously this does not *a priori* make any difference to their sedimentary history. We shall see also that basins, geosynclinal or not, may either be asymmetric, formed on the margin of a continent, or symmetric, i.e. on the continent. The second kind is the inter-cratonic basin. This makes a great difference in their sedimentary history. The asymmetric basin receives its sedimentary material from one side only. Its thickest accumulation will be on the continental slope, and when it becomes a geosyncline it may develop volcanic arcs on its ocean-bounded side. Furthermore, the incipient stage may be marine, just as its final stage, though this is not necessarily the case. In contrast with the circum-continental basins the inter-cratonic basin always starts and finishes with a continental facies. Transgressions and regressions play an important role on the continental margins of both types of basin.

Their most typical characteristic is the epicontinental calcareous facies, and in particular its epineritic subdivision (i.e. from 10–40 m depth of water). Biohermal limestones on the littoral side or on ridges, and biostromal limestones on the shallow shelf are the most typical members of the epineritic facies, witnessing the quiescence of its environment. Slow sedimentation with no strong relief nearby are the predominant conditions. The long time interval during which this sedimentation continues and the slow but unbroken subsidence of the basin, make it possible for very large thicknesses of sediments to accumulate. The stratification is usually well marked, the beds being well sorted by wave and current action. Quartzites, marls, and mud-stones predominate. The prevailing shallow depth of the sea means that slight changes in coastlines or depth are immediately expressed in their fossil content by faunal breaks. The lithology of the limestone is also very sensitive to any depth change. These conditions, continuous sedimentation, and sharp faunal and lithological changes, mean that the epicontinental facies is the "dorado" of the stratigrapher. The epineritic facies is also the domain of cyclic sedimentation, either in facies of coal-bearing sequences, or in marine cycles of limestone-marl-shale and sandstone.

A characteristic which is of major importance for oil accumulation is the facies changes which take place from the margin of the basin to its centre. In the centre the finer grained clay accumulations are the source rock of oil; and the sand-tongues that enter the centre from the margins are the natural conduits of the oil, liberated from the shales by compaction through the ever increasing load of new sediments. The reef limestones on the margins of the basin offer the same possibilities in slightly different circumstances. Their detritus accumulates in front of the reefs and stretches out far into the basin centre where the oil is generated, thus giving it its access to its later reservoir. Towards the border of the basin the formations wedge out, either by regressional or by transgressional processes, bearing witness to the rhythm of the advancing and retreating shore line, and building up reservoir rocks for oil in the form of beach-sand ridges and similar sedimentary traps.

The epineritic facies is not only the domain of carbon and hydrocarbon accumulation, it is also the environment of accumulation of sedimentary iron, manganese, and phosphorus. Ferruginous sandstones, either in the form of iron oxide coating quartz grains, or in the form of pisolitic iron oxide concretions, are typical of the stable shelf. Its manganese counterpart is more restricted to the continental margin of the shelf. The large thick phosphorite accumulations of North Africa and elsewhere, on the contrary, are related to somewhat deeper water conditions than the iron-bearing sandstones. The curious fact that only one particular element — carbon, iron, manganese, or phosphorus — is predominant in one particular kind of neritic facies of stable conditions due to its immediate environment is understandable. But why it should be bound to one particular stratigraphical stage, as often happens, is less intelligible.

As we have seen, the neritic facies occurs in two types, the sand-claystone type and the limestone-marl type, which correspond in the first place not to the immediate environment but to that of its continental surrounding. When erosion is active the supply of detrital matter prevents the development of the limestone type, which needs clear water. The two types are therefore in principle mutually exclusive, but numerous transitions of course exist.

Whereas pure quartz and sandstones are typical of the stable shelf, subgrauwackes, grauwackes, and arkoses, characterized by a certain content of felspars and micas, indicate less stable conditions. The reworking of the newly deposited sediments is less thorough, the sorting less complete. Intra-formational irregularities such as unconformities and disconformities will become more frequent. Unstable shelf conditions grade into real geosynclinal environment, where grauwackes predominate and limestones are entirely restricted to the margins. There is no fundamental difference between ordinary basin accumulations and shelf accumulations because the sea bottom itself remained more or less stable, the subsidence being matched by the accumulation of sediment. Only gradational differences exist, chiefly due to the instability of the surrounding land and the consequent variation of detrital supply, but also to variation in subsidence. The extreme type of instability is reached in the flysch facies.

One more facies of a distinctly geosynclinal character ought to be mentioned here, i.e. the bathyal clay facies represented in the Pennine Alps by the "schistes lustrés" (phyllites), in the Northern Apennines by the "Argille scagliose" or scaly shales, and in the Californian coastal geosyncline by parts of the Franciscan sequence. The clays, shales, or phyllites are characterized by the absence of bedding, by their uniform character, dark colour, and high plasticity, and above all by their remarkable association with on the one hand ultrabasic rocks and on the other by very fine-grained limestones and radiolarites.

The facies is typical of the first geosynclinal stage, and indicates a considerable deepening of the basin, before the border regions were elevated. Its association with basic rocks of the initial magmatic stage points in the same direction, since it suggests a direct connexion between the crust-substratum and the basin-bottom.

Chapter 21

Contorted Beds

CAUSE OF CONTORTION

Contorted beds, which may be regarded as microstructures restricted to particular layers, have been described from various environments. They have been attributed to widely different causes of which the following are the main types:

1. slumping and loading
2. action of ice flows
3. movement in thawed beds above a permafrost floor, so-called "cryoturbate contortion"
4. gravitational gliding
5. thrusting
6. intraformational tectonic contortion

One is nearly always justified in assuming that a decrease of the grain pressure has (in consequence of a relative increase of the hydrostatic portion of the rock pressure) played an important role in all these disturbances. The non-lithified rock then becomes a suspension of grains in water, and can flow under almost any stress-gradient. In arctic climates, for instance, near the surface, when the permafrost has been forced down a few feet or more by thaw of the surface layers, the latter may start flowing or may allow upper portions of sand to sink down into an underlying clay because the water has not yet had time to escape to the surface, and cryoturbate phenomena are the result.

Folding stress may create an extra stress above the rock pressure (thus diminishing by an equal amount the grain pressure), and in unconsolidated sediments, covered by an impermeable clay layer, the same effect may give rise to complete contortion of sands and clays with but little tectonic movement. Afterwards, when the surplus

300

water has escaped by slow filtration, the sediment regains its solid phase but preserves its thoroughly contorted aspect.

When one compares, for instance, the photographs accompanying the papers by Arkell, Barrington Brown, and Baldry (1938 volume of the Quarterly Journal of the Geological Society of London), it becomes clear that the present aspect of a contorted rock can hardly be expected to give us a clear understanding of the cause of disturbance. The structures illustrated by the first author, which are ascribed to internal movements due to Tertiary folding, show a marked similarity to those described by the latter two authors, which are convincingly attributed to the gravitational sliding of great masses of sedimentary rocks. The complete similarity of all these contortions convinces us that they have a similar origin, controlled by different factors.

Because the circumstances in which the flow takes place are almost identical, it seems unnecessary to look within the contorted beds themselves for distinguishing features indicating the stress origin, as Kuenen (1949) and Rich (1950) have done.

Nevertheless, there are some general considerations which have to be taken into account:

1. Cryoturbate contortion is necessarily limited to glacial deposits, of Quaternary or of the older ice ages.
2. When the contorted bed is also a break in the stratigraphical sequence, e.g. forms the lower boundary of a thrust-mass, its contortion is obviously due to tectonic movement, either gliding or thrusting.
3. When the contorted bed is in direct connexion with sandstone or silt "dikes", its structure cannot be due to slumping and must be due either to gliding or to folding.
4. When the contorted beds are horizontal and belong to a non-tectonized region, the contortion is obviously either slumping or loading.

LOAD STRUCTURES AND SLUMPING

Loadcasts, one of the most common basal characteristics of sandstone beds overlying shales or marls, are due to the loading of a mud deposit with a sandbed. The mud, having a lower permeability than the sand, keeps its connate water longer than the sand, has a looser packing than the sand, and has therefore a lower specific gravity. As a consequence, the sand is able to sink into it, forming basin-shaped hollows. This can happen only directly after the deposition of the lower sandbeds, because otherwise the mud would lose its surplus water content to the sand. Hence the upper part of the sandbed is not concerned in the sinking mechanism, as is shown by the fact that its surface is often perfectly plane (Fig. 228). As the mud is still oversaturated with water when the loadcastings are made, it still has a very low viscosity and a great fluidity. One might expect, therefore, that any stress-gradient, the slightest slope for instance, would result in an internal movement of the mud. That is exactly what has often been observed. The more compact sand has often moved a little as a solid sheet over its fluid substratum, deforming the loadcasts, which then show a singular asymmetry, as in Fig. 229. The horn-shaped mud intrusions between the sand-pockets are all curved in the same direction, i.e. the direction of movement of the overlying bed. When the

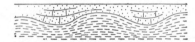
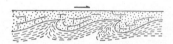

Fig. 228. Loadcast of sand in shale. Fig. 229. Loadcasts deformed by gliding of upper sandbed.

movement of the upper sandsheet is somewhat greater, the sand protuberances in the mud may be entirely severed from the overlying sandbed and form sand balls in the mud (Fig. 230).

Eventually the gliding movement of the sandsheet may be so great that the flat sand balls are turned over and even contorted themselves. All these phenomena can be observed on the cliffs of the Millstone Grit and higher Carboniferous exposures along the coasts of Pembrokeshire, from Amroth to Tenby and near Broadhaven.

The internal motion mentioned in the last paragraph is itself a kind of slumping, and further flow leads to completely slumped beds, sometimes including both the sandbed and its underlying mud deposit. Slumping is the mechanism which causes the most common type of local contortion, and is explained by the movement inside a water-saturated mud due to sliding down a slope which need not be more than a few degrees. Real slumping must take place before the deposition of the next bed, and is therefore a purely superficial phenomenon. However, there can be little doubt that slumping can happen after — and is probably even stimulated by — the deposition of an overlying sandbed, as explained above. On the Pembrokeshire coast one can even observe violent slumping in which the whole overlying sandbed of some 5–8 feet thickness becomes eventually involved in the slumping of the mudbed. It seems unreasonable to draw a distinctive line between purely superficial slumping and the same phenomenon after the deposition of another bed; on the contrary it is probable that in certain circumstances the gliding will take place only after a considerable sequence of layers has been deposited. This leads naturally to the phenomenon of gravity gliding as described by Baldry (1938) and Brown (1938) from Peru (Fig. 215).

The introduction of the concept of slumping processes into geological thought is mainly due to O. T. Jones (1937), and the definitions are due to him. Jones is anxious to avoid ascribing any contortion whatsoever to slumping, and advances as his most important criterion for real slumping that the next sandbed deposited on the slumped bed should truncate the slumped structures of the mudbed, as in Fig. 231. In cases where the gliding started only after the deposition of the next sandbed this condition cannot of course be fulfilled, and structures like those described by Rich (1950) can result, in which the types described as "anticlinal" contortions show considerable thinning of the constituting layers, but no truncation.

In such a case of slumping without truncation the contortion of

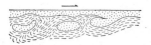

Fig. 230. Sand balls in contorted shale formed by severance of loadcasts due to gliding of upper sandbed.

Fig. 231. Slump structure. (*After Kuenen. Published by permission of the American Association of Petroleum Geologists.*)

the mudflow could just as well be due to origins other than superficial sliding down a slope. Much later folding, for instance, could have originated the same kind of internal structures.

Cryoturbate contortion is nothing but a special kind of loadcast, and there are consequently only circumstantial criteria to distinguish them as a special group. The fact that they are due to a shallow melting of a permafrost surface gives the loadcasts of this type a rather extreme development, because the contrasts in fluidity are exceptionally large.

Tectonic Contortions. They can have different origins. Limestone mylonites on thrust planes, as they have been described for instance from the base of the Helvetian thrust sheets, represent typical tectonic contortions. Such thrust sheet contortions might also be expected in the tail-end of all thrust planes of thrust anticlines, where the thrust plane runs over long distances in the same incompetent bed, as has been described in Chapter 17. There are, however, much simpler structures in which we might expect tectonic contortion in incompetent beds. In young clay sediments, where compaction has not yet got rid of much water because of the low permeability of clays, any source of additional pressure will create a great fluidity, as explained in Chapter 2. When this additional pressure is due to a lateral folding stress, the unconsolidated clay with very low viscosity will absorb most of the internal movement necessitated by the folding, and contortion will be the result. A proof that this actually occurs in many young structures is given by mud volcanoes and by silt and sandstone dikes, described from many parts of the world. The "heaving shales" encountered in bore holes, where the sudden decrease of pressure in the hole originates a mudflow towards the drill hole, often stopping all drilling operations, are another proof of the existence of extremely fluid muds at considerable depth. As long as the superfluous water cannot escape, this state of fluidity remains.

GLACIAL LOADING AND GLIDING STRUCTURES

A special case of non-tectonic disturbances is that of certain glacial structures, partly due to the loading effect of the ice sheet, partly due to the ice movement, partly to the thrust in front of the ice sheet on its unconsolidated sediments.

Many examples of contortion in strip-mined lignite beds have been described from Germany. The beds have apparently been shorn off from their basal beds by the advancing glacier and crumpled up in front of it (Fig. 232). The example gives an exceptionally good instance of oblique shear-folding.

Another section, Fig. 233, shows more rounded forms, and its basal shear is not exposed. Slater (1927a) gives many examples of extremely disturbed sections in which the bulging up of the Eocene London Clay on the floor of the glacier and the deposition of slices of London Clay, Pleistocene boulder clay, and Pleistocene sands form a very intricate pattern (Fig. 234). Slater explains the slices as being mainly due to very slow melting of the glacier, which leaves behind its own laminated structure in the form of englacial material. Thus the structure as observed now represents a fossilized glacier.

Sharp faults are also often observed in fluvio-glacial and glacial

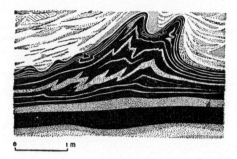

Fig. 232. Folded lignite bed in strip mine near Borna-Gnandorf.

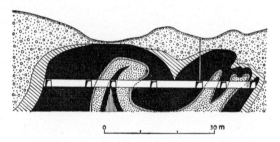

Fig. 233. Folded lignite bed from the Merkur mine near Drebkau.

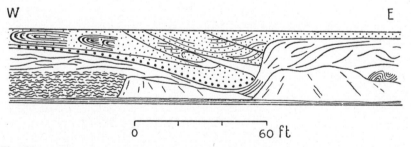

Fig. 234. Disturbed glacial drift and London clay in clay pit near Ipswich.
(After Slater, Proceedings of the Geologists' Association, vol. 38, 1927. Published by permission of the Geologists' Association.)

sands. Sometimes they are ascribed to thrusting of an ice-lobe (Fig. 235), sometimes to drag of an ice-blanket, sometimes to loading by a local ice-lobe. They could also be caused by differential sagging due to unequally distributed melting.

The whole gamut of glacial disturbances is very ably treated by Fairbridge (1947), who advances many examples from various parts of

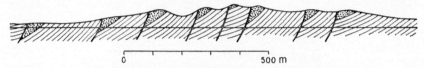

Fig. 235. Thrust structures in the Pleistocene sands of Archemerberg, Netherlands. *(After de Jong, Geol. & Mijnb., vol. 14. 1952.)*

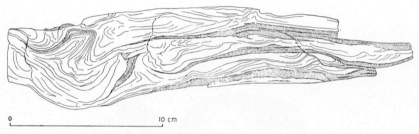

Fig. 236. Slumping in Ordovician siltstone from the Western High Atlas, Morocco.

the world and to whom I refer the reader for greater detail. He agrees with the modern view that many contortions formerly ascribed to glacial activity may be due to slumping.

A particularly instructive example of intraformational slumping is given by Fig. 236, a drawing representing a polished slab of rock from the Ordovician of the Western High Atlas in Morocco. We observe in these slices, which truncate one another, a thinning at their origin and a considerable thickening accompanied by crumpling at the end of the flow. In this micro-example the principle of slumping is admirably expressed by recurrent flows, truncating one another, each successive one gathering in speed and volume by incorporating material from its substratum and finally arriving at its end in a great turbulent whirl.

Chapter 22

Microfolds, Macrofolds, and Faults

MICROFOLDS, MACROFOLDS, AND FAULTS

In order to demonstrate the complex nature of a natural fold we will discuss two examples of microfolds, first a hand specimen microfold of chert-banded limestone, and secondly an ordinary fold from the Rheinisches Schiefergebirge (after H. Cloos, 1948). Both Cloos and myself have come to the conclusion that the complex of compression, shear, and tension phenomena, each acting in different directions, which are together responsible for the final shape of the fold, clearly demonstrates that a simple observation of one of these features situated somewhere on a large fold can never lead to any conclusion about the general character of the whole fold.

Narrow Microfold in Limestone with Chert Bands. In this fold the limestone is the incompetent rock and the chert the competent rock, but in section the limestone covers a larger surface than the relatively thin chert bands. When we consider Fig. 237 we notice that the anticlinal hinge of the triple chert band c has risen vertically quite a distance above that of the triple chert band b. This means that there has been a considerable slip in the limestone band B. The lateral stress has at the same time sharply compressed the fold of c above that of b, but the chert band d does not show this dent in the flank; it remains more or less straight. Outside c the dent is filled up by local thickening of the limestone C. A similar dent is observed in chert band a. The chert band b shows in the left flank a doubling along a vertical thrust-fault parallel to the axial plane, which certainly expresses the same upward motion as band c underwent in relation to b. In the same left flank of b we notice a series of subparallel step-faults, more or less perpendicular to the bedding. They can be understood as vertical rotational joints due to a couple acting parallel to the bed which results in tilt of the detached blocks. In the anticlinal hinge of b we

Fig. 237a.   Microfold in limestone with chert bands, Devonian, Valle de Aran, Spanish Pyrenees.

notice a slight crestal thrust due to the same upward movement as the flank thrust in the left flank.

The chert band c shows many peculiarities. In its hinge the uppermost band of the triplet shows a crestal thrust of the same kind as in chert band b, the middle chert band showing beautiful tension cracks. In the left flank we find first of all rupture due to the extra compression above the hinge of b. The chert band has been scattered in small blocks. Below the dent the chert band c still shows its curve towards the original anticlinal hinge, formed before the later upward movement. Further down in the left flank the chert band c shows a series of small

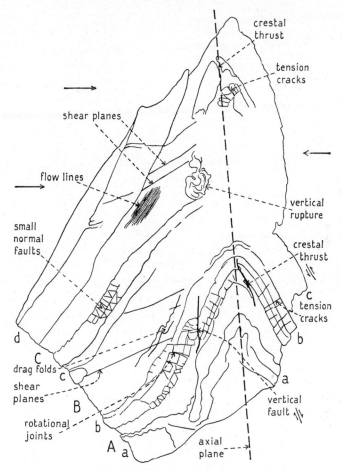

Fig. 237b.   Key to Figure 237a.

normal faults, witnessing the tension to which it has been submitted, and which later resulted in the rupture and the upward surge. In the right flank we notice similar tension cracks and movement by normal faults.

In the limestones *B* and *C* there are many flow-lines parallel to the bedding and a set of shear-joints, seen as a number of parallel lines making an angle of 60–65° with the axial plane, or 20–25° with the direction of the stress. Where these lines in the limestone touch the chert bands they sometimes continue as an offsetting fault. The most interesting feature of the limestone deformation is perhaps the drag-folding of a very thin siliceous band in limestone *B*. The axes of the drag-folds are roughly parallel to the axial plane; they show the conventional asymmetric shape and are, as it were, the limestone replica of the offset joints in the chert bed.

Summarizing the observed deformation types we can conclude that:

1. The chert bands react by means of cracks, joints, etc. to the deformative stress, and the limestone by flow

2. The chert bands show:
   a. Tension cracks on the anticlinal hinge
   b. Rotational joints in the flanks
   c. Tension cracks and normal faulting in the flanks

3. The limestone shows:
   a. Flow-lines parallel to the bedding
   b. Drag-folds
   c. General shear-joint traces

The structure as a whole gives evidence of: a concentric folding (flow-lines in limestone, rotational joints in chert), b cleavage folding (drag-folds in limestone, disharmonic upward rise of upper portion of fold accompanied by faults in flank and crest faults), c tension parallel to bedding (tension-joints, and normal faulting in chert and thinning of limestone), d shearing (shear-joints in limestone with a 20–25° angle to stress) independent of folding mechanism.

All these different tension and stress expressions are together perfectly consistent with one general stress-field, a horizontal compression.

The Flexure Fold of Schuld (The river Ahr, Rheinisches Schiefergebirge) described by H. Cloos, 1948.

The fold is exposed in three almost complete sections by a meander of the river Ahr. Cloos likens the fold to the human knee and foot joints, the straight flat flanks being the thigh, and the foot and the straight vertical flank the shin. The thigh consists of grauwackes divided by bedding-shear into two halves, of which the lower half turns downwards in a simple fold, whereas the upper half has glided further forwards and joins the lower half only after having described a sharp overturned fold. To the right we find only normal tension-joints in the upper half. The bedding shear-plane runs straight into this overturned fold. The stretching noticed in the right hand side of the thigh is compensated by the thrust in the frontal part. Another overturned anticline has developed in front of this asymmetric fold. The vertical shin part of the fold is of course not exposed in its vertical length, but is demonstrated by a horizontal section through its slightly overturned strata. It is divided into two halves by a fault-line, the right half being considerably more overturned and more crushed than the steeper quasi-vertical left portion. The fault-line is subparallel with the bedding and has the throw of a normal fault.

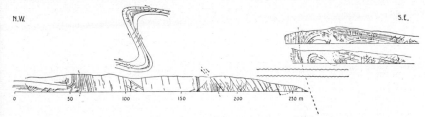

Fig. 238.   Flexure of Schuld.   *(After H. Cloos, Zeitschrift der Deutschen Geologischen Gesellschaft, vol. 100, 1948.)*

In the most overturned part of the fold we notice many other similar gliding planes, all in the bedding and with the same movement. They are accompanied by diagonal shear-planes with a contrary movement. The two shears are completely contradictory and we notice also that some of the bedding-shear is later than the diagonal shear.

The ankle joint is very similar to the knee joint, mostly characterized by bedding-plane shear. In the foot itself we find a whole set of tension-joints, indicating a stretching of this horizontal part of the fold comparable to that of the upper flank.

In this case of a flexure fold the whole fold is not exposed, only a horizontal section of some 15 to 20 m high. In that section we find occasional tension phenomena, some thrusting, bedding-plane slip almost everywhere, and ordinary jointing. The main thrust plane is the one dividing the vertical intermediate flank into two halves. Above this thrust plane we find stretching by diagonal joints, and in another section several secondary folds. The whole structure is some 600 m wide. All the details are compatible with one general horizontally directed stress-field, or to quote H. Cloos (1948, p. 302): "all structural detail which seems confused and fortuitous or unintelligible can be explained as mechanically derived from one large-sized simple deformation".

From these two examples, one 600 m wide, the other 12 cm wide, we learn that a locally restricted tectonic analysis without a knowledge of the whole structure to which the local structure belongs will often be misleading, because it can contain in its separate parts widely divergent structural features, both tensional and compressional.

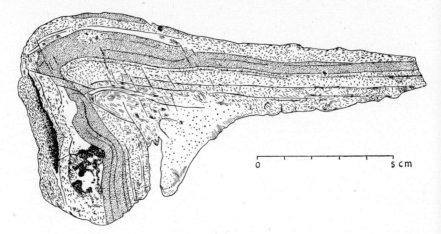

Fig. 239. Overthrust in microfold, metamorphic limestone, Ordovician, Pyrenees.

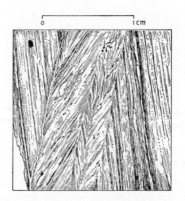

Fig. 240. Accordion-fold in Ordovician schists from Vicdessos Valley, Pyrenees.

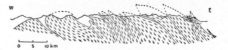

Fig. 241. Section through Pelvoux massif, Western Alps.

In Chapter 4 I drew attention to the remarkable conformity between microfolds and macrofolds.

Figure 239 shows an overthrust in a handsize specimen, which is perfectly similar to many large thrust folds. The lower flank shows a tension zone just below the thrust plane, characterized by recrystallization of quartz and calcite in large crystals, just as one would expect. The upper flank carries a few small thrusts comparable to the oblique shear-planes in the disharmonic folds of Fig. 165.

Figure 240 shows an analogy, in the form of a microfold, to the accordion-folds of the Ruhr district (Fig. 162) and the Australian gold district (Fig. 158), and could also be compared to the micro-accordion folding of Fig. 66. It would not be difficult to multiply the examples of conformity between microfolds and macrofolds a hundred times.

The Relation of Microfolds to Large Structures. The few examples of microfolds will have to suffice for the demonstration of the fundamental analogy between microfolds and macrofolds. In Chapter 4 I have already referred to this analogy, and concluded on the evidence presented in that chapter that the very close resemblance between microfolds and macrofolds gives us an opportunity of studying folding and faulting in the microfold sample and applying the conclusions in tectonic deformation in general. This method is subject, however, to certain limitations. Because the mass of the microfold is a thousand times smaller than that of the macrofold, the influence of gravity will be much less important, and the overall shapes may therefore differ considerably. The importance of the analogy lies much more in the relation between faults and folding than in the comparison of shapes. In cleavage folding of a microfold, for instance, we often notice cleavage-planes with slip which is ten or a hundred times larger than normal. These "faults" are identical in function to those of Fig. 158 (Bendigo), where they occur in a synclinorium, and with the mylonite zones of some of the Alpine massifs such as those of the Pelvoux massif (Fig. 241). The close study of microfolds will probably reveal many such analogies. When combined with a microscopical analysis of the preferred orientation of minerals in metamorphic rocks it might give us a much firmer basis for structural petrology.

Chapter 23

The Interference of Structures
of Different Phases

Interference of two Consecutive Folding Phases of one Orogenic Period. In many instances peculiarities of fold and fault patterns have been ascribed to a pre-existing system superposed by a younger system of another direction. Sometimes the inference is purely hypothetical, when the older system is not exposed independently in the same region, for instance, but careful analysis can sometimes achieve reliable results.

The fact that in a folded belt one may be able to distinguish, apart from the obvious anticlinal and synclinal axes, other oblique lines – joining, for instance, culminations of successive anticlines – is no proof of a separate folding phase with a deviating compressive direction.

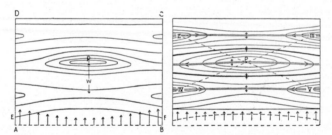

Fig. 242. Development of plunging and alternating folds.

When a compressive force is acting in a block of sedimentary strata *ABCD* (Fig. 242), some irregularity in the sedimentary series will localize the first fold at some particular point, *P*. As we have seen, the width of the fold, *w*, is soon established by the thickness of the strata involved. From the point *P*, the future culmination, the anticline will develop to the right and left, and after some compression the straight line *AB* will be in the position *EF*, with a bulge in the centre due to the culmination in the anticline at point *P*. The growing load on the first anticline due to its uplift will favour the birth of new

314

anticlines. Their distance from the first (i.e. the wavelength) is roughly
fixed at any one time by the amplitude of the first fold. As the compressive stress will be greater to the left and right of the bulge in the line
EF, because the yield of the material has been greatest opposite this
bulge, the starting points and therefore the future culminations of the
new anticlines will be located at points II, III, IV, and V, either
simultaneously or successively. The lines joining II, P, V, and IV, P,
III are not then due to a compressive stress perpendicular to these
lines; the pattern is determined solely by the thickness of the section
involved in the folding and by occasional irregularities in this section.

On the other hand one can find several examples where two distinct
directions of folding can be discerned, and where particular irregularities in the folding pattern must be attributed to their interference.
We find a good example in the High Atlas, where a post-Eocene and
a post-Miocene folding interfere with one another (Fig. 243); this has
been described in some detail (de Sitter, 1952). The most convincing

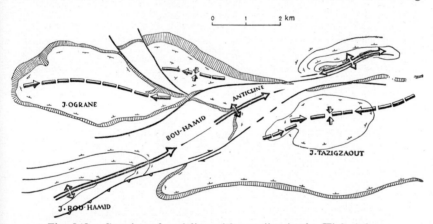

Fig. 243.   Crossing of anticline with syncline in the High Atlas.

element in this structural pattern is an anticline crossing a syncline.
The anticline of Bou-Hamid plunges in a NE direction, and is still
discernible crossing obliquely the broad EW syncline of younger age
(the J. Ograne — J. Tazigzaout). It emerges again at the other side in
a sharply folded and slightly displaced anticlinal culmination (Fig. 243).

The actual crossing of the anticline is accompanied by two wrench-
faults in its flank. The south-western of these finds its origin in a
thrust-fault of the Bou-Hamid anticline and the synclinal flank of the
Bou-Kandill curves sharply against the fault. In the north flank of the

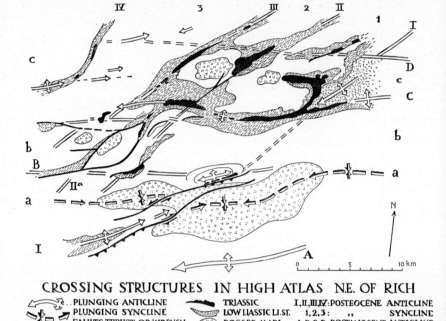

CROSSING STRUCTURES IN HIGH ATLAS N.E. OF RICH

PLUNGING ANTICLINE	TRIASSIC	I,II,III,IV:POSTEOCENE ANTICLINE
PLUNGING SYNCLINE	LOW LIASSIC LI.ST.	1,2,3: ,, SYNCLINE
FAULTS,THRUST-OR WRENCH-	DOGGER MARL	A,B,C,D:POSTMIOCENE ANTICLINE
MOVEMENT INDICATED	HERC. SCHISTS	a,b,c: ,, SYNCLINE

Fig. 244.   Structural pattern of crossing folds in High Atlas.

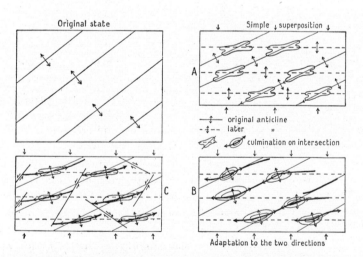

Fig. 245.   Diagrams of interference of successive directions.

syncline, the western fault probably disappears in the strike of the Dogger marls, and the north-eastern one becomes a thrust-fault along which the anticline north of the syncline is pushed into the synclinal flank in a southerly direction.

In accordance with the general situation in North Africa we may presume that the ENE–WSW trend is older than the EW trend, the first being Pyreneic (post-Eocene), the second post-Miocene, the Miocene syncline passing through a depression of a pre-existing Eocene anticline.

On the evidence of this structural feature we can explain many other peculiarities of the adjoining folds. It appears that in general the more or less diapiric Triassic cores of the culminations of the anticlines are situated at the crossing of two sets of anticlines, and that the basin-like synclines are situated in the centre of the lozenges formed by the anticlinal axes with two different directions (Fig. 244). In this case we clearly have a superficial kind of folding where the Mesozoic (largely Lower and Middle Jurassic) cover has glided along the detachment-plane of the Triassic on its Hercynian basement. In such a case we might be able to distinguish different kinds of adaptation of the older parallel anticlines to the new compressive stress. In Fig. 245 three possibilities have been sketched, and all the irregularities of the fold pattern of Fig. 244 can be attributed either to one or to a combination of these possibilities.

Influence of Basin Structure on Subsequent Folding. In the last two examples the same stratigraphical section has been folded twice, but in many other instances it is supposed that the grain of the basement rock, due to an older folding phase, has influenced the folding direction of the younger sedimentary cover. In general, such interference remains highly hypothetical because the structural features of the basement can be inferred only from observations a long distance from the folded sedimentary cover. Nevertheless there are some clear examples where older structures do influence the younger folds. One of the most striking examples is furnished by the influence of the shape of the basin on the alignment of the folds in the sedimentary rocks.

We have seen that the position of a fold is largely determined by the sedimentary structure, or in other words that the location of a fold is related to a large sedimentary feature such as the sharp edge of a competent layer which is wedging-out. We have studied this phenomenon in vertical section, but it will be equally true in the horizontal plane. There the anticlinal axis will have a tendency to follow the

edge of the wedge, which will be parallel to the border of the
basin. Although in general the folding force is directed perpendicular
to the longer axis of the elongated basins, this need not be true everywhere in one basin nor for every basin. In some cases the folding
direction will make an acute angle with the border of the basin and
therefore with the edges of the wedging competent layers. In such
cases there are two factors which tend to determine the direction of

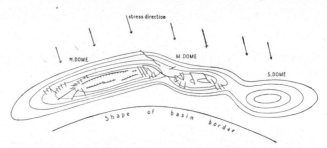

Fig. 246.   Kettleman Hills en échelon structure.

the fold-axis: the sedimentary structural feature, and the direction of
the force. The result is usually an arrangement of short folds en échelon,
each of them perpendicular to the folding force, but together forming
a string of beads parallel to the basin border. The famous three domes
of the Kettleman Hills demonstrate this principle clearly (Fig. 246).

We find the same en échelon arrangement in the normal faults which
together constitute the Mexia fault-zone, west of the Cretaceous basin
of the Texas embayment (Fig. 104). Their alignment is parallel to the
basin border, but each of them makes an acute angle with this direction.
I think it extremely probable that their general alignment is determined
by the overall structure of the basin, but their individual directions
by a tensional force perpendicular to the actual faults; but it may be
true that a deep-seated shear-fold, parallel to the basin border, has
originated the normal faults at the surface in the same way as has been
proposed for the fault-belt in Creek and Osage counties in Oklahoma
(cf. Chapter 11, p. 173).

We have described, for instance, in Chapter 12 the compressional
North Pyrenean fault which has an en échelon structure possibly
due to the superposition of a Tertiary phase on a Hercynian phase.
(Fig. 120.)

In many cases the location of folds in the blanket sediments on a
known basement rock has been attributed to faults in the basement.

There exists for instance the controversy between Goguel (1952) and Glangeaud (1944, 1949), the first maintaining that the folds of the pre-Alpine western Alps are perfectly independent of the basement, the other advocating the contrary for the narrow folds of the table Jura, the external zone of the Jura Mountains. In the same way Buxtorf (1910) believes the Jura folds to have glided over a plane, unbroken basement surface, whereas Aubert (1945) draws thrust-faults in the basement below the larger folds.

From a general point of view the gliding of the blanket rocks would be opposed or even prevented by strong fault-scarps in the basement. When the fault-scarps are small, however, it may be imagined that the irregularity at the bottom of the folding blanket localized the folds; but this is different from simultaneous faulting in the basement and folding in the blanket.

One can detect differences in level of the basement when the general level of the synclines in one zone of the folded chain is lower than in another, but even then I would prefer to suppose a bending of the basement rather than faulting, when positive information is lacking.

Influence of the Structural Grain of the Basement on a Younger Folding Phase. In the last two examples the control of the folding direction by the general shape of the basin has been described, but the basin formation and the folding both more or less relate to one and the same structural cycle of one basin. However, when an inhomogeneity in the structural grain of the basement rock is supposed to influence the folding of its sedimentary cover, the two determining factors are even wider apart, and therefore still more difficult to prove. One can often notice that the original grain has no influence whatsoever on the later folding. In the western plunge of the High Atlas, for instance, the grain of the Palaeozoic basement rock is NS, whereas the Tertiary folding is EW. But on the other hand the Middle Atlas chain is rigorously parallel to the NE–SW trend of the Palaeozoic structure. Hence the supposition that the Hercynian trend of the Moroccan Meseta determined the folding (and faulting) directions of the Middle Atlas is considerably weakened by the evidence of the western High Atlas.

Similar arbitrary suppositions are frequent in geological literature, and it is rare that real evidence can be brought forward to their support.

In general the evidence supports the view of Argand that an older major orogenic phase has consolidated the basement and that it will

no longer move except in large blocks. I should like to add that
although the basement cannot be folded again in the ordinary sense
of the word, it may still be compressed by metamorphic processes
ranging from simple cleavage to gneissification, which will not be
parallel to the original grain but perpendicular to the younger compression.

Basin formation, the deformation phase preceding the compressional
phase, may on the other hand be influenced by the older structure,
and therefore may have an indirect influence on the subsequent
folding of the basin. It seems probable, for instance, that the strongly
indurated migmatized arcs of the older Hercynian structures remain
the positive areas in the new basin formation, but quite possibly
different in arrangement from their original alignment – the Brabant
mass between the North Sea and the Parisian basins for example.

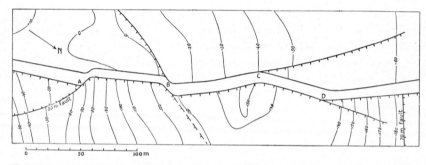

Fig. 247.   A Tertiary fault deflected by older Carboniferous folds in South
Limburg. *(After Sax, 1946.   Published by permission of Geologisch Bureau
voor het Mijngebied, Heerlen.)*

Also it is certainly true that the Caledonian and Hercynian belts
envelop the Pre-Cambrian shields, extending the shield outwards, as
will be explained later. The Alpine folding, however, seems to be
independent of the folded Palaeozoic belts.

I can point out in detail some instances where older structural
features have actually influenced later tectonic features to some
degree.

The normal faults of southern Limburg in the Netherlands, step-
faults limiting the Roer Valley rift, have been mentioned before
(Fig. 101). They are particularly well known within the coalfield,
where the Hercynian structure of the Coal Measures is equally well
known. In several instances it has been shown that post-Palaeozoic

normal faults have been deflected for some distance from their original trend by striking an older Hercynian fault. In Fig. 247 we notice that each time the younger normal fault encountered an older fault, as at the points *A*, *B*, *C*, and *D*, it followed the course of the older fault for a short distance, but then resumed its own course again. This example shows clearly the interaction of the younger and main fault directions and the older structure, but at the same time the dominating factor of the younger tensile stress.

A very instructive example of the influence of a basement structure on its blanket rocks, described by Reed and Hollister (1936), can be found in the Newport-Inglewood belt of the Los Angeles basin (Fig. 248). A long row of domes and diagonal faults is located on this belt;

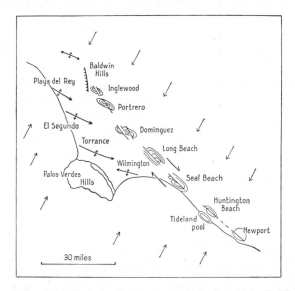

Fig. 248.   The Newport-Inglewood belt in Southern California.

many of the structures are oil-bearing. The belt is flanked to the west by a straight syncline which separates it from the NW striking anticlines of Playa del Ray, El Segundo, and Torrance.

Evidently the main stress had a SW–NE direction and caused, besides the last named anticlines, a dextral tear-fault in the basement, parallel to the St Andreas fault further to the NE. The deep-seated tear-fault sometimes reaches the surface, as in the Seal Beach anticline (Fig. 145). Sometimes, however, domes such as those of the

Dominguez oilfield are formed, diagonal to the fault but parallel to the western anticlines; sometimes diagonal tear-faults cross the domes, as in Inglewood; and sometimes normal faults are formed, as in the Baldwin Hills. All of these structures comply with the single stress-field mentioned above, although the parallelism is not very precise.

The relative independence of the Tertiary mountain chains from the grain of the Hercynian folding is however in general much more striking than are a few isolated instances where an interaction is discernible.

The moderately folded Hercynian belt of Europe extends from Cornwall to the Saharan border, whereas the Tertiary folded chains are perfectly individual units, with many different directions. We certainly cannot assume, therefore, any large-scale influence by the grain of the Hercynian on the Tertiary folding; on the contrary, the two are largely independent.

But even in this Hercynian belt, there are a few examples of large-scale conformity between the Hercynian and the Alpine directions. The most conspicuous instance is without doubt the Pyrenean orogeny, which is principally a Hercynian EW mountain chain, rejuvenated in two phases, late Cretaceous and early Tertiary, with only a slight variation of deviating strike. It seems probable that in this and similar cases both the earlier and the later orogenies are influenced by a common invariable factor, in this case the border of a long enduring cratonic block.

In conclusion, I may say that interference between successive phases of the same major orogenic period is common, but can be observed only when the two phases are not parallel. Interference of the shape of a basin on the folding of the subsequent folding phase can also be quite often observed although it is often difficult to prove. The shape of the basin may in its turn have been influenced by an older folding phase, particularly by granitization or batholith intrusions. On the other hand it is improbable, except in detailed minor structural features, that the grain impressed by an older major orogenic period on the basement influences to any great degree the alignment of younger structures, unless the same cause which originated the older strike is still active in the younger orogenic period.

Part Three

Geotectonics

Chapter 24

Fundamental Concepts of Geotectonics

EPEIROGENESIS – OROGENESIS

When we study in any detail in any part of the world the succession of the sedimentary strata and their relationships, we are struck by the fact that there are apparently long periods of quiescence and continuous sedimentation, and shorter periods of deformation, indicated by unconformities, transgressions, and other irregularities. From observation on the sedimentary sequence we conclude that during the quiet periods also there has certainly been some vertical motion in the earth's crust in that particular region, either downward or upward; this is suggested either by non-deposition during certain periods, or by the excessive thickness of some stratigraphic units. But these motions appear to have been very slow and did not result in folded or faulted structures and unconformities. The conclusion has been expressed in the terms "Orogenesis" and "Epeirogenesis". The first term designates the quick deformation of a belt of sedimentary rocks, the other the slow motion of basin formation and upheaval of large blocks. In recent years, a tendency to connect the two phenomena has developed, and the hypothesis of isostasy, combined with other concepts of the origin of tectonic forces, has been used to a large extent in order to establish a theoretical basis for this connexion.

Haarmann (1930), and after him Escher, have pointed out that the term "orogeny", meaning "mountain building", is as a matter of fact a misnomer when we use it to designate the actual folding, because the mountain chains have as a rule been formed by the upheaval of a previously folded belt. They therefore proposed the term "tecto-genesis" for the folding and faulting action, and the term "orogenesis" for the later upheaval of the folded belt. Orogeny would then mean only a kind of epeirogenesis. The term "tectogenesis" has however never been widely accepted, its predecessor "orogenesis" being too firmly established in the minds of geologists. Moreover, it is certainly not true that folding causes only a down-warping in the crust; on the contrary, we know for certain that in some cases, like the Jura, most of the compensation to horizontal compression is upwards, and in other cases syn- and post-tectonic sediments prove that at least some of the vertical movement was upwards. Nevertheless, we must recognize a more or less independent post-tectonic phase of upheaval, which we might call the "morphogenic phase." A causal connexion between the folding and a later upheaval has been given by the buckling hypothesis of Vening Meinesz, which I will examine later on, but it has not been generally accepted. Personally I prefer the term "orogeny" as a general term for all relatively swift and severe deformations of different kinds which have more than a local extension. An "orogenic phase" embraces the deformation that happened in a distinct time interval, and an "orogenic period" is constituted of successive phases. A "mountain chain" or "orogeny" is a comparatively narrow deformed zone, and an "orogenic belt" consists of one or several related mountain systems, which have been deformed in one orogenic period. The definition of the term "epeirogenesis" is much more difficult. In general one may say that both the sinking of a basin and the slow lifting of a part of the earth's crust may be called epeirogenic. But when one talks about the sinking of a rift valley block, opinions are divided. There is, moreover, in modern thought, a tendency to blot out the limits between epeirogenesis and orogenesis, the former being regarded as a slow motion process of the same origin and function as the latter.

Stille is a fervent supporter of the view that orogenesis and epeirogenesis are two quite different processes, and advocates the theory that all folding and accompanying faulting activity are short-lived and more or less of a world-wide nature, in distinct short periods separated by long periods of quiescence. He gave every recognized unconformity a distinct name, and thought that future knowledge would increase the evidence that each of them had been active in a large part of the world. The original idea is much older of course; since Haug (1900) published his famous book we know that we can distinguish four major orogenic periods, the *Huronian* at the end of the Pre-Cambrian, the *Caledonian*, in the Lower Palaeozoic, the *Hercynian* (or Variscean) period at the end of the Palaeozoic and the *Alpine* period, starting at the end of the Cretaceous period with the Laramide phase. Stille subdivided each of the major periods into many phases and subphases, all of which were assigned to well-defined, distinct short periods of the earth's history. He originally named three Caledonian, five Hercynian, and eleven Alpine phases. The names of his principal phases have won wide acceptance but the principle has lately been under severe attack.

In the first place, the growth of our exact and precise stratigraphic knowledge has shown that there are innumerable small unconformities in any sedimentary series. Gilluly (1949) found that there were forty-three in the Miocene of California alone and that any of them might locally be of importance. Furthermore, the dating of the Stille phases is often so inexact, as Rutten (1949) and Gilluly pointed out, that it is very doubtful whether certain unconformities really belong to the same folding phase or not. In many instances an observed unconformity representing a wide stratigraphical gap has been placed at a convenient place in the time scale simply because that place had a Stille phase-name. More and more the conviction has grown that although the Stille phases are very convenient to indicate the general situation of a folding movement in the stratigraphical scale, we must not have too many phase-names and not attach to them too much theoretical value. A certain phase may easily vary a little in time from one end of a mountain chain to the other, or from one border of a basin to the opposite one.

I am also convinced that much confusion has arisen from the fact that once a certain well-dated unconformity has been locally observed, whatever its size, it has been apt to receive a phase-name, and forthwith placed as an equal to all other phases. After all, one can and ought to distinguish major phases such as the pre-Oligocene "Pyreneic" phase in Europe, which coincides with major paroxysms in the Alps, Pyrenees, and elsewhere, from a small unconformity noticed locally between some sub-stages in the Pliocene. There is furthermore always a tendency to place unconformities in between two strati-graphic stages, for instance between the Eocene and the Oligocene, notwithstanding the fact that the palaeontological evidence allows only a broader dating, perhaps post-Middle Eocene — pre-late-Oligo-cene. The deformation of the earth's crust is probably the result of a slowly growing stress which at a certain height exceeds the elasticity limit of the rocks concerned; hence the exact moment of the yielding-point of rocks depends on the rate of growth of the force and the nature of the rock. As both factors may vary widely and even influence one another because the yielding at one place may suddenly increase or decrease the stress somewhere else, we may expect that even in one structural unit the time of movement of the yield will vary as well. Therefore we must accept the notion that a stress condition acts at one place in the earth's crust for a long time, long in the geological sense of the word, and that the actual intensity of folding or faulting may vary somewhat erratically in time and in place over the whole period and over the whole stressed region, so that we can discern only certain maxima, i.e. the orogenic phases and subphases.

Moreover, the fact that gravity-gliding tectonics have been recognized means that spectacular tectonic movements may be the result of a slow epeirogenic rising of a part of a folded belt, and need not coincide with any known orogenic phase. The same is true for the rising of salt-domes, which are often initiated by folding-stress but then continue independently of any stress condition and are controlled by the gravity field only.

From this point of view we can distinguish, in both hemispheres, at least three major orogenic periods: a Pre-Cambrian period; a Hercynian period at the end of the Palaeozoic, and an Alpine period, starting with the Laramide folding; with an extremely quiet period embracing almost the whole of the Mesozoic between the Hercynian and the Alpine. But even these are not fully equivalent in America and in Europe. The major phase along the Pacific coast, for instance, is the Nevadan phase, which occurred in the later Jurassic and not at the end of the Palaeozoic. On the Atlantic coast of America we find a Taconic phase (Caledonian), an Acadian (late Devonian) phase and an Appalachian phase (Hercynian). All three phases are known in Europe too, but it is a question of opinion whether one reckons the Acadian phase as a late Caledonian manifestation or as an early Hercynian phase.

This brings us to another question which I should like to put, concerning the supposed cyclic development of the earth's crust and its world-wide synchronism. In sweeping simplification, it is suggested that fixed periods of some 200 million years of epeirogenic character are separated by equally fixed periods of some 50 million years of orogenic phases forming together an orogenic period, a cycle which is furthermore emphasized by glaciations (Pre-Cambrian, Hercynian, and Quaternary), volcanic activity and evolutionary steps of plant and animal life (cf. Umbgrove, 1947). Such a schematization is perhaps valid for glaciations but it is not valid for mountain building; for between the Pre-Cambrian orogenies of 500 to 600 millions of years ago and the Hercynian orogenies about 250 millions of years ago,

we find the Caledonian phases, about 350 millions of years ago.
Between the Tertiary phases beginning with the Pyreneic phase (30
millions of years ago) and the Hercynian (230 millions of years ago) we
find the Laramide phase (about 70 millions of years ago) and the
Nevadan phase at 100 millions of years ago, of which the first is
of world-wide significance. The schematization is not always true
either for one large mountain chain or one orogenic belt. Nevertheless,
it is true for the Mediterranean area that a late Palaeozoic orogenic
period is followed by a Mesozoic period of quiescence and then disturbed again in the late Cretaceous or early Tertiary; and that in
the Appalachians, *s.str.*, a Pre-Cambrian orogeny was followed by a
Palaeozoic period of quiescence and subsequently by a very late
Hercynian folding phase.

The very detailed stratigraphic work of oil geologists in particular
has shown that there is never a really tranquil lapse of time; the
forces are always working, but show small accelerations, of which the
important groups – the orogenic phases – are more or less simultaneous
over a whole continent. The controversy about the world-wide
applicability of the simultaneity of the orogenic phases is resolved
when the Stille principle of simultaneity is accepted only for the orthotectonic regions for which it was intended, in each of the continents
separately, but not for the paratectonic regions. Paratectonic phases
are much more erratic, although they often reflect the orthotectonic
phases of nearby mountain chains.

Nevertheless, the orogenic phase and period names are in such
common use that it would be foolish to propose abandoning them
altogether. But when we accept them we shall have to bring some
order to the chaos by disregarding many minor, insignificant, or badly
defined names. Moreover, it would be expedient to give others a
somewhat wider meaning because their time definition may vary
greatly from one place to another.

I should like to propose the following list in which the designation
"Jurassic", for example, is intended to embrace all inter-Jurassic
dates *including* a post-Jurassic – Pre-Cretaceous age; and "Lower
Cretaceous" all inter-Lower Cretaceous ages *and* the post-Lower – pre-
Upper Cretaceous age:

Holocene	Passadenian	⎫
Pliocene	Attic	⎬ Alpine
Miocene	Skytic	⎪
Oligocene	Helvetic	⎭

Eocene	Pyreneic	Pyreneic
Upper Cretaceous	Laramide	Austrian
Lower Cretaceous	Oregonian	
Jurassic	Nevadan	Cimeric
Triassic	Pallisade	
Permian	Appalachian	
Pennsylvanian (Upp. Carb.)	Asturian	Hercynian
Mississippian (Low. Carb.)	Sudetic	
Devonian	Acadian	
Silurian	Erian	Caledonian
Ordovician	Taconic	
Cambrian	Sardic	
Proterozoic	Lake Superior	−550 m.y.
	Huronian	−760 m.y.
	Karelian	−850 m.y.
	Laurentian	−1000 m.y.
	Archean	−1350 −2900 m.y.

In the next paragraph we shall see that the principle of isostasy is in accordance with this principle of continuity of the deformative forces in the earth's crust.

ISOSTASY

Isostasy means that the larger units of the earth's crust, continents and oceans, mountain chains and plains, are not just irregularities carved in the upper layers of a rigid crust and wholly supported by them, but that each of them is compensated by a relative mass-defect or mass-surplus underground. The simplest way of imagining isostasy is by comparing the mountains to icebergs floating in the sea, where the mass-surplus above sea level is compensated by an equal mass-defect (difference of weight of the ice and the replaced water) below it. This image, however, is not the only solution to the problem. Different geophysicists have offered different solutions, not necessarily as actual physical conditions of the earth's crust but more as a method of putting the hypothesis of isostasy into calculable form (Fig. 249).

Pratt imagined that above the equilibrium surface each volume of material had its own specific weight, the higher the lighter. The bottom of his columns rested on the substratum on one plane surface.

Airy followed another method, and imagined all columns of equal specific weight, floating in a heavier substratum. Airy's columns therefore reach different depths, like icebergs.

Heiskanen admitted an increase of density in the floating columns of Airy; hence they penetrated less deeply into the substratum than Airy's.

Vening Meinesz imagined that an extra load on the surface caused an elastic bending of a much larger surface than the diameter of the actual load, and hence a diffusion or a regionality of the compensating mass below. The radius of the regionality round the disturbing mass can then be chosen so that with the measured values of gravity the best result of isostatic compensation is reached.

The principle of isostasy introduced the idea that the upper crust has a lighter density than its substratum, i.e. the granite layer or *sial* rests on a heavier *sima* layer. As gravity is more or less equal on the

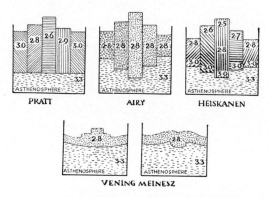

Fig. 249. Physical interpretation of isostasy by different authors.

continents and on the oceans (in both cases reduced to sea level), it is thought that the sial is thickest on the continents, absent in the Pacific Ocean and thin in the Atlantic Ocean, a notion which seems to be corroborated by seismic evidence.

The upheaval of mountain chains, or subsidence of basins, is accordingly accompanied by respective thickening or thinning of the sialic blanket. Such vertical movements are apparently slow. The best-known example of recent isostatic adjustment is the rising of the Scandinavian block, after the melting of the ice-cap, which is demonstrated by the elevated beaches along the Scandinavian coast.

It is reasonable to presume that on the same principle the erosion of the elevated mountain chain must activate the upward motion, and that the deposition of sediments must maintain the sinking of the basins. But the original uplift of a mountain chain cannot be due to erosion, nor can the sinking of the basin be due to accumulation of sediments. Both the elevation and the sinking must have had an independent origin. Because all the great Tertiary mountain chains of the world are more or less folded structures, bearing witness to great compression, it is obvious that the thickening of the crust beneath them can be directly related to the folding; and later elevation of the mountain chain, the morphogenic phase, can be regarded as an isostatic adjustment of the thickened crust.

The fact that every mountain chain has a root of sialic matter, presumably due to the folding process, has been revived by Vening Meinesz in his buckling hypothesis. Vening Meinesz found, in Indonesia, a zone of strong negative anomalies (Chapter 28), without a mountain chain on top; he concluded from this evidence that the crust had buckled downwards, pressing a narrow zone of sialic matter into the heavier sima layer below. By analogy with his buckling

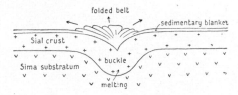

Fig. 250.   The downwards-directed buckle of the earth's crust in an orogeny with its sedimentary core pressed out. (*After Vening Meinesz, Publ. Neth. Geod. Comm., vol. 2, 1934.*)

hypothesis and with the known zones of negative anomalies in the gravity field of Tertiary mountain chains like the Alps, it became a very attractive hypothesis that all Tertiary mountain chains — and before that, older orogenic belts also — were formed by a downward buckle of the earth's crust, with a pressed-out, crumpled sedimentary cover above, subsequently elevated by isostatic adjustment (Fig. 250). In the next chapter we will occupy ourselves to a greater extent with the consequences of this theory; but here I shall straight away point out that serious objections can be raised against such generalization, on the grounds that many Tertiary mountain chains of great elevation show only very minor compression compared with the Alps, and that the upheaval sometimes happened only after tens of millions of years had elapsed, sometimes immediately after the folding.

For the basin structures, which are negative vertically displaced structures, comparable in size to the positive mountain chains, a thinning of the crust cannot be explained in such a simple way. I have always wondered why, in general, so much stress is laid on the isostatic cause of uplift, and so little on that of subsidence. Why should geosynclines not be related to thinning of the crust due to tensions, as Staub suggested, in analogy with uplifts supposed to be the result of thickening due to compression?

In general, it is a hazardous occupation to try to derive a geotectonic reality from the mass distribution which the geophysicist has presumed in order to explain the observed gravity field. There are so many factors which are uncertain, and the geophysicists always proceed by a method of trial and error starting from a certain general conception; the reality may be very far removed from their supposition. Nevertheless, geodetic and gravimetric measurements definitively prove that between a depth of 50 and 100 km the crust material gives way and hydrostatic equilibrium is reestablished in a relatively short time, say in some tens of thousands of years. All major topographic deviations above or below sea level can persist only when they are isostatically compensated; this certainly applies to deviations equivalent in size to blocks 100×100 km, and probably to any block greater than 20×20 km.

THE INTERIOR OF THE EARTH

We are not concerned in this book with the physics of our globe in general, but we have to consider what is generally regarded as the most probable constitution of the earth's crust and interior and to what extent the respective hypotheses form a solid basis for theories dealing with the deformation of the crust.

There are a number of independent sources of information about the substratum which is hidden beneath the visible layers of the crust. In the first place, the nature of the volcanic and intrusive rocks gives us valuable indications about some zones of the crust. These rocks, however, do not afford direct evidence of the actual depths from which they originate. Secondly, isostasy proves that there must be some more or less plastic layer, the so-called "Asthenosphere" at a depth of about 100 km. In the third place, the velocity of seismic waves in different zones is different. And finally, theoretical deductions about temperature and hydrostatic pressure at depth may give us some purely hypothetical information.

It must be borne in mind that discontinuity planes for different physical properties need not coincide at depth, even when they are apt to coincide at the surface of the earth. For instance, the depth of melting points and the bases of the zone capable of carrying transversal shock waves need not be identical. The great hydrostatic pressure and high temperature at depth create circumstances which are difficult to imagine or to extrapolate from experimental data.

All the views which have been formulated about the earth's interior are influenced by one of two preconceived ideas, either that the earth was once hot, fluid, or even gaseous, and then cooled down to its present state; or that the earth was once cold and became heated by radioactivity and gravity.

The proponents of the originally hot earth are in favour of a core and mantle which are still hot; those in favour of a cold origin of the earth consider that the mantle at least is solid. Both agree in general on the existence of a hot and fluid core, because of its incapacity to transmit transversal seismic waves, and both, of course, agree about the solid state of the crust. Their difference of opinion concerns the mantle.

Their concepts of the origin of the earth itself are also dependent on their concept of the mantle. The hot earth is thought to have been derived from the sun by a cataclysm caused by a near-collision with another star; the cold earth is thought to be a result of a slow accretion of galactic matters, dust, and meteorites.

The opponents agree that the division into core, mantle, and crust is not a question of gradual downward increase of temperature and pressure increase; the two first-order seismic discontinuity surfaces separating these shells are too clearly pronounced. The concentric shells must be due to differences of phase, of material, or of both. But they disagree again on how the separation in concentric shells originated.

The hot earth proponents think of a process of segregation by gravity and chemical selection; the cold earth proponents propose a selective accretion and in the beginning gravitational selection as well. Astronomers know more about stars, but look to the geophysicist to tell them particulars about the planets, and the planets certainly differ much between themselves.

The only contribution the geologist can make to this controversy is that going back in time, the surface of the earth certainly appears to have been hotter and hotter. Both plutonic and volcanic activity were greater in bulk in relation to sedimentation in the Archean than later. This evidence, although pretty definite, may not be conclusive, since it is concerned only with the upper crust and goes back only 2,000 or 3,000 million years, little more than half the life of the earth.

There is of course a strong interaction between the conclusions and premisses in every geophysicist's mind. A seismologist does not like a fluid mantle because it transmits transversal seismic waves. Hence he prefers a cool earth, and will be careful to draw his temperature depth curve in such a way that it does not cross the melting point of silicates before reaching the core. But someone who believes in contraction as the mechanism responsible for orogenies does not hesitate to admit higher temperatures; neither does a convection current enthusiast. The present trend is certainly towards a solid mantle and a liquid core.

Seismic Evidence. Our knowledge about the constitution of the deeper layers of the earth is almost wholly derived from measurements of seismic wave velocities, because they are practically the only geophysical data giving direct measurements below the immediate crustal layers. Unfortunately, the interpretation of the data is very difficult and different authors arrive at widely varying conclusions. The general result indicates, however, that in the upper 100 km at least, three, and perhaps four layers can be distinguished on the continents: namely, at the top, the lithified sedimentary veneer of varying thickness with a mean velocity of 3.6 km/sec; then the "granite" layer some 15 to 25 km in thickness with a mean velocity of 5.2 km/sec; below that, an intermediate "basaltic" layer of 10–40 km thickness, in which the velocity increases to 6.5–7.2 km/sec. limited by a pronounced discontinuity surface, the Mohorovicic discontinuity. Below that discontinuity a considerably higher velocity of 8.2 km/sec. is observed. The nature of the rock material in this sima layer beneath the Mohorovicic discontinuity is of course unknown; it is sometimes referred to as the dunite or ultra-mafic layer.

Below the Mohorovicic discontinuity we find a rapid increase of the velocity, as far as a depth of 950 km; here, at the Repetti discontinuity, the rate of increase slows down. Formerly, various workers, including Gutenberg in particular, advocated the existence of several such discontinuities of the second order, for instance at 1,200, 1,900 and 2,150 km depth; but Gutenberg seems now to have rallied to the idea of only one well-pronounced discontinuity of the second order (i.e. a change in the rate of increase of the velocity; a first order discontinuity is a sudden jump in velocity) at 950 km depth. Finally, at about 2,900 km depth, another first order discontinuity leads to the core. Figure 251 gives the curve of velocity increase and variations from crust to centre (Gutenberg, 1951, p. 276). The two first order discontinuities are very definite, the Repetti discontinuity at 950 km is less certain, and there may be others in the mantle and in the core; but with our present instruments and theory and with the variability, inconsistency, and changing nature of the seismic waves themselves, their determination is very hazardous. The Repetti discontinuity is often explained as a level of change of phase due to the increasing pressure, and Birch (1952, 1954) thinks that a closer packing of the

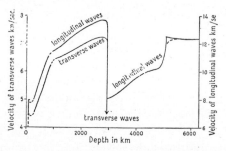

Fig. 251. Velocity of longitudinal waves and transverse waves (scales right and left) as a function of depth. *(From "Internal Constitution of the Earth" by Beno Gutenberg. Reprinted by permission of Dover Publications Inc., New York 10, N.Y. $ 5.50.)*

oxides of the magnesia–iron–silica system is responsible for the discontinuity. This concept is referred to as polymorphism in the mantle. The thickness of the crust layers above the Mohorovicic discontinuity varies considerably from place to place. The granitic layer is thickest below the Alps (40 km) and thins along the edges of the continent. It is certainly absent in the Pacific and perhaps in the Atlantic but even below the continents various authors report varying depths. The same is true for the Mohorovicic discontinuity itself. Recent work has even shown that the basaltic layer is much thinner on ocean bottoms, only 3–4 km, than under the continents.

Physiographic Evidence. It is well known that 35.3 % of the earth's surface is occupied by continents and their surrounding shelf, with an average altitude of $+250$ m; 51.15 % by the oceans, with an average depth of $-3,800$ m; and only 13.2 % by the continental slope. This is good evidence that there must be some fundamental difference between the continental shelf and the ocean bottom. Combined with the fact of isostasy, which means that there is a hydrostatic equilibrium between the two units, the assumption is warranted that the continental blocks of granite, and sial, float on a heavier substratum, the sima.

The peculiar distribution of these sialic blocks on the earth's surface has given rise to many speculations. First of all, the Pacific hemisphere is nearly all ocean, and the continents are concentrated on the opposite hemisphere. Secondly, all the continental blocks taper off towards the south. And finally, the antipode of every continental block is an ocean. The congruency of the eastern and western Atlantic coasts, and the tapering off of the continental slopes, inspired Wegener with his famous theory of drifting continents once conjoined to form a single shield, "Pangaea".

Geologic Evidence. The Pacific Ocean is characterized by the uniform basaltic composition of all extrusive rocks and by the absence of any other rocks apart from coral limestones and ordinary loose sediments on land and on the sea bottom. The continents, on the other hand, are characterized by the great profusion of all kinds of sedimentary rocks and by the fact that granites predominate to a large extent amongst plutonic rocks whereas volcanic rocks vary from the flood basalts to rhyolites. The basalts, however, predominate in bulk.

The circum-Pacific belt on the continental shelf carries numerous volcanoes on island arcs, among whose products andesites predominate. The line separating the occurrences of basaltic rocks from the occurrences of andesitic rocks is called the "Andesite Line" and in the east of the Pacific, coincides more or less with the coast, and in the west with the outer festoons of island arcs.

Basalts, and in particular basalt and diabase dikes and sills, are numerous and dispersed over almost all continents and are of all ages. It is therefore logical to expect the basaltic layer of the Pacific bottom to extend below the continents. There is good evidence, however, that the constitution of the Pacific basalts is not exactly the same as that of the continental flood basalts (cf. Chapter 25).

The limit between the granite layer and the basaltic layer need not coincide with the transition from a crystalline to a less rigid — let us say vitreous—layer. Since the specific weight of granite is 2.8 and that of an ultrabasic rock 3.2, we may assume that a granite (sial) continent is floating on an ultrabasic (sima) basement; but it is generally accepted that there is an intermediate basaltic layer, the source of the basaltic lavas, between these two. The rock wave-velocity is

5.2 km/sec. in granite, 8.2 km/sec. in the ultrabasic layer, and 6.5 km/sec. in the intermediate layer.

We may presume that in the continents the crust consists of a granitic layer of 15–18 km in thickness, and a crystalline basaltic layer 15–22 km thick, underlain by a glassy basaltic layer and below that the ultrabasic layer. The transition from crystalline to vitreous basalt is indicated by the velocity of seismic waves, which decreases slightly with increasing depth. In the Pacific the granite layer is probably almost absent, though we may expect some thickness of very fine-grained sediment on top. In the Atlantic and Indian Oceans the granitic layer is certainly much thinner than on the continents and is, perhaps, locally altogether absent as in the Pacific, for velocities of as much as 7 km/sec. have recently been measured below the sediments.

Between the crystalline and the non-crystalline phase of the basaltic layer, we may expect a semi-crystalline phase with liquid between the crystals.

I have left out of our consideration many controversial questions which do not invalidate the conclusions mentioned above. All the suppositions about the properties of the mantle are extremely uncertain; the only thing we know about it is that down to 700 km it still has the strength to generate shock waves. Its density probably increases to 9 next to the core (Fig. 252). The core itself must have

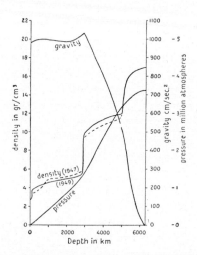

Fig. 252.   Density, pressure, and gravity as a function of depth. *(From "Internal Constitution of the Earth" by Beno Gutenberg. Reprinted by permission of Dover Publications Inc., New York 10, N.Y. $ 5.50.)*

a still greater density of about 11, otherwise the mean density of 5.5 of the whole earth could not be attained; and it is supposed to consist of the heavy metals, iron and nickel, by analogy with the composition of iron meteorites. It can be assumed to have no rigidity because it cannot transmit transversal shock waves, and is supposed to be really fluid and to contain the origin of the earth's magnetic field (Runcorn 1954).

The depth of the isostatic plane is variously calculated by different authors. In general a depth of 120 km is accepted, but it may vary considerably from place to place. Its position has nothing to do with any of the other discontinuity surfaces between the shells.

From a global point of view the Tertiary orogenic zones coincide only in the circum-Pacific zone with the boundary between the granitic crust and the sima basement. Neither the Indian nor the Atlantic Ocean shows this feature.

Temperature. The increase of temperature below the surface, i.e. the temperature gradient, is known from such sources as drill-holes, obviously not very deep in comparison with the thickness of the crust. This temperature gradient varies widely from some 20 m per C° to ± 100 m per C°. It is generally higher in sediments than in crystalline rocks. This variation is easily understandable when we think of the variation of thermal conductivity in rocks of different kinds and of differences caused by varying geologic history, such as upheavals and subsidence, intrusions, circulation of mineralizing solutions, compaction, flow of water, and so on.

Van Orstrand, 1951 (in Gutenberg, 1951) concludes from all the available data that in basins the isogeotherms tend to reflect the depths of the basement, and are therefore elevated over domes and anticlines. As a rough estimate of an average gradient in sedimentary areas he gives 33 to 60 m per C°.

Obviously these data cannot be used for extrapolation for the great depths of the basaltic layer and for the mantle or core, except in a general way.

The temperature of the earth's surface depends on the incoming solar radiation, of which some 70 % is absorbed, and on the radiation from the earth. Deeper down, however, the temperature is regulated by the conductivity of the rocks and by the heat produced inside the earth by disintegration of radioactive matter. The heat flow in the upper layers can be calculated from the numerous temperature gradient measurements, and indicate that on the continents at least, it is much more uniform than the gradients (0.95 − 2.00 × 10^6 cal cm^2/sec. average = 1.3). It is believed that this heat is mostly produced by disintegration in the sialic crust itself; or, in other words, that the earth is not cooling at present. But we know nothing whatever about the loss of heat below the oceans.

All speculations about the change of temperature with depth below the measured temperature gradients depend on various assumptions about the amounts of radioactive elements in the crust and mantle, and about the presence or absence of convection currents and various other unknown qualities. Figure 253, represents the results of the speculation by different authors. Verhoogen (1954) is in favour of a somewhat lower temperature, perhaps not rising above 1500° C at the boundary of the core.

Density and Pressure. Both astronomy and geodesy give us very meagre information about density distribution within the earth; the only source of information is seismology. It would lead us too far to enter into the considerations which guided various authors to their conclusions; I simply include their figures in the graph of Fig. 252, from the tables in Gutenberg (1951). The jump on the 2,900 km surface

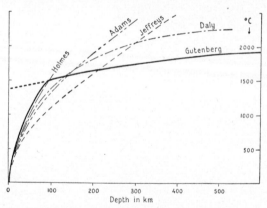

Fig. 253.   Temperature as a function of depth according to various authors. *(From "Internal Constitution of the Earth" by Beno Gutenberg. Reprinted by permission of Dover Publications Inc., New York 10, N.Y. $ 5.50.)*

is obvious; the discontinuities in the core are obviously highly hypothetical and wholly based on seismic data.

Chemical Composition of the Earth. Actual knowledge about the chemical constitution of the earth is derived from two sources, that of the igneous rocks and that of the meteorites, since these latter are supposed to have their origin in an exploded solid planet cooled from a liquid. There is evidence that this latter supposition is fully warranted (cf. Rankama and Sahama, 1949). There are recognized in general two kinds of meteorites: the stony meteorites consisting mostly of olivines and pyroxenes, which are called chondrites when they have a considerable iron-nickel content, and achondrites when FeNi is lacking; and siderites, or iron meteorites, which contain almost nothing else but nickel-iron. Table XII gives a comparison of their composition with the average composition of igneous rocks.

Table XII

	Average Igneous rocks (after Daly)	METEORITES		
		Iron Meteorites	Stony Meteorites	
		Siderites	Chondrites	Achondrites
O	46.59	—	37.10	42.05
Si	27.72	—	18.34	23.00
Al	8.13	—	1.55	3.26
Fe (metallic) . . .	—	90.67	11.46	1.18
Fe (silicate). . . .	5.01	—	12.88	12.33
Ca	3.63	—	1.65	5.09
Na	2.85	—	0.59	0.5
K	2.60	—	0.11	0.22
Mg	2.09	—	13.54	10.91
Ti	0.63	—	0.01	—
Ni	0.02	8.5	1.31	0.33
Co	0.001	0.6	0.07	0.04
P	0.13	0.17	0.06	0.06
S	0.05	0.04	1.98	0.54
Cr	0.04	—	0.28	0.31

The stony meteorites are presumably of igneous origin and they differ mostly from basic volcanic rocks on the earth by their iron-nickel content.

From these data it has been concluded that the interior of the earth has to some extent the constitution of the meteorites, the core resembling the siderites and the mantle the stony meteorites. From this general consideration Goldschmidt developed the idea that the composition of the earth resembles that of a blast furnace, with iron and nickel in the core, elements with a strong affinity to sulphur in the mantle, and the oxidized slag in the crust. The partition of the elements with depth is admirably demonstrated when their atomic number is plotted against their atomic volume as Goldschmidt (1924-26) did (Fig. 254). The resulting curve shows at the tops the elements having a complete electronsphere, the lithophile elements and at the minima those with free electrons; the siderophile elements, and the chalcophile elements are in between. The concentration of the elements in the different spheres is a result of many factors — their chemical properties, along the lines explained above, but also gravity and pressure. Gravity will favour a concentration of the heavier elements in the core, but will drive the lighter chemical compositions upwards according to their affinities; pressure will favour heavy and compact compositions down-

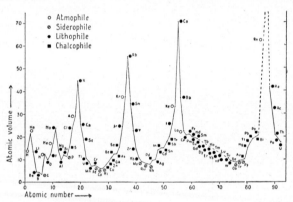

Fig. 254. Atomic volume of elements as function of atomic number. (*From "Internal Constitution of the Earth" by Beno Gutenberg. Reprinted by permission of Dover Publications Inc., New York 10, N.Y. $ 5.50.*)

wards. Near the centre gravity is small, and we might perhaps expect there a centre of the original undifferentiated matter in a compact form. Perhaps the discontinuity indicated by seismic evidence at 5,000 km depth indicates this central core.

Magnetic Field of the Earth. It has been shown by Hospers (1953) that during the Cenozoic no drifting of the poles in any important measure has taken place; but Runcorn (1954) has shown that we might have to reckon with a pole shift of considerable extension during the Palaeozoic and Mesozoic, perhaps from the Equator to the present position. Hospers' evidence was obtained by measuring very accurately and with all possible precautions the magnetization of lava streams and sediments. The results, in particular those on the Cenozoic lava streams of Iceland, were surprising; they indicated that every two million years or so the magnetic field became reversed in the sense that the North Pole became the South Pole and vice versa. The reversal happened very quickly in comparison with the stable periods. This reversal must have an origin in some change in the core of the earth in which the magnetic field of the earth is generated.

As the orientation of the magnetic field is certainly bound in some way or other with the orientation of the rotation of the earth, the reversals have nothing to do with any shift of the axis. The Cenozoic measurements on lava streams and sediments seem to be very conclusive, but the measurements on older strata, mostly on sediments which have a much weaker magnetic field, are in many instances still contradictory. If they really indicate that magnetic pole-shift took place in the Palaeozoic and Mesozoic, then they are most probably linked to shifts of the rotation axis, perhaps brought into effect by changes in the core of the earth. From a structural point of view these changes interest us because they would call forth considerable stresses in the crust when the flattening of the earth was shifted in relation to the continents. Vening Meinesz (1943), considered this stress problem and fitted the lines of maximum stress to the structural lines of the crust. The result is not very convincing but nevertheless we can note that consistent leverage of shields like that of the Canadian and Baltic shields towards the Mediterranean zone might have something to do with this pole shift.

MOUNTAIN CHAINS

A glance at the globe will tell us that the Tertiary mountain chains are distributed according to a very definite pattern. We find one circum-Pacific belt and another equatorial belt, the Tethys, or Mediterranean belt, both meeting in the West and East Indian archipelagos. We might expect the characteristics of the circum-Pacific belt, situated between large continental sialic regions and the one great territory which has no sialic crust, to be different from those which are typical for orogenic belts between two continental regions, i.e. between Eurasia in the north and Gondwana in the south.

Looking further back in history we find a different though similar pattern for the Hercynian orogenic belts, and again another one for the Caledonian orogenies. We find that some orogenic belts surround a stable shield; others are situated between such shields; and finally we may perhaps consider the circum-Pacific belt as a distinctive unit. We must investigate each of these on its own merits, although in many instances it will be difficult to decide to which group a particular belt belongs.

The following list may provide a preliminary base for our survey:
Caledonian orogenies — Circum-continental mostly, round the Angara, Canadian, and Australian shields.
Hercynian orogenies — Circum-continental, round the Angara, Baltic, Brazilian, Australian, and Canadian shields; Intercontinental, between the Gondwana and Eurasian shields (Palaeozoic Tethys), and between the Llanorian, Appalachian, and Canadian shields.
Alpine orogenies — Intercontinental Alpine Tethys and Circum-Pacific belt.

It would be premature to suppose that all mountain chains belonging to one particular type of orogeny have the same characteristics. A short survey of some mountain chains of the European Tethys orogeny and of their mutual relations can convince us of the wide variety presented by such a small group.

The Alpine Structural History of the West Mediterranean. The Western Mediterranean belt is enclosed between two shields, the Sahara shield in the south, and in the north the French Plateau Central with its western extension in the Aquitanian plain and its eastern extension in the Vosges Mountains and across the Rhine Valley rift in the Variscean mountains of central Europe. The two shields are very different in almost every respect. The Sahara shield is an old African shield covered by sub-horizontal Palaeozoic, the European shield has had a long and complicated Palaeozoic history with many Hercynian orogenies which extend far into the Alpine mobile belt.

In the Alpine belt we can distinguish a northern belt bordering the European shield – the Pyrenees, Alps, and Carpathians; and a southern belt, the High Atlas in Morocco and Sahara chains in Algeria (Fig. 255).

Right in the centre of the belt we find the Betic Cordillera extending into the Balearic Islands, and the Moroccan Riff trending further along the coastal region of Algeria. Both are roughly parallel to the main EW trend.

Besides these longitudinal belts there are some diagonal mountain chains, the Apennines and the Dinarides, the Middle Atlas and the Tunisian chains.

In between these Tertiary mountain chains we find numerous blocks relatively undisturbed by the folding going on around them. They include the Moroccan Meseta, the Spanish Meseta, the Hauts-Plateaux

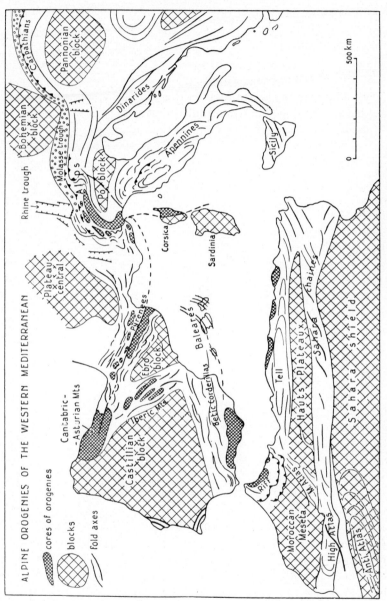

ALPINE OROGENIES OF THE WESTERN MEDITERRANEAN

cores of orogenies

blocks

fold axes

Fig. 255. Alpine orogenies of the Western Mediterranean.

in Algeria, some undefined blocks in the Western Mediterranean, perhaps one in the Tyrrhenian Sea, the Hungarian Pannonian block, and perhaps many more of smaller size. We can sometimes trace the Palaeozoic history from one block to the next across the Tertiary mountain chain when the latter contains sufficient exposures of older rocks in a not too metamorphosed state. The Pyrenees are an example. The conclusion that the blocks formed one continuous unit before the Tertiary folding is fully warranted. In this vast peneplained territory, sinking basins developed and were filled first with Mesozoic and later with Tertiary sediments. The folding, as the sinking set in at different times, was repeated with varying frequency in the different mountain chains. The claim that the folding was sharply restricted to the geo-synclinal basins is not quite true because we find both non-basined parts of the crust and strongly folded geosynclines included in the mountain chains. Nevertheless, in broad lines, the basins and folding zones coincide with the exclusion of what has been termed parageo-syncline by Schuchert. The blocks or nuclei sometimes became partly nuclear (parageosynclinal) basins, and partly remained continuously above sea level. The same arrangement is still visible now; some of the blocks are sunk beneath sea level, some form high platforms.

The orogenic belts never became clearly defined before the present mountain chains were actually there. It would certainly be erroneous, for instance, to suppose that anyone could have predicted the present configuration of orogenies with any accuracy from the geologic map in the middle of the Upper Cretaceous.

When the real folding started in the Upper Cretaceous after some preliminary earlier Cretaceous movements, the borders of the African and European shields approached towards one another, pressing up the border zones, geosynclinal or not, pushing the intermediary blocks in various directions, sometimes breaking them, and causing their intervening links to fold in various stages of compression.

In this sequence of events it is clear that the Sahara block was by far the most solid and stable one (none but the Upper Cretaceous transgressions ever covered it for instance), and that as we go further north the geosynclinal subsidence is deeper and larger, and the folding becomes more intense. The northern boundary of the orogenic belt is, in accordance with this fact, much less clearly defined; and one could easily defend the thesis that the Betic Cordillera in the south of Spain, which has a great pile of nappes on its northern flank, like the Alps, is the real northern boundary, and not the Pyrenees which have been folded only moderately in the Alpine period. On the other hand one might assign the Wealden dome in southern England, the Paris basin or the North German basin, all of them lightly folded by Tertiary or Mesozoic movement, to the orogenic belt of the Tethys.

A very short review of three major mountain chains of the Western Mediterranean belt will show us how different they are. (For further analysis see Chapter 26.)

The *High Atlas*, bordering the Sahara shield to the north and partly separated from it by a marginal trough filled by younger Cretaceous and Tertiary sediments which are partly of continental facies, was a Lower and Middle Jurassic geosyncline folded in post-Eocene time, and again to a lesser degree, in Miocene time. A peculiarity is that the Tertiary chain extends much further west than the Jurassic basin did. In the central High Atlas the pre-Cambrian and Palaeozoic was never covered by the Jurassic nor by the regional Upper Cretaceous transgressions; nevertheless its upheaval surpasses that of the calcareous High Atlas further east. Further east along the border of the Sahara shield the geosyncline is mainly of a Lower and Upper Cretaceous age, and the folding is quite different from that of the High Atlas. Towards the Atlantic the High Atlas chain disappears with a sharp plunge, towards the east it flattens out. Apparently both geosynclinal basining and folding are bound to the Sahara shield border but are independent from one another. The folding is very superficial, and of the type encountered in the Jura Mountains. There is no central crystalline mass, and the marginal troughs are only slightly developed. A very interesting feature is the longitudinal zoning by faults, separating blocks of relative intense folding and blocks with hardly any folding. There is some magmatic activity in post-Lias time (Cretaceous) of a basic (anorthosite-trondhjemite) nature. It is at any rate later than the geosynclinal phase and earlier than the folding.

The present altitude of the High Atlas chain is due to a Pliocene uplift.

The *Pyrenees* represent a real orthotectonic Hercynian orogeny, simply rejuvenated by uplift; paratectonic folding took place in its marginal troughs during the Alpine orogenic period (an Upper Cretaceous and a post-Eocene phase). A large longitudinal fault (see Chapter 12) reached down below the crest into the basic layer and permitted the ascension of small masses of basic rocks and metasomatizing solutions. The marginal troughs remained free of any magmatic activity. Towards the west the southern marginal trough develops into an independent Cretaceous geosyncline with the same kind of folding as further east. Towards the east the axial zone plunges a little and is then cut off by the Mediterranean. Its northern marginal trough flattens out to some extent towards the east and can be followed along the coast into the western Alpine front zone. Long after the last folding a general uplift, in the Miocene or Pliocene or both, gave the Pyrenees their present level.

The *Alps* are characterized by a whole series of geosynclines separated by geanticlinal ridges. The southern geosyncline is Triassic, the middle is Jurassic and the northern is of Cretaceous age. The central geosyncline developed into the Pennine Alps, and is characterized by a basic initial phase and by extreme folding accompanied by strong metamorphism.

The northern geosyncline, the Helvetides, had no magmatic phase, was very strongly folded and thrusted, and finally glided down the northern slope of its originally northern geanticlinal ridge into the marginal trough.

The southern Triassic geosynclinal region, the Lombardy Alps, was strongly disturbed by longitudinal faults and subsequent folding. It had no proper magmatic phase, but on the very deep-reaching fault-line which now separates it from the Pennine Alps we find several post-tectonic granitic intrusions, and one pre- or syntectonic basic intrusion, the Ivrea zone. The folding was very intense over the whole breadth of the structure and occurred in many phases, the oldest in the centre, the younger ones in the marginal parts. To the west, the structure curves round southwards and becomes simpler and less intensely folded. Finally, it plunges towards the Mediterranean and is cut off by the sea. Towards the east its northern units merge into the Carpathians and its southern units flatten out and are replaced by other structures.

The final uplift occurred in the Pliocene, not long after the strong Miocene orogenic phase.

Its southern marginal trough merges into the independent Po basin, the sediments of which cover, in the west, all of the original southern Alpine unit.

Its northern marginal trough is well developed in the centre and to the east, but disappears in the west, where the Jura Mountains join with the Alpine structures.

To detect fundamental characteristics of mountain chains of the intercontinental type, one should enquire if there are any properties which these three chains have in common. There are very few indeed. A Pliocene uplift after largely varying intervals of quiescence following the last folding phase is perhaps the most obvious common trait.

In addition, the thickness of sediments in the marginal troughs is perhaps roughly in accordance with the intensity of folding; and finally, the pattern of longitudinal zoning is common property to all of them. But all their most prominent characteristics are totally different, and hence it would be a fallacy to look *a priori* for a common origin.

When we direct our attention to circum-continental mountain chains we need not wonder that we again find great differences and little in common in the Appalachians and in the western Cordilleran belt. It is somewhat doubtful whether these last mountain chains can really be regarded as a separate group, for in both cases, and perhaps in all circum-continental chains, there is good reason to suppose that these chains were flanked originally by some emerged land outside their present location; land that has disappeared since then, warped down in the adjoining ocean.

But more recently these hypothetical outer land regions have been replaced by largely hypothetical island arcs, often volcanic, and themselves a portion of the orogenic belt. (Chapter 27.)

Finally, in reviewing the typical island arcs of the Pacific (Chapter 28) we shall again find other different characteristics.

GEOSYNCLINES AND BASINS

I have already remarked that there is a close connexion between a mountain chain and a geosyncline, the geosyncline being the forerunner of a mountain chain. But this relation has proved to be loose. We find many basins which were never folded and we also find portions of mountain chains which have never been geosynclines. The non-folded basins are numerous, the folded mountain chains not preceeded by a geosynclinal phase are perhaps exceptions.

The conception of the relation between a mountain chain and a geosyncline is due to James Hall, who published in 1859 the third volume of his "Palaeontology of New York", containing his conclusions that mountain chains are apt to occupy elongated belts with exceptionally thick sediments, the sinking and the folding being due to the loading of sediments on a relatively narrow strip. Since then the causal connexion between sinking and sedimentation and between

sinking and compression has been continually discussed; but no
generally accepted conclusion has been reached, although the necessity
of a causal connexion has been recognized as valid.

There are two problems. The first is simple: Is the sinking the
cause of sedimentation, or is the sedimentation the cause of the
sinking? The answer is definite: to start more intensive sedimentation
in one place than in another, there must be a basin in the first place; to
sustain the basin as a place of extra sedimentation the sinking must at
least keep up with the rate of sedimentation, and this result can never
be reached without active sinking. The load of sediment helps, but
isostatic adjustment is always only a fraction of the load and the
sinking must therefore be primary in order to keep up with the filling.

The second problem is the causal relation between mountain building
and the geosyncline. If the compression were the result of basining,
all ordinary longitudinal basins ought to have been folded, which is
certainly not the case. The original conception of James Hall that the
loading caused the folding cannot be sustained any longer. If, on
the other hand, basining were due to compression one could expect
that the arrest of compression could occur either before or after actual
folding took place, resulting either in an unfolded basin or in a mountain chain. This point of view is all the more attractive because we
have already concluded that basining is the cause of sedimentary
infilling. Our final result, then, is that compression causes the sinking
of the basin and the mountain building; and therefore that the
connexion between geosynclines and mountain building must be
sought in a common cause and not in a direct interaction.

The result of our reasoning is not new in any way, but was already
reached by Dana in 1873. Dana recognized the division of the crust
into continental and oceanic areas — a division inherited from the time
when the crust was first formed — and thought that lateral stress first
caused basins to form on the margins of continents by a downbending
of the crust, and then threw up the mountain chains, simply because
these margins were the weaker portions of the crust. It is to be regretted
that the basic truth and soundness of Dana's reasoning have so often
been neglected, and that so much new but irrelevant evidence has been
used to challenge his views. Most of the confusion has arisen from the
fact that the definition of a geosyncline had from the beginning a dual
character, because both Hall and Dana saw it as a combination of
thick sediments and folding. The question therefore arises as to whether
a geosyncline is mainly characterized by its sedimentary rocks or by

its folding. Haug (1900) for instance, defined a geosyncline as sedimentation in his bathyal zone (800 m), and therefore considered deep-sea troughs as typical geosynclines, though admitting the existence of shallow water geosynclines. For others, e.g. von Bubnoff (1931) and Stille (1936) the main characteristic of a geosyncline is its intensity of folding. An excellent discussion of the development of thought in this respect has been given by Glaessner and Teichert (1947) to which paper I refer my reader for details. I shall not enter into the complicated nomenclature that has sprung up in recent times, culminating with Kay (1947).

In accordance with the original concept of James Hall and Dana, I propose to use the term *geosyncline* only for those accumulations of sediments of great thickness which have been severely folded. The term *basin* can then be used for thick sediment accumulations which have not been folded or, in a historical sense, which have not yet been folded. A deep-sea *furrow* which has not been filled with sediments can be referred to as a furrow or a trench. A *rift* is a depressed strip between faults.

A basin, as defined above, conforms to general use, and is a synonym for the "parageosyncline" of Schuchert and Stille, and for some of the nuclear and discordant basins of Umbgrove. Some of Umbgrove's nuclear basins I would however call "blocks". Umbgrove made a subdivision of nuclear basins in our sense, and distinguished "isochronous" ones, concordant within a territory with a single trend; "anisochronous" ones, which were enclosed between different trends, and finally discordant basins, superimposed upon any kind of trends in the basement. A close study of basins reveals, however, that one can always detect some kind of connexion between the elongation or axis of the basin and the trend of the basement, and I think that the subdivision is therefore superfluous. A typical discordant basin like the Michigan basin, for instance, is enclosed between broad arches in the Pre-Cambrian basement of the Canadian shield; and the Paris basin is distinctly parallel, its older formations in particular, with the Hercynian trend of the Brabant massif. Some of Umbgrove's nuclear basins are blocks between mountain chains which have sometimes been submerged and received sediments, the Pannonian block for instance (the Hungarian Plain); others such as the Castillian block in Spain have been mainly elevated. In general, the thickness of their sediments is smaller than in the surrounding geosynclines, and their facies is apt to be continental.

Other basins are situated on the margin of a continent, e.g. the Gulf Coast basin which is a "paralia geosyncline" in Kay's nomenclature. But here also the older sedimentary series show distinct parallelism with the continental border, and their transgression on the continent is not fundamentally different from any other circumcontinental geosyncline. In our terminology it is a basin because it has not been folded — yet.

The "rift" in our terminology becomes a "taphro geosyncline" with Kay. I prefer the shorter word which every geologist knows.

A deep-sea furrow becomes a "geotectocline" in Hess's nomenclature because this author suspects that a deep-sea furrow will become the axis of a major orogeny; I feel safer with the purely descriptive term.

The proper geosyncline certainly merits a closer examination. According to its definition it is an elongated basin with a thick series of sediments which has been strongly folded in contrast with the mild folding that many basins show.

But this definition leaves a very wide range of epeirogenic and orogenic structures of different character under one heading. We have seen already in the preceding pages how totally different mountain chains of the same period and the same elevation may be; and their original basins were at least as different. I do not think however that the current subdivisions are satisfactory, for they are mostly genetic and not descriptive and therefore tend far too much to generalize special features of particular orogenies.

As in mountain chains, I should like to distinguish three groups: *intercontinental geosynclines*, like the Urals (mesogeosyncline = Mediterranean geosyncline of Schuchert); *circum-continental geosynclines*, like the Appalachian geosyncline; and *circum-oceanic geosynclines*. We have to admit that in many cases one is in doubt whether at the time of formation the basin was of circum-Pacific or circumcontinental character. Perhaps the types are not so very different. But the subdivision is clear in its purpose, and their characteristics may emerge later. Besides this orographical distinction one can distinguish clearly two types, those that precede the main folding and those that come after. The latter type of basin is called a *marginal trough* ("Saumtiefe" of Stille; idiogeosyncline of Umbgrove), and it may be folded or not. The molasse basin of the Alps is a very gently folded marginal trough; those of the Pyrenees have been more strongly folded. The marginal trough is short-lived and filled with syntectonic and post-tectonic sediments; it is the effect of the folding and it is marginal to the folding. The geosynclines which preceded the folding may be called *orthogeosynclines* when they are large. They are long-lived and show several stages during their development and end in an orogeny. Sometimes they show an initial magmatic phase in the beginning of their history (exogeosyncline, Stille and Kay); sometimes this is absent (miogeosyncline, Stille); and they are apt to split up into separate basins (epieugeosynclines, Kay) towards the end. But I think that many more subdivisions would have to be created to do justice to the great variety of geosynclinal development. Since we are not yet far enough advanced in our knowledge about the genesis of a mountain chain, I prefer to restrict the term orthogeosyncline to large, severely compressed geosynclines; the smaller ones like that of the High Atlas we may call minor geosynclines (the monogeosyncline of Schuchert, 1925).

When we want to emphazise the fact that a particular orogenic zone is characterized by an initial basic magmatic phase we can use Kay's term of exogeosyncline.

An orthogeosyncline has a special characteristic, a shifting centre; when it is an intercontinental geosyncline we can generally recognize an epicontinental facies on both margins; and on one margin when it is peripheral to a continent. The centre may be filled with grauwacke facies, which for some people is the typical geosynclinal facies (O. T. Jones, 1938, and Krynine, for instance), and which is called flysch facies in Switzerland. There they regard the flysch facies of alternating sands and clays not only as typical of the central zone of the geosyncline, but in particular of its later phases when intergeosynclinal ridges have emerged and have increased the slopes. Others, like Haug, think of the epicontinental facies of well-stratified limestones and marls as the typical geosynclinal and bathyal facies (cf. Chapter 20). The shift of the geosyncline may be either towards the continent or away from it; but one can state in general terms that a shift towards the continent occurs during the development of one single geosynclinal period, as in the Alps, for instance; and a shift away from the continent takes place when different geosynclines separated by orogenic periods are peripheral round the same continent, as in north-east America, where the Laurentian, Taconic, and Acadian orogenies are concentric round the Canadian shield (Grabau, 1940). In the Palaeozoic Cordilleran geosyncline, the original orthogeosyncline of very large width was eventually split up into two by a central geanticline (the sequentgeosyncline of Schuchert). There is, however, a distinction in geosynclines which may be of some importance in their later development but which is not made in the current systems of subdivision.

A basin like that of the present Gulf Coast is decidedly asymmetric in the sense that it is bordered by land on one side and by sea on the other, with the result that the thickest sedimentary series is represented by the accumulation on the continental slope, and that it wedges-out landwards by transgressive and regressive series and seawards by simple thinning of each member, i.e. by facies change. The same situation can be found at the end of the Lower Cretaceous of the central Alpine geosyncline, where the Upper Cretaceous has a deep-sea facies, in the southern Alps, which continues southwards in the Apennines. Subsequently a ridge, separating the centre of the geosyncline from its seaward extension, was warped up in the Upper Cretaceous, during the first Alpine folding phase in the centre of the geosyncline, but in the early geosynclinal phase the geosyncline had one shelf margin and one deep-sea margin.

In contrast with this asymmetrical shape stands the symmetrical geosyncline; we may take the Welsh Caledonian geosyncline described by O. T. Jones (1938) as the prototype of this group. Such a symmetric geosyncline has shelves on both sides, and its sediments have the typical grauwacke facies of graded sandstones in its centre, a facies which is lacking in the asymmetric open geosyncline.

Whether the symmetric type and the asymmetric type have a different orogenic history cannot be ascertained at present with our incomplete knowledge of too few mountain chains. One would suppose that the asymmetric geosyncline would develop into an asymmetric structure like the Alps or Appalachians, and the symmetric type into a more or less symmetric structure like the Pyrenees or High Atlas; but whether this is a rule or just a coincidence is difficult to decide.

In summarizing the subject of the nomenclature of sedimentation areas, we can formulate our point of view as follows. As a first subdivision we recognize:

Blocks: stable units within an orogenic system, either submerged (ocean blocks) or emerged (continental blocks) or outside the orogenic systems (shield blocks).

Basins: subsided, sediment filled, only slightly folded or unfolded areas on the shield or on their margin.

Rifts: elongated, subsided strips between faults.

Furrows: (trench or trough), elongated strips on the margins of ocean, not filled or only partly filled with sediments.

Geosynclines: elongated, subsided, strongly folded basins, containing thick sedimentary series.

They may be asymmetric or symmetric.

They may be large and continuous, i.e. *orthogeosynclines*, or smaller and then will be called minor or *monogeosynclines*. On the other hand they may be *intercontinental, circum-continental* or *circum-Pacific*. They may have an initial magmatic phase (exogeosynclines) or may be of the epicontinental type (miogeosynclines.)

A *Marginal trough* is a basin, folded or not, which is marginal to a mountain chain and is due to the folding.

I think that we have to be content for the moment with this subdivision because our knowledge of geosynclines in general and their orogenic history in particular is too scanty to warrant any genetic system.

CONTINENTS AND OCEANS

The permanency of the continents and oceans has been discussed to a great extent. We have seen the evidence which points very convincingly to the existence of granite floes floating on a basaltic layer, the floes being the continents and the basaltic or ultrabasic layer the bottom of the oceans. The discussion does not centre round the question of whether a continental area can change into part of an ocean, but of whether the continents and oceans are stationary and have been in their present positions since the earth's crust came into existence.

On the one hand we find those who want to explain the world-wide distribution of faunas by land bridges spanning the oceans; and on the other, those who want to let the continents drift away from one another after a period of established faunal or floral conformity. In my discussion in Chapter 33 of the different orogenic theories we shall find that continental drift is very unsatisfactory from an orogenic point of view, and that the conformities of land faunas or floras for a certain period can always be matched by dissimilarities, whereas the better known marine faunas can be followed for long distances along former coast lines. I cannot enter into anything like a full discussion of the arguments, but will state only that the permanency of the oceans and continents seems to be no longer seriously questioned from the palaeontologist's point of view.

Quite another question, however, is how far the present continental shelf boundaries are permanent. Obviously the continental coasts have never been permanently at their present position. On the contrary, the old shields have been growing by addition of orogenic belts and have been losing by subsidence of peripheral blocks. But it is often believed that all these additions and subtractions are confined to changes in the continental shields, and that the continental slopes have therefore been more or less permanently fixed in their present position since the Archean.

We shall however find that there is evidence that the continental Archean shields have continued to grow; that throughout geological history the continents have encroached on the oceanic region – not very much perhaps, and more in one place than in another, but still to such a degree that strict permanency of the boundaries of the continental shelves can hardly be accepted.

On the other hand the continental slope is often not very well defined, and one is often at a loss where to place it on the map. Also, we know of numerous instances in which it is clear that large chunks of the continents have sunk to oceanic depth and have apparently never risen again.

The coastal regions of the continents have widely differing characters. The west coast of the American continent is, in its large sweep of the Cordilleran system, the most simple coast line to be found on the globe. Nevertheless, in detail many irregularities occur; for instance, it looks probable that the coast ranges of California are cut off by the coastline in the north, and die out on the shelf or in the ocean. The west coast of the Pacific, with its island arcs, is less simple but still offers quite a comprehensible picture. The Atlantic coast of North America with its Appalachian mountain system on the margin is comparable, but not quite, to its west coast. It is difficult to believe that the Piedmont province is not bounded in the east by a less metamorphic zone of some breadth, and one is tempted to believe that much of this structure is hidden beneath the Cretaceous blanket on the shelf.

When, however, we turn our attention to the east coast of South America, or the eastern Atlantic coast, or the coast of the Indian Ocean, there is much less concordance between the structural lines on the continent and the boundary line of the shelf.

The Caledonian mountain chain of Scandinavia, for instance, is parallel to the coast although some of it is covered by the sea; but in the south of Norway it is cut off by the coast line and emerges again in Scotland and also in the north of Ireland. Obviously a large north-westerly portion of the chain has sunk beneath sea level and is contained in the continental shelf. Some geotectonicians like to draw a line across the Atlantic to link it up with the Taconian (Caledonian) chain of the maritime provinces of North America, which have much in common with the European portion and would form a welcome land bridge for migrations of coastal marine fauna.

The EW trending Hercynian orogeny of south-west England is cut off by the Atlantic in South Wales, an area where there are major tectonic effects such as the overthrust of Pre-Cambrian on Carboniferous in Pembrokeshire.

What happened to the Hercynian folds of Brittany — were they cut off by the Atlantic? In Spain the cutting off is less abrupt; and in the west coast of North Africa we find, both in the case of the younger Tertiary Riff Mountains and in that of the older High Atlas, that their orogenies die out before reaching the coast. All these orogenic features, abutting against the Atlantic coastline and sometimes finding a possible homologue on the other side, make us doubt the permanent character of the Atlantic Ocean. On the other hand, seismic evidence is distinctly in favour of only a thin sialic crust on the ocean bottom, and the presence of the NS feature of the Atlantic ridge is in direct contradiction with any tectonic feature crossing the ocean. Nor can we expect a direct connexion between the Mediterranean orogenies and the Antillean island arcs. The latter forms a closed loop, and the former really dies out before it reaches the coastline.

Our information about the ocean bottom and shelf bottom structures is obviously too scanty to allow any definite conclusions, but as far as we can judge at present I certainly prefer to accept the view that the continental shelf border can often sink to great depths and thus conceal the structural dying-out of the mountain chains which enter it from the continent. On the Moroccan coast, for instance, we find not only that the structures flatten out before they reach the coast, but also a narrow downbent strip along the coast which constitutes the beginning of the continental slope. The east coast of Greenland shows the same kind of continental border flexure.

Apparently the continental margin is always a mobile zone, being warped up and down even when no geosyncline or mountain chain is in the making.

In the Mediterranean we must accept large blocks of continents which have sunk down to great depths. The north coast of Algeria, for instance, is cut off right along the centre of a geological uplift where the crystalline cores of an orogenic system come to the surface. There is also every reason to look for the continuance of the Betic orogeny of southern Spain in the Balearic Island structures, and to suppose that the islands of Elba and Corsica are only small remnants of much longer orogenic systems. The disappearance of the Pyrenean mountain chain in the Mediterranean towards the east, and its continuation in the sea along the south coast of France, linking it up with the Maritime Alps, can hardly be doubted. All these numerous vertical movements are incomprehensible from the point of view of isostatic compensations, but any other theory explaining the pattern of positive and negative radial crust movements is lacking. A contraction of the earth's interior could, of course, explain the sinking in itself, but does not offer a reason for the particular pattern. I think it is obvious from this bewildering variety of often contradictory evidence that we are not yet in a position to form an opinion on the function of the continental shelf border. Extensive research is needed and fortunately is in progress in many quarters.

Chapter 25

Magmatic Phases in Orogenesis

Orogenic belts and rift valleys are both accompanied by magmatic phenomena which are clearly connected with their formation. On the other hand, there are magmatic manifestations which are outside the rupture zones of the earth's crust and are typical of the shields. An interesting symposium on this question can be found in "Tectonic Control of Igneous Activity" published in 1954 by the Department of Geology of the University of Leeds.

The orogenic belts, being without doubt the most profoundly disturbed of the earth's crust, have also the most complex magmatic history, with migmatization and batholiths, basic intrusions and volcanic zones, whereas the rifts and shields are characterized only by volcanism.

The subdivision of magmatic phenomena into those related to mountain chains and those related to stable shields is therefore genetically warranted.

THE OROGENIC MAGMATIC CYCLES

The most simplified picture of the magmatic cycle of an orogenic belt contains three distinct phases:

1st phase, basic rock intrusions (ophiolites) and extrusion of spilitic lavas in the geosynclinal stage.

2nd phase, syntectonic migmatization accompanied by pegmatitic granitic magma and late-tectonic granodiorite batholiths.

3rd phase, post-tectonic volcanism.

The magmatic cycle in three phases is often not complete, or cannot be ascertained to be complete because the region has not been sufficiently denuded. The connexion between the 2nd and 3rd phases is often obscure; sometimes they are supposed to be contemporaneous, the volcanoes being the surface indications of an active batholith; in other instances the volcanic action is very much retarded and it becomes doubtful whether it may still be regarded as belonging to the past orogenic phase.

Nevertheless, large mountain chains generally show all three phases and the less intense the orogenesis the less complete are the magmatic phases. Moreover, the older chains have a much stronger magmatic character than the younger ones, and the Mediterranean belt less than the circum-Pacific belt.

The Initial Phase. The initial magmatic phase is either a volcanic phase of basic rocks of which pillow lavas are the most typical components, or equally typically an ultra-mafic intrusive phase, or both. The volcanic rocks alternate with the sedimentary rocks; the olivine-bearing ultra-mafic rock is intrusive in these sediments. As these ultra-mafic olivine-bearing rocks, peridotites or dunites, are often very much serpentinized, they are often referred to as the serpentine belt of a mountain chain; a better term would be "peridotite belt" (Hess). The peridotites seldom cause any thermal metamorphism in the surrounding rocks, although in some cases, as in the Pyrenees, the enclosing limestones are highly metamorphosed and altered into scapolite and hornblende-bearing carbonate rocks. In this case the field evidence shows, however, that the metamorphism cannot be due to the intrusion of the basic rocks but is an independent phenomenon although probably related to the same compression which caused the peridotite (and gabbroic) intrusions. The temperature of the intruded rock must therefore have been low, not more than 500° C, and probably less (Turner and Verhoogen, 1951, p. 245). Hence it is supposed that the rock consisted largely of olivine crystals, with small quantities of magmatic water or other liquid lubricating the whole mass (Bowen, 1928). The association with spilitic lava or other basic volcanic rocks would suggest that the peridotites represent the gravitative basic differentiate of a spilitic magma. The widespread and often very deep-reaching serpentinization of the peridotites can in most cases be attributed partly to the action of this water-rich lubricating intergranular liquid, but principally to the water content of the invaded sediments, and not to weathering, which would attack only the surface of the rock. In the case of the North Pyrenean fault, it is more probable that the connexion between the surface (or the near-surface) and the great depth at which the peridotite accumulation must have originated is not made by the subsidence of a deep geosynclinal basin, but by a fundamental fault reaching down to this great depth and followed by compression. All peridotite belts need not therefore be in the axis of a geosyncline. The peridotites are often associated with radiolarites and very fine grained limestones in a pelitic sediment, indicating a large basin of deep water far from the emerged land.

The intrusive bodies are often small sized in comparison with granite stocks and batholiths; and their distribution in the invaded rock is mostly very chaotic, at any rate, as regards smaller bodies. This is also due to the extreme distortion these plastic rocks often undergo in the centre of a compressed geosyncline. Their very smallness contributes to their susceptibility to serpentinization by the activity of connate water. Other instances are however known, in the Mediterranean Belt, Cyprus, Syria, and Celebes, for instance, where the peridotites have accumulated in great masses with very little sediment, and very little compression.

The volcanic rocks belonging to the initial magmatic phase are usually of the spilite-keratophyre class, although rhyolites occur also. Many of the spilitic lava flows form pillow lavas, assumed to indicate a subaqueous effusion. The sodic nature of the spilite rocks is assumed by Turner and Verhoogen to be due to a contamination of a basaltic intrusive, deep down in the geosyncline, by the sodic environment of arkosic grauwackes typical of this kind of geosyncline and by their connate water; but the relation grauwackes-spilites is not always present. On the other hand, there are numerous examples of the relation of arkosic grauwackes with spilites, of which one of the simplest is that formed by the Algonkian Dal-formation of south-west Sweden. Both below and above the spilite bearing middle Dal-formation there occur thick arkosic grauwackes, and there is every reason to believe the spilite flows to be subaqueous (Overeem, 1948), but there is no field evidence whatsoever of contamination. In the Appalachian belt of the eastern United States the Cambrian and Ordovician rocks include large quantities of basaltic and rhyolitic lava flows, but as in many other cases it is difficult to decide whether the volcanic phase belongs to a post-Pre-Cambrian orogeny or to a pre-Caledonian orogeny, both being probably present in that region. The classic spilites of the Devonian of the Variscean chain reaching from Cornwall to Germany are a much better example because they occur outside a Caledonian orogenic belt. In general, one has to admit that in the older orogenies the volcanics of the initial magmatic phase do not consistently show the typical spilite association. Often they are of the basalt-andesite rock association. Nevertheless the spilites are more or less confined to the initial magmatic phase. The Alpine orogenies of the Mediterranean belt seldom have an initial volcanic phase but only intrusive peridotites; whereas the American geosynclines, both eastern and western, have very large initial volcanic phases (Marshall Kay, 1951).

In the better-known mountain chains the peridotite belt is often, but not always (Anatolia for instance is a notable exception), restricted to one longitudinal zone only — to the Piedmont province of the Appalachians, for instance, or to the Pennine zone of the Alps. Hess (1937) made a fairly complete analysis of all the known peridotite belts and I refer the reader to his work for more details.

The origin of the basic melt is difficult to ascertain, but its restriction to the most central and deepest part of the largest geosynclines, in the younger orogenies at least, proves that it is formed only in special circumstances of the geosynclinal belt and that it is derived from a deeply buried level which can be tapped only by a geosyncline which has subsided deeply.

Whether we accept the sodic character of spilites as a secondary feature acquired during the ascension of the magma, or see it as a special differentiation trend of basaltic magma, there is in neither case any objection to the supposition that the origin of the ultrabasic magma must be sought somewhere in or below the basaltic substratum, which also furnishes the igneous rocks of the shields, the flood-basalts.

How this magma reserve is tapped and how it is formed, and why it is different from the next phase of the orogenic magmatic cycles, will be shown in the next paragraph and in the final chapter.

The Syntectonic and Late-Tectonic Phases. When Turner and Verhoogen (1951, p. 360) consider the generation of magma, they come to the conclusion that, although the total amount of energy available from the radioactivity of crustal material is largely sufficient to raise its temperature from 800° to 1100° C, no mechanism can be found to effect such a local concentration of energy, although the amount is relatively small. Neither the blanketing effect of a 10 km thick layer of sediments in geosynclines nor the transport of heat from below by convection currents seem to offer a sufficient increase of temperature. The authors conclude with the remark "that its precise nature remains an unsolved problem". The question of the generation of magma with temperatures like those of lava streams, gets quite another accent when we regard it from an orogenic point of view. Both the influence of decreasing pressure and the presence of water will lower the melting temperature of rocks. The lowering by decrease of pressure is estimated at $\pm 4 \%$ per unit of pressure equalling the weight of 1 km of crust rock and from an increase of 0 % to 7 % of water, a decrease of 1100° to 600° C in the melting temperature is probable (Daly, 1933, p. 67). Both factors combined would certainly allow liquid magma to form and to intrude from below into higher levels of the crust at relatively low temperatures. The addition of water to the melt would certainly take place when an intrusion reached the sedimentary rocks at the bottom of a deep geosyncline which still contains considerable amounts of connate sea water, or produces water by the thermal metamorphism of its rocks. A decrease of pressure is equally probable as soon as folding takes place, in particular at the beginning, because the start of an uplift is always characterized by a decrease of pressure below the centre of the uplift. When a certain amount of lateral compression has taken place the deficiency of pressure is replaced by an excess of pressure. It is exactly the same process as takes place in an ordinary fold at the surface and particularly well exemplified by diapiric salt structures, where salt first accumulates in the core of the anticline and is later squeezed out towards the surface.

Hence the optimal conditions for melting of rocks are realized at the start of an orogenic phase, and those for intrusion in a later phase (cf. Fig. 256).

The origin of the intrusive magma has been the subject of many speculations, and this is not the place to enlarge on these problems. We will follow the well-considered opinion of many modern scientists, that migmatization and the genesis of granite magma are closely associated, for the field evidence is strongly in favour of this relation. It has been principally the Scandinavian school, Sederholm, Eskola, Backlund, Magnusson, and Wegmann, which has developed the concept of the differential fusion of basic rocks of the simatic substratum in which it is emphasized that the constituents of lower melting point will melt first, and that thus a mixture of mafic crystals and an acid granitic melt will be formed. The heat is generally believed to be derived from radioactive energy from the overlying primitive granitic shell, increased locally by the approach of the latter through down-bending in the geosynclinal axis. It would be erroneous to imagine this two-phase aggregate, solid crystals and interstitial melt, as a fluid containing floating crystals. At the start at least it would resemble much more a honeycomb structure in which the walls predominate, a solid mass containing a certain amount of fluid. It is even doubtful whether it ever reached the stage of a fluid with floating crystals,

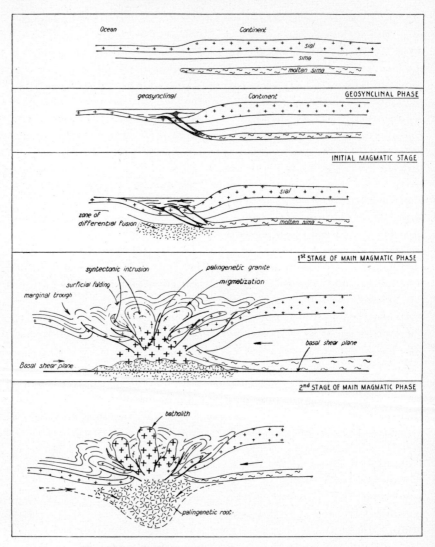

Fig. 256. Sequence of events in a major orogeny.

because long before that happened the orogenic stress would press out the melt from its pores. This tectonic process can be compared to the shearing that takes place in a water-saturated sand, as described in Chapter 2. The moment the walls of the honeycomb structures are broken by the stress, the hydrostatic pressure of the fluid phase is immensely increased because the grain pressure drops to zero, and the full weight of the rock pressure and lateral stress has to be borne by the fluid. The resistance to deformation suddenly falls to a fraction of the stress that was needed to break the walls, and catastrophic events are obviously apt to follow. The origin of the greatly accelerated distortion which we call an orogeny must be sought partly in this sequence of events: weakening by differential fusion of a basal layer; rupture by the stress which is causing the epeirogenic downbending of the geosyncline, hence mechanical separation of the upper layer from its substratum; great reduction of resistance to this stress; and therefore passage from elastic strain to plastic strain with the consequence of accelerated distortion.

The melt, under excessive pressure, will take advantage of the deformation of the rocks above and will insert itself in all possible fissures and shear-planes, lubricating them and thus contributing to the decrease of resistance. In the beginning of the folding process there is a notable decrease of pressure on the horizontal stratification planes, as a result of the elastic arching, and much of the inserted melt will follow these planes, forming minute concordant veins and sills and large laccoliths. In other words, the process of migmatization has set in under the influence of the high-pressure melt intruding from below. The maximum of pressure decrease will be found in the cores of the large geanticlinal structures, where the elastic process of lifting up the central arch of the anticline causes a strong decrease of the grain pressure. Later, aided by the rapid decrease of pressure and the admixture of connate water from the invaded sediments and of water freed from clay minerals by thermal metamorphism, palingenetic granite magma is formed on a large scale, partly by accumulation of the differentially fused melt from below and partly by fusion of the already migmatic rock. Thus we must distinguish between two processes: at the bottom of the structures, palingenetic granitization; and higher up, migmatization with acid intrusions, usually parallel to the bedding and folded with it.

The palingenetic granite will stay in its chamber unless further lateral shortening causes an extra pressure on the granite, or unless it finds a way out by melting and stoping. There can be little doubt that the late tectonic granitic or grano-dioritic batholiths and stocks find their origin in these palingenetic magma chambers. Their emplacement is still difficult to understand. The large bodies like the Sierra Nevada or Idaho batholiths are certainly not intruded in a single upsurge of magma; on the contrary, careful fieldwork has shown that they consist of many sheets intruded one after the other. It is also true that in many cases of large bodies it can be shown that the invaded rock has been pushed aside, but not to such an extent that room was made for the whole body. The small bodies and stocks are in general more discordant to their environment; they, perhaps, did not elbow their way into their present surroundings as did the larger ones. These late-tectonic intrusions are often referred to as post-tectonic phenomena, on the ground of their discordant position in relation to the trends of the tectonical structure of their surroundings. The theory of "overhead stoping" proposed by Daly (1933) as a means of the emplacement of these bodies, and involving fusion supplemented by detachment of small and large blocks from the roof, was principally a theory to explain the discordant character of stocks and batholiths. The point of view of the ultra-transformists who suppose that even these bodies are the result of metasomatic processes of the rocks *in situ*, either by reaction in solid state or helped by diffusion of hydrothermal or pneumatolitic agencies, is another approach to the same problem. Both explanations have met with serious objections. The overhead stoping implies that all the rock that has been replaced by granite must have been assimilated in the magma, leaving no trace whatsoever, except in the margin of intrusive bodies, a view which is difficult to accept, particularly in view of the homogeneous nature of the granite. On the other hand, a chemical reaction in the solid state on such a large scale is in itself a very doubtful process; and again, the small variability of these granites (or granodiorites), their homogeneous character, their relatively high temperature as indicated by their contact aureoles, and in particular their sharp boundaries against the host rock, all bear witness against metasomatism or metamorphism *in situ*.

By rejecting both the transformist point of view and overhead stoping, the problem of emplacement becomes largely one of structural geology.

First of all, we have to ask ourselves whether the discordant position is really a proof of their post-tectonic character. Although a post-tectonic emplacement certainly would be characterized by discordancy, it is obvious that a syntectonic emplacement of a large body, large in comparison with the amplitude of the folds in which it penetrated, must also necessarily be discordant. Even a pre-tectonic intrusion would not lose its discordant character by folding. Let us think of a fluid but very viscous magma, intruding during the folding; it will find its place not only by pushing aside the layers of rocks and inserting itself consistently between two particular layers; but in addition these layers will be cut by faults and left behind in the upward surge due to lateral stress, making place for the more plastic magmatic mass. The whole process will be very comparable to the diapiric action of incompetent shales and evaporites. There is for instance in principle very little difference on the map between the distribution of salt diapirs in a folded region like North Germany or Tunisia and that of granite bodies like those of Brittany. The analogy between the two phenomena has already been pointed out by Wegmann (1930) but only on the basis of his experience of the Pre-Cambrian rocks of Fennoskandia and Greenland, where the migmatic or highly metamorphosed rocks curve round the granite bodies; and it may well be that in those circumstances the granite bodies were more viscous than the migmatites.

Even if the palingenetic magma in its original chamber had a more or less concordant position, it would be very probable that upon entering the overlying structures it could never find there a concordant position unless it intruded in very small bodies. There is undoubtedly a strong disharmony between the structures at depth and those near the surface, and disharmony always means a multiplication of folds; a large body coming from below therefore enters into a region of relatively small folds and has to find a discordant position.

Almost every batholith or stock shows some "ghost structures" of metamorphic limestone or basic rocks, which sometimes can be directly connected with similar rocks of the host. Such features are generally regarded as a proof either of the melting capacity of the intruder, leaving the ghosts as more resistant portions, or of the formation *in situ* of the granite, also leaving alone those rocks which are less suitable for transformation into granite. Some of these ghosts certainly may have this origin, in particular those that are imbedded in the granites of the first phase, which were much hotter and much more fluid, but many of them have another origin. In almost all Triassic diapirs, for instance, we find drifting floes of the surrounding rock, sometimes made unrecognizable by metamorphism, sometimes still connected at one end to the particular layer of the country rock, sometimes entirely detached from it but still marking its original position by a string of blocks, sometimes just floating around in any position whatsoever. Figure 257 gives some examples of these floating blocks of limestone in a diapiric gypsiferous marl of one of the anticlines of the Tunisian-Algerian region. In the centre of the figure we see a folded and disconnected block floating on the marl, and on the

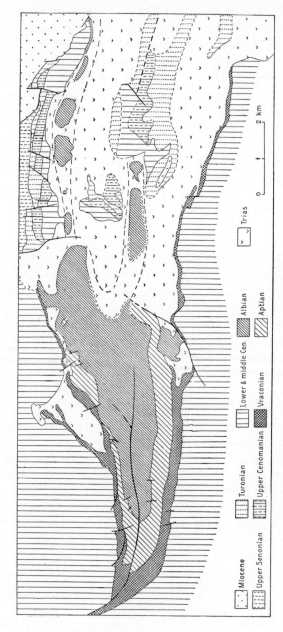

Fig. 257. Ghost structures in Triassic diapir of Ouenza anticline, Algeria.

northern margin of the Triassic diapir we see a string of vertical limestone blocks which form the direct continuation of a particular limestone in the flank of the non-diapiric portion of the anticline. Evidently the intruder has left the hard limestone in place, has broken through it here and there, but has not dislocated it. In other instances, it has detached blocks from their original place and has carried them along, disturbing the original structure. With these examples in mind, it is obvious that one could never prove or disprove the intrusive character of a granite by measuring the strike and dip of the ghosts. Only in the case where intricate structures can be followed from the non- or less metamorphic country rock into the highly metamorphic facies of the "true" ghosts in a palingenetic granite, as Read has done in Donegal, can one prove the palingenetic genesis of the rock *in situ*.

Post-Tectonic Volcanic Phase. The post-tectonic volcanic phase either follows the second phase almost directly or, as often happens, is separated from it by a long period of denudation. The most striking examples of a long retardation of the post-tectonic phase are the Permian volcanics of Europe, which are certainly closely related with the late Carboniferous folding and granite batholiths (Asturian phase); this is shown both by the field evidence and by the close resemblance of their differentiation diagrams (de Sitter, 1949). The retardation is here represented by a long denudation period, and the volcanic rocks are deposited on a new peneplain. There are other examples, however, where post-volcanic rocks are directly connected with their own synchronous granites, which then have a more alkaline character, as for instance in the late Pre-Cambrian of the Anti-Atlas (Choubert, 1952).

These volcanic rocks are very often accompanied by an intricate system of dikes showing all kinds of differentiation tendencies in the magma, and are themselves equally variable, but all of them have a calc-alkaline character in contrast with the alkaline character of the non-orogenic type. No doubt the long period allowed all sorts of magmatic differentiation, by gravitational differentiation or by assimilation or both. These volcanic rocks and dikes originate from the batholiths of the foregoing phase which did not reach near to the surface, or remnants of the original magma chamber, or small bodies of intruded rocks tucked away in inaccessible spots. Their great diversity is very well explained by the long lapse of time and their varying surroundings, size and depth. Their vents have sometimes a linear arrangement, showing that late fault movements tapped the reservoirs. In other instances they are distributed without any appreciable relation to tectonic lines. The difficulty of explaining their emplacement does not lie in their origin, or in their location but only in their high temperature.

When one accepts the view of Turner and Verhoogen, 1951, that the batholiths and palingenetic granites never reached temperatures rising above 500°–600° C, which is certainly strongly corroborated by the structural features of their intrusion, it is difficult to understand how the high temperatures of the volcanic rocks which reach 1100° C and 1200° C are generated. As has been mentioned, Turner and Verhoogen call it an unsolved problem.

Since the palingenetic granite and its sequence of volcanic rocks is as much a tectonic as a petrological problem, I should like to suggest that the source of energy must again be sought in the radioactive energy of the lower granitic crust in which the palingenesis takes place. There would be no reason to expect an accumulation of heat energy in one particular spot if no special circumstances intervened; it must be connected with the particular emplacement of these bodies.

The Relation of Stress and Magmatic Phases. The sequence of the magmatic cycles in orogeny as it has been sketched in Fig. 256 need not be complete in any one orogenesis. In particular, the initial stage is independent of the next stages because it has quite a different origin. Its presence does not imply continuation, neither does its absence imply the absence of the next stage. The initial stage is bound up with the proximity of a continental shield and a deeply submerged geosynclinal bottom, or deep-reaching faults. The second and third stages are bound up with the presence of a sufficiently thick sialic crust in the geosynclinal region and a sufficiently deep subsidence of its bottom. In short-lived and shallow basins it should be absent, but then the folding cannot be of the same intensity. A typical basin of this shallow kind is the marginal trough of a main chain like the Molasse basin of the Alps. Whether the migmatic zone becomes accessible at the surface is a question of depth of denudation. The migmatite front may rise much higher in one instance than in the next. The batholith stage is certainly bound up with the palingenesis and thus with the preceding migmatite stage, but whether the two will be nicely separated or not, depends entirely on the stress development. With a relatively small stress at the beginning, the palingenesis can proceed without a previous long or intensive migmatite stage, and the diapiric structures and the later volcanic stage may be formed without apparent migmatization. The Cascade mountain volcanics are perhaps the largest examples of this kind of development. On the other hand, a strong stress at the start of the maximum diastrophism will create strong migmatization, which may not be followed by a batholith stage when the stress diminishes after this first stage. In the same way, the development of the volcanic stage may depend on the stress conditions. We have seen that much of this volcanism may be related to a much later arching of the geanticline, causing tension-faults on its summit; failure of this posthumous arching may prevent the development of the volcanic phase.

Besides stress conditions, the total available amount of differential fusion melt may influence the development, and there may be other conditions as well which locally can be of great importance.

The reader will have noticed that a variable stress is invoked in order to explain variations in intensities of the different phases although he will perceive later on, in the final chapter, that a constantly growing global stress is postulated as a fundamental principle. The contradiction is apparent only because the local stress will always depend on local circumstances, and a strong yield to stress at one point will always cause an increase in the neighbourhood and a subsequent decrease at the same spot.

Plutonic and Volcanic Rocks of Continents and Oceans. The occurrence of plutonic and volcanic rocks on the continents, outside the orogenic belts, is much less a structural than a petrological problem, and a short summary will accordingly suffice.

They may be subdivided into three groups:

    a. Basaltic rocks of the oceans

    b. Flood-basalts of the continents

    c. Volcanic rocks of continental regions

In these three groups the basaltic rocks predominate. Each of the first two groups is far greater in volume than the third. From this world-wide predominance of basalts stems the belief that the primary magma is basaltic and that from such a magma all other plutonic associations are derived.

Basaltic Rocks of the Oceans. In the Pacific, all the non-coral islands consist of volcanic rocks, and olivine basalt is by far the most predominant kind. The line that separates the basaltic rocks of this type from the volcanoes associated with the island arcs along its western margin and those of its eastern margin is called the Andesite line, since andesites predominate in this circum-Pacific belt. The line is thought to separate the ocean floor, characterized by the absence of a sialic cover, from the continental border formed by a sheet of sial. The basalts are of the olivine basalt type, and show a differentiation to trachytes and phonolites which is generally thought to be due to fractional crystallization of the parent magma. It is noteworthy that the Indian and Atlantic Ocean volcanoes do not differ in any respect from those of the Pacific; apparently the thin sialic cover of these oceans, if present, does not enter into the magma evolution.

Several attempts have been made to relate the volcanoes to fracture lines or shear-zones, but except in the case of the mid-Atlantic ridge, there is no convincing evidence that these lines represent any reality.

The Atlantic ridge is dotted with volcanic islands from its northern tip, the island of Iceland, over the Azores and St Helena to Ascension. From the ridge itself basaltic rocks were picked up by Ewing (1948) so that it looks as if the ridge is a pressed-up part of the basaltic substratum.

The Atlantic ridge is, next to the circum-Pacific zone, one of the most prominent lines of seismic activity. As such it constitutes a unique phenomenon on the earth's crust, a single structure running almost from Pole to Pole, a disturbed area which never developed into a geosyncline. The close relation of its shape with the coasts of Europe-Africa in the east and the Americas in the west suggests that it has something to do with a general EW directed pressure acting from continent to continent. It would be tempting to relate the ridge in some fashion with the equally long and roughly parallel tension zone of the African–Red Sea–European rift system, but there is no evidence to warrant such relationship.

Flood-Basalts of the Continents. The flood- or plateau-basalts cover very large regions of the stable part of the continents of today but definitely belong to a rather late period of their history. They range from the Jurassic to Recent. Their chemical and mineralogical composition is slightly different from the oceanic basalts, olivine is much scarcer because the magma is slightly oversaturated with silica, and its rare differentiation products are different from those of the olivine basalts of the oceans. The parent magma is called the tholeiitic basalt magma (Kennedy, 1938). The volume of perfectly fluid basalt expelled from the interior is enormous, and is far greater than that of any other kind of rock ever produced by volcanism. Through all these thousands of lava streams very little variation in composition occurs and the conclusion is warranted that they all tapped the same layer, which must be somewhat different from that which produced the olivine basalts of oceanic regions. Because the vents are always covered by the lavas themselves it is doubtful whether the mode of extrusion is of the fissure type. Nevertheless their horizontal attitude, and their occurrence in undisturbed regions only, prove that their upwelling is in principle not a tectonic process; but they seem to be strictly bound, nevertheless, to orogenic phases. It is thought that their ascension has to do with gravity because the lava, with a density of 2.7, is lighter than the overlying rock. The flood-basalts are simply pressed out by hydrostatic pressure. The supply of molten rock at depth must be limited to a certain extent, for after each lava flow, which is often not thicker than 5 m, there follows a long interval during which even lateritic weathering can develop before the next flow covers the weathered ground. The great and unsolved problem is that of the local heat supply which each time can heat up this particular layer of the substratum to the temperature at which the basalt is fluid enough to be expelled. But this problem is a general problem, equally true for all volcanic activity whether it be of oceanic, orogenic, or of continental origin.

Volcanic Rocks of Continental Areas. Many volcanic rocks outside the orogenic belts have definite associations with tectonic trends, mostly rift valleys. They are either of the olivine basalt type and its differentiates, or of the tholeiitic basalt type with strong alkaline differentiates (Shackleton, 1954). Apparently the olivine basalt type is not exclusively oceanic in the same way that the tholeiitic basalt is definitely continental. Typical of the continental type of volcanic rocks are the leucite-bearing rocks, but their distribution, often haphazard, shows that their alkaline character must be due to local circumstances. The rocks of the eastern rift in Africa, for instance, are of the olivine basalt type, wheras the western rift shows some highly alkaline rocks.

There can be little doubt that the great rifts provided opportunity for magma to rise to the surface. All along the European-African rift system volcanoes have arisen, from its southern extremity in Africa to the Oslo region in Norway. The different ages of the volcanics, ranging from Permian to Recent, show the fundamental function of these rifts. It is to be noticed that their time range is about the same as that of the flood-basalts.

In the case of the rifts there is some reason to ascribe a special function of magma differentiation to tectonic factors. The rifts are without doubt regions of tension and dilatation, and there is every reason to suppose that at the bottom of the rift valley a region of minimum pressure was created; we can even advance further and suppose that the thinning of the crust at the bottom of the stretched layer caused a flow of rock to this strip of the crust. In this magma chamber considerable reduction of hydrostatic pressure favoured melting, and when renewed activity along the faults opened a vent, the magma, which had time to develop all kinds of fractional differentiation, could send up different kinds of its derivates. Most of the rifts are broad enough to allow their normal faults, even with a dip of only 45°, to reach below the sialic crust into the basaltic layers. Stress periods which occurred occasionally could also add to the upward surge of magma.

The problems connected with magmatic evolution are largely of a petrological nature, but as we have seen they enter also into the province of structural geology. This in particular is the case in orogenic belts, which have received much more attention in this chapter than the quiet regions of the earth's crust, but even there structural considerations are of importance.

MAGMATIC CYCLES IN THE COURSE OF THE EARTH'S HISTORY

In this chapter we shall learn that the magmatic cycles of an orogenesis have a somewhat different aspect in the older Pre-Cambrian orogenic phases from the younger systems. In Scandinavia, where the sequence of igneous events has been followed up most closely, Backlund (1936) and Magnusson (1937) propose the following phase sequence:

- a. Primorogenic granites, granitization and extensive basic and ultra-mafic volcanic action
- b. Serorogenic granites, migmatization and granitization with special emphasis on pegmatitic igneous action
- c. Post-orogenic granite

This compares extraordinarily well with the schematic picture I drew before, principally from evidence from Palaeozoic mountain chains. The difference lies in the intensity. Whereas our younger orogenies include in general in their initial phase only an intrusive, and more seldom an extrusive, phase of basic and ultramafic rocks, the Pre-Cambrian and more so the geosynclinal phase of Archean orogenies are characterized principally by supracrustal rocks, volcanic and pyroclastic rocks, among which pillow lavas are sometimes predominant. In the more central parts of the orogenies these supra-crustal rocks are granitized, or are in relation with so-called primeval granites. In the second half of the geosynclinal period the igneous activity diminishes, both in Canada and in Scandinavia. The descriptions of the second phase with their widespread migmatization, granitization, and gneissification are only more severe versions, intensifications, of the syn-orogenic phase of the Palaeozoic orogenies I have already described. Pegmatites are typical for both.

The post-orogenic phase embraces mainly granite intrusion and is the same as our late-tectonic phase.

The post-tectonic volcanic phase has probably been washed away by denudation in the Archean regions — or is represented only in the post-orogenic conglomerates which are also typical of the post-volcanic phase of the Palaeozoic orogenies.

I have already drawn attention to the fact that in the youngest Alpine orogenies of the Mediterranean the magmatic cycle appears much reduced. The initial phase is sometimes present, sometimes absent; the syn-orogenic phase is sometimes absent; the late-orogenic batholiths are much less frequent; and a post-tectonic volcanic phase is also very much reduced.

This is true only for the Mediterranean region, and not for its continuation in the Near East—Iran, Caucasus, and Turkey—where the initial phases are very important. Nor is it true for the circum-Pacific region; initial and post-tectonic volcanism is very prominent there. The Californian coastal region, for instance, starts with almost as active an initial volcanism in the Jurassic (post-Nevadan) as in the Archean of Canada and Scandinavia, and is even repeated in the Miocene, perhaps as a post-tectonic phase of the Cretaceous folding but more probably as an initial phase of the Pliocene folding. The Nevadan (late-Jurassic) folding is characterized by large syntectonic intrusions and migmatization and late-tectonic immense batholiths. The post-tectonic volcanic phase is present in profusion (Yellowstone Park blanket, for instance) but is not easily distinguished from flood-basalts of the continental type (e.g. the Columbia Plateau).

The intensity of the magmatic action in orogenies is dependent on the localization on the earth's crust, the intensity of the orogenic forces, and the relative age of the orogeny. It would also be possible to regard the magmatic activity as the primary cause of an orogeny, as van Bemmelen does, for instance. Its intensity could then be decreasing with the increasing age of the earth and vary with the thickness of the crust. However, such a hypothesis is unsatisfactory because all the paratectonic phenomena (tectonic activity without any magmatic phases, outside the mountain chains) become incomprehensible, and even in orthotectonic activities there is no simple and direct relation between the intensities of compression and magmatic activity. Hence we prefer to see the three above-mentioned factors as more or less independent factors, with the compression as the primary cause of any orogeny whether of para- or orthotectonic character. The thickness of the sialic crust has then a preponderant influence on the intensity of the magmatic activity, preventing it on the shields (paratectonics), and favouring it on its borders (circum-Pacific zone). Moreover the initial magmatic phase certainly stands in a different relation to the orogenic disturbances from the syntectonic phase; but the cause of this difference in relation will remain obscure until we have better understanding of the relations themselves.

Chapter 26

The Intercontinental Mountain Chains
of the Mediterranean Type

A comparative structural review of mountain chains is an extremely difficult problem because so few are sufficiently explored to allow a reliable comparison. Moreover, it is difficult to visualize such a complicated structure without personal knowledge, and one person cannot be personally acquainted with more than a few. Those five or six with which I have a more than casual acquaintance are in addition so fundamentally different in structure that I suspect — and my suspicion is confirmed by what I read — that the rest will show also a great variety. Whereas simple structures, anticlines and synclines, can always be referred to a limited amount of types, mountain chains have evidently a much greater variety. When one looks closer, however, one can distinguish in each chain one or several zones each characterized by its own style, and the structural styles are again comparable from one chain to the next. It is the preponderance of one style over the others or the combination of different styles in different ways which classifies each mountain chain as a separate type.

It is obviously an impossible task to give adequate descriptions of mountain chains in the limited space of a few chapters, but I shall try to give some general idea of a few of them.

The sequence — High Atlas — Pyrenees — Alps is inspired by the fact that evidence from the simpler structure helps to understand the more complicated one. Thus some features of the High Atlas are repeated in an exaggerated form in the Pyrenees, and they in their turn can assist us to explain the even more complex Alpine structures.

THE PYRENEES

In contrast with the Alps, the Pyrenees are more of a rejuvenated Hercynian mountain chain than a Tertiary structure. In the Alps we know very little about the Hercynian structure, because it is strongly masked by Tertiary deformation. We suspect, however, that the

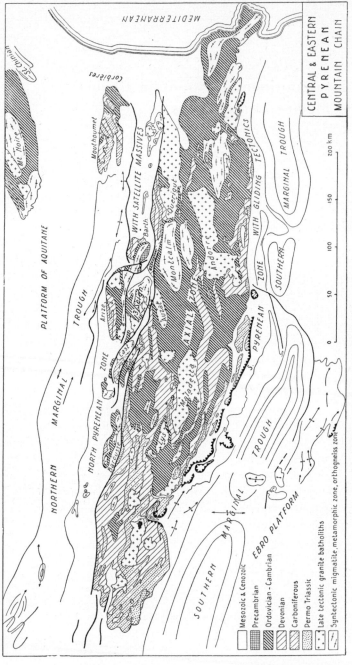

Fig. 258. Map of the Central and Eastern Pyrenees.

trends of the Permian and Triassic basins of the Lombardy-Austrian Alps are a Hercynian inheritance, and that the Briançonnais zone is primarily a Carboniferous basin, with an original structure of its own. But little is known about these old structures.

In the Pyrenees the Hercynian structure is exposed over large areas and can be studied in detail because the degree of camouflage by metamorphism is low. The younger structure is simpler and consists of only two phases, and both were much less severe than in the Alps.

We can distinguish (1) a central or axial zone consisting almost exclusively of Palaeozoic rocks (2) a northern zone separated from the axial zone by an important fault-zone, the North Pyrenean fault-zone, and characterized by folded Mesozoic rocks surrounding domes of Palaeozoic series, the so-called satellite massives, and (3) a sub-Pyreneic zone, the marginal trough filled with folded post-tectonic Upper Cretaceous and Eocene and covered by unfolded Neogene. In the south the zone of early Mesozoic sediments, equivalent to zone 2 in the north, is narrower and steeper and has a quite different structure without any satellite massives but with small gliding nappes. From this zone we step down to the southern marginal trough filled with thick Eocene deposits (Fig. 258).

Thus the Pyrenees present themselves as a more or less symmetrical structure with a Hercynian core, a Mesozoic mantle, and Palaeogene marginal troughs.

The Hercynian structure of the Pyrenees needs some elaboration in order to come to a better understanding of this mountain chain.

We do not know anything about an initial magmatic phase, which could be expected in the infra-Ordovician sequence. The little-differentiated series below the Silurian consist of a rather uniform sequence of mostly psammitic rocks, with at the base possibly some Cambrian limestones and at the top Upper Ordovician limestone, the latter combined with local thick conglomerates. It was a geosynclinal development in different basins with some ridges rising above sea level at the end of the period. The base is exposed only at one locality, and there the Ordovician series are thin and cover a highly metamorphic basement of unknown, probably pre-Cambrian, age. The Silurian with its widespread thin graptolite schists represents a very quiet period. In the Devonian the approaching Hercynian orogeny is already proclaimed by greater facies differentiation in a horizontal sense, and in the Lower Carboniferous the centre of the chain was probably already partly emerged.

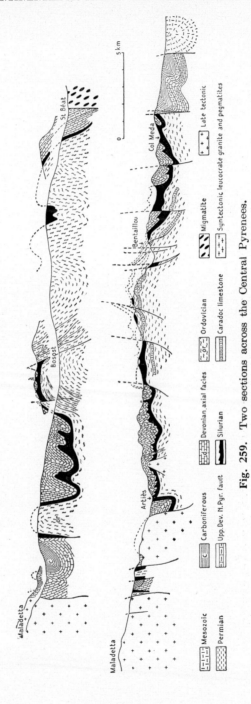

Fig. 259. Two sections across the Central Pyrenees.

The orogeny started in the Upper Devonian, and reached its maximum somewhere in the middle or towards the end of the Carboniferous.

A syntectonic magmatic phase is very well represented by large-scale but local migmatization, intrusion of white granites and granite gneiss, sills of pegmatites and thermal and dynamic metamorphism. The late-tectonic phase is represented by numerous intrusive granodiorite or biotite-granite bodies, non-tectonized and discordant, ranging in size from small stocks to sizeable batholiths. The post-tectonic volcanism is known to exist in the Permian discordant cover, in particular on the south flank.

The syntectonic magmatic phase is particularly suited to study because it is restricted to a previously undisturbed formation, the infra-Ordovician, which was not seriously disturbed by any later Alpine diastrophism. In the central axial zone we find several large domes of Ordovician penetrated by large flat bodies of granite-gneiss, in its thickest part developed as an Augen-gneiss with large porphyroblasts of felspar, in between migmatite or mica-schists, curved into a great arch. The original structure is sometimes rather disturbed on its margins by Alpine compression, but this deformation is mostly connected with a large fault-zone, the North Pyreneic fault, and confined to a steepening of the northern flank of the axial zone. A somewhat schematic cross-section (Fig. 259) shows the main structural features.

The schistosity of the Augen-gneiss is often very pronounced and always parallel to its roof and therefore sub-horizontal over large distances. The origin of this lamination must be sought in the combined action of flow of the subcrystalline granite mass of large and small crystals with still partly fluid interstitial matter in between, and of folding along concentric arched planes.

Smaller bodies of the same kind of white granite are also almost invariably concordant in the host rock; the pegmatites are mostly concordant sills, but sometimes discordant dikes. Somewhat later intrusions of small bodies of the same white granite in a fine grained facies are discordant; these, too, often grade into pegmatites.

The white granites never rise above the upper limit of the Ordovician, although they caused thermal metamorphism in the Silurian and Devonian rocks.

The folding of both the Ordovician and the younger Palaeozoic rocks up to the Devonian is of cleavage type, sharp and with very numerous small folds, steeply plunging anticlinal and synclinal axes, all combined in synclinoria and anticlinoria, and cut by many longitudinal faults of which some are late tectonic, even subsequent to the late tectonic granites, and some have been rejuvenated in the Alpine cycle. The Silurian slates act as a detachment and lubricating horizon, so that folds of the Devonian are apt to be independent of the Ordovician structure, perhaps particularly where the latter formation has been migmatized.

The North Pyreneic fault cuts obliquely through the EW trend of the Palaeozoic structure. It had an important horizontal movement from east to west which can be ascertained by the displacement of the cut-off parts of some of the late-tectonic batholiths. At the same time the northern block was folded in broad waves which accentuated the uplifts of the migmatized domes, and the domes were separated by other tear-faults. Thus basins were prepared for the later Triassic sedimentation, and there were uplifts which were only gradually covered by transgressing younger Mesozoic sediments.

The Alpine orogenic period comprises two major phases, an older phase between the Lower and Upper Cretaceous, and a Pyreneic phase (post-Lutetian).

It is doubtful whether the axial zone was ever covered to a large extent by Jurassic or Cretaceous sediments; the only Mesozoic remnants we find belong to the Triassic.

The Triassic has everywhere a continental facies, the Jurassic is incomplete but marine, the marine Lower Cretaceous is thicker and of some importance in the northern and southern zones. The axial zone was never a geosyncline in the Mesozoic; on the contrary, it maintained the geanticlinal character it obtained from the Hercynian folding.

Its emergence, which started before the Cretaceous folding, caused marginal troughs to be formed at both its flanks; these remained narrow, however, and had more of a shelf character than a typical geosynclinal sedimentation. The Cretaceous folding, which was not strictly parallel to the Hercynian structure, accentuated the North Pyrenean fault-zone and the emergence of the axial zone. It shoved the marginal troughs further outwards. The Pyreneic folding affected the marginal troughs of both flanks but had no influence or very little on the axial zone.

The Hercynian orogeny had an EW strike, but both Alpine phases show an WNW–ESE trend, roughly parallel to the late Hercynian North Pyreneic fault.

The North Pyreneic zone, with its domes with their migmatized cores, was severly compressed in the Cretaceous phase, a compression which was localized mainly along the front of the axial zone. The lower Mesozoic series became pressed in a narrow and vertical syncline between the axial and northern Pyreneic zone. This rejuvenated fault-zone also became the site of intrusions of ultrabasic to gabbroic intrusions, and of large scale intensive metasomatism of the scapolitization type in the Lower Cretaceous limestones.

The Pyreneic phase principally affected the marginal troughs of the Cretaceous phase. It threw up the southern margin of the north Pyreneic trough in very long and rather sharp folds, often accompanied by thrusting, and threw down the centre of the trough. The southern Mesozoic zone was strongly compressed and numerous gliding nappes slipped down from the uplifted axial zone; some of these have been described in Chapter 19.

After this last orogenic phase came a long period of denudation, creating enormous fans of conglomerates and sandstones at both sides of the central chain. The present lofty position of the central zone is due to discontinuous emergence in the Miocene and Pliocene.

The Alpine structure of the North Pyrenean zone is very much like that of the southern Alps. Large domes of the Hercynian basement, separated by steeply compressed strips of Mesozoic rocks leading down in steps to the Aquitanian plain to the north, are characteristic. On the other hand, neither large thrusts nor gliding nappes have been mapped. The southern Mesozoic zone has several gliding nappes and has the peculiarity that the thick sub-horizontal Oligocene conglomerate blanket dips a few degrees towards the centre of the mountain chain. Evidently a collapse of the axial zone preceded the youngest upheaval.

There is a direct connexion between the Pyrenees and the Alpine system by means of the Pyreneic folds which extend from the North Pyrenean zone almost without interruption into the western sub-Alpine zone; but in contrast with the sub-Alpine region, this link was not refolded by a later Alpine (post-Miocene) phase. The late-Cretaceous phase is present in both chains, but is very much less intense in the Pyrenees. The basic intrusions of the North Pyrenean fault-zone could be compared to those of the initial magmatic phase of the Pennides, or better still, with those of the Insubric fault-zone; the North Pyrenean fault-zone itself could be compared to the Insubric fault-line, and the satellite massives of the North Pyrenean zone to the external massifs of the Alps; but all other features of the two mountain chains are totally different.

THE ALPS

The Alps are without doubt the best known and the most complex mountain chain we know of on the earth, and have often been taken, quite unwarrantedly, as the prototype of an orogenic system. I shall restrict myself to a mere outline of their structure.

The chain consists of several longitudinal zones, which are, however, not quite parallel. In the south, we have the southern Alps, containing the Lombardy Alps and Tyrolese Alps. This zone is separated by a very conspicuous tectonic fault-line of deep significance, the Insubric line, from the next zone, the Pennine Alps, which again are separated, by a series of central massifs, from the next northern zone, the Helvetides. Situated to the north of the Helvetides is the marginal trough of the Molasse which is surrounded by the arc of the Jura Mountains; the latter we can leave for the moment, as a not essential part of the main chain. Each of these longitudinal zones is characterized by its own stratigraphical sequence, differing in facies and in age from that of the others (Fig. 260):

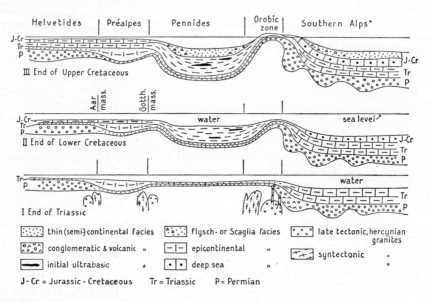

Fig. 260. Schematic development of Alpine basin during the Mesozoic.

Southern Alps – thick Permian (volcanics) and Triassic (limestones facies)

Pennine Alps – thick monotonous Liassic to Cretaceous schists with initial magmatic phase (schistes lustrés facies) Upper Cretaceous to Tertiary Flysch facies

Helvetides and Préalpes – Jurassic – Cretaceous shelf – limestone facies with Flysch blanket

Molasse basin – Oligocene – Miocene clastic facies

Structurally the four units are characterized first of all by the geanticlines which divide the Lombardy Alps from the Pennides, and the Pennides from the Helvetides, and in the second place by their own style of folding.

Southern Alps. Moderately compressed series of gigantic arched steps leading up to the geanticline of the Orobic zone, separating them from the Pennides. Further east the Southern Alps sedimentary unit is developed in gigantic low-angle thrust sheets or nappes, the Austrian nappes.

Pennides. Involved nappes characterized by flow-structures, wholly consisting of crystalline rock, part of which may belong to a pre-Hercynian basement. Alpine metamorphism masks earlier history to a high degree.

Helvetides and Préalpes. Surficial thrust sheets of non-metamorphic sediments which glided down the slope of an elevated basement ridge (the external massifs) and piled up one on the other on its front.

Molasse Basin. Slight folding in the basin, steep thrusting on its southern margin.

In describing in a few words the events which created this complex mountain chain, I have obviously to simplify a great deal, and thus my description will be open to much criticism.

In the Middle Cretaceous, before the great diastrophism of the Alps really started, there was a deep-sea basin in the south, separated by a submarine ridge, the Orobic zone, from the Pennine geosyncline (Fig. 261). North of this geosyncline we find the Helvetian shelf.

Each of these concentric units, the Austrides (including the Southern Alps), the Pennides, and the Helvetides (including the Préalpes) had its own sedimentary characteristics, as depicted in Fig. 261, and subsequently had its own structural development. The later orogenic trends were never quite parallel to the earlier epeirogenic structure; and in particular, during the older sedimentary phases of basin

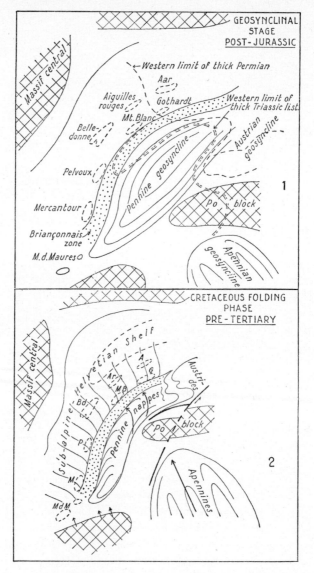

Fig. 261a.   Development of Alpine orogeny.

structures we find considerable deviations from the general trend. The Permian, for instance, was deposited as thick conglomeratic and volcanic series in a NE–SW trending basin, cutting almost perpendicularly through the later pattern. The thick Triassic limestones of

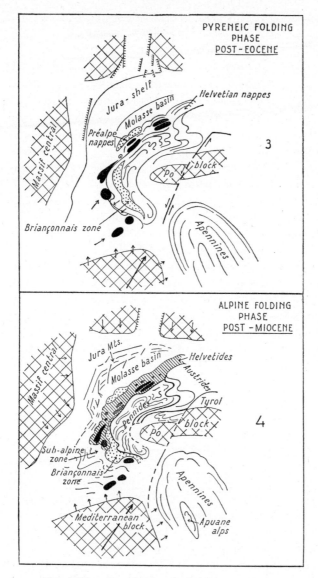

Fig. 261b.   Development of Alpine orogeny.

the Austrian basin were also far from parallel to the present trend. We presume that these NE–SW trends were roughly parallel to the Carboniferous basin in the west, the Briançonnais zone, and thus represented a posthumous-Hercynian trend. With the development of the Liassic trough of the Pennides the true Alpine trend was inaugurated and then persisted to the end. This interference of the Hercynian direction with the Alpine trend created an EW zoning in the Alps (Western, Central, and Eastern Alps), and caused the very strong axial plunges which are seen even in relatively small units.

Structurally the three sections are characterized as follows:

Western Alps. No molasse basin. The autochthonous folds of the Jura Mountains merge into the Helvetides. Strong compression in Briançonnais zone, advancing on thrusts as gliding sheets between Belledonne and Pelvoux massifs. No central massif. Pennine nappes well developed. Southern Alpine zone absent.

Central Alps. Jura Mountains and Molasse basin well developed. Helvetides in thrust and gliding sheets pushed over external massifs together with Préalpes. Pennine sheets well developed. Southern Alps narrow but broadening eastwards.

Eastern Alps. Helvetides as narrow frontal zone, Molasse marginal trough widens towards the east. Pennine belt disappeared, in the west partly covered by the Austrian thrust sheets. Southern Alps broad and developed in autochthonous flat folds.

In this schematic picture I have included two controversial subjects. In the first place we consider the Préalpes as the direct continuation of the Briançonnais zone and therefore as having originated from a zone north of the Pennides, in accordance with the French school of thought represented, for instance, by Tercier (1945). But the older conception placed the zone of sedimentation of the Préalpes to the south of the Pennine geosyncline. Both points of view are based on facies comparisons, but the French conception has in addition strong structural arguments in its favour. In the second place I do not think, in contrast with Argand (1916) and Staub (1924), that the Austrian thrust sheets ever extended much further west than their present extension in that direction, and therefore never covered an appreciable portion of the Pennine nappes. Neither do I think that the Pennides extend much further east below the Austrian sheets. Both convictions are based on the realization of the non-parallelism of the older and younger Mesozoic trends of basin development, as outlined above.

In the Upper Cretaceous the folding became paroxysmal, and the deep Pennine geosyncline was narrowed. In its basement the syntectonic migmatizations and intrusions facilitated flow-structures; the secondary ridges and basins, which had already developed to some extent, became pressed together, and produced a single basin filling

with detrital sediments derived from its rising northern border (the
central massif), and its southern margin (the Orobic zone), but principally from the Austrian sheets which were in full development (Fig. 262).

The Southern Alps became separated from the advancing thrust-
masses of the Austrian thrust sheets by the Insubric fault-line, and

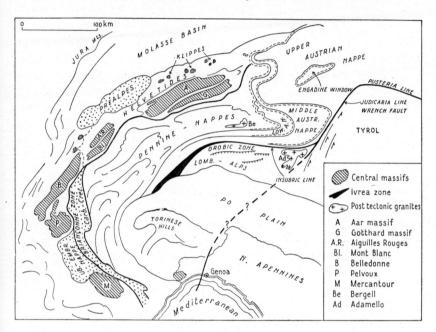

Fig. 262.   Present state of Alpine orogeny.

formed the stepping stones by which the ascent to the rising Orobic
zone became possible (cf. Fig. 177) (de Sitter, 1949). The Austrian
nappes consist principally of the thick Permo-Triassic cover and on
their fronts Jurassic and Cretaceous sediments sheared off from its
basement; but often thick slices of the basement were included,
proving that originally the thrust-faults cut deep into the basement,
and cut obliquely through the present EW trend of the whole chain
(Cornelius, 1940).

The compression which started in the east progressed westward.
The Pennine infrastructure developed under the influence of intruding
syntectonic granites and strong migmatization into the involved
nappes, now enveloping its Mesozoic sedimentary cover. In the west
the Pennine structures slipped along the continental shelf, curling up

against it like an oblique surf against the coast (Argand, 1916). The continental shelf border arched up in the central massif of the Gotthard and Mont Blanc. On the shelf, new welts were formed in the epicontinental plateau, the future external massifs. The Préalpes zone was pushed over and on the Helvetic zone. Several geanticlinal ridges rose above sea level and were eroded down again, delivering coarse syntectonic sediments in the deep tectonic troughs, the typical Flysch facies.

The next orogenic phase occurred after the Eocene, although the intervening time was never really a time of quiescence. The Helvetides and Préalpes were definitely sheared off from their basement, which was itself thrust into great imbricate structures. In front of the rising shelf margin, coinciding with the central massifs, a deep trough was formed — bounded in the north by another welt, the future external massifs. In this trough the sedimentary blanket became thoroughly compressed in low-angle thrust-faulted structures like those in the Valley and Ridge province of the Appalachians. Eventually these thrust sheets were pressed over the welt of external massifs, and glided down its northern slope after the latter became uplifted to its present height (cf. Fig. 212). The Préalpes sheets came somewhat earlier and were partly carried forward on the back of the gliding Helvetic nappes. Towards the west the intensity of compression became less and less. In the Dent de Morcles and Wildhorn nappes the Helvetides are almost autochthonous, and the Préalpes disappear as thrust-structures west of Geneva. The pressing upwards of the external massifs caused the thrust-structures to come into motion again, first one fold, then another, in an intricate pattern of advancing waves, tumbling down in the marginal trough which in the meantime was filling up with coarse detritus derived from the advancing folds which often rose above sea level.

At the same time the Pennides and Southern Alps rose to greater heights. The youngest sedimentary cover of the Pennides, Cretaceous and Palaeogene flysch, took part in the northward gliding of the Helvetides and Préalpes and became strongly involved in their folds and nappes. The elevation of the Orobic zone by lateral compression accentuated the stepping stones, which acted as buttresses against which the lower steps were pressed in thrust-faults and folds. Finally even the sedimentary cover of the higher steps slid down southwards on the lower adjoining ones (see Fig. 218). The southern marginal trough was filled with flysch sediments derived from the rising Lombardy Alps.

The great advance of the Austrian nappes of the Orobic zone, consisting of the Mesozoic cover of the Southern Alps, with cut-off slices of the basement at their bottom, was greatly increased by a large wrench-fault, the Judicaria fault-line offsetting the Insubric fault-line to the north.

We are not concerned here with the innumerable controversies which have arisen and subsided or are still unsettled about the continuation of the individual folds and thrust sheets from west to east. Their argument is always based on facies, tectonics, and other similarities. Neither are we concerned with the actual origin of each thrust sheet. I only want to point out that the shearing-off often occurred not in one sheet containing the whole Mesozoic sequence, but along many horizontal planes which first divided the sedimentary sequence into individual sheets, or along oblique planes separating different facies zones, one advancing above the other, and sometimes carried forward by a lower sheet, as I have already explained with regard to the Helvetian sheets of central Switzerland (cf. Figs. 222 and 223). Probably the first unit of the Pennides to glide down north was the Flysch cover with chunks and slices of its Mesozoic base forming the Wildflysch and the Ultrahelveticum, on which all the Pre-Alpine and Helvetian sheets were later deposited. Part of the Ultrahelveticum probably originated from the Pennine geosyncline itself, another part from the Helveticum.

Summarizing, I want to point out that each epeirogenically formed basin played its own particular role with its own characteristic style in the drama of diastrophism in its own particular phase of compression. The orogenic history started in the south and east in the oldest unit; it reached its maximum in the central unit and progressed northwards to the younger units on the continental shelf. Nevertheless it appears that the central unit, the Pennine geosyncline with its initial and syntectonic magmatic phases, contains, if not the motorizing force, then at any rate the capacity to unclench the diastrophism. Compression deep down in its basement, when the sedimentation of its youngest sediments was still in progress and the geosyncline was still rapidly subsiding, started the Austrian nappes. The later phases of its folding accompanied by upheaval started the movement in its Helvetian epicontinental border.

The arched shape of the Western Alps is certainly due to a further advance of the central part; the strongly decreasing complexity and total contraction towards the west, proves it. The famous Argand

(1916) note explains the mechanism admirably. Argand explains the origin of the curvature by supposing a bay in the northern continental border. I do not think this bay is the only cause of the Alpine arch. The stronger advance of the eastern position is sufficiently explained by the presence of the Austrian nappes which are lacking in the west, and by the stronger compression in the Pennides in the centre. The reason why this portion of continental border geosyncline was more strongly compressed can perhaps be found in the fact that the Italian peninsula, having already acquired a cylindrical cross-section by its geosynclinal development in the lower Jurassic, could not be further folded in EW folds and was therefore driven into its foreland as if it were a beam.

It is therefore clear that the central zone, the Pennine geosyncline, is the fundamental portion of the Alpine structure.

STRUCTURE OF THE PENNINE NAPPES OF THE ALPS

The peculiar shape of the Pennine nappes in cross-section has always been a puzzle to structural geologists; not least to Swiss geologists, who, however, were never troubled much about their unique character. The main enigma is the fact of the predominant horizontal structure in the most compressed centre of the mountain chain, where one would expect a wholly vertically directed schistosity and gneissification of the exposed infrastructure.

I think that after having made acquaintance with the structure of the axial zone of the Pyrenees we are now in a better position to understand the Pennine nappes of the Alps.

In many large domes of the axial zone of the Pyrenees we are in the presence of a granite-Augen-gneiss, intruded in the shape of laccoliths or sills between the syntectonically metamorphosed mica-schists and migmatites of the Ordovician. The pronounced schistosity of the granite gneiss body is parallel to its roof and wall and therefore horizontal in its centre and steeply inclined towards the north (and south) borders. Such a horizontal schistosity is difficult to understand as a result of lateral compressive forces, and equally difficult to see as a result of the load it carried on its back since that load never surpassed some 1,200 m, at the most (Silurian (200 m) + Devonian (600 m) + Carboniferous > 400 m). But as there is overwhelming evidence for the syntectonic character of the intrusion of the granite gneiss (folded pegmatite dikes, sills, etc.), I think we can regard this schistosity as the result of two activities, namely the flow of the partially crystallized granite and the more or less concentric shear in each great dome. Both shear movements, by flow and by folding, were parallel and created the Augen-gneiss texture round the large felspar eyes, and the schistosity in the fine-grained varieties of the granite gneiss. In other words, the mobilization of the material in the core of the mountain chain, due to the rise in temperature and the injection of granite magma, had the effect of forming predominantly horizontally directed structures.

When we return to the Pennine nappes, we remark that their recumbent fold character is established without any doubt by the presence of the enveloping Mesozoic mantle as reentrants between the frontal lobes and the central bodies of the nappes, dividing them into three large units, the Upper, Middle, and Lower Pennine nappes.

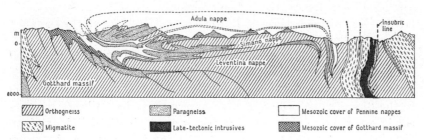

Fig. 263. Section through the Pennine nappes in Central Ticino. *(After Nabholz, XIXe Congrès Géologique International, Alger, 1953, Compte Rendu, sec. 3, fasc. 3.)*

But each unit is built up in its turn by a core of granite gneiss, locally developed as Augen-gneiss, and a mantle of paragneiss within another mantle of Mesozoic phyllites often accompanied by basic igneous rocks. The paragneiss zone comprises mica-schists and migmatites (Fig. 263). All of this crystalline core, ortho and paragneiss, is regarded by many Swiss geologists as the Hercynian crystalline basement. This opinion is based on the irrefutable evidence of the much less disturbed Southern Alps and on the central massifs in the north, where both syntectonic granite gneiss and late tectonic granite of Hercynian age have migmatized the Palaeozoic or older metamorphic rocks. But Kündig (1934) and Wenk (1953) are, however, very much in favour of regarding at least some of the granites and granite gneisses of the Pennine sheets as Alpine intrusions, and there is apparently no direct field evidence which contradicts their thesis.

The advantages of this point of view are manifold and often obvious. First of all we are satisfied that in the most severely compressed mountain chain we know, the syntectonic magmatic phase is no longer lacking between its well-expressed initial magmatic phase and its admittedly poorly developed late-tectonic granite phase.

Secondly, the root-zone of the Pennine nappes, this peculiar vertical, very much compressed, zone, which in the conception of Staub and Argand was originally a zone of flat lying thrust planes which, only later, in a late Alpine ("Insubric") phase, were put in their present vertical position, has quite another aspect when we regard it — as does Wenk (1953) — as principally the vertical part of the intrusive syntectonic granites. The Insubric phase of steepening of Argand is in direct contradiction to all the evidence of the Lombardy Alps, where parallel steep thrusts, often even with a flattening southerly dip, occur very frequently and can certainly not be regarded as basculated older low-angle thrusts. In the conception of Wenk the steepness of the so-called "root-zone" is, then, partially due to the steep ascent of the intrusive granite gneiss and only partially to lateral compression.

Because we can follow the Mesozoic, probably Triassic, dolomites right from the frontal lobes along the horizontal bottom of a nappe to the "root" zone, where it often appears as a lime-silicate rock, we can be assured that each nappe represent an originally individual dome with its own syntectonic intrusion. During its intrusion the nappe developed as a flow-structure. The flow-structure style is emphasized by peculiar steep and highly metamorphosed zones, starting from the "root" but penetrating deeply in between the horizontal nappes in a NS direction.

When regarded from this point of view, the Pennine nappes become an example of a strongly tectonized central core of a mountain chain with a strong syntectonic magmatic phase, comparable to other simpler structures.

A very difficult problem is reserved, as Wenk (1953) remarks, for the petrologist, i.e. to disentangle the possible syn- and late-tectonic granite gneisses and granites of Hercynian origin from those of a syn- and late-tectonic Alpine origin, because we must be prepared to meet all of them in the Pennine nappes. It is possible of course that the Hercynian intrusives are absent and that the central geosyncline and its later compression were located — just because of this absence — in this particular belt, flanked to the north and south by belts of Hercynian intrusions now exposed in the Aar and Gotthardt massifs and in the Lombardy Alps, belts which became too rigid for further folding because of their Hercynian granitizations.

The fact that the supposed Alpine laccolithic intrusions of the Pennine sheets never intruded the Mesozoic cover, need not surprise us so much when we recall that in the Pyrenees the granite gneiss nowhere went higher than the top of the Ordovician, although it caused slight marmorization and thermal metamorphism both in the overlying Silurian and Devonian. Apparently this syntectonic magmatic phase is a typical infrastructure phenomenon, closely connected with the infrastructural tectonic style of large-scale doming beneath a cover of tightly compressed superstructure.

THE HIGH ATLAS

I should like to add one other mountain chain to my survey of the Mediterranean orogenic belt in order to demonstrate the wide differences in structure between Tertiary mountain chains which otherwise

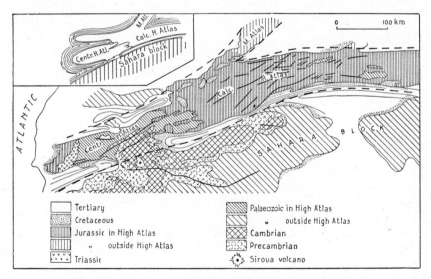

Fig. 264. Structural sketch of High Atlas Mountains.

have but two main features in common, their elevation in the Pliocene to about the same height, and their longitudinal zoning, but hardly anything else.

The High Atlas (Fig. 264) is situated on the border of the Old Sahara shield, which except for the mild arching of the Anti-Atlas, its marginal zone, has been extremely quiet since the Pre-Cambrian. The High Atlas zone has a Hercynian history of some magnitude, but its Mesozoic history is extremely simple. During the Lias and the Dogger a broad strip along part of the Sahara shield border, sank, and a thick series of limestones and marls accumulated upon a blanket of continental Trias. A slight marginal trough was formed between this geosyncline and the Sahara shield after a mild Pyreneic folding phase. Figure 129 shows the kind of Jurassic folding it caused in these well-stratified limestones. A very mild post-Miocene folding with here and there a slightly different direction, gave rise to some interesting features of cross folding (cf. Figs. 243 and 244). In the strike of the folded geosyncline the Jurassic strata wedge-out towards the west, but not the uplift, with the result that at the meridian of Marrakech the chain becomes nothing else but upwarped Hercynian structure of the type of the axial zone of the Pyrenees, but with the big difference that here the Hercynian structure is almost perpendicular to the axis of the chain.

Longitudinal faults limit the whole structure to the north and the south (cf. Fig. 179), and other longitudinal faults can be found in the structure, separating sub-horizontal or arched blocks from folded blocks by a very sharp line. Both its shallow marginal troughs were filled with younger Tertiary sediments, mostly continental. Those of post-Miocene age are unfolded.

A Pliocene upheaval lifted the mountain chain to its present altitude; a similar uplift affected the unfolded Anti-Atlas chain.

Towards the Atlantic Ocean the whole mountain chain plunges sharply, with the result that along the coast very little of the specific High Atlas structure is left. Its Jurassic and Cretaceous strata are simply a part of the coastal sedimentation area, striking SE–NW, and unconnected with the Mesozoic High Atlas basin. To the East the folds of the High Atlas flatten and the chain merges into the central platform of Algeria, an elevated continental block separated from the Sahara shield in the early Mesozoic. Between this block and the Sahara shield a Cretaceous basin has developed; this, in the sense of the marginal basin of the Sahara shield, is the continuation of the High Atlas geosyncline.

Chapter 27

The Circum-Continental Mountain Chains of America

THE CORDILLERAN SYSTEM

The most grandiose of the younger mountain systems of the earth is that of the Pacific coast of the American continents, where a single system runs from Alaska to Tierra del Fuego.

The time has not yet come to give a description of the whole chain, for large areas are totally unknown, others have received only scanty attention, and in general our knowledge is far too unequally distributed to allow a coherent picture to be drawn. Even in the United States large areas are virtually unknown, either because of their inaccessibility, produced by an extensive volcanic blanket, or of the fact that they are hardly explored. I shall chiefly confine myself to a single cross-section from California over Nevada and Utah to Wyoming.

From west to east we pass the younger Tertiary coastal ranges of California, its central — or San Joaquin — basin, the Sierra Nevada orogenic belt, the large Basin and Range province, the Laramide Central Rockies in Utah. We can cast a glance at the Colorado Plateau to the south, and at the basin structures of Wyoming, and shall finally arrive at the stable shield of the Mid-Continent area.

The Palaeozoic Cordilleran Geosyncline. At the beginning of Palaeozoic time we can already discern a pronounced basin on the continental border, with a relatively thick Cambrian section in the geosyncline, as compared to the thin one in the continental plateau of the Utah-Wyoming shelf. Its western margin remains unknown because it is covered by the Pacific Ocean. The Cambrian basin is an extension of a much narrower Algonkian basin in the north. We notice that from Ordovician times onwards the western half of the basin becomes characterized by frequent volcanic intercalations, in contrast with the eastern half, which retains an essentially carbonate shelf facies. After the Devonian the very large and elongated basin (some 800 miles wide) develops a central geanticline, the Cordilleran geanticline,

397

which accentuates the separation into two geosynclinal basins; a basin with volcanic intercalations in the west, and a marine basin in the east. The western basin, consisting of the Alexander trough in the north and the Klamath trough in the south, lasted into the Permian, somewhat longer than the northern and southern Rocky Mountain troughs in the west, which were filled with Pennsylvanian rocks (Fig. 265).

The traces of many minor orogenic phases can be found in the Palaeozoic rocks of both geosynclines, in the form of unconformities, disconformities, or the stratigraphical evidence of conglomerates; but the major phase did not arrive until much later, in the Jurassic.

The Nevadan Orogeny and the Coastal Ranges of California. The whole west coast of North America is characterized by a strong orogenic period in the Jurassic, comprising several phases reaching from the early Jurassic into the Cretaceous. It is called the Nevadan orogeny and is typified by its unusual date of occurrence — unusual in the European sense — between the Hercynian and Alpine cycles of the Mediterranean area.

The last phase of geosynclinal sedimentation started in the Triassic with thick volcanic deposits and marine sediments, and continued in the Jurassic (Fig. 266, I). This Nevadan trough was severely folded and elevated by the late Jurassic Nevadan phase. The Nevadan orogeny was accompanied by the intrusion of the Sierra Nevada batholith, and the sediments of the original Nevadan trough were strongly metamorphosed and migmatized (Fig. 266, II). After this first major orogenic phase a marginal trough, the Californian trough was formed further to the west; this became filled with Upper Jurassic and Cretaceous sediments, again containing a large amount of volcanic deposits and intrusive rocks (Fig. 267).

The history of the Californian geosyncline is characterized by numerous disturbances, throughout the Cretaceous, and later in the Tertiary, when the geosyncline became split up into a multitude of smaller basins. Although no marked orogenic phase divides its Tertiary and Cretaceous history, the difference between the two epochs is very pronounced, because of this splitting up of one great geosyncline into many small basins which are not parallel to one another or to the general NS trend of the Nevadan orogeny. The end of the Cretaceous was marked by a regression which was certainly due to regional crustal movements, partly folding and partly of an epeirogenic character, creating the uplifts between which the future basins were formed.

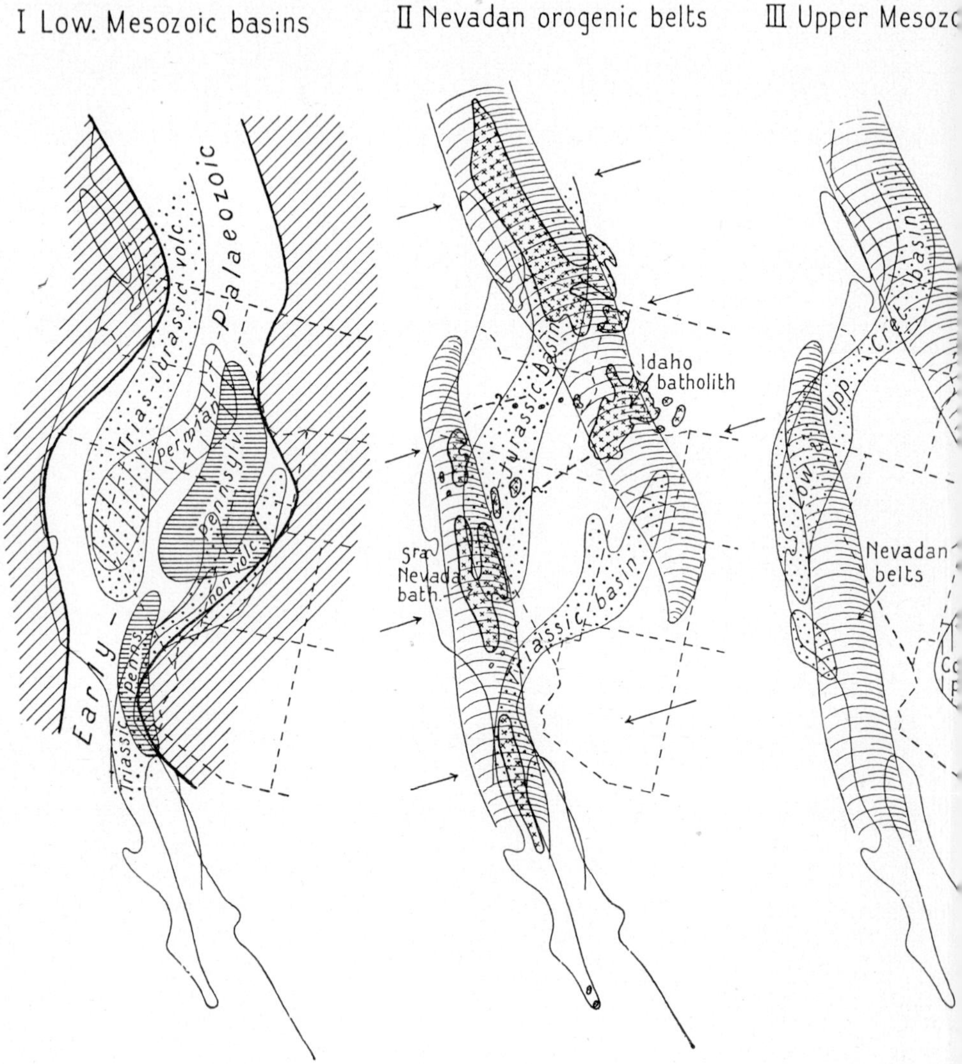

I Low. Mesozoic basins   II Nevadan orogenic belts   III Upper Mesozo

Early – *Palaeozoic*

Trias-Jurassic volc.

Permian?

Pennsylv.

Permian volc.

Triassic-Permian

Idaho batholith

Jurassic basin

Sra Nevada bath.

Triassic basin

Upp. Cret. basin

Lower Upp.

Nevadan belts

Cc F

Fig. 266. Successive stages in the development of the Cordilleran geosynclin
of Messrs Ha

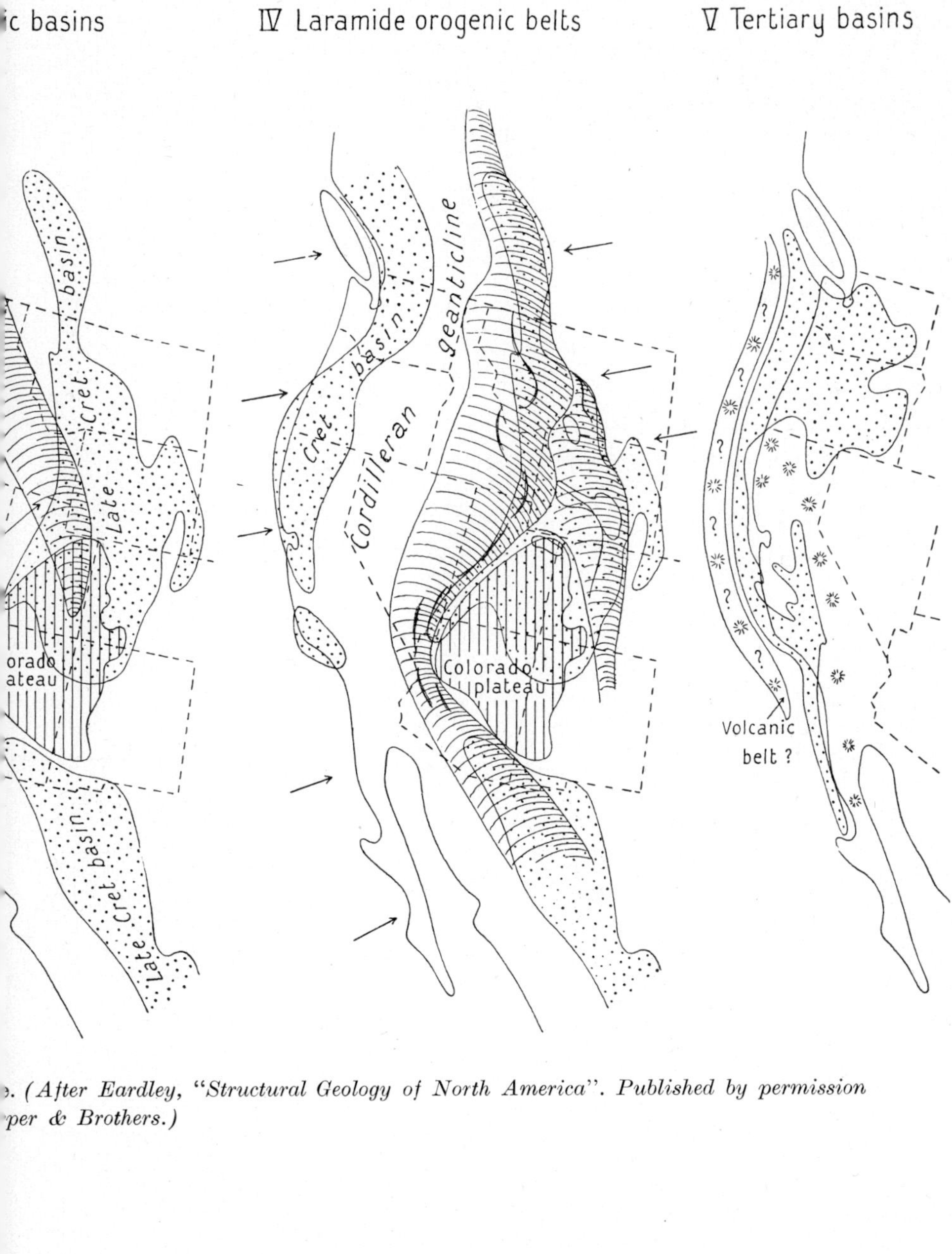
ic basins
IV Laramide orogenic belts
V Tertiary basins
Cret basin
Late
orado
ateau
Late Cret basin
Cret basin
Cordilleran geanticline
Colorado
plateau
Volcanic
belt ?

. (*After Eardley, "Structural Geology of North America". Published by permission* *per & Brothers.)*

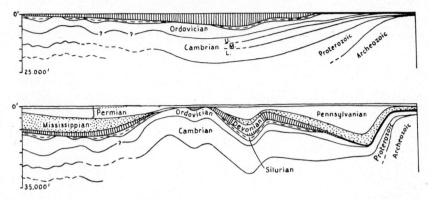

Fig. 265. Development of the Cordilleran system in two stages, at the close of Devonian and at the close of the Permian. *(After Eardley, "Structural Geology of North America". Published by permission of Messrs Harper & Brothers.)*

These basins – the San Joaquin, Santa Barbara-Ventura, and the Los Angeles basins, which already showed the peculiar transverse position which coincides with the flat S-curve of the San Andreas fault (see Fig. 292) – indicate that horizontal movement along this fault is one

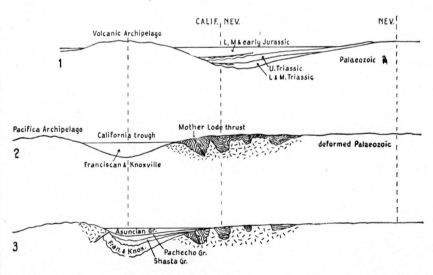

Fig. 267. Mesozoic phases in California and Nevada. *(After Eardley, "Structural Geology of North America". Published by permission of Messrs Harper & Brothers.)*

of the conspicuous features of this late-Cretaceous disturbance. Hill and Dibblee (1953) arrived, as we saw earlier (Chapter 11), at the same conclusions by comparing homologous elements at both sides of the fault. Both phenomena, the oblique position of the transverse ranges and the tear-fault, are due to a new stress-direction oblique to the Nevada range and its marginal trough. The uplift of Salinia is, then, partly due to this ancestral tear-fault which separated the Great Valley as a marginal trough from its original extension into the Los Angeles basin. Apparently the basculating movement of the Nevada block, subsiding in the west and rising in the east, must be connected with this tear-fault; but it probably preceded it.

The basin formation, and the subsequent Miocene and Pliocene folding, are one of the clearest examples of the common origin of epeirogenic and orogenic crustal distortions that can be brought forward. The tear movement of the San Andreas fault is doubtless a result of an ENE–WSW stress, the same stress which formed the Santa Barbara embayment and the quickly subsiding Ventura basin and their later folding, with thrust-faults such as the Santa Ynez fault. The interference of the original NNW–ESE strike of the Nevadan orogeny and the Tertiary ENE–WSW directed stress formed the intricate pattern of thrusts, folds, subsiding and folded basins which characterize the Californian coast.

The original Nevadan orogeny was of the syntectonic migmatite type, i.e. with steep structures with vertical schistosity, steeply plunging fold-axes, thoroughly migmatized and invaded by granites and granodiorites, as was shown by the detailed survey of Mayo (1941). As I had occasion to mention before, it is only this kind of orogenesis, causing an almost complete recrystallization of the rocks, which creates new stiff blocks that can be moved only as blocks when cut by faults and which will not fold.

The early Mesozoic basin of the Nevadan orogenic belt is situated in north-west Nevada and west Oregon, whereas the orogenic belt itself extended much further to the south into the area of the Sierra Nevada batholith and the southern Californian batholithic intrusions. The Tertiary basins of southern California could be regarded as a southward extension of the Mesozoic basin (Fig. 266, V). The California trough shifted southwards in the time between the Permian and the Pliocene, with interruptions halfway through this interval by the Nevadan orogeny and towards its end by the younger Tertiary orogenic phases.

The Internal Laramide Orogeny of the Rockies. The Californian trough was flanked towards the east by the Cordilleran geanticline, a vast and broad positive belt in which the Palaeozoic rocks are reduced in thickness. During the Upper Carboniferous and then during the Mesozoic — and in particular during the Cretaceous — several basins developed on the western border of this geanticline, and were folded in the Laramide orogenic period (Fig. 266, III and IV), starting in the Upper Cretaceous and continuing far into the Tertiary.

The Mesozoic geosynclinal trough of the Rockies is interrupted by the Colorado Plateau, but sets in again in Mexico. The Laramide orogeny roughly followed these eastern Cretaceous troughs, which encroached towards the west onto the geanticlinal shelf, but the centre of the geanticline was left outside the orogenic movement. This remnant of the broad area of Palaeozoic sedimentation is therefore the only portion of the wide Pacific belt which remained relatively undisturbed by folding during the whole of the Mesozoic and Tertiary periods. Its numerous faults show, however, how severely it was attacked by the two orogenies, at both its sides. This desert region is still little known, but its block-faulted character seems well-established. The fault system, sometimes limiting long rift valleys, sometimes tilted blocks, is partly superimposed on Laramide and Nevadan structures. Most of the fault-blocks are well represented by physiographic features, and must therefore be younger than both orogenies, and are probably contemporaneous with the Plio-Pleistocene folding of the coast ranges. The nature of the tensional stress which caused the faulting remains obscure; it might be the expression of the collapse of a formerly arched structure or structures.

On the inner side of the Cordilleran geanticline, a series of basins was developed, mostly in late Cretaceous time. Their further extension southward was hindered by the rigid cratonic block of the Colorado Plateau, which had probably already acquired this property in the Pre-Cambrian. The Laramide folding phase is exceptional in the sense that it does not occupy the centre of the basin (Fig. 266, IV), but only its eastern margin. The adjoining eastern shelf was submitted to much stronger distortion than was the centre of the basin, except in the Sierra Madre Oriental of northern Mexico. As a result, the front of the Rockies is characterized by very long wide thrust sheets of the higher shelf region, overlying its sunken foreland, such as the Lewis thrust on the Canadian border, the Beartooth range thrust, the Darby and Bannock thrusts and many others (Fig. 268). Some of these thrust sheets seem to reach several hundreds of miles in width. In view of the often very thin slices that have been transported over such long distances I suspect that many thrusts are partly gliding structures.

In front of the Laramide orogenic belt we find a multitude of basins filled with Cretaceous and Eocene sediments, only moderately disturbed and gradually merging into the stable inland shield (see Chapter 30).

Looking back at the long and complicated history of the eastern Pacific mountain system, we can discern some important general principles. Here as elsewhere we find that the geosyncline development shows certain laws. At the start there is a large chiefly marine basin which becomes differentiated in later stages into smaller and deeper basins, which shift consistently in one of two directions. First, a large Palaeozoic basin, then a Jurassic basin which shifts westwards to the

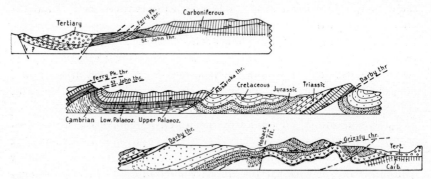

Fig. 268. Section through low-angle thrust of the Rocky Mountains. *(After Eardley, "Structural Geology of North America". Published by permission of Messrs Harper & Brothers.)*

Californian basin, and later further west to the coastal Tertiary basins. At the same time an Upper Cretaceous basin develops far to the east by means of a rising geanticline in the centre.

Here as elsewhere we observe that the orogenic belts do not coincide consistently with the geosynclines. The two Nevadan orogenic belts are apparently arranged en échelon. Even when one supposes that they are connected by a sharply arcuate curve west of the Idaho batholith, their main direction is WNW–ESE. The Cretaceous basins developed on the outsides of the previous folding belts, but their intervening geanticlinal belt, the Cordilleran geanticline, cuts obliquely through the older orogenic belts and runs from the crest of the northern belt to that of the southern belt; it thus acquired a curved shape which was followed by the Laramide orogenic belt on its inner side, and later by the younger Tertiary folding on its outer side. The origin of the Colorado Plateau as a separate block, and that of the great central basin, are due to this interference of older structures with younger geosynclines.

When we attempt a comparison between well-known structures in Europe with those of the Pacific coast, we have to take into account their size. The total length and breadth of the Alpine chain is comparable to that of the Nevadan chain from Oregon to Baja California, and the total width of the Pacific system is comparable to that of the whole Mediterranean system from the Pyrenees or Alps to the Sahara shield. From this point of view any large-scale analogies are obviously improbable. The Mediterranean zone is far less homogeneous, orogenic belts alternate with a multitude of blocks separated by transverse chains, and there is no central geanticline flanked by orogenic belts at both sides.

Comparing the Pyrenees with the Sierra Nevada, for instance, there are great differences and some analogies. The Cretaceous basins to the west of the Nevadan orogenic belt, are in a way marginal troughs comparable to those of the Pyrenees; but the Pyrenees have a trough on both sides and the Sierra Nevada only on one side. The migmatization and late-tectonic intrusions of the Sierra Nevada are comparable with those of the Pyrenees, but are more numerous and larger, and more intensified. Moreover, in the Pyrenees there is a long period of quiescence between the Hercynian and the Pyreneic orogenies, whereas in the Sierra Nevada the Nevadan orogeny started much later and continued longer. The typical basculating movement of the Sierra Nevada, which causes a wedging-out of the strata towards the inner and older orogenic belt, has no replica either in the Alps or in the Pyrenees, where the greatest thickness of the marginal basin lies next to the older orogeny and the wedging-out occurs towards the foreland, in contrast with the shape of the Great Valley.

The Laramide belt with its relative scarcity of volcanic phases and absence of intrusive bodies would be more comparable to the Tertiary chains of Europe; but such large-scale low-angle thrust sheets are unknown round the Mediterranean, except in the Alps, where they have another character.

THE APPALACHIAN SYSTEM *

The Appalachian mountain chain stretches for more than 1,200

* In general I shall follow the summaries by P. B. King (1950) and by Eardley (1951), which contain extensive lists of references.

miles along the east coast of North America. This long stretch can be
divided in two distinct halves, the Southern Appalachians or the
Appalachians, *s.str.*, from New York southwards, and the Northern
Appalachians north of this city. Very roughly, the Northern Appalachians represent the Taconic (Caledonian) system, and the Southern
Appalachians the Appalachian (Hercynian) system; but it is believed
that the Taconic orogeny had a great influence in the eastern part of
the Appalachian system too, and some Hercynian movement can be
traced north of the Hudson River. Marshall Kay (1951) calls the
Taconic system the Magog belt, and the Appalachian system the
Champlain belt.

In the Appalachian system, *s.str.*, we can discern three major longitudinal divisions, from west to east; the Appalachian mountain province
or the Valley and Ridge province, the Blue Ridge province, and the

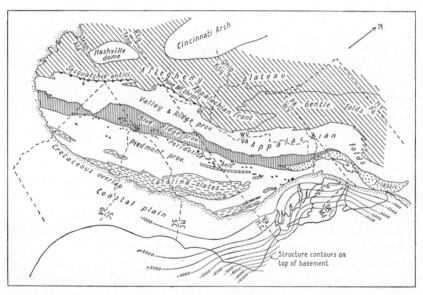

Fig. 269.   Structural sketch of the Appalachian, *s. str. (After Eardley and
King. Published by permission of Messrs Harper & Brothers and The American
Association of Petroleum Geologists.)*

Piedmont crystalline province (Fig. 269). The Piedmont crystalline
belt belongs (according to Kay) to the Magog belt, the other two to
the Champlain belt. Since the eastern margin of the Piedmont crystalline belt is covered by younger Cenozoic sediments, we know very

little about the possibility of another eastern longitudinal zone, although boreholes indicate that the metamorphism decreases eastwards and southwards.

The Valley and Ridge Province. It is characterized by a complete series of Palaeozoic rocks, some 10,000 to 13,000 m in total thickness, of which the lower half is of the carbonate-shelf type and the upper half of clastic rocks. Its western front, a distinct tectonic line, separates it from the Appalachian Plateau, the unfolded continuation of the geosynclinal shelf of the Appalachian geosyncline, of which the Valley and Ridge province is the folded part. All Palaeozoic formations thin out westwards (cf. Fig. 1, Chapter 1). There is no distinct break in facies or thickness of the sediments in the Appalachian front line. The eastern limit of the Valley and Ridge province is again a tectonic line only; the original geosyncline probably simply deepened further eastwards, but the absence of younger Palaeozoic in the Blue Ridge province prevents a closer comparison. A recent account of the Valley and Ridge province by J. Rodgers (1953a and b) gives an excellent description of the Tennessee section. Along the whole length of this section of the Appalachians we find a number of parallel thrust anticlines which remain constant over vast lengths, for hundreds of miles. Their consistency is due to the absence of axial plunging and of any cross folding or faulting, and this phenomenon is itself due to the unchanging facies and thickness of the sedimentary sequence in a direction parallel to the basin axis. Although some disconformities can be discerned, as a whole the sedimentation was remarkably uniform between two major unconformities — at the top of the Pre-Cambrian, and at the top of the Pennsylvanian or within the Permian period. The Taconian and Acadian orogenic periods are represented by only slight disconformities or local slight non-conformities, increasing in importance towards the NE.

The parallel thrust folds are all characterized by low-angle thrusts always following some incompetent bed in the Middle Cambrian, and by the total absence of any trace of an inverted flank. Consequently the Pre-Cambrian and Lower Cambrian up to the Rome formation (M. Cambrian) are seldom exposed. As King (1950) and Rodgers (1950 and 1953) point out these significant facts lead to the same conclusion as Buxtorf (1916) drew for the Jura Mountains — that the folds are superficial folds, disharmonically folded on the basement. This conception is all the more probable when we take into consideration the fact that in the Blue Ridge province and in the windows beneath the marginal thrusts of this province over the Appalachian folds, this same basement, including the Pre-Cambrian and Lower Cambrian, comes to the surface. Evidently the superficial sequence is stripped of its basement in the Blue Ridge too.

The low-angle thrusts reach great width, particularly in the frontal north-western area. The Pine Mountain thrust (Fig. 192) and the Sesquatchie anticline are the most spectacular examples of the mechanism of these thrusts, and it seems quite natural that the thrusts of the centre of the basin had similar horizontal extension in cross-section before the top of the folds was eroded away. A peculiar character of these thrusts is that the width of thrust is very large, perhaps up to 20 miles, whereas the actual slip is not more than 4 or 5 miles.

The Blue Ridge Province. The rocks of the Blue Ridge province belong to the older section of the Palaeozoic sequence from Lower Cambrian downwards, are non-fossiliferous, often volcanic and have consistently a slaty-cleavage or marked schistosity. The great difference in altitude of the stratigraphic sequence between the Blue Ridge province and the Appalachian folds is often, though not always, marked by high or low-angle faults on their boundary. At many places the younger Palaeozoic rocks of the Blue Ridge have overridden their foreland, the Appalachian folds, with small nappes which invariably show some of the typical characteristics of gliding structures. The thrust plane plunges down from the high altitude of the Blue Ridge uplift and emerges again further to the west (Fig. 270). Further, the thrust sheets have no great lateral extension, but each has its own individuality, and many consist of several superposed slices. Apparently the thrust planes have been bent again after the emplacement of the nappes.

In the north-east, the Blue Ridge has the appearance of an imbricated geanticline with a core of migmatites and flanks of Pre-Cambrian volcanics and clastic rocks. In the south-west, the Upper Pre-Cambrian becomes much thicker — the Ococe and Upper Talladega series, of sedimentary origin. The origin of the Appalachian geosynclines in the Upper Pre-Cambrian (Algonkian) must probably be sought here.

The character of the Blue Ridge deformation is everywhere of the schistosity-cleavage type, accompanied by migmatization in the lower reaches of Pre-Cambrian. Its great difference from the structural type of the Appalachian folds may be due to several factors, of which the fact that the Pre-Cambrian was submitted to several orogenic periods, one Pre-Cambrian, one Taconic, and one Hercynian, may be the principal factor. The structural type has been worked out in detail by Ernst Cloos (1947b) (see Fig. 53, Chapter 6). But here again we are confronted with the question as to whether the cleavage shear was contemporaneous with the folding or a later superimposed feature. In Chapter 6 we found that contemporaneity is very probable.

The Piedmont Province. The Piedmont area represents the metamorphic and plutonic belt of the orogenic system of the Appalachians and as such it is its most fundamental feature. Unfortunately it is very difficult to interpret and has been little studied from a structural

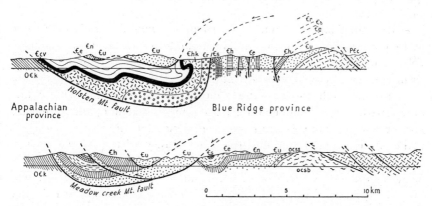

Fig. 270. Thrusts, perhaps gliding nappes, in Tennessee in front of the Blue Ridge. *(After Rodgers. Published by permission of the Department of Conservation, State of Tennessee.)*

point of view. The age-relations of its constituent rocks are still largely unknown, because of their high metamorphism.

It consists mainly of a gneiss complex of katametamorphic character, most probably of Pre-Cambrian age, with granite plutons of different ages. Rodgers (1952) recognized plutons mainly of about 600 and 800 million years old, representing Pre-Cambrian orogenies, but some of them seem to be younger (Hercynian?).

Besides these Pre-Cambrian rocks, one finds long and narrow belts of meta-sedimentary rocks of the epi- or mesozone, which are probably younger, and in addition peridotite intrusions, scattered through the whole crystalline belt but mostly arranged in long streaks. These latter are regarded by Hess (1946) as proof of the initial magmatic stage of a great orogeny, and this may be true, but as their age is completely unknown it is still highly problematic whether they belong to a Palae- ozoic or a Pre-Cambrian orogeny. The latter looks more probable. The limit between the Blue Ridge and Piedmont province is in general not very distinct, indicating that the Blue Ridge tectonics are only the up- and overthrust margin of the Piedmont crystalline basement.

The only conclusion that can be drawn from these facts is that a Pre-Cambrian orogenic belt apparently lies parallel to the Appala- chian geosyncline and has been warped up to considerable height during the Appalachian diastrophism. Whether it forms an intrinsic portion of the later orogeny or not is very doubtful, although most authors presume that this is the case on the ground of the evidence of its parallelism with the later belt and of its intimate connexion with the Blue Ridge province. Personally I would prefer to consider it as the east flank of the Appalachian geosynclinal belt; strongly folded, it is true, and perhaps containing a folded belt of Palaeozoic or at least Algonkian rocks, but not necessarily its central geosyncline. An analogy with the Pennine zone of the Alps seems wholly un- warranted, and it cannot be regarded as a root-zone of thrust sheets, for large thrust sheets themselves are lacking (cf. Lombard, 1948).

The New England and Maritime Provinces. North of New York the Appalachian system has quite a different character. The age of the orogenic periods is greater — Taconic and Acadian (Caledonian, one would say in Europe). The system has a different general strike and the rocks themselves are also different to a large extent. It is generally believed that the Southern and Northern Appalachians belong in some way to the same system. Hess (1946) for instance, draws its peridotitic zone as a more or less continuous trend, and Kay (1951) also regards them as one unit, but I would suggest that the two are really different, and that we have to discriminate between a northern Taconic and a southern Appalachian arc, which intersect north of Long Island. The intersection is largely obscured by a blanket of Triassic rocks. The large Taconic thrust sheets are rather academic constructions, the existence of which is largely based on supposed facies differences, and they certainly need more detailed structural evidence to become firmly established. The Acadian (late Devonian) orogenic phase is more restricted to the eastern part of the belt, but has the same general strike. The influence of the Taconic or Acadian orogenies in the Southern Appalachians can be found in the Palaeozoic series of the Appalachians, *s.str.*, but only as minor effects. I venture to suggest that it would perhaps be more profitable to regard the Northern and Southern Appalachians as two different belts, the younger one cutting nearly at right angles through the older one in the coastal regions of New York and Connecticut. They have perhaps a common Pre-Cambrian history.

Chapter 28

Island Arcs

Among the most striking and conspicuous phenomena in the structural pattern of the earth's crust are undoubtedly the island arcs which bound the Pacific Ocean to the west and reach from Alaska to Australia (Fig. 271). The discussion of island arcs starts from a number of general data which are rarely realized in any other typical feature of crustal disturbance. Nowhere do we know so much of the general character and, I am tempted to say, so little of the geologic detail. This is due to the fact that the island festoons which decorate the western border of the Pacific are morphologically conspicuous features; deep-sea troughs and lines of volcanic activity draw a remarkably consistent and, in many details, regular pattern, emphasized and brought into a three-dimensional perspective by the arrangement of earthquake foci and the zones of negative and positive gravity-anomalies discovered by Vening Meinesz. The scarcity of geological data is due to the fact that most of the territory is covered by sea and that our knowledge of these remote islands, often covered by dense tropical forest or by thick recent volcanic products or coral reef terraces, is naturally scanty.

General Properties of the West Pacific Island Arcs. As mentioned above, the festoon of arcs possesses a series of remarkable, unique, and constant features which give us opportunity of gaining an insight into the connexion between superficial shape and deep subsurface structure.

1. Their *location* is very significant; they lie exactly on the border of the sial crust of the Asiatic continent and the sima crust of the Pacific Ocean, just inside the Andesite line, a line separating the basaltic volcanics of the Pacific from the andesitic volcanics of the island arcs.

2. Their *shape*, arcs en échelon with their convex sides facing the ocean, and intersecting one another, gives a strong impression

410

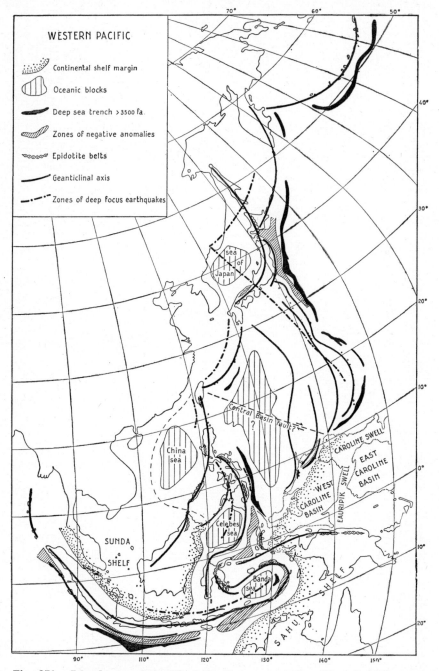

Fig. 271. Island arcs of the West Pacific coast. (*After Hess. Published by permission of the Geological Society of America.*)

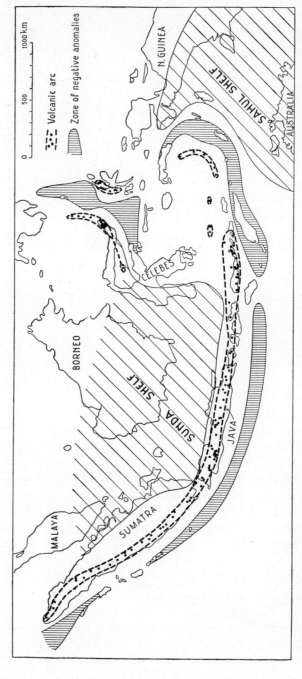

Fig. 272. Negative gravity-anomalies in the Indonesian archipelago. (*After Vening Meinesz, Publ. Neth. Geod. Comm., vol. 2, 1932.*)

of ocean waves with a directed movement. Complications of the pattern arise only in the eastern portion of the Indonesian archipelago, which is squeezed between the Australian continent and the Sunda shelf.

3. *Deep oceanic furrows* invariably accompany them on their convex side.
4. A zone of large *gravity-anomalies* is equally constant in its presence on the convex side of the arcs.
5. A zone of *volcanism* is present but not always active on the inner side of the arc or on the arc itself.
6. *Seismic activity* is very great in this zone and has the peculiarity of possessing foci descending in depth inlandwards to a depth of 700 km.

The first three properties are superficial features, the last three are manifestations of the infracrustal structure. Let us start with the zones of large gravity-anomalies, which Vening Meinesz discovered by his famous pendulum measurements during several trips aboard a submarine. His field of observation is principally concerned with the Indonesian archipelago (Fig. 272), but two crossings further north were made across the Nero deep and the Yap deep. The sections from Java to the Indian Ocean all show negative anomalies, coinciding with the row of islands which lies on the oceanic border of the isle of Sumatra and is continued south of Java by a submarine ridge; the latter emerges again in the arc formed by the row of islands from Timor over the Tanimber Islands to Ceram and Buru. The deep furrow lies to the south and west of this line. Between the outer arc and the main arc of Sumatra and Java we find depths ranging from 1,500–3,500 m, and on the main island arc we find rows of active volcanoes.

The Pacific sections are somewhat simpler because they contain only a single row of islands, accompanied by a deep marine trough. The gravity-anomaly sections show exactly the same kind of narrow zone of negative anomalies but it coincides roughly with the furrow and is asymmetric.

The narrow strip of negative gravity-anomalies has been interpreted as a narrow zone of sialic material of low density pressed down into the heavier sima layer. Because of the narrowness of the negative zone the crustal disturbance cannot reach much deeper than about 100 km.

The gravity sections are not always symmetric, as for instance in

the Guam section, which might indicate an asymmetry in the shape
of the sial mass replacing the series. All kinds of other structures
can be imagined which will satisfy the gravimetric curves, and we
have no geophysical means of determining which one really exists.

Three suggestions have been made (Fig. 273a, b, and c): according
to the first one the crust has been compressed and thickened along a

Fig. 273.   The origin of the downward buckle according to *a* Bijlaard, *b* Vening
Meinesz, *c* Umbgrove.

narrow zone; according to the second, the crust has buckled down;
and according to the third, a thrust plane has been formed.

The second is the original suggestion of Vening Meinesz (1932)
which was exemplified by the experiments of Kuenen (1935) and
Griggs (1939) and used by Hess (1938b) and Umbgrove (1938) as
the obvious solution. The first suggestion was made by Bijlaard
(1935) who proved by purely theoretical reasoning that a plastic
deformation oblique to the stress would be much more probable
than the elastic buckle; Vening Meinesz later rallied to Bijlaard's
opinion. The third suggestion is from Umbgrove (1945). I do not think
that Bijlaard's theory is sound because none of the mathematical–
physical theories is as yet capable of embracing the simultaneous
elastic *and* plastic nature of rock deformation. A deformation as
represented in Chapter 13 by Fig. 124 seems quite adequate for the
buckle, if it exists.

We shall have to look for geophysical or geological evidence other
than gravimetrical data in order to choose between these suggestions.

Fortunately we have a very illuminating series of seismic evidence
to guide us in our choice. All the island festoons are characterized by
great seismic activity with shallow foci on the island arcs next to the
deep marine troughs, by foci of intermediate depth (200–500 km)
further away from the Pacific, and by deep foci (500–700 km) in a
zone still further inwards, below the sialic crust. When we presume
that the shocks originated on shear-zones, as the primary shocks
indicate, the shear-planes have a dip of some 50° away from the ocean.
Consequently we may assume that the suggestion of a thrust of the
continental shelf over the Pacific Ocean floor is right—the thrust plane

mistake

cutting through the rapidly thinning sialic crust, and forming simultaneously the root of the zone of negative gravity-anomalies and the deep furrow bordering the ocean basins.

The relations of the geological and geophysical features are best represented in a section (Fig. 274) slightly modified after Gutenberg (1951) across Japan.

The superficial features, a deep-sea trough in front of a geantic lina

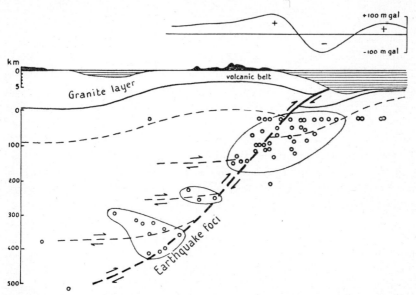

Fig. 274. Earthquake hypocentres, relief, and gravity-anomalies along a profile in the Northern Japanese region. *(After Gutenberg and Richter. Published by permission of the Geological Society of America.)*

volcanic arc, with a basin at its back separating the geanticline from the continent, are seen in relation to the geophysical data. The island arc is a zone of positive gravity-anomalies, the trough or its slope towards the geanticline is the site of a zone of negative anomalies. The epicentres of the deeper earthquakes are situated in clusters on a plane sloping with a dip of about 50° towards the continent.

All these facts are consistent with a thrust movement of a marginal geanticline of the continent over the Pacific Ocean floor. The gravity minimum on the convex side of the belt marks the line where the buckle downwards was formed, here drawn as an overthrust where the two flanks together form the necessary light sial displacement in the heavy sima basement. The geosyncline at the back of the volcanic

ridge is then the corresponding flank movement of the thrust. There
is no need to suppose any subsequent flow of sima material to the left
or right away from the downward buckle of the oceanward flank, for
the thrust movement itself has already redistributed the masses. The
volcanic belt can be understood as the result of tension in the upper
arc, which is sometimes clearly demonstrated by a longitudinal rift
valley on top of the anticline, as in South Sumatra (the Semanko rift
described by van Bemmelen, 1949), but we can hardly expect such
fissures to reach very deep down into the crust.

A section across the Malayan geosyncline, across the island of
Sumatra for instance, has a slightly different pattern. The zone of
negative anomalies coincides with a secondary non-volcanic outer
ridge, separated by a shallower longitudinal trough from the volcanic
arc. It is supposed that this is due to a greater age of the orogeny in
this region, adjustments either below or in the crust having taken
place in the meantime.

The Development of the Buckling Hypothesis. The buckling hypothesis of Vening Meinesz has been further developed, mainly by Hess
(1938 and 1939), Griggs (1939), and Umbgrove (1938, 1945, and 1949).

Hess considered that the buckle probably underwent at least two
compression periods separated by a period in which the flanking
geanticlines emerged above sea level and were partly eroded. Its detritus
and the volcanic material from the inner arc filled up the deep-sea
trough. This trough, seen as a central basin, Hess called the "geotectocline". The second diastrophism compressed the accumulated sediments
of the geotectocline and created the complicated thrust-structures
which are considered to be typical for a great mountain chain. The
serpentinized peridotite intrusions which accompany island arcs and
folded orthogeosynclines are believed to belong to the first diastrophic
period. Hess thinks that the serpentine belt is one of the most trustworthy indications of a real tectogene. An interesting feature in Hess'
analysis of the Antillean arcs is the function of the supposed great
sinistral wrench-fault along the northern scarp of the Bartlett trough
from Guatemala to the Windward passage, still active, as is proved
by its frequent earthquakes, Fig. 275. Hess believes that the fault
movement relieved the area south of the fault of compression, and
the area north of the fault was also much less compressed, as witnessed
by the decrease of the negative anomaly zone west of Haiti.

Umbgrove (1945 and 1949) puts special stress on the double arc
feature, the outer non-volcanic arc being situated on the negative

anomaly zone. He accepts the explanation of Hess that this outer
arc is due to squeezing out of the accumulated sediments between the
two jaws of the geanticline crusher.

Umbgrove also advocates recurrent action along the same zone. And
he particularly stresses the lateral flow of simatic material as a consequence of the downbuckling and its isostatic readjustment, a flow
which would be directed first away from the buckle but afterwards
towards the buckle – when it was lifted up by isostatic adjustment.

In the meantime, according to Umbgrove, the sialic buckle melted
at the root and also flowed sideways, causing further uplift of the
geanticlines or of the troughs between the double arc. All this flowing

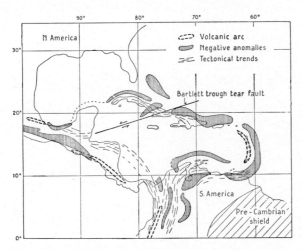

Fig. 275.   The island arcs of the Caribbean region.

hither and thither of sialic and simatic material is of course very
conjectural and can be used for any elevation inside the island arcs.
What is valuable in Umbgrove's analysis is the stress he lays on the
different nature of the inner and outer arcs. The elevation of the inner
arc is a true geanticline due to elastic bending with fault or slip-plane
relaxations and is consequently favourable for volcanism. The emergence of the outer arc is due to isostatic adjustment, and the thickening
of the crust prohibits volcanic action.

The fact that all island arcs are not double arcs, but that many are
single arcs with the marine trough on the convex side of a volcanic
arc, is explained by Umbgrove as due to a much thinner sialic crust
in these regions: Guam with the Nero trough, Yap with the Yap deep,

which is actually situated on the margin of the Pacific non-sialic ocean floor. His drawings are suggestive but there is no cogent reason why the frontal hinge should be volcanic in one case and not in the other.

Hess returned to the same subject (in 1948) now armed with much more detailed knowledge acquired during the war, and Gutenberg and Richter (1949) commented upon it. The old concept of the relation between deep ocean furrows, island arcs, volcanic zones, and earth-quake zones was confirmed everywhere, but extremely interesting details throw much light on the mechanical problem.

First of all, it became established that the southern Pacific must

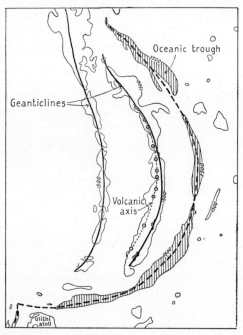

Fig. 276. Slight shift of volcanic axis from geanticlinal axis in Marianas arc. *(After Hess. Published by permission of the Geological Society of America).*

be regarded as a separate unit, different from the northern Pacific and much more like the southern Atlantic, and characterized by swells and basins (see map Fig. 271). The shapes of the West and East Mariana arcs and the Palau arc strongly suggest that the Caroline-Pacific acted as a block against which the westward movements of the surficial layers abutted and could fully develop only to the north of it, with the great swing of the Eastern Mariana arc.

Secondly, Hess made it clear that in the Japanese islands the earthquakes whose foci are of moderate depth follow the geanticlinal axes of the Bonin, Honshu, and Kuril arcs; but that the deep-focus earthquake-lines have a simpler pattern, clearly indicating that there is a difference in the thrust zone pattern below and above a 300 km depth level (Fig. 277).

In the third place, Hess showed that the line of volcanoes is not always coincident with the geanticlinal axes but tends to diverge slightly in direction (Fig. 276), again indicating that at a much slighter depth we may also expect a separation and shifting of one layer over the other.

Another feature of great interest is the arrangement of the deep-focus earthquakes in clusters of greatest activity separated by zones of much less frequency, which together still show the 50° landward slope mentioned before (see Fig. 274). Again we might conclude that there are horizontal layers of different character possibly slipping one over the other. Moreover, Hess succeeded in distinguishing two sets of arcs differing in age. The older one runs in larger festoons, the first festoon from Sakhalin to Hokkaido and along Honshu, the second festoon from the Ryukyu arc to Taiwan, the third festoon from Taiwan over Luzon to Borneo; together they form more or less a straight line, or in other words have one single direction of compression, NW–SE.

The younger set is different in having one northern set of festoons, first the Aleutian arc, and next the Kurilean arc, with a NNW–SSE direction of movement; and a southern set, formed by the Mariana and Bonin festoons supplemented in the background by the Iwo-Jima geanticline, the West Caroline and Palau-Kyushu geanticlines and the Philippine geanticline, all with an EW direction of movement.

The two younger directions meet in Japan; the well-known cross-structure in Honshu, the Fossa Magna, is their meeting point. At depth, they meet — as is shown by the cluster of deep-focus earthquakes — just on the mainland of Asia, north of Korea (Fig. 277). It is obvious that the geanticlinal arc of Honshu and its present trench in front are partly the old geanticline, and partly a result of the interference of the two younger directions in the higher (less than 300 km depth) reaches of the crust.

When we turn our attention to the Indonesian archipelago we find

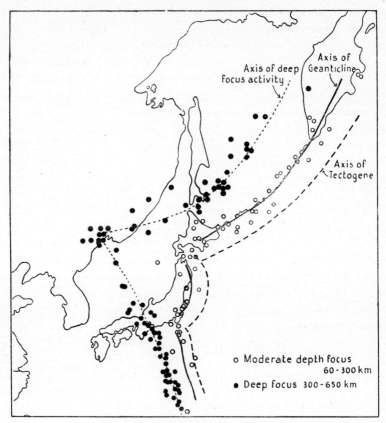

Fig. 277. Divergence of the arcs of deep-focus seismic activity from arcs at moderate depths and island arcs. *(After Hess. Published by permission of the Geological Society of America.)*

the third direction, approximately NS, which originated the Malayan or Sunda geanticline with its trench, its volcanic arc, and its deep-focus earthquake zone. As we shall see further on, the older intercontinental Banda geosyncline has been reshaped in this last NS compression, causing its exaggerated S-shaped curve.

All these ideas about the origin of the pattern of the west Pacific island arcs are of course highly speculative. Still, they are of some interest because, in particular, they do make us realize that first of all we have to consider the necessity of separating older from younger structural features and their interference. Moreover, we get the strong impression that the crustal deformations are entirely dependent on much deeper-seated and wholly unknown factors. The recurrent conclusion that the crustal layer is detached from its substratum by orogenic stress can be observed only in this particular instance, where the absence of sialic crust on the North Pacific floor allowed the upper crust to glide forward.

Furthermore, the section of Fig. 274 shows that the medium and deep foci occur in clusters, sometimes of two, sometimes of three, each having a slightly greater extension in a horizontal direction than in a vertical one. A further separation of horizontal layers, and differential gliding of these layers, one over the other, accompanying the general eastward (or southward) thrust, could explain this localization of earthquake foci.

The Indonesian Archipelago. Although the Indonesian (or East Indian) archipelago is perhaps not a typical example of island festoons, it cannot be omitted from our discussion of island arcs, for it has become a much discussed and controversial object which has unfortunately been taken, because of its spectacular features, as an example for other regions. Our knowledge of the region as a whole is relatively extensive and certainly very diverse, but in detail and exactness it is woefully inadequate.

The Indonesian archipelago is situated on a point of intersection of two large and long orogenic belts, the western circum-Pacific belt ending in the Philippines and entering by the northern arm of Celebes, and the north-eastern Indian Ocean belt running from Malaya into the arc of the greater Sunda Islands (Sumatra and Java).

On the other hand the archipelago is also an intracontinental zone between the Asiatic and Australian continents.

This dual character has perhaps not been sufficiently realized by the various authors who have analysed its geological history; the present configuration, with the separate units welded in one continuous pattern, is often misleading.

The boundary between the Australian and Asiatic continents is formed by the intercontinental Banda geosyncline (Fig. 278) described by Umbgrove (1938 and 1949) as having had almost continuous, although very variable, sedimentation during the whole of the Mesozoic, and a strong Laramide and subsequent Miocene folding. Its extremely curved shape is probably due partly to the shape of the edges of the continental plateau, partly to differential movement in these continents, and partly to the Miocene orogenic phase. At its southern extremity it is met and joined by the Malayan geosyncline,

and at its northern extremity by the circum-Pacific belt. No wonder
that the regular pattern of the Malayan belt, with its double arc,
negative gravity-anomaly zone on the outer arc, volcanism on the inner
arc, and longitudinal basins at the concave side, becomes deranged and
unrecognizable when it merges into the older intercontinental Banda
geosyncline. The same is true for the less well known Philippine arc.

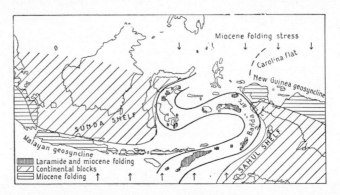

Fig. 278. Banda geosyncline with strong mesozoic sedimentation and Laramide
orogeny. *(After Umbgrove. Published by permission of the American Association
of Petroleum Geologists.)*

There can be little doubt, for instance, that a considerable amount
of shearing took place between the island of Timor of the Banda
geosyncline and the island of Sumba of the Malayan outer arc.

Kuenen (1935) gave a good summary of the existing "explanations"
of the structural features. At that time he had four so-called "geotectonic" maps, by H. A. Brouwer, van Es, Staub, and Smit Sibinga,
at his disposal. Since then many others have been added to the list,
most of them engendered by the negative gravity-anomaly zones of
Vening Meinesz. All of them consist of a curve-pattern joining islands
and ridges. Some draw tear-faults; some prefer curves when the lines
do not join up very well; and in doubtful cases they differ in linking
up the different islands. It is the same game as that which has been
going on in Southern Europe for a long time. Do these lines inform us
about the unity (in time or in space?) of an orogenic system or of the
unity (again in time or in space?) of basin formation? It is impossible
to represent the ever-changing pattern of geosynclinal basins, fold
directions and their interference through geological history by a single
set of lines. And worse, it is misleading. The set of palaeographic maps

by Umbgrove, 1949, gives a much better picture, and from them the
dual character of the Malayan geosyncline running from Sumatra
through the Banda arc to the Philippines becomes evident.

There is a distinct omission, however, in all the more theoretical
sections of Umbgrove — the fact that the limit of the Sunda continental
shelf lies not somewhere on the south coast of Java or Sumatra, but
just on the border of their north coasts. We have there a very rapid
decrease, within some tens of kilometres, of the whole Tertiary
geosynclinal series; from several kilometres in thickness to a few
hundred metres on the shelf. The real continental border is therefore
on the north coast of Java and Sumatra, and further south we probably
have a thinner sialic crust, which perhaps extends into the outer arc.
This limit of the shelf border is also expressed in the difference between
the volcanic rocks on the shelf and on the volcanic arc. The volcanic
arc is andesitic, on the shelf we find typical alkaline rocks (cf. van
Bemmelen, 1938a; Willems, 1940).

Finally, I should mention two other facts: The first is that Vening
Meinesz himself admits that the negative zone together with its flanking
positive zones are about isostatically compensated, and that therefore
a regional isostatic adjustment of the buckle has been accomplished.
Nevertheless, he is not content with this very simple explanation of
both the geanticlinal volcanic arc and the inner basins as results of
the regional uplift, because he believes that the curved shape of the
buckle could never be sustained in the crust once the lateral force
had subsided.

An entirely new approach to the problem of the relation of the deep-
sea furrow to the gravity minimum zone has been opened by Ewing
(1952, 1954). This author, with his collaborators, made a seismic
investigation of the ocean floor over the deep-sea furrow of Puerto
Rico. He found first of all that north of the trench the ocean basin was
covered by a layer of sediments, 1 km thick, overlying a 4 km layer
of basaltic (7.17 km/sec velocity) material above the Mohorovicic
discontinuity; ergo, complete absence of a sialic crust. In the trench,
the flat bottom was underlain by a very thick column of loose sediments
4 to 8 km in thickness, but the bottom was not actually reached.
South of the trench, near the island of Puerto Rico, a layer of 5.5 to
6 km/sec velocity with a minimum depth of 9 km, corresponding to a
sialic layer, was found. When the gravity data are compared with this
general picture it becomes evident that the loose sediment filling of
the trench, roughly 6 km thick together with its water-filled portion,

adequately explains the gravity minimum. There is no need for any sialic buckle beneath the trench, and there is probably no sialic layer at all in the trench beneath the sediments (Fig. 279).

If we are justified in generalizing from this result we should have to conclude that all the gravity-anomaly zones of Vening Meinesz have nothing to do with a configuration of the bottom of the sialic crust, but are simply due to a much deeper furrow along the island arcs than we thought; a furrow partly filled with loose sediments whose accumulation is probably due to turbidity currents starting on the continental inner

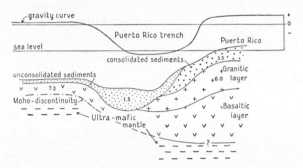

Fig. 279. Puerto Rico trench, gravity curve and constitution of crust after seismic evidence. *(After Ewing. Published by permission of the Geological Society of America.)*

slope. The furrow is just on the limit between the sialic crust and the ocean bottom. The thrust movement of the sialic crust over the ocean bottom causes the furrow, either by buckling or just by pressing it down. The deep furrow is isostatically compensated by a regional adjustment, throwing up the island arc along its inner border.

The Banda Arc. The most conspicuous arc of the whole western Pacific is the Banda arc, and it has been used extensively as a prototype of three other arcuate structures, viz: the Antillean, Alpine, and Gibraltar arcs. We will examine it in some further detail. We have seen that we can regard the Banda arc as the deformed intercontinental geosyncline between the south-east point of the Asian continent and the Australian continent, which in its original shape must have been considerably straighter than its present exaggerated S-shape. The Banda arc is limited to the north by a long straight structural feature, the EW geanticline passing from the Salu islands over Obimajor and Misool into the western extension of New Guinea. In the south, the Banda arc is limited by the Australian continent, which does not show any Tertiary deformation phases but may have moved as a block, and merges into the Malayan folded geosyncline, which also has an EW strike. There can be little doubt that in the Miocene folding phase there was a considerable shortening, in a NS direction, of the whole region occupied by the present Banda arc. A shortening by compression in one direction is always accompanied by an extension in either one or two directions at right angles; the vertical direction is preferred by the surface layers, and sometimes we may presume that the horizontal direction is preferred by the substratum. The vertical extension of the superficial layers is shown by their numerous folds and thrusts. The horizontal extension perpendicular to the main stress can be perceived at the surface only by the general shape of larger structural units or by dilatation features like oblique wrench-faults. The EW stretching which inevitably took place in the Banda arc, combined with the strong compression in a NS direction, deformed the original slightly curved geosyncline into an extreme S-shape (Figs. 272 and 278). One could compare this mechanism with the formation of ptygmatic folds of aplite veins in a gneiss. In the same way that the aplite is somewhat more rigid than the gneiss, and therefore follows another mode of deformation, the geosyncline is, as a result of its cylindrical cross-section, somewhat stronger than the surrounding part of the crust.

The peculiar deep-sea trench behind the Banda arc, the Weber deep, and the adjoining inner Banda arc on which the island of Banda is situated, are also readily explained by the proposition of narrowing and compression of the outer Banda arc. As anyone can see when performing a simple experiment with a folded tablecloth, by compressing an already arched fold one deepens a furrow at the convex side of the arc.

The folded geanticline of the Salu islands — New Guinea — apparently became stretched; so much so that its nose pressed into the southern extension of the Philippine arc, causing the inverted arc of Celebes.

The interference of the EW direction with the slight S-shaped Laramide geosyncline of the Banda arc is also clearly demonstrated by the surface features of their southern junction. The Malayan arc penetrates into the Banda arc west of Timor. The arrangement of the island ridges en échelon, probably accompanied by vertical shearing, is typical of such interferences, as I had occasion to point out in Chapter 23.

Arcuate Structures. Sollas (1903) and Lawson (1932) explained the arcuate shape of the festoons by pointing out that a plane and flat overthrust would intersect the sphere of the earth along a curved line. The overthrust plane, however, must then have a 15° dip, whereas the seismic evidence points to a 50° dip. It is possible, of course, that the thrust plane flattens out near the surface as a result of difference in altitude between the sialic crust and the Pacific or Indian ocean bottom. But there may be other reasons, and when one considers the very long curve from the Tanimber islands deep into Burma, and the strong curvature of the Aleutians and Mariana arc, the suggestion of Sollas and Lawson seems difficult to accept.

I think it much more probable that the thrust plane itself has an arcuate shape, varying from almost straight to the strong curvature of the Mariana arc. In this respect we might recall that in general a deformation sets in at one particular point and then spreads to the right and left, upwards and downwards. But the fact that the central point gives way first alters the stress conditions on both sides of that point. First of all we shall find in the centre a stress much smaller than at the initial stage, but still capable of thrusting the broken block forwards; and much larger stresses towards both extremities, which diminish again outwards to the degree of the initial stress (Fig. 280).

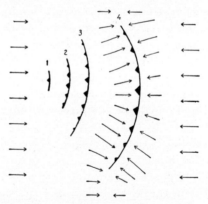

Fig. 280. Origin of arcuate structures.

The unequal stress yield will also change the stress-directions which will become divergent outwards. Seen from this point of view, the curvature of the island arc has the same nature and origin as the curvature of an asymmetric anticline. But having established a strong NS stress in the southern area of the Indonesian archipelago, we might also expect this stress-field to have extended much farther north. It would then certainly have attributed to the arcuate shape of the Japanese group of arcs by adding a NS compression to the eastern advance.

Without doubt the island arcs of the west Pacific border are the most instructive examples of orogenic deformation. We have seen that the detachment of one horizontal zone from the next is one of the most principal features of the folding, which can develop particularly well here because the upper continental layer can actually be shoved over the Pacific floor. It is the same principle that prompted us always to distinguish the distortion typical of the upper sedimentary layer as opposed to that of the basement, a principle which we already deduced at an earlier stage of our investigation when we had opportunity to point out that every incompetent layer between competent series is apt to become a detachment horizon originating disharmonic folds. I should like to suggest that these incompetent layers, or at any rate the upper ones, are the layers that furnish the magma of the extrusive lavas and the intrusive basic rocks.

We deduced from the development of island arcs that two perpendicular directions of stress can act either at the same time or alternately but that in either case both stresses contribute to the final shape. Moreover, we inferred that the cylindrical cross-section of a pre-existing geosyncline constitutes an exceptionally strong element in the structure of the basement, which may be bent if it has been arched beforehand, but will withstand great stress if originally straight.

Furthermore, we learned that the stress condition is certainly not limited to the upper 60 or 100 km of the crust but reaches at least to 700 km depth, and that it is very probable that discontinuity surfaces split this section up into two or three concentric zones.

As I have gone rather extensively into the problems of the Japanese and Indonesian island arc, I will leave alone the Antillean arc, which has many features in common with the Indonesian arc. We find there the same connexion between volcanism, seismicity, gravity-anomalies, and arcuate island festoons, accompanied by wrench-faulting (the Bartlett trough) and folding.

Whether or not the double arc of the Lesser Antilles is a replica of the Banda arc, with a similar later compression of a Laramide geosyncline of simpler shape, seems undecided. But from a general point of view we need not expect any great analogy because the Banda arc is an intercontinental structure and the Antillean arc more of a circum-continental one. According to the gravity map of de Bruyn

(1951) the negative zone does not curve round to the north into the Leeward trench as Hess (1938) drew it but enters the mainland of South America in the Orinoco delta in good accordance with purely geological considerations (Bucher, 1952).

A comparison of the Banda arc with the Gibraltar arc is certainly not warranted. The Gibraltar arc (see Fig. 255, Chapter 24) is *not* a true arc because the structural lines do not curve round from their EW position in south-east Spain to a NS direction west of Gibraltar and an EW direction in North Africa. On the contrary, the two units, the Riff in North Africa and the Betic cordilleras in southern Spain, are two orogenic units, which are perhaps connected in one two-sided orogenic system, or more probably separated by a block, but are not connected by an arc round the Strait of Gibraltar.

On the other hand the S-shaped curve of the Western Alps has an origin which is similar but not exactly analagous to that of the Banda arc, as we have seen in Chapter 26, because part of its curved shape seems to be due to a compression of an already existing curved geosyncline.

Whether the western Pacific arcs and their volcanic rows are an analogue of the volcanic activity of the eastern Pacific is an open question. As we have seen in Chapter 27, the latest (Pliocene to Recent) volcanoes of the Cordilleran system, are probably to be regarded either as a post-tectonic volcanic phase or as a continental phase, and can hardly be compared to the volcanic island arcs. The volcanic activity in the Jurassic and Miocene may have had a similar origin to that of the island arcs, as advocated by Kay (1951) but the geology is still so obscure that a well-considered opinion is impossible. Personally, I would hesitate to take the island arcs of the western Pacific with their unique assembly of geotectonical and geophysical features as a prototype of any other structural feature of the earth's crust except the Antillean arc, and perhaps the Falkland Island arc, although their separate characteristics may certainly be present elsewhere.

Chapter 29

Shields

The structural study of the Pre-Cambrian shields is one of the most difficult tasks of geology, because the relative age of their rocks cannot be determined by fossils, but only by comparison, analogies, and finally by physico-chemical methods (Pb/U and Pb/Th ratios).

A shield is a part of the earth's crust which manifestly has not been seriously disturbed since the Pre-Cambrian. As we shall see, the Pre-Cambrian history bears witness of very severe and profound disturbances, and the rigid nature of a shield is therefore only a relative property. The Hercynian blocks, for instance, which have been severely folded in the mid or final stage of the Palaeozoic but have withstood deformation during later Mesozoic or Cenozoic periods, could also be considered as part of a shield. There is, however, a special reason for drawing the line at the end or near the end of the Pre-Cambrian and not at a later period, namely the highly metamorphic state of most of the Pre-Cambrian shields; they show phenomena of migmatization and granitization over larger areas and in a much higher degree than does any Palaeozoic orogenic belt.

There is a general notion that the Pre-Cambrian shields form the nuclei around which first the Palaeozoic, and later the Alpine chains, came into existence, in concentric zones. I shall refer to this again in Chapter 32. This notion, however, needs an important restriction, because the Palaeozoic geosynclines certainly had a bottom, consisting of a Pre-Cambrian basement; and there was therefore undoubtedly a part of the Pre-Cambrian shield that did *not* resist deformation. As a matter of fact, one might as well postulate the thesis that the present shields are those portions of a much larger Pre-Cambrian continent which were not affected by later geosynclines and orogenic belts or mountain chains. And as the Caledonian and Hercynian belts in their original geosynclinal stage were nothing but basins on the Pre-Cambrian shield, their folding did not add anything to the shield.

429

THE CANADIAN SHIELD

In the Canadian shield the age relations have been established by
Pb/U, Th ratios, and other radioactive elements. Ellsworth started this
investigation in 1932. Three ages of pegmatitic igneous rocks are
prominent, one around –1,800 to –2,200 m.y. in the shield itself, one
around – 1,050 m.y. in the Grenville series, and some of about – 1,350
m.y. in isolated patches. The Northern Appalachians are younger,
Caledonian and Hercynian, with most probably a basement of a
younger Pre-Cambrian phase of about – 600 m.y., and another of
– 800 m.y., which is also present in Ontario and in the Piedmont province
of the Southern Appalachians (Fig. 281). The method assigns the
significance of an orogenic period to a rock-series containing pegmatites
whose age-determinations are comparable; it is based on the assumption that pegmatites occur only once in connexion with syntectonic
granitization in the course of the geosynclinal and orogenic cycle. We

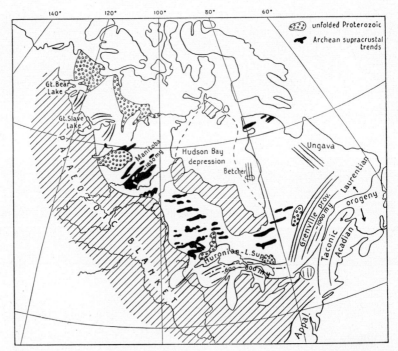

Fig. 281. Areas of Proterozoic rocks in the Canadian Pre-Cambrian shield.
(After Gill, Jubilee Volume of the Canadian Institute of Mining and Metallurgy,
1948.)

have seen that this assumption holds good in Palaeozoic and Alpine mountain chains and it is confirmed again and again in the Pre-Cambrian shields.

To the west, the Canadian shield is covered by younger sediments, increasing in thickness towards the Pacific orogenic belt.

In its centre we find the great depression of the Hudson Bay, whose subsidence started in the Ordovician and continued in the Devonian. On the shield we find large and small patches of undeformed late Pre-Cambrian rocks (Jotnian), as on the Baltic shield. They are located south and west of Hudson Bay. To the south-east the shield is limited by the Northern Appalachians, and to the south by the Palaeozoic cover reaching far into the interior states of the U.S. As in the Baltic shield, the provinces in the Canadian shield can be distinguished by the prevailing strike and general nature of the rocks; and, if possible, ages are given to each province after their determination by radioactive methods.

By far the greater part of the rocks of the Canadian shield consists of granites and gneisses of which little is known. But enclosed in these igneous and highly metamorphic rocks, there occur long stretches of little metamorphosed but highly disturbed sediments and volcanic rocks. The strike varies, but they can be grouped by similarity of strike into three large areas. In the south-east, there occurs a special province with a SW–NE strike, the Grenville province, which is regarded as a true orogenic belt of somewhat younger date. Towards the south, the shield is limited by the Huronian orogenic belt, with an EW trend.

These supracrustal formations of the shield outside the Grenville and Huronian provinces fall into two groups, an older Archean group typified by conglomerates, arkose, grauwacke, and slate, and a younger Proterozoic or (younger) Pre-Cambrian group of quartzite, dolomite and limestone, slate, grauwacke, arkose, conglomerate, and iron-bearing formations. Lavas make up a large part of both groups and they are dominantly of a basic type. They are more prominent in the Archean rocks than in the Proterozoic sequence.

The trend of the folding is given by the stringers of folded Archean rocks in the granite-gneiss basement. Inside the shield no great orogenic belts have been recognized up till now, but unless the granite-gneiss basement is better known this can hardly be expected. At present the pattern of the less deformed Archean supracrustal formations suggests a multitude of oblong, relatively shallow basins filled with lavas, pyroclastics and coarse sediments, strongly compressed and invaded by granite intrusions.

The relations between the three great provinces are in no way clear. Obviously they represent different stress-fields, probably at different times, but the succession is unknown.

The detailed structure of the supracrustal rocks is known at many places from underground mining works and is almost invariably of

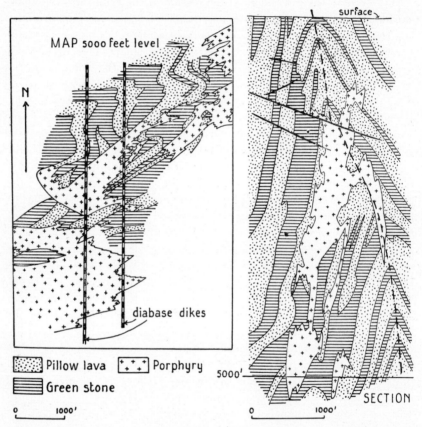

MAP 5000 feet level

N

diabase dikes

Pillow lava   Porphyry

Green stone

5000'

surface

SECTION

0   1000'   0   1000'

Fig. 282.   Map and section of Coniaurum Mine. *(After Caster, Jubilee Volume of the Canadian Institute of Mining and Metallurgy, 1948.)*

the type in which the internal movement has been concentrated on parallel planar schistosity-planes. Figure 282 gives an excellent picture of this kind of folding. The anticlinal axis dips here at 70° from the surface to the 3,500 feet level, and below that at nearly 90°.

The fold-axes are far from straight, as is shown by Fig. 283; the granite intrusions are more or less localized on the anticlinal axes, and are bent together with the anticlinal axes of the invaded rocks, indicating a change in the orientation of the stress-field.

Taking account of the relatively short distance between the synclinoria of supracrustal rocks, some 40–60 miles, Gill (1952) concludes that the crust at the time of the thick lava-flows was thin and relatively weak, and subject to frequent and rapid deformations in swells and troughs. The resulting narrow mountain chains were less lofty than present ones and more numerous. The age-determinations of these

Fig. 283. Geological map of area round Flin Flon Mine. *(After Stockwell and Harrison, Jubilee Volume of the Canadian Institute of Mining and Metallurgy, 1948.)*

Archean rocks include two main periods; Keewatin, around − 2,000 m.y., and Algoman (or Manitoba) − 1,750–1,800 m.y. The period from − 2,000 m.y. to − 1,500 m.y. was particularly favourable for gold mineralizations. Apparently we are here in the presence of one of the oldest recorded histories of the earth's crust, older than the most of the Baltic shield, and it may well be, as Gill supposes, that the nature of earth crust distortion was fundamentally different then from what it has been since the Laurentian (− 1,000 m.y.) Grenville province.

To the south-east the Canadian shield is bordered by a broad belt, some 200 miles wide, of highly metamorphic rocks in which the Archean rocks seem to be absent, and which is characterized by anorthositic intrusions; this is the Grenville province. It certainly represents a mountain chain trending north-east, and can be followed into the Adirondacks in New York State. Its pegmatites indicate an age of −1,030 m.y., and its orogeny is named the Laurentian orogeny.

In the south of the Canadian shield, north of Lake Huron, and south of Lake Superior, another belt of orogeny is disclosed; this we may call either the Huronian chain or the Lake Superior chain. The rocks belong to the Huronian system and the orogeny is also called Huronian and has an age of −760 m.y. The Keweenawan series overlap unconformably on the Huronian rocks, but have been folded themselves, and are intruded by granites whose age has been determined as −550 to 600 m.y. This orogeny has been given the name of Lake Superior. Both the Lake Superior and the Huronian periods are also represented in the Appalachian Mountains (Rodgers, 1952). The nickel mineralization of Sudbury probably belongs to the youngest orogenic period, the Lake Superior period.

In the north-west some additional Archean folding has been mapped recently in the neighbourhood of the Great Slave Lake and Great Bear Lake. Of the Great Bear Lake an age of −1,350 m.y. has been reported.

The Canadian shield thus consists of an immense central mass which has been consolidated by a series of orogenic periods older than 1,000 m.y. In each period basins were filled with pillow lavas and other basic lavas, pyroclastics, and coarse sediments. The sediments were intruded by porphyries and later by granites, and severely compressed between large granite batholiths. The stress-fields of the succeeding compression periods vary in orientation; and the general character of the cycles as a whole differs from that of later periods of geological time not only in the nature of the sediments, which are dominated by volcanic rocks and include no limestones, but perhaps also in the width and distribution of the geosynclinal zones.

THE STABLE INTERIOR OF THE NORTH AMERICAN CONTINENT

To the south and south-west the Canadian shield is bordered by younger orogenic belts, in which there are supracrustal formations of great thickness. These formations are partly of the same character and age as those that lie unconformably and hardly disturbed on the shield. Limestones are present; volcanic rocks are still very frequent; migmatization and granitization are prominent. The Grenville or

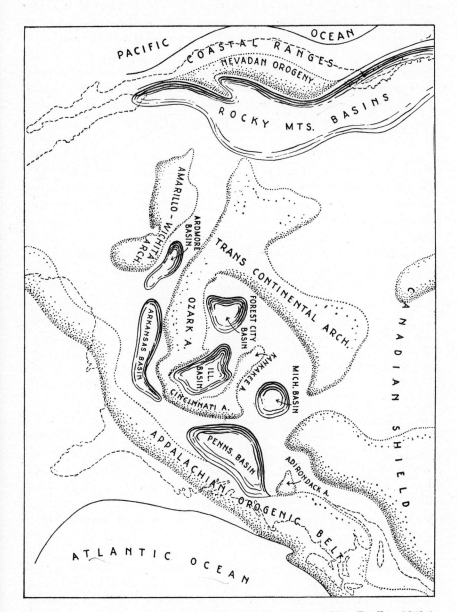

Fig. 284.   Tectonic features of the Midcontinent region. *(After Eardley, 1951.)*

Laurentian belt is followed to the east first by the Taconian (post Silurian) and then by the Acadian (post Devonian) orogenic belts, both roughly parallel to it and each further removed from the centre of the shield. The Huronian belt is not followed to the south by any younger belt. On the contrary the shield conditions reign undisturbed for a great distance until they are interrupted by the Palaeozoic chain of the Ouachitas, an EW chain. This central stable region of the North American continent is covered by Palaeozoic sediments, which allow us to observe ridges and basins of epeirogenic character. The basins are located on both sides of a central NE–SW trending arch, the transcontinental arch (Fig. 284) with later cross-arches trending NW–SE. Some of those cross-arches developed into more sharply expressed features, such as the Arbuckle-Wichita belt, and later the strongly compressed Ouachita-Marathon mountain chain. But even after these late-Palaeozoic interruptions the stable character of the shield persisted far to the south, subsiding, it is true, its subsidence variations imposed in Palaeozoic times, but still essentially stable as far south as the Antillean arches of the Caribbean region. Thus we find here essentially the same picture as the Baltic shield presents, a northern region of Pre-Cambrian rocks which are covered by Palaeozoic rocks towards the south; showing epeirogenic deformation and occasional late Palaeozoic orogenies but remaining stable as far south as the Caucasus and Balkan region of the Mediterranean.

THE BALTIC SHIELD

In northern Europe, just as in northern America, we find a large tract of land where Pre-Cambrian rocks form the surface, and it is only occasionally, in rift valleys, that they are covered by younger sediments. Since it extends both west (in Sweden) and east (in Finland) of the Baltic sea, we can call it the Baltic shield.

The Baltic shield consists largely of gneisses and granites, with some less metamorphosed supracrustal formations. The age-relations have been worked out by Finnish and Swedish geologists, by patient fieldwork. Most of this work was done before the advent of radioactive methods of investigation. The latter have been little used in this region up to the present. It is to be hoped that they will soon be applied more widely, in order to allow a correlation with Canada, Africa, and Australia. Such age-determinations are also highly desirable to solve several correlation problems within the shield itself. At present we can distinguish three or four major periods, each ending with a major diastrophism (Fig. 285).

Algonkian (Jotnian — Eo-Cambrian) Charnian folding (−600 m.y.?).

Karelides, Lake Superior folding (−800 m.y.).

Gothides. Folding age also −800 m.y.?

Sveccofennides or Svionides. Laurentian folding (−1,000–1,200 m.y.).

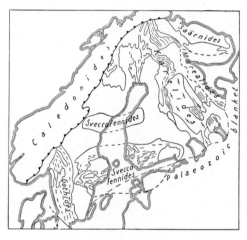

Fig. 285. The Baltic shield and its orogenic regions.

Backlund (1943) unites the middle periods as the Gotho-Karelides, a point of view which cannot be refuted without absolute age-determinations because the two regions are widely separated, the Karelides in north-east Finland, the Gothides in south-west Sweden.

The Algonkian has its own well-defined position at the top of this sequence, since its formations show little or no metamorphism. It consists of volcanic rocks (Dalaporphyries) and continental sandstones, and their erosion products, the Jotnian sandstones, which have been intruded by the youngest granites (Rapakiwi alkaline granites), by monzonites and numerous porphyry and diabase dikes, and finally by curious small stocks of very alkaline rocks. To me it looks probable, as it does to von Bubnoff (1952), that the Dal-formation west of Lake Vänern in south-west Sweden is a geosynclinal facies of the Jotnian, by analogy with similar formations in central Europe which also consist of spilites and grauwackes; but most Swedish geologists regard it as a Karelian basin. If the Dal-formation were Jotnian, its intense folding, which includes large-scale thrusting of older gneiss-granite over the core of its geosyncline (see Fig. 286), should be late Jotnian; and the Eo-Cambrian formations, which consist mostly of grauwackes (Sparagmites), tillites and finally orthoquartzites and slates, would be the denudation product of the late Jotnian peripheral folding, round the western margin of the Baltic shield, which has been largely obliterated and over-run further north by the still later Caledonian folding.

The Karelian System, the principal part of which is located in northeast Finland, has a NW–SE strike. It consists of numerous complex synclinal zones, pressed between domes and elongated masses of older rocks. The base of supracrustal rocks, according to Väyrynen (1933) is found in the eastern part of the Karelian region, where a coarse conglomerate lies on the abrased surface of older Sveccofennide rocks; the rocks above the conglomerate consist mainly of arkoses, and thick quartzites (700–800 m), followed by dolomites, and then by a thick

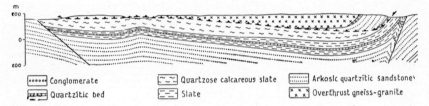

Fig. 286. Overthrust over the Jotnian geosyncline of Dalsland, Sweden.
(After Heybroek and Zwart, Leidse Geol. Med., vol. 16, 1949.)

volcanic series of a basic nature. In the centre of this zone we find a different facies, above the thick basal quartzites, called the Kalevian facies, which is more metamorphosed and has been intruded by granites. It consists chiefly of phyllites with ophiolites and serpentines, a typical eugeosynclinal facies. The orogenesis of the system comprises, besides the ophiolitic initial phase, acid granites accompanied by strong migmatization and metamorphism, and late-tectonic porphyric granites. The sections of Wegmann (1928) show the complicated Alpine type with important overthrusted structures.

The Gothides. In western Sweden we find a gneiss region with a NS trend, sharply separated from the younger post-tectonic granites, and along that contact there occurs a series of ultrabasic intrusions. There seem to be transitions in the form of granite gneiss between the west-Swedish gneisses and the Småland granites, and it is supposed that the gneisses are a tectonized facies of the granites. They have their own supracrustal formations in the form of lavas and tuffs of the Åmålformation, and these are regarded as the equivalent of the Småland porphyries. The line separating the eastern granite region from the western gneiss region is characterized by a strongly developed zone of schistosity (Fig. 287).

With this general picture in mind it seems probable that the western gneisses together with their supracrustal volcanic rocks are an orogenic belt younger than the Sveccofennides, and more or less synchronous with the post-tectonic granites of the eastern region. The Gothide orogenesis ended with post-tectonic granites (Bohus- and Karlshamm granite).

The Dal-formation, mentioned above as an Algonkian basin, is certainly discordant on the Åmålformation and represents one of the few remnants of the youngest Pre-Cambrian geosynclines surrounding the Baltic shield. The Ural Mountains contain a cycle of the same age.

The sequence of events in the pre-Algonkian orogenesis is characterized by a profusion of granites. The supracrustal formations of the geosynclinal

	Post-Cambrian sediments		Younger Archeozoic
	Magnetite-gneiss		Jotnic sandstone
	Foliated granite		Dala-porphyry
	Granite		Basic intrusives

Fig. 287. The boundary line, marked by hyperite (ultrabasic) intrusions, between the western gneiss region and eastern granite region in middle and south Sweden.

stage are largely volcanic and are connected with their own granites; the syntectonic phase is again characterized by granites, strongly migmatizing the older supracrustal formations; and the post-tectonic phase again consists of granites and volcanics, which at the same time forms the initial phase in a peripheral region of the first orogenesis, thus linking the great cycles together in one continuous series of granitization and volcanic activity.

The picture we gather from the Baltic shield is very much like that of the older part of the Canadian shield, although it is probably considerably younger and roughly synchronous with the Grenville and Huronian belts.

The Sveccofennian System. The most important Sveccofennian structure is an orogenic WE belt reaching from central Sweden to southern Finland. It has been thoroughly explored in the central Swedish iron ore belt by Magnusson and Geyer (1944), in Finland by the classic work of Sederholm (1932), and by Wegmann and Franck (1931).

In the coastal regions of central Sweden the axis plunges sharply eastwards into the Baltic Sea and emerges again in Finland. The rock types on both sides are closely comparable.

The Sveccofennide sediments, or Svionic cycle as Magnusson (1936) calls them, start with the leptite formation, mainly pyroclastic rocks and lavas, which can be divided in a lower group with volcanic rocks and limestones, and an upper group with grauwackes and schists. The iron ores of central Sweden are restricted to this leptite formation. The leptite formation has been strongly granitized and migmatized by the oldest syntectonic granites, mostly forming laccoliths and sills. These granites range from basic to acid types. The folding and granitization were followed by the intrusion of numerous diabase dikes (now amphibolite), along fault systems; and by a new granite phase, of the Fellingsbro-Stockholm potash granite type, rich in pegmatites. This granite phase has again migmatized and penetrated the surrounding rocks with pegmatites and in Finland forms large batholiths (Hängo-granites). This is the serorogenic phase of the Scandinavian geologists, comparable to what we call the syntectonic type of granization. The more solid and uniform Finnish granites represent the deeper palingenetic state, the Swedish granites being the higher pegmatitic migmatizing state, resulting in streaked gneisses. Still younger are the Philipstad and Småland granites, on the western margin of the Sveccofennides; they are clearly post-tectonic and are accompanied by porphyries and pyroclastic rocks.

The Stable Interior of Eurasia. The extension of the Baltic shield towards the south is found in the Russian and North German plains, as far as the Alpine belts of the Alps, Carpathians, and Caucasus. This part of the shield is covered by Palaeozoic and younger sediments, and has been transformed in the west and south-west and south by many Palaeozoic orogenic belts. Outside these belts we find a gently undulating plain, partly covered by younger sediments as in the North German plain, or still open to surface study as in the Russian plain. The two are separated by a NS welt or arch, the Scythian arch, comparable to the transcontinental arch of North America. East of this arch a great basin has developed, the Moscow basin, deepening towards the east where it merges into the marginal trough of the Ural Mountains chain. Its history has been described in great detail by S. von Bubnoff (1952) whom I shall follow here (Fig. 288).

The Moscow basin forms, together with the Baltic shield, one great basculated and slightly bent block of the earth's crust, elevated in the north and sinking in the south. As a whole, it is bounded on all sides by orogenic mountain chains; in the north-west by the Caledonian chain of Norway, in the east by the repeatedly folded Ural Mountains, in the south and south-west by a sequence of Nevadan to Alpine

Fig. 288. The Moscow basin, the Baltic shield, and the Alpine orogeny in Europe. *(Mainly after von Bubnoff, Fennosarmatia, Abb. 48. Published by permission of Akademie-Verlag, Berlin.)*

orogenic mountain chains. The interior of this Palaeozoic shield has been influenced by all these surrounding mountain chains; it has been arched up in broad arches and sunk in marginal troughs. The age of these arches and basins varies. The sinking of the coal basin of Southern Russia, for instance, started only in the Upper Devonian, whereas the subsidence along the Urals is of a much older origin. The Moscow basin is the result of these marginal movements. It measures some 1,600 km in diameter, and took its present form only after repeated epeirogenic movements, shifting and changing in direction, but apparently always in connexion with impulses from its marginal orogenic zone, the Urals.

Although the pattern of the Sarmatian (Russian) shield is different

from that of the North American shield, we find the same kind of
epeirogenic movements in relation to its surrounding orogenic belts.

THE CENTRAL AFRICAN SHIELD

It is of considerable importance to compare the structural features
of two of the great shields of the northern hemisphere with those
of the southern hemisphere; the latter differ from their northern

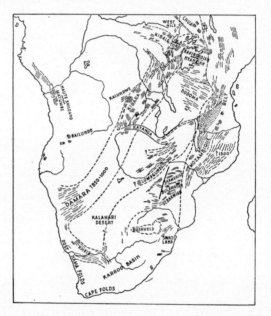

Fig. 289.   The   African   orogenies.   (*After A. Holmes,* 18th *International
Geological Congress, London,* 1951.)

counterparts in that they have remained more stable since the Pre-
Cambrian. The African shield is in parts better known than either the
Australian or the Brazilian shields (Fig. 289).

The characteristics of the older rocks of the Central African shield
have been described by Macgregor (1951). "The basement complex of
Southern Rhodesia," he writes, p. XXIX, "is composed of granites of
different ages, enclosing masses of mainly older rocks which were
formed at the earth's surface as lavas or sediments. These masses are
widely scattered in the granite areas but they are in the main very
similar in their constitution."

The supracrustal rocks of the Bulawayan system consist of basic lavas, often pillow lavas, andesitic breccias, and interbedded coarse sediments. They overlie unconformably the older Sebakwian system, which contains ultrabasic rocks intrusive in coarse sediments, migma-tized and granitized sediments, gneisses and granites. The Bulawayan system itself is overlain unconformably by the Shamvaian system, consisting of arkoses, grauwackes, and conglomerates.

The sedimentary rocks of these formations differ from our ordinary sediments in that they consist predominantly of undifferentiated arkoses and grauwackes, and with a few exceptions do not contain clay or limestone. The exceptions are some quartzites and banded ironstones. This is what one may expect in the oldest Archean sediments, where the decomposition of igneous minerals like felspar, pyroxenes and micas, which in more modern rocks has resulted in abundant clay minerals, produced during a long sequence of periods of deposition and erosion, has not yet had time to develop. The granites and gneisses are partly older than the Bulawayan system and partly younger. The larger batholiths are round or ovaloid bodies, and the sedimentary systems fill up the "pore space" between them (Fig. 290). The typical triangular synclines of the sedimentary rocks (Fig. 291) suggest that their formation is not so much due to lateral compression as to the vertical rise of the granite masses. Inside the triangles we find numerous small granite cupolas, often on the synclinal axes, suggesting that the axial planes are potential fault-lines, perhaps of the kind we often find in similar folds. The granite cupolas could represent either recrystallization of the sediments in zones of vertical tension on the axial planes or intrusions from below.

The oldest granites have a gneissic character caused by the segregation of biotite in parallel seams between wider lenticles of felspar and quartz. The banding is parallel with the margins of the larger batholiths. The younger granites are clearly intrusive. The migmatites are very much contorted and do not show preferred directional texture. The logical conclusion from the facts, it seems to me, is that we still find the same cycle as we found in Palaeozoic mountain chains — early syntectonic migmatization and gneissification, and late-tectonic intrusion. The abundance of ultra-mafic rocks in the oldest sedimentary system, the abundance of pillow lavas and serpentine intrusions in the Bulawayan rocks, and the coarse undifferentiated sediments of the youngest system also suggest one single cycle.

The age-determinations of the Shamvaian pegmatites give an

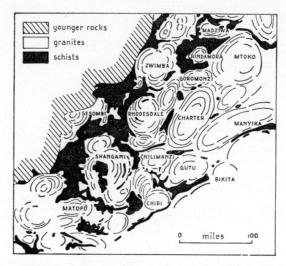

Fig. 290. The structure of the oldest orogenies in Rhodesia. *(After Macgregor. Published by permission of the Geological Society of South Africa.)*

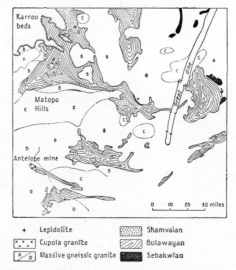

Fig. 291. Distribution of triangular geosynclines between granite masses in Bulawayo district. *(After Macgregor. Published by permission of the Geological Society of South Africa.)*

average of 2,650 m.y. (Holmes and Cahen, 1955). The Rhodesian region of great age described above is only a tiny patch in the great African shield. Much of that shield is covered by the Upper Palaeozoic Karroo formation, sub-horizontal everywhere and disturbed only by the faults of the African rift systems. Around the enormous basin of the Congo, a series of apparent Cambrian or Eo-Cambrian rocks comes to the surface, however, and extends into South-West Africa; these rocks have been studied in some detail by Belgian geologists, mostly in connexion with exploration of the copper, gold, and radioactive minerals of Katanga, and the gold belt of the Great Lakes, east of the Congo basin.

The Katanga system is well dated by the Shinkolobwe pegmatites. It has an age of -630 ± 35 m.y., and has been taken as the limit between the Cambrian and the Pre-Cambrian in Central Africa. The belt to which these pegmatites belong has a roughly east-west direction, and is almost perpendicular to a much larger system, the Kibara-Urundi belt, the orogenic age of which has been determined as $-1,200-1,400$ m.y. The intervening -800 m.y. orogeny is unknown in Africa up to the present. The Katanga sedimentary series, subdivided with the use of many local names, ends with well-established tillites, again showing that an ice age may be expected at the end of an orogenic period.

PRE-CAMBRIAN AND YOUNGER OROGENIC SYSTEMS COMPARED

What we have learned about the oldest history of the earth differs in many ways, in its structural and its stratigraphical aspects, from our experience of Palaeozoic and Cenozoic mountain chains. The sediments differ in several respects; they tend to be less assorted, grauwackes and arkoses are much more important, limestones become definitely rare and often are altogether absent. This is understandable when we realize that the chemical separation of calcium from the silicates, as with the formation of clay minerals from felspars, is a very slow process. The mechanical separation of quartz from felspar and mica will also become more and more complete when the sediments are reworked by erosion and sedimentation.

The most striking difference from the younger rocks is without doubt the great bulk of volcanic rocks, which are often predominant in any supracrustal rock series.

The magmatic phases, which we got to know as initial, syntectonic, late- and post-tectonic phases, and of which only the middle ones were characterized by granites, are here all accompanied by granitic intrusion, migmatization, granitization, etc. The curious fact remains, however, that the initial magmatic phase still contains, in its oldest manifestations, the ultra-mafic rocks which we have already met as the most characteristic feature of this phase in the youngest Alpine orogenies. We are thus confronted from the beginning of the geologic history of our Earth by the contrast of the ultra-mafic and granite rocks.

The folding characteristics do not differ from those we know from younger chains; most of it is of the schistose type, but occasionally we meet purely concentric shapes. Our detailed structural knowledge is however very restricted — confined to a single mine or exploration field here and there. The larger belts appear only with the 1,000 m.y. Laurentian orogeny, like the Grenville belt, the Sveccofennides or the Kibara-Urundi belt. The older ones seem to be much less confined to specific belts, they appear more scattered on a large surface, often with a specific trend as in Canada, but this impression may be due only to insufficient knowledge. On the other hand we find a certain provisional synchronization of orogenies round the figures of $-1,000$, -800, and -600 m.y. on the several Pre-Cambrian shields, although the -800 one seems to be missing in Africa.

Chapter 30

Basin Structures

THE SEDIMENTARY AND STRUCTURAL PROPERTIES OF A BASIN

The structural history of a basin has been recorded by its sediments during its epeirogenic development, and by its structural features during its orogenic periods. Nowhere else is the close relation between the two kinds of development more clearly demonstrated than in folded basins; and no structures are better known, for it is in these basins that oil occurs, stimulating an extensive research reaching to great depth.

The filling up of a basin, geosynclinal or cratonic, with sediments is in itself a complex and peculiar phenomenon. Two factors must contribute, otherwise the mechanism would stop: namely, the sinking of the basin, and the rising of land at one or both sides. If the sinking stopped, the sediments would be carried further away and deposited elsewhere; and if the rising of the land stopped there would be no further source of material. The fact that so many basins have been continuously supplied with sufficient material to maintain a relatively unchanging depth of the sea within the basin proves that the two motions (downward within the basin, and upward at its margins) are so closely related, that the sinking and the filling are neatly balanced. This balance is thought to be controlled and maintained by isostatic sinking of the basin as a result of the increasing load of the accumulating sediments and by the isostatic rise of the land as a result of denudation. Isostasy can of course never be more than a controlling factor; the amount of sinking due to loading can never be more than a fraction of the thickness of the load.

The classification of areas with particularly thick sedimentary series into geosynclines and basins is arbitrary. Some basins are clearly subdivisions of geosynclines; others are independent units on a shield. In general, a sedimentary region which is of limited size and not severely

447

folded is referred to as a basin, as I have outlined in Chapter 1, whereas geosynclines are either themselves folded and uplifted in mountain chains or are closely connected with such mountain building. They are, moreover, of a larger size and much longer than they are broad. Some geologists ban the term basin from their terminology. I prefer to retain it for areas of relatively thick sedimentation without severe folding. Whether they are in close connexion with mountain building or not is immaterial. Thus a basin may be a latent minor geosyncline if one supposes that in the future it will be folded into a real mountain chain; and a basin may also have a typical geosynclinal facies of the grauwacke type, like the Ventura basin (Natland and Kuenen, 1951).

A basin, like a geosyncline, has a long sedimentary history, and usually passes through various orogenic phases, none of them very severe. It might be wholly continental or wholly marine or anything between. In simple basins we can recognize one cycle of sedimentation, starting with a continental facies (transgressive series) followed by the gradual incursion of marine conditions, and ending in another continental facies (regressive series) as the basin becomes shallower again. Its development may be interrupted once or several times by the orogenic phases of a nearby mountain chain, and we are often in doubt as to whether its present state really is its final stage. Usually its borders shift a little, widening when it deepens, and narrowing when it becomes shallower; but in general the shift of its borders is very restricted, indicating that the subsidence is not due to a rise of the sea level but is really a sinking of its bottom in relation to surrounding stable or rising borders characterized by much thinner sedimentation.

Some basins are hardly folded at all. Some are folded towards the end of their history. Some are disturbed by folding during the early stages in their development.

In order to get a better insight into their characteristics I shall describe some of them in greater detail.

THE SOUTHERN CALIFORNIAN BASINS

I shall follow Reed and Hollister (1936), Reed (1933 and 1943), and Taliaferro (1943a) in my description of the Californian basins.

The San Joaquin Valley is the southern extremity of the Great Valley of California, situated west of the Sierra Nevada, and is the best known portion of the Valley because of extensive exploration for oil (Fig. 292).

The Capistrano embayment with the Los Angeles basin originally made part of the same basin but was separated from it by the Mid-Cretaceous folding of the transverse ranges which also created the Santa Barbara embayment and the Ventura basin.

The Great Valley basin is without doubt the Tertiary and latest stage of a much longer geosynclinal history. It started as a separate unit in the coastal area of the great Cordilleran system, after the Nevadan orogeny (cf. Chapter 27, Figs. 266 and 267) near the end of the Jurassic. West of this great mountain chain of the Sierra Nevada, with its strong magmatic phases there developed a new geosynclinal trough filled with uppermost Jurassic and lower Cretaceous (Franciscan-Knoxville, Shasta, etc.) sediments; these were derived partly from the east, from the rising Nevadan chain, and partly from the west, from a hypothetical island arc which provided the volcanic content of these sediments. The Franciscan is characterized by numerous spilitic lavas and ultrabasic sills, which constitute the initial magmatic phase of the coastal geosynclines. This new coastal geosyncline was not a true marginal trough, due to the uplift and thrusting of the Nevadan mountain chain; as we shall presently perceive, it was a new geosyncline with its own initial magmatic phase and its own stress-field. The Upper Cretaceous Chico formation (Cenomanian and Senonian) derived its coarse sediments from the west and its finer sediments from the east. The axis of the Chico basin is shifted to the east, indicating that a gradual emergence of a western chain was under way (Fig. 292).

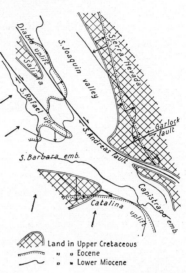

Land in Upper Cretaceous
 "   "   Eocene
 "   "   Lower Miocene

after Reed 1943
and Eardley 1951

Fig. 292.   The development of the Upper Cretaceous—Tertiary basins of Southern California.

Although local unconformities exist between the Tertiary and the Chico formation, the general picture is a continuation of the process which started in the Upper Jurassic, that is, a further emergence of the western arc, accompanied by a shift to the east of the axis of the basin.

The Tertiary history of the San Joaquin basin is merely a repetition of its earlier history. A further uplift of the coastal range, accompanied by slight folding at the end of the Miocene, shifted the axis of the Pliocene basin further east and narrowed the basin again. Further folding took place after the Pliocene, and was the strongest since the Nevadan orogeny which originally started the basin. The final stage was the filling up with Pleistocene continental detritus and alluvium; and the trough axis was again shifted further to the east (Fig. 293).

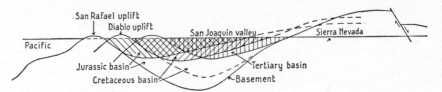

Fig. 293.   The shift of the basin axis of the Great Valley, California, from Jurassic to Tertiary.

There is a strong evidence of volcanic activity on the Pacific side in the Upper Jurassic and in the Miocene. The supposed Pacific volcanic arc, which at the beginning of this long Mesozoic-Cenozoic history constituted the western margin of the marginal geosyncline of the Nevadan mountain chain, became more and more distant from the centre of sedimentation because new territory emerged to the west of it, narrowing the basin and shifting it to the east. The later stages of this emerging coastal chain are preserved in the San Rafael uplift and San Diablo uplift, separated by the shallow basin of the Salinas Valley. The cumulative effect of the three stages of subsidence, separated by minor but clearly defined folding phases in the Mid-Cretaceous and Post-Miocene, is a fairly symmetric basin, so far as the shape of the basement is concerned. The eastern limit of the basin was the basculating block of the Sierra Nevada, rising in the east where a large fault separated it from the Cordilleran geanticline, and subsiding in the west (Fig. 293).

The initial magmatic stage of ultra-mafic intrusions subsided in the Lower Cretaceous. The Mid-Cretaceous orogeny split the Mesozoic geosyncline into separate basins. We have seen in Chapter 11 that the San Andreas fault dates also from this orogeny. It seems very probable that the fragmentation of the original basin was due to the deflected direction of stress, now acting from the south instead of from the south-west, giving rise to the San Andreas fault and the transverse ranges, and thus causing the separation of the Great Valley from the Los Angeles basin (Fig. 292). The Laramide orogeny and the Post-Miocene orogeny had the same southerly stress-direction. The Miocene volcanic activity had the character of what one is used to call the post-orogenic-type, varying from andesites to rhyolites; but as the Miocene folding phase certainly does not represent a major orogeny it cannot be regarded as a typical example. The relatively strong post-Pliocene folding restricted the basins further, and put a stop to the whole geosynclinal development as far as we can judge. In the Pleistocene there was strong volcanic activity, mostly of basaltic character, in the Sierra Nevada range, but none in the coastal regions or in the basins. Again we are at a loss to insert this volcanism into the schematic picture of magmatic phases which we developed for the Mediterranean mountain chains. Probably we can better regard them as continental flood-basalts, escaping through fissures opened by Pleistocene stresses. The two directions of folding which we have observed in the development of the coastal ranges and basins of California are evident in the folds within the basins, as well as in the foundation of the basins. On the west side of the San Joaquin basin, for instance, we find three WE spurs, each of them extending deep into the basin, and slowly turning to a NW–SE direction with an arrangement en échelon such as we have already noticed for the three Kettleman domes (Chapter 23, Fig. 246). The basin structure itself is strongly influenced by the waves of uplift and subsidence along the ancestral San Andreas fault.

The east side of the San Joaquin basin is not folded. The thin veneer of sediments on the basculating Nevadan block was protected against folding by their solid basement. The oil accumulations are all determined by unconformities and faults.

In the Los Angeles basin, we find both directions again. The Newport-Inglewood trend is located on a wrench-fault parallel to the San Andreas fault (Chapter 23, Fig. 248), the structures of the Los Angeles area all trend roughly EW, but the Capistrano embayment is parallel and the direct continuation of the San Joaquin basin.

The Santa Barbara embayment and the Ventura basin are a purely EW structure, dating from the Mid-Cretaceous. Here the fold axes are parallel to the basin borders. No doubt the extremely thick Pliocene of the Ventura basin, witnessing the rapid subsidence of the basin is due to this parallelism of the basin with the folding-stress, and further evidence of the identity of orogenic and epeirogenic stress.

Our experience from the Cretaceous-Cenozoic Pacific coast geosyn-

cline teaches us that its trough was formed between a flexible ridge on
the Pacific continental border and the rigid block of the former Nevadan orogeny. The block basculated as a whole, the ridge moved inward.
The NW–SE trend of the trough is determined by the original Nevadan
trend, but the folding-stress had a direction oblique to the block.
This stress caused several wrench-faults, of which the San Andreas fault
is the largest, cutting with a 45° angle to the stress, into the Nevada
block. Furthermore it caused the fragmentation of the trough into
several basins by throwing up transverse ridges and forming basins
perpendicular to the stress, and folds in all the basins. The two conflicting trends, the older grain of the basement and the younger folding
direction, together formed the intricate pattern of the Californian
basins.

BIGHORN AND WIND RIVER BASINS, WYOMING

Both adjoining basins belong to a row of Cretaceous basins in front
of the big Laramide orogeny of the Rocky Mountains. They are a part
of the stable inland, and are at the same time an integral part of
Laramide orogeny in the sense that they represent the direct influence
of the orogeny on the shield. Both are surrounded by uplifted areas
of the Pre-Cambrian — the Bighorn and the Laramie uplifts to the
east, the Sweetwater uplift to the south, the Wind River, and Beartooth uplifts to the west, and the Owl Creek uplift between the two
basins (Fig. 294).

The stratigraphic sequence is built up by four cycles: an older
Palaeozoic cycle from Cambrian to Lower Ordovician, a younger
Palaeozoic cycle from the Devonian up to the Jurassic, a Cretaceous
to Palaeocene cycle, and finally a post-orogenic filling with Eocene and
Oligocene rocks. The Palaeozoic rocks are relatively thin, and thicken
towards the west; in other words they represent the epicontinental
border of the Palaeozoic orthogeosyncline. In the centre of both basins
the Palaeozoic section is some 3,000 feet thick, and is followed by
continental deposits of Triassic and Jurassic age, of some 1,600 feet.
The Cretaceous starts with non-marine strata some 200 feet in
thickness, and continues with a marine series of 4,000 – 6,000 feet.
The uppermost Cretaceous and Palaeocene are again non-marine. The
major folding occurred between the Palaeocene and the Eocene, and the
post-orogenic filling with the detritus of the uplifted surrounding
blocks and volcanic deposits was wholly continental in both basins.

Intensive erosion in the Wind River basin preceded the deposition of coarse river deposits of Oligocene age.

Both basins have an extremely simple structure, but the Wind River basin is strongly asymmetric. Its two main bordering Pre-Cambrian uplifts, the Owl Creek arch to the north and the Wind River

Fig. 294. Bighorn and Wind River basins. *(From tectonic map of U.S.A. Published by permission of the United States Geological Survey.)*

uplift to the south, are blocks which have been upthrusted towards the south and south-west with the result that the axis of the basin is just in front of the Owl Creek uplift.

Both basins are characterized by a series of mostly asymmetric anticlines, often oil bearing, parallel to the uplifts and folded against the gently dipping flanks of the basin. The central area of the basin probably contains folds also, but much of it is covered by unconformable Eocene strata which hamper their detection. In the basin extremities, however, where this uncomformable blanket is missing, many folds are present, still parallel but more symmetric. The two basins selected from among the large group of Rocky Mountains basins are typical of this province. They represent a type in which the structural

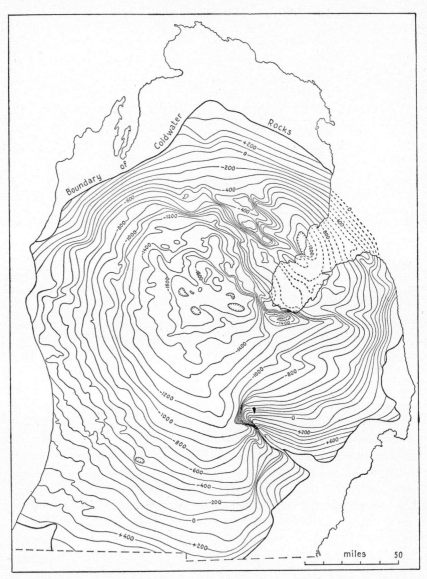

Fig. 295. Michigan basin, structure contours on the Cold-water formation. *(After Brown–Monnet, 1948. Published by permission of the American Association of Petroleum Geologists.)*

history is not quite so closely bound to the preceding sedimentary history as we have found elsewhere. Neither the Palaeozoic sediments (as the border of the great Cordilleran geosyncline) nor the Cretaceous strata (as an epicontinental margin of the Cretaceous basin preceding the Laramide orogeny) foreshadow the future separation of this shelf region into separate basins. The basin structure is wholly post-tectonic and only the Eocene filling is truly a basin sedimentation. The differentiation into separate basins by the strong uplift of the boundary arches is due to a great variety of causes among which the Pre-Cambrian structure of the basement is possibly an important factor.

MICHIGAN BASIN

The Michigan basin is remarkable for its practically undisturbed condition, its symmetric shape and its great size; its diameter is about 450 miles. Its sediments range from Cambrian to Pennsylvanian. Its present structure is always referred to as a pile of saucers, each higher one being smaller than its predecessor. Until the Devonian, the Michigan basin was an extension of the Illinois basin to the south, the two together forming a depression east of the great transcontinental arch, the backbone of the continent (Fig. 284). This depression is limited to the east by the Cincinnati arch, another NS swell in the Pre-Cambrian shield.

Beginning in the Devonian, a transverse arch with a NW–SE direction developed, the Kankakee arch, which separated the Michigan basin from the Illinois basin.

Oil exploration discovered several flat anticlines roughly parallel to the Kankakee arch. In some of them faults have been proved in the lower beds, indicating that they overlie faults in the basement, which are probably contemporaneous with the Kankakee arch. The total thickness of the Palaeozoic, which is overlain by glacial drift only, is nowhere greater than 10,000 feet.

The Michigan basin can be considered as the most perfect example of the stable shield basins: a long, very slow undisturbed subsidence, with only 10,000 feet of accumulated sediments in the whole Palaeozoic (Fig. 295). Its development is governed by two perpendicular directions, the older NE–SW transcontinental and Cincinatti arches and the younger NW–SE direction which we find in the line from the Ozark dome to the Ellis arch, and the Amarillo-Wichita system further south. Again we find that a basin formation is due to two fold directions, which in this case cause fold amplitudes 500 miles across, a width that is perhaps dictated by the thickness of the strata involved, which in this case means the whole solid crust of the earth.

THE PARIS BASIN

The Paris basin is one of the north-west European basins which developed during the Mesozoic on the abraded Palaeozoic surface. Their emplacement is strongly influenced by the Hercynian structure of this area, but in their present configuration on the map they have certainly a discordant character. We can distinguish in the south the Alpine geosyncline, the future site of the Alpine mountain chain; its prolongation towards the west, the Languedoc basin; and the Aquitanian basin north of the Pyrenees, originally extending southwards towards the Hercynian Pyrenean mountain chain. The Languedoc and

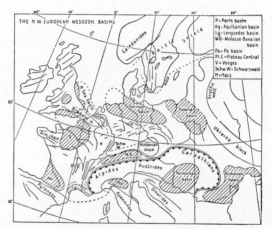

Fig. 296.   The north-west European Mesozoic-Tertiary basins.

Aquitanian basins are separated by the Hercynian Montagne Noire orogeny, which was connected with the Pyrenees (Fig. 296).

To the north of these southern basins we find the great shield of the French Plateau-Central–Rhineland, a broad uplifted plateau, with western extension in the Armorican mountain chain of Brittany. On its eastern slope there developed the Bavarian basin, originally the northern epicontinental extension of the eastern Alpine basin. Still further north the Hercynian orogeny of south England and Belgium, and the Variscean chains of Germany form the southern boundary of

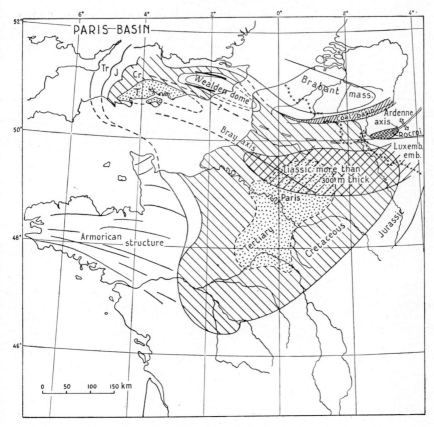

Fig. 297. The Paris basin.

the Baltic shield of that epoch. The Paris basin developed between the Armorican orogeny in the south, the Hercynian orogeny in the north and the central platform in the south-east and east. The English North Sea basin and the North German basin, separated by a buried ridge running from SE to NW through Holland, together form the North European basins, with an extremely complicated Mesozoic history, largely buried beneath a Tertiary blanket.

In outline these basins are therefore the Mesozoic reflections of Hercynian structures. This relation is demonstrated in particular in their earlier history; it is only in the later epeirogenic phases that the transgressions of the younger series, in particular Upper Cretaceous, give these basins a discordant character.

In the northern part of the Paris–southern England basin proper

are reflected the structure of the Brabant massif, which had probably
originated during the Caledonian orogeny, and that of the Hercynian
chain of the Ardennes (Fig. 297). South of the Brabant massif the
Carboniferous geosynclines of the Ruhr - Liége - Charleroi - North
French coal basin developed. This Upper Carboniferous basin was
bounded in the south by the core of Ardennes mountains, the Stavelot
and Rocroi Pre-Cambrian massifs. It is south of this older basin that
the Paris and Wealden basins started to develop in the Jurassic as a
longitudinal basin parallel to the old Brabant massif. Only later did
it extend to the south and acquire its round shape. The post-Eocene
doming of the Wealden-Boulonnais dome is also mainly restricted to
this original Jurassic basin.

Structure of the Wealden Dome. The Wealden district basin began
to develop in early Mesozoic times. Thin Liassic strata wedge-ou

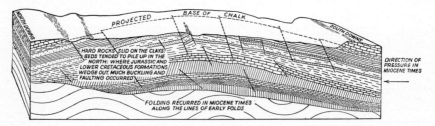

Fig. 298.   Structure of the Wealden Dome. *(After Edmunds, "British Regional
Geology : The Wealden District", 1948.   Published by permission of Her Majesty's
Stationery Office.)*

in the north against the Palaeozoic mass, which represents the westerly
continuation of the Brabant mass. The same strong tendency to
increasing thickness towards the south is exhibited by the Middle and
Upper Jurassic and is accentuated by the Lower Cretaceous Wealden
delta deposits, which are slightly transgressive. The transgression
caused overlapping to the north and eventually passed over the
northern ridge in Upper Cenomanian times. The Chalk still shows,
however, a thickening towards the south. In the Eocene the whole
basin was folded into one large dome striking EW, most of the area
emerged above sea level and only in its southern flank continental
Eocene deposits are preserved. They wedge-out towards the north.
Oligocene and Miocene are practically missing (Fig. 298).

The inception of the movement occurred in pre-Eocene post-
Cretaceous time, the maximum was reached in the Miocene.

The Wealden dome is complicated by many parallel and asymmetric folds, also trending east to west, and with their steep-dipping flanks to the north.

The combined effect of the epeirogenic and orogenic movement is a gently dipping Palaeozoic floor with southwards-thickening Mesozoic sediments on top, arched in a large dome with secondary asymmetric folds, probably due to faults in the basement.

Structure of the Paris Basin. South of the Ardennes chain there developed in earliest Mesozoic times a relatively deep furrow parallel to the trend of the Ardennes, starting in the east and gradually extending westwards, filling with Triassic in the east and Liassic in the centre. Although its axis is north of the Seine River the transgression reached much further south in the Dogger, encroaching on the Central Plateau and the Armorican chain of Brittany and Normandy and the Hercynian chain of southern England. In the Lower Cretaceous the basin narrowed, to its central part around Paris and eastwards; it became enlarged again, in the Upper Cretaceous, to its former extension. In the Eocene, the basin became much smaller — around its present centre, Paris, and its southern England centre, around Southampton.

The total thickness of the Mesozoic sediments is relatively small, some 5,000 feet in the centre.

The folds of the Paris basin are in general very gentle, parallel to the general NE–SW trend of the northern border. Whether they reflect faults or fold movements in the basement or not is difficult to tell. Their general asymmetric shape, like that of the largest one, the Bray anticline, and their large wavelength indicate that the basement is concerned in the tectonics. The faults on its southern border, trending north to south, are certainly basement faults; they extend from the southern border into the basin, and belong to the Limagne rift and a Plateau-Central system of Oligocene faults.

The Paris–southern England basin is thus a basin feature very much like the Michigan basin, developing on an older abrasion surface as a new feature. It is unlike the Michigan basin in being much more dependent on the structure of its basement, but this is readily understandable; the Hercynian structure of the North European region had much younger and more pronounced trends in its mountain chains and its basins of sedimentation, than did the Pre-Cambrian of the Canadian shield in relation to the Palaeozoic sedimentation of the Michigan basin.

From my short review of these selected basins we can see that the style of relationship between basin formation and orogenies varies widely. On one hand, we have the examples of the Californian and Rocky Mountain basins which can both be compared to post-tectonic marginal troughs. On the other hand, the Michigan and Paris basins are remote from such a direct relation. The Californian and Rocky Mountain basins differ again, since the history of the Californian basins is wholly post-orogenic in relation to the Nevadan orogeny but eventually developed into a dismembered geosyncline in its own right; whereas the history of the Rocky Mountain basins is essentially pre-orogenic in relation to the Laramide orogeny, and they received their basin structure only at the last moment during that phase.

The Michigan and Paris basins differ in that the first is formed by swells parallel to contemporaneous geosynclines which were forming elsewhere, and the second by subsidence parallel to preceding orogenies.

Chapter 31

Blocks

Our perusal of the Mediterranean region brought us into contact with relatively stable regions, between the mountain chains, which we designated as "blocks". We recognized in North Africa the Moroccan block and the High Plateau of Algeria; in Spain the Castillian block; and a probable submerged block in the western Mediterranean. Further east we can recognize the Pannonian block, the east Mediterranean block, and the Anatolian block (cf. Fig. 255).

In the Cordilleran system of North America we found the Colorado Plateau, surrounded by Laramide belts of folding; and in the Antillean system of island arcs, several submerged blocks may be anticipated.

The same arrangement of stable blocks surrounded by folded chains is represented by the pattern of the Indonesian island arcs. Apparently the stable block within extensive mountain systems is quite a common occurrence and it certainly merits a somewhat closer examination.

The difficulty in this respect is that the historic development of many of these blocks is virtually unknown because they are either covered by the sea or by flat-lying young sediments.

The Colorado Plateau. One of the best-known blocks is the Colorado Plateau, well exposed by the deep section cut into it by the Colorado River and its tributaries.

Its Pre-Cambrian abrasion surface, which has distinct topographical features, is covered by a maximum of 5,000 feet of Palaeozoic sediments and 9,000 feet of Mesozoic.

In the Pre-Cambrian we find a tilted Algonkian series on a highly metamorphic basement. The Palaeozoic is very incomplete, the Cambrian is mostly present, the Ordovician very reduced. The Devonian is either absent or thin; some Mississippian limestone may be present; only the Pennsylvanian and Permian reach large thickness — often in a red bed facies.

The Mesozoic shows a similar development of intermittent sediment-

461

ation; only the Cretaceous reaches great thicknesses and then only in small basins.

Disconformities are therefore numerous; folding is practically absent, and anticlinal belts and shallow basins exist, but are ascribed mostly to fault movements in the basement because their shape is very asymmetrical. The uplifts are often called monoclines, because the opposite flank is nothing but a flexure. The Cretaceous basins are certainly related to the Laramide folding of their surroundings, and thus represent the faint reflections of the stress-field in a particular stable block. Some narrow structures are due to longitudinal salt diapirs with accompanying collapse due to solution. Elsewhere on the plateau, most perfectly developed laccoliths, fed from a central vent, have been described (Hunt, 1946). Their age is probably Pliocene; there was extensive contemporaneous volcanic activity which produced basalts, andesites, and rhyolites.

After the late-Cretaceous Laramide deformation, the origin of the elongated uplifts and faults, the basins were filled with Eocene and younger sediments. The plateau was uplifted as a whole in the Pliocene (Longwell, 1946) and the volcanic activity continued from then to the Recent.

From a general point of view we can conclude from this evidence that the Colorado block has acted as a stable block since the Archean. It was submerged only in those periods preceding a major orogenesis in the neighbourhood, the upper Palaeozoic and the Cretaceous. Its volcanic activity is of the continental type.

The Moroccan Meseta. Between the very mildly folded Tertiary chains of the Middle Atlas in the east, the High Atlas in the south, the Atlantic in the west, and the strongly folded Riff arc in the north, there extends the Moroccan Meseta, a stable region during the whole of the Mesozoic (Fig. 299).

Its Palaeozoic history, however, is different. The Palaeozoic in the western part of the Meseta reaches great thicknesses; there is some 4,000 m of Cambrian and Ordovician of similar thickness; on its eastern border the Devonian and Mississippian also attain similar thicknesses. Caledonian and Hercynian periods of folding can be distinguished; the direction is mostly NS or NE–SW.

Its Mesozoic history was extremely quiet, in strong contrast with this Palaeozoic history. On its eastern border are some transgressive Jurassic limestones, in the centre some Cretaceous – Eocene strata, both on the original widespread Triassic cover of the Hercynian abrasion surface.

The Tertiary orogeny had but slight influence on the now stable block. In the south a geanticline with an EW strike, the Jebilets, was warped up and flanked on both sides by shallow depressions. Its Atlantic margin was bent down towards the ocean, particularly in the south, and its eastern margin was warped up along faults striking NE–SW, parallel to the mildly folded Middle Atlas chain. Its northern border became depressed by the load of advancing gliding nappes of the Riff.

This block, which in the Palaeozoic period still belonged to the

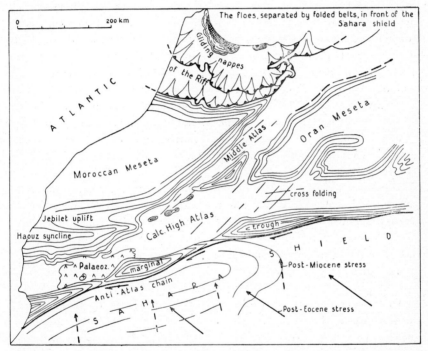

Fig. 299. Blocks in the Moroccan region between Sahara and Riff orogeny. *(After Choubert, Notes et Memoires du Service Géologique, no. 100, 1952, Rabat.)*

flexible part of the earth's crust, became stable after the Hercynian folding and acted as a block during the Tertiary diastrophism, weakly reflecting the stress-fields around it.

Oceanic Blocks. If we considered other blocks we should find the same characteristics. Some have been stable since the Pre-Cambrian, some only since the Mesozoic. Some have been filled up with Tertiary sediments, often of continental facies like the Oligocene-Miocene cover of the Castillian block or the Hungarian Plain; but others are far below sea level. Kuenen (1935) has made a special study of these blocks in the Indonesian Archipelago. His first group of ocean basins are characterized as "large, broad and deep (5,000 m) basins with steep sides and a flat, horizontal bottom" (p. 38). He thinks that a basin of this type is due to downfaulting of a stable area, because "its considerable size, the box-like section, the equi-dimensional shape, the absence of complication of the floor are so many features opposing a folded structure". (p. 41). The situation of these basins is shown in Fig. 271, and we see how the folded belts curve around them. There can be little doubt that structurally they have the same function as the continental blocks we have already considered, their only distinguishing feature being their extremely low level. An explanation of the difference in level offers itself almost automatically, the continental blocks are sial blocks, the Indonesian blocks are oceanic without, or with, a very thin sial blanket. This explanation has been proved correct by seismic refraction measurements made by Ewing (1952). Their depth of 5,000 to 6,000 m is exactly what one might expect from an isostatic point of view for a sial-free ocean bottom.

The Saxonic Structural Type. The function of the blocks from a structural point of view is not altogether passive. They are active in the sense that a large block, like the Moroccan Meseta, can divert the stress from its original direction. As it is pushed in one direction it may be slightly rotated, with the result that one of its other sides exerts a stress in another direction on its margin, and causes folding with another strike, different from that which the original stress would cause.

This phenomenon, with all its intricate results of tear-faulting, tension-faults, thrust-faults, and localized folding, has been the subject of a very extensive research by Stille (1924a and b) Lotze (1938, 1953) and many of their pupils in Germany. Stille has coined the term "Saxonic folding" or "Germano-type orogeny" and still later "Para-tectonics" for this structural type in contrast with the "orthotectonics" of mountain chains; and in a series of publications entitled "Geo-tektonische Forschungen" this subject has been treated extensively.

The typical Saxonic field is situated between the Alpine mountain chains in the south and the Baltic shield in the north. This territory has been severely folded after several extensive geosynclinal phases during the Palaeozoic, causing an intricate pattern of mountain chains — Pre-Cambrian or early Palaeozoic blocks like the French

Massif Central, the Brabant massif, and the Harz Mountains, with different trends and different grades of mobility or rigidity. During the Mesozoic, basins were formed, some extensive and persistent, some only very limited in space and time, and the whole platform was broken up and pushed about by the great Alpine stress directed NS.

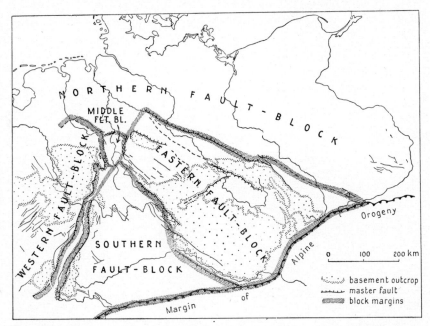

Fig. 300. Blocks north of the Alpine orogeny. *(After Lotze, Geotektonische Forschungen, vol. 9/10, 1953. Published by permission of E. Schweizerbart'sche Verlagsbuchhandlung, Stuttgart.)*

The heterogeneity of the substratum, an inheritance from its Palaeozoic history, caused a great heterogeneity in structural trends in its Cenozoic history. These trends have mostly been named after the trends of old mountain chains, Hercynian for the NW trend of the Armorican chain * for instance; but others have a younger date, e.g. the Upper Rhine Valley rift, which is an Alpine structure. Its NS trend has been called the Rhine direction.

The fact that the NW Hercynian direction, the NE trend of the Variscean systems further east, and other old trends, are represented again and again in the younger fault and fold systems, is in itself proof

* This is the reason why "Hercynian" as a time indication is not used in German but has been replaced by "Variscean".

enough that the heterogeneous basement has had a great influence
on the trends of its Alpine paratectonic structure, although it must be
admitted that the principle has certainly been overworked.

In Fig. 300 is reproduced Lotze's conception (1953) of the way in
which this foreland of the Alpine chain has been broken up into blocks.
The blocks have to be considered as mobile units, moving together
and relatively to each other, each gliding on the substratum, the asthenosphere. The block margins are characterized by greatly increased
tectonic mobility in relation to the centre of the blocks. There may be
extensive normal faulting, as along the Upper Rhine rift; but elsewhere we may find very flat and peculiar overthrusts, as on the margin
of the western block in the Osning zone (Fig. 301); or we may find
tear-faulting.

The intensity of movement need not be equal along one border-zone;

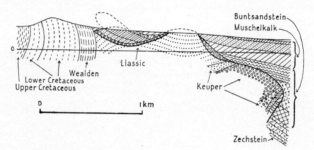

Fig. 301. Overthrusts in the Osning zone. *(After Stille, Abhandl. Preuss.
Geolog. Landesanstalt, N.F., vol. 95, 1924.)*

it is often masked by younger discordant formations, or it may grow
consistently in one direction, or one kind of movement may be replaced
by another; but all along their borders we find the same increase of
intensity of tectonic features.

The blocks themselves are not free from structural deformation;
parallel faults are frequent both in the eastern and in the central
blocks and which zone of disturbance one considers as a master-fault
is often a matter of taste.

In the northern block in particular, we find secondary complications
due to a horizontal detachment within the block along incompetent
salt horizons of the Permian, where smaller blocks drifting on this
salt horizon create their own style of diapiric disturbance. The great
Hercynian northern master-fault of the eastern block can be followed
in the northern block along a row of salt diapirs, for instance. Figure

200, Chapter 18, gives a good example of the tectonics of this block movement on a salt-layer. Along many of the master-faults one can recognize contrasting movements in succeeding periods. Thus we find, both along the Osning zone and along the Roer Valley rift, that a particular block was raised in all the pre-Upper Cretaceous movements, sank in the Upper Cretaceous, and rose again in the Miocene phases. Such contrasting movements are comprehensible in a block field where the individual blocks sometimes drift asunder and sometimes press against each other. When we consider the pattern of the master-faults of the German foreland of the Alpine mountain chains in Europe (Fig. 300) we are struck by the fact that the bisectrix of the sharp northern angle of the central block is exactly the stress-direction of the Alpine orogeny. The conclusion seems warranted that the Rhine trend (NNE) and the Hercynian trend (NW) are in their origin a simple conjugate set of tear-faults, caused by the NS directed Alpine stress.

But before we can form a good judgement on the great Rhine rift we shall have to consider large rifts in general.

Tension or Dilatation Zones in the Earth's Crust. Great tension (dilatation) regions, of which the principal ones are the African rift system and the Great Basin fault system, are not very numerous. On the other hand dilatation is a constant companion of stress, as one of its secondary consequences in all minor structures.

The question now arises whether the great dilatation areas could be the secondary consequences of other large structures, mountain chains or orogenic belts. Some of their general characteristics can be formulated as follows: there is recurrence of movement during long periods; their total dilatation is small in comparison with total compression of mountain chains; they are typical of stable regions.

The thought that the dilatation in the stable shelves is the reflection of orogenic processes in their surrounding mobile belts is very suggestive, and can be more or less proved for the best-known rift, the Rhine Valley rift (cf. Fig. 98). There the start of the subsidence of the rift is synchronous with one of the major phases of the Alps (post-Eocene), and its situation and that of its accompanying fault-blocks (see Figs. 98, 255, and 296) make it almost imperative to link the two phenomena in one catastrophic event. The picture arises in one's mind of the blunt bow of a ship crushing into an ice sheet and pushing the floes in front. This image is not necessarily false, although it is too much of a simplification; and questions immediately arise — how the Rhone Valley rift, the Limagne faults, and the Lower Rhone faults, which are certainly expressions of the same dilatation but have a totally different orientation in relation to the Alpine arc, are to be accounted for.

The subsidence of the rifts may have been initiated by the orogenic push of the Alps, that is to say their bordering faults were the direct result of this push; but the subsidence itself was a slow process, with all the characteristics of cyclic epeirogenic motion. Moreover, as Cloos (1932, 1936) has demonstrated very convincingly, the actual rupture of the faults is preceded by a long process of bulging, of arching of the shield (cf. Fig. 98, Chapter 10). Therefore our image of the ship bumping against an ice sheet is wrong in so far that the process is not one of a sudden bump but a slow process which at a moment of maximum pressure caused rupture. The pressure existed before and continued after the rupture. This result is in perfect accordance with our general conception of epeirogenic and orogenic stress, in which the orogeny is the moment of yield in a continuous stress-field. Accordingly the notion of a close relation between folding and rift formation is strengthened by a closer examination of the characteristics of both processes, but the mechanism is perhaps less obvious.

We shall have to go back to another of our fundamental concepts of earth distortion, the notion of the different tiers of the earth's crust which react differently under stress. The lower tiers are characterized by homogeneous deformation, the upper tier by discontinuous deformation. Obviously the rift faults originate in and are typical of the upper tier, but what happens in the lower tier? There we shall find compression in the direction of the main stress, and dilatation but no tensional stress in the two perpendicular directions; or, in the case of the foreland of the Alps, compression in the NS direction and dilatation in the vertical and EW direction. The vertical dilatation caused the bulging of the Rhine shield; and not only there, but also further west and east, in the whole stable shield north of the Alpine belt. The horizontal EW dilatation in the lower tier apparently caused, here and there, a tensional stress in the upper tier, expressed by rift valleys and their subsidence. The tensional stress in the upper reaches of the crust is not necessarily bound to the bulges in the crust, but would only have a preference for them. A rift was initiated as in the region of the Upper Rhine shield, starting in the centre of the bulge and progressing to the north and south, and not just in front of the Alpine arc as we would expect if our metaphor of the ship and the ice floes were right. And because the deformation of the lower tier is not limited by the surficial expression of stress, it is evident that the faults can extend into the outer reaches of the Alpine arc — where they have been traced, in the Jura Mountains and even in the Molasse trough (Schuppli, 1952), and even across the entire chain by seismic evidence (Oulianof, 1947). Once the rift had been formed, one could understand that it was widened by further thrust of the Alpine chain in particular because a wedge at its southern extremity was driven into the gap.

Nevertheless the bulge of the Rhine shield was not the only effect of the compression in NS direction in the block facing the Alps. On the contrary, the compression also manifested itself in great tear-faults which divided the European continent in separate blocks, as could be expected on the principles laid down in Chapter 8. The Rhine Valley rift is a secondary feature due to the Rhine shield bulge and its accompanying tear-faults with NW and NNE trends.

The African rift system is much less directly connected with any major mountain chain than the Rhine Valley rift is with the Alps. Nevertheless, we find here in the same way a direct connexion between a NS stress-direction and an EW tensional direction. Different authors have pointed out that the pattern of the system is built up by two directions, NNW and NNE striking faults. Such a consistent conjugate set of faults is compatible with a NS stress-direction, which would be in harmony with an EW dilatation, but the faults are apparently not tear-faults but normal faults. Again the conclusion is warranted that the fault direction has been dictated by the main stress, but the fault type by the actual movement; or, in other words, the fault pattern is due to the stress condition in the lower tier, and the fault movement to the resulting dilatation in the upper tier.

Both the European rift systems, the Rhine and Limagne faults, and the African rift systems, are characterized by extensive volcanism on the faults, proving that the faults cut deep into the substratum.

The fault system of the Great Basin in the North American Cordilleras has another character and another cause. It consists of innumerable relatively small faults, small in length and width and not necessarily small in slip; they have mostly the same strike and dip-slip movement, and form instead of prominent rifts a series of basculated blocks. Their strike is parallel to the general strike of the flanking orogenies, and not perpendicular to it as in the case of the Rhine Valley rift. We may suppose that this general character is a result of a superficial dilatation due to arching of the old Cordilleran geanticline in Mesozoic and Cenozoic time. They differ also in one important aspect from the great rift faults: they are not accompanied by any volcanic activity.

The Function of Blocks in the Structural Pattern of the Earth. My survey of the stable blocks has revealed that we can distinguish two different kinds of blocks, those which are remnants of the continental or oceanic shields engulfed between orogenic belts, and those which are simply part of the continental shield.

The first kind has been called "Zwischengebirge" by Kober (1928) and nuclear basins by Umbgrove (1947) and we can distinguish amongst them continental blocks and oceanic blocks, proving once more that the earth's crust is not less rigid in the oceanic region, where it consists exclusively of basalt and its ultra-mafic substratum, than in the continents where a sialic blanket is provided.

The second kind of blocks is much less universally recognized; it has been described in detail and fully analysed only in the European foreland of the Alps. One might expect a similar structure, for instance, in the Indian peninsula in front of the great Himalayan chain where long fault-zones are known to exist, and in Anatolia and Persia. The fault systems which divide the Arabian, Syrian, and Abyssinian shields into separate blocks certainly form a similar pattern to that which we found in Europe, but here the blocks are more rigid, still more of the cratonic type, and the intervening channels are not folded.

We found that the great rift systems of Africa and Europe are the most spectacular form of master-faults in the crust, but are not fundamentally different from other block boundaries. In this respect it is of some interest to recall what I wrote in Chapter 12 about some great compression faults, such as the North Pyrenean fault-zone and the Anti-Atlas fault-zone.

There is one other very long zone of disturbances which could be associated with the same group and that is the Mid-Atlantic swell, also characterized by a long row of volcanoes reaching from Iceland to Ascencion; but this remains, for obvious reasons, an uncharted feature of the earth's crust.

Looking back over all this evidence of large-scale cracking of the earth's crust, we must conclude that the stress-field in the crust has apparently never subsided. It causes world-wide fault-zones on continents and oceans, it loosens small blocks from the great shields, and it thus changes continuously the shape of the continents.

Chapter 32

Relation in Time and Space of Orogenies

DIFFERENCE IN MECHANISM OF DIFFERENT OROGENIC PERIODS

We have already had occasion to observe that the conception of world-wide revolutions of short duration separated by world-wide long periods of quiet must be revised, in the sense that the earth's crust has never been absolutely quiet and that the paroxysms are only culminations in deformation which goes on continuously; that they are certainly not world-wide although there are cycles of some 200 million years of relative quiescence separated by shorter periods of greater activity; and finally that folding phases in paratectonic regions are different from orogenic phases in orthotectonic belts.

It has also been suggested that the great orogenic periods, those of the Pre-Cambrian and of the Hercynian and the Alpine periods, are not true equivalents. This is certainly true when we consider the magmatic phases. No doubt the deeper erosion of the older orogenic belts exposes the infrastructure to a greater extent than in the younger belts, with the result that the intrusive rocks occupy larger surfaces and that the metamorphism is more intense and more extended in the older belts; but the scarcity of Tertiary granites in Tertiary belts (none in the Atlas, none in the Pyrenees, and very few in the Alps) as compared with their abundance in the Hercynian period and the predominant role of granitization phenomena in the Pre-Cambrian belts, cannot be explained exclusively by this difference in denudation level. No doubt the magmatic phases decrease in importance from old to young. In this sense the orogenic phases are not equivalent.

On the other hand it has also been suggested by Fallot (1944) and Goguel (1952) that the surficial structural characteristics are also not equivalent in the different phases; that the Alpine period is

471

characterized by greater compression and more frequent overthrusts than the older periods. There is certainly a marked difference, but I should like to find another kind of definition than that of Fallot and Goguel. In the first place, the deeper denudation level explains to a certain degree the absence of typical surficial phenomena such as nappes; and secondly, large overthrusts are not so uncommon in the older periods. The first large nappe ever described is the Sparagmite nappe of the Caledonides of Scandinavia (Törnebohm, 1896).

I had occasion myself to see the imposing nappe of older granite and gneiss in the youngest Pre-Cambrian in Dalsland, south-west Sweden (Heybroek and Zwart, 1949) (Fig. 286), a perfectly horizontal sheet of a width of at least 15 km, of Pre-Cambrian age. In the Montagne Noire the plunging frontal lobes of Hercynian age are of the same size as the Helvetian nappes (cf. Figs. 224 and 225, Gèze, Trümpy, de Sitter 1952). The Moine thrust of Caledonian age in Scotland is one of the most famous overthrusts of the world.

Surficial folding with a basal detachment-plane, typical of Alpine structures, is also quite frequent in Hercynian orogenies, but perhaps less easy to discern. The Devonian structures of the axial zone of the Pyrenees have undoubtedly been detached to some degree from their Ordovician basement, along the plastic shale horizon of the Silurian, and the great thrust-faults of the Ardennes indicate a frequent detachment along several horizons. Besides the difference in denudation level and the fact that the older the phase the less detail has been mapped, there is another factor that obscures the real original structure of the older orogenic belts.

There is a striking difference in the physiographic expression of the structure in Alpine belts as compared with Hercynian (or Caledonian) and Pre-Cambrian belts, which is perhaps best felt by the photo-geologist who tries to infer the structural details from aerial photographs. When working in favourable circumstances on Tertiary structures one is able to analyse their structure in great detail; but in the same circumstances a Hercynian structure is often not revealed at all. One important restriction must be made, however: there are some Hercynian structures of paratectonic character which show the same degree of physiographic expression as any Tertiary belt. I think for instance on the one hand of the Hercynian structures of the axial zone of the Pyrenees, where the physiographic features are almost completely independent of the structure and very little can be learned from the aerial photographs; and on the other hand of the wonderful clear physiographic expression of the Anti-Atlas folding. The same experience was found by comparing the central Hercynian High Atlas, with very little physiographic expression, with for instance the largely Hercynian Asturian-Cantabric mountain chain, which shows beautiful physiographic structural detail.

As far as I can ascertain, this striking difference is due to an Alpine cleavage of the older Hercynian structures; this does not demolish the structures, but does reduce their physiographic expression by obliterating the differential resistance to erosion of the different lithological rock types. A limestone is then no longer more resistant than a schist. Another factor is the weathering which the Hercynian mountain chain underwent in the post-orogenic period; its effects were conserved beneath the Mesozoic blanket. The rocks were again exposed to weathering agents after the Alpine folding. Then a granite may form a valley instead of a mountain.

In order to ascertain in what measure the difference in structure of orogenies of different age are apparent, we have to make a more thorough comparison. For convenience sake I have tabulated the characteristics in Table XIII.

From this table we learn that almost every characteristic of an

Table XIII

Characteristics	Archean	Palaeozoic	CENOZOIC	
			Circum-Pacific (Laramide)	Mediterranean
Initial magmatic phase	ultrabasic and granites	ultrabasic	ultrabasic occasionally	ultrabasic occasionally
Syntectonic magmatic phase	granites, pegmatites, granitization	granites, pegmatites, granitization	absent	occasional granites and migmatization
Late tectonic magmatic phase	frequent granites	frequent granites	frequent granites	rare granites
Post tectonic magmatic phase	undistinguishable	frequent volcanism	active volcanism	rare volcanism
Metamorphism	profound	important	rare	rare
Concentric folding	absent?	frequent	common	almost exclusively
Low-angle overthrust	absent?	rare	rare	common
Schistosity and similar folding	almost exclusively	common	rare	rare
Island arcs	absent?	rare?	common	occasionally

orogeny may be present in any kind of mountain chain, but that some are much more frequent in the older ones than in the younger ones and vice versa. There is apparently one group of phenomena, intensity and magmatic phases coupled with schistosity and similar folding, which is common in the older mountain chains and much rarer or absent in the younger chains. On the other hand, concentric folding and overthrusts are typical of the youngest chain and scarce in the oldest ones.

The difference, for instance, between Alpine and Hercynian (or Caledonian) mountain chains is striking. In the first we find little magmatic activity, and concentric folding as the leading principle, whereas the second group is characterized by a much more intense magmatic activity and a metamorphic state which favours schistosity and similar folding. The same trend can be noticed when we pass from Palaeozoic to Archean orogenies. One is tempted, of course, to connect the difference of folding with the metamorphic state, i.e. to suggest that similar folding is connected with schistosity and a slight metamorphic state, and concentric folding with non-metamorphic rocks. In this respect we have to remember that at the time of their folding the Palaeozoic rocks were as fresh as the Mesozoic rocks now, and that the difference in type of folding can therefore not be due to stronger lithification of the older rocks. Nor can it be true that the epimetamorphic state of the folded Palaeozoic rocks can be due to any Alpine folding phase, for there are many Hercynian chains which have not been submitted to any noticeable Alpine stress, yet have the same general habit. On the other hand, unfolded Palaeozoic sediments can be as little lithified as unfolded or folded Mesozoic rocks; one has only to remember the perfectly unconsolidated Palaeozoic sedimentary rocks of the Russian and American shields.

The difference in metamorphic state must therefore be closely connected with the folding itself, and we are tempted to assume that the much greater frequence of the magmatic phases in the Palaeozoic chains is the deciding factor.

In Chapter 7 I reasoned that the difference in the mechanism of folding between sandstone and slate in the same rock sample was due to their difference in competency, the stronger rock-type being folded concentrically, the weaker rock being deformed by schistosity; and that the rock with the higher strength was apparently deformed in the elastico-viscous field, and the incompetent rock in a more plastic field, both with the same stress. The relation of stress to the strength of the competent or incompetent rock-types was found to be the determining factor. When the stress only just passed the strength the deformation was elastico-viscous of the concentric type; when the stress could rise well above this limit the deformation was of the similar type, accompanied by schistosity or cleavage.

In general, the yield point of a rock mass, whether it be a single layer or a mountain chain, can be reached either by a fall in the resistance below its original strength, the stress being uniform, or by the rise of the stress far above the strength, the resistance being uniform.

Now it seems possible that the explanation of the frequency of schistosity and similar folding in Palaeozoic mountain chains, in contrast with the concentric folding and absence of schistosity in Mesozoic rocks, lies principally in the function of the syntectonic magmatic phase. That this phase brings about a strong rise in temperature is proved by the migmatization and thermal metamorphism of the infrastructure; the effects often rise quite high into the superstructure, though with less intensity.

If the folding started in the elastico-viscous field, just above the strength, with the addition of heat and perhaps lubricating substances from below in an early stage of the paroxysmal deformation, the strength of all rocks would be lowered considerably, and the result would be that with the same stress the rock material entered into a more plastic state and changed from concentric folding to similar folding combined with schistosity and epimetamorphism, and lower down even to flow. This action would be much more intense in the infrastructure, but would also be noticeable in the superstructure.

If this reasoning is sound, we have to accept the view that even in the Ruhr coalfield, the lower part of the structure, which shows typical accordion-folding (a type of similar folding), has undergone and been influenced by heating, although a syntectonic magmatic phase of Asturian age is unknown to me in this Variscean chain. On the other hand the concentric habit of the Appalachian Ridge and Valley province with its absence of any magmatic phase is well in accordance with this view. The Pyrenees, with a strong syntectonic magmatic phase, are schistose almost throughout the lower formation, and show cleavage folds in the upper formation. One of the rare instances of schistosity in Mesozoic formations is found in the phyllites of the "Bündnerschiefer" of the Pennine core of the Alps, which probably had a well-developed syntectonic magmatic phase (cf. Chapter 26).

The same effect could be reached, however, when the stress, for some reason or another, had the occasion to rise further above the strength. I shall refer to this possibility at a later stage of my reasoning.

OROGENIC CHARACTERISTICS OF MOUNTAIN CHAINS

I think that at this point of our investigation into the nature of the orogenic deformations of the earth's crust, we have to look back and try to summarize our experience.

We started from the point of view that we might expect great differences in the nature of mountain chains, and that any general rules should be formulated only after we had studied the characteristics of several mountain chains of different ages and in different positions in relation to continents and oceans.

After this review there can be little doubt left that our original presumption was justified, that each mountain chain has its own character and that it will be difficult to find a common basis for any specific rule of development.

We can perceive, for instance, a striking analogy in shape in cross-sections through the Appalachians and the Alps (cf. Lombard, 1948). The Ridge and Valley province can be compared with the Jura Mountains and Molasse basin, the Blue Ridge province with the thrust zone of the so-called Main Anticline south of the Molasse basin (cf. Figs. 270 and 303), and the Piedmont province with the Pennine nappes. But the Molasse basin is a typical marginal trough of post-orogenic origin, and the Ridge and Valley province is a marginal zone of an orthogeosyncline. The Helvetic zone of the Alps with its external basement massives is missing in the Appalachians and it is, to say the least, very doubtful whether the Piedmont and Pennine zone have anything in common apart from their high metamorphism. Again the so-called root-zone of the Pennine nappes cannot be identified in the Piedmont province, and the southern Alps zone is missing or not exposed in the Appalachians. The only characteristics that remain are the typical steep thrust zone of the Blue Ridge zone and the front of the Helvetian nappes against a sunken basin, and the high metamorphism of the central zone. The latter conformity may only be apparent, because it seems quite probable that the metamorphism of the Piedmont province is largely due to Caledonian and Pre-Cambrian orogenies. The steep thrust zone separating a less deformed sunken foreland from a more compressed and elevated central orogenic zone can be found in some other mountain chains, for instance the western border of the internal Rockies, where the thrusting is, however, largely of the low angle thrust type. But even this characteristic is by no means universal in mountain chains. When we consider the boundary between the central Nevadan orogenic zone and its foreland to the west, we see, on the contrary, that the Sierra Nevada has acted as a basculated block and that there is no trace of any thrusting on its boundary with the great valley; instead we descend a gently tilted block whose sedimentary cover is hardly folded and is disturbed by only a few small faults.

In the structure of the Californian coastal basins we faced a distinct element of non-parallelism between earlier and later compression directions, which also played an important role in the history of the Alpine area, although less easily identified. The strong axial plunges in the coastal basin structure are certainly due to this element, and we may presume that the same reasoning holds good in the Alps, although former basement heterogeneities have no doubt also had their influence on the axial plunges of the external massives of the Helvetian zone. In the Pyrenees we found the same discrepancy in folding directions, but here between Hercynian and Alpine phases and not between phases of the same period. Hence the satellite massives of the Pyrenees are primarily due to a preconceived heterogeneity of the basement. In strong contrast with these examples of the strong dismemberment of a formerly large unified basin into smaller units, we find the whole of the Appalachians, and in particular the Valley and Ridge province, in a state of perfect unity with hardly any axial plunges or individual domes.

When we turn our attention to the island arcs we find a consistent pattern of surficial expression of earth-crust deformation.

We found minor internal geosynclines with mild or very mild folding round the continental basement, enclosed in turn by slightly elevated geanticlines with frequent volcanism. This geanticline is surrounded either by an external basin and geanticlinal structure, or by an immediate deep-sea furrow. Evidence of strong lateral orthotectonic compression is rare, and the whole structural pattern looks as if most of its deformation is directly expressed by its morphological features. It is wholly unwarranted to assume anything like a central metamorphic zone of strong compression below the blanket of Cenozoic volcanics that covers the geanticlinal arc; on the contrary, when anything of the structure is revealed below this blanket, we find either mild folding and arching or tension rifts, both consistent with a large arching of a geanticline. Can we take this kind of structure as the prototype of an orogeny? Obviously not; it might perhaps eventually develop into an orogenic system comparable to the Cordilleran system or the Alpine system, but it certainly has not done so yet. The only general rule that can be derived from its structural features is that volcanism can be particularly frequent on the external side of an orogeny; this we also found in the Cordilleran system, and to some extent, but much more doubtfully, in the Appalachian system. On the other hand the Mediterranean chains are completely free from this external volcanic arch, which is therefore more or less confined to the circum-Pacific zone.

We can express the differences in structure of the various mountain chains by two schematic cross-sections better than by words, Fig. 302.

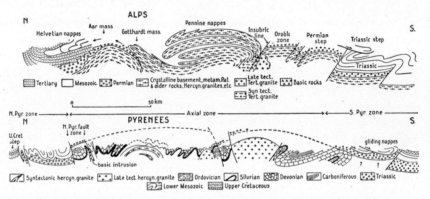

Fig. 302. Schematic cross-sections through the Alps and Pyrenees.

We see the great diversity in size and structure, and we despair of ever finding two mountain chains which are built on the same pattern.

There are simply too many contributing factors which determine its structure: thickness of the crust, depth of geosynclinal subsidence, thickness and peculiarities of sedimentary blanket, position of the mountain chain in relation to the continental border, nature of the ocean basement, degree of compression, number of orogenic phases, heterogeneity of continental basement, and many others less obvious, which in their endless possibilities of combination determine the ever-varying structural features of a mountain chain.

It is therefore impossible to establish any kind of prototype of an orogenic system; but it is not a hopeless task to determine the influence of each factor separately.

First of all there are large tracts of the earth's surface which are apparently unsuitable for orogenic deformation, and generally it is assumed they are simply too rigid. Under this heading we can classify in the first place the truly oceanic regions. A cooled basalt crust, for some reason or other, constitutes a very rigid crust. We might presume, however, from the island arcs, which apparently advance from the continent oceanwards in the course of geologic history, that under strong lateral stress and under the influence of the continental border it may bend down and arch up — with the result that differentiation of basaltic magma starts in the fields of minimum stress below the arches, and thus locates volcanic activity on the geanticlinal welts. Presumably such an action is the start of a sialic crust on a narrow strip which may eventually develop by a shift of the axis or by multiplication of the volcanic arches, and thus contribute to the encroachment of the continent on the ocean. The blocks of oceanic basaltic crust thus separated from the general ocean floor remain rigid and form the obstacles around which later folding concentrates.

Besides these oceanic bottoms and blocks we have the large Archean shields, equally rigid, with a thick sialic crust formed in an early stage of the earth's history. The boundary region between the sialic and basaltic blocks became the most unstable regions of the earth. Orogenic stress often had opportunity to break off blocks of the sialic crust, which were pushed away, and the intervening strips remained mobile strips in the crust and became again and again the scene of orogenic deformation. Sometimes a large shield became broken up by a long crack which developed as a geosyncline like the Urals, or remained just a shatter-zone like the African rift zone.

The continental border-zones became the most intensively deformed zones of the crust. When the boundary lay between a large continent and a large ocean, as in the Cordilleran or the Appalachian orogenies, we find an encroachment of the continent on the ocean by repeated orogenies, each adding a new strip to the rigid continental crust. Sometimes the orthogeosyncline becomes split into two by a central geanticline, the internal one having no volcanic activity, the external one being more active and much more volcanic. When the boundary was between a continental block or shield and smaller oceanic basins with drifting oceanic and (or) continental blocks, the resulting orogenies became more localized and smaller in longitudinal extension, but not necessarily less active.

A very important factor is the subsidence of the geosyncline. In the case of a long and profound subsidence, we are apt to find a well-developed initial magmatic phase, and what is more important, a strong syntectonic magmatic phase. If the latter can develop, we get a metamorphosed core of the orogeny with strong compression, flow deformation in the deeper infrastructure, and schistose folding above it. The subsidence alone is, however, not the only determining factor for the occurrence and intensity of the magmatic phases. The latter are more frequent in older mountain chains, as we have seen, and are also more frequent on the Pacific border than elsewhere. The thickness of the sedimentary filling in the geosyncline is primarily a function of the subsidence of that basin, but it nevertheless exerts its own influence. A thick mass reacts differently from a thin blanket. In this respect the presence of particular incompetent layers between thick competent ones is of great importance. We have seen how in the epicontinental facies of both the Helvetides and the Valley and Ridge province the low-angle overthrusts were determined by the clay-marl horizons between the limestones. On the other hand, a sand-clay alternation gives much less occasion for such predominant horizontal detachments, and therefore more occasion for local and varying disharmonies in the folding, as in Tertiary oilfield basins and Carboniferous coal basins.

The position of the geosyncline, on the continental margin or between continental blocks, is obviously a very important factor in its orogenic development. The intercontinental geosyncline such as the Pyrenees or the Welsh Caledonian chain is by nature more or less symmetric, whereas the Alps or the Appalachians are already asymmetric in their geosynclinal stage. In cross-section, the symmetric one extends outwards on both sides by adding its successive marginal troughs to its main body as it passes through successive phases of orogeny, whereas the asymmetric geosyncline with one continental border and one oceanic border advances only in one direction in its successive geosynclinal and orogenic phases. It is important to note that in both the Alps and the Appalachians, and to a certain extent in the coastal Cordilleran system also, the geosynclinal development exhibits a phase where a barrier is warped up between the ocean and the basin. This barrier, the Orobic zone in the Alps, the central zone of the Piedmont province, and the coastal ranges in the Tertiary Cordilleran system, is steeply inclined towards the continent and has at its foot the deepest part of the asymmetric geosyncline. In the orogenic period this steep face becomes a zone of high-angle thrusting accompanied eventually by gliding structures. In the Alps, this kind of sequence of events has happened twice, once on the northern face of the Orobic zone and once on the northern face of central massives. In the Cordilleran coastal region it happened once, and was less well developed as a result of the oblique stress-direction.

This asymmetric barrier is no doubt a result of failure of the sialic crust in the deepest part of the original geosyncline. Along this line of failure it was pressed upwards, forcing the continental border further

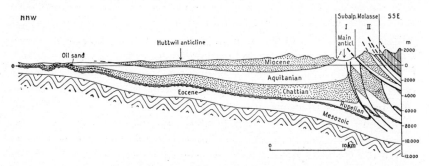

Fig. 303.   Section through Molasse basin of the Alps. *(After Schuppli. Published by permission of Schweizerische Geotechnische Kommission, Zürich.)*

down (Fig. 303), and initiating the folding of the epicontinental part of the geosyncline. In this way we can understand the remarkable feature that in its long and violent geosynclinal history a circum-continental geosyncline encroaches on the continent, and that its path is followed by a sequence of orogenic ranges.

Which factors determine the degree of compression I cannot tell, but there is a certain correlation between the depth of subsidence of the geosyncline and the violence of the orogeny. The shallow and short-lived High Atlas basin, for instance, was submitted only to very mild folding, and the same is true for most marginal troughs. The number of orogenic phases in one period also contributes to the severity of the total compression, but in general one of the phases is the major paroxysm, preceded by some introductory phases and followed by some posthumous phases in the marginal troughs.

A factor of major importance in any orogeny is the heterogeneity of the basement, not only in the geosyncline itself but also in the surrounding continental or oceanic regions. We have seen how strongly the development of the Mesozoic and Tertiary Cordilleran orogenies were bound up with the peculiarities of its Palaeozoic history. We found, both in the Alps and in the Pyrenees, special features indicating how strongly the Alpine orogeny was dependent on the Hercynian structure.

Nevertheless, there is also a remarkable independency of a younger orogeny with regard to an older one, in the sense that the trends may be perfectly independent. The westerly plunge of the High Atlas structure, for instance, parallel to the Sahara shield border, cuts perpendicularly through the strong NS Caledonian and Hercynian trends of the Moroccan Meseta.

Hence on the one hand we have a concentric structure of one orogeny round the other, together surrounding a continental shield, and on the other hand we find them cutting one another in all possible directions.

We may presume that when prominent structural features of the earth's crust, such as the Pacific Ocean basin or large shields like the Canadian shield predominate, they will impose their own boundaries as orogenic trends on the folding-stress, whereas when the region is broken up in blocks, or has been folded before and still carries its own grain, the local stress-direction prevails, influenced by the hazards of shifted blocks and similar irregularities. The Mediterranean orogenic zone is therefore much less regular than the Pacific zones. The reason for the NS trend round the Pacific in contrast to the EW trend of the Mediterranean will be discussed in the last chapter.

Chapter 33

Theories on the Cause of Orogeny

Theories about the origin of tectonic forces are numerous and diverse. It would take far too much space to review them all, and we shall therefore have to restrict ourselves to the most prominent theories of today, although there is no adequate reason why older ones, now more or less discarded, should be less valuable.

Before we start on this excursion into the realm of conjecture I should like, however, to point out the extremely flimsy grounds on which such theories are built.

First of all we have seen hardly anything of the earth's crust below a depth of 2 km; secondly, only one third of the globe is open to geological investigation—the rest is ocean; thirdly, a large portion of the continents is covered by shallow water or alluvial deposits, and of the remaining fraction only a very small portion is really well known.

Of all the great mountain chains of the world we know well only a very few, the Alps, for instance. Even in Europe there is little known about such important chains as the Betic Cordilleras or the Carpathians. The Ardennes are much better known, but the Caledonian chain of Scandinavia is known only in very broad outline. I do not think that either the Appalachians or the Rockies can be regarded as well-known structures. And when we turn our attention to the South American Cordilleras or the African Pre-Cambrian structures, or, as a matter of fact, to any other orogenic belt, our knowledge of their structural features is woefully scanty. It is obviously most premature to attempt an all-embracing theory of orogeny. Nearly all the fundamental data are lacking. The most weird conceptions are therefore often just as well founded as the more sober ones, and we have no adequate reasons for rejecting one or accepting the other.

In all my descriptions of deformations of the earth's crust I have avoided mention of the origin of the forces that caused these deformations, because we are still completely in the dark about these causes.

Many theories have been advanced and many have been rejected, but from each of them something has stayed in our collective mind, with the result that the total picture is far from clear. When we try to classify the various theories we can distinguish two large groups:

1. those based on lateral-tangential forces, and
2. on radial forces

but very often the two are combined in one theory.

In historical sequence we can distinguish as major theories the following:

1. The classical contraction theory, contraction due to cooling of the earth
2. Joly's theory of expansion due to radioactive heat
3. Wegener's theory of continental drift
4. Haarmann's, Bailey Willis's and v. Bemmelen's oscillation and undation theories
5. Convection-current theory (Vening Meinesz)

In 1, 2, 3, and 5, lateral forces in the crust are the origin of all deformation, whereas in 4, the cause is sought in vertical forces. In 4 and 5, the origin of the force is located in the interior of the earth, in 1, 2, and 3, the cause is located in the crust itself.

Evidently the central problem of the origin of orogenic deformation is twofold: on one hand we find the controversy as to whether the obvious lateral compression is a secondary manifestation of primary vertical movements or whether it is in itself the primary cause; and, on the other hand what is, in both cases, the origin of the force and energy?

Without doubt the first question is more within the scope of our possibilities of observation than the second question, and the answer depends to a large degree on our adjustment to the second question. In this book I have continuously reasoned from the central conception of a primary lateral compression, and have advocated vertical movements as the origin of lateral movements only in the case of occasional gravitational gliding structures in a comparatively restricted sense. This traditional point of view has been strongly attacked by van Bemmelen, and it behoves us to check it again in relation to our present knowledge of the great mountain chains.

A fundamental question which must be put to each theory is whether the supposed driving force is adequate or not, and whether the physical phenomenon can or cannot exist. The classical contraction theory, based on the consideration that the earth is constantly losing energy by radiation and therefore cooling, had to be abandoned because with the recognition of radioactive energy, probably concentrated in the crust, the cooling itself becomes very doubtful. The other extreme, that radioactive energy is heating an expanding earth is equally improbable, and had also to be abandoned. Nevertheless, both theories taught us viewpoints which have their advantages, which we are reluctant to throw overboard with the theories.

Wegener's theory of drifting continents started from the obvious resemblance in shape of the South American and African continents, and found many other homologues on the two continents; these again, we should be sorry to lose altogether. The force that caused the drift, however, is lacking; the wandering Poles, which are not essential to the theory, looked suspicious from the beginning.

A similar observation can be made about the convection currents. The possibility of convection currents following on a chaotic state before any crust or core had been formed, has rarely been challenged, but their formation in simple adjoining cells turning in opposite directions is theoretically unproved, and looks improbable when one takes the rotation of the earth into consideration. Moreover, as soon as the application of the simple cells is carried forwards in time and has to explain all kinds of peculiarities in the configuration of the pattern of the earth's crust and of its gravitation field, one again becomes suspicious. Nevertheless, it would be a pity to have to lose the advantages of imagining the primeval state of the large convection current by rejecting the later stages.

For all these reasons I shall have briefly to review some of the more prominent hypotheses of the cause of the distribution of the earth's continents and oceans and of the orogenic forces that have been acting throughout its history.

THE CONTRACTION THEORY

The idea of the contraction of the earth through cooling was formulated in the middle of the 19th century in Europe by Elie de Beaumont (1852) and in America by James Dana (1847).

The generally admitted conception that the earth at the dawn of its history was very much hotter and lost its heat gradually by radiation, and that at the same time its heavy core and light crust were formed, has survived all criticism. The consequence, that since the crust had been formed the loss of heat has since proceeded, at a much lower rate to be sure, but has never stopped, leads naturally to the conception of a shrinking earth.

As only the crust is solid, enveloping the whole earth, a shrinking results in tensional stress in the interior and compressional stress in the crust. In between there must be a surface of no tension or stress, the *asthenosphere*, at something like 60 km depth according to Jeffreys (1929). The tangential stress in the crust would result in more or less uniform crumpling unless it possessed special zones of weakness between continental blocks of greater rigidity. Hence the rigid portions of the crust glide over the substratum along a surface in the asthenosphere, and the shortening is concentrated in the zones of weakness, the orogenic belts. The continental blocks are therefore surrounded by orogenic belts, which, when once folded and thickened by this folding, acquired the same rigidity as the original block, and thus the shield grew outwards, each orogenic period adding another circum-continental ring to the shield.

It was, in particular, Ed Suess (1909) who insisted on the accompanying phenomenon of collapse, of zones of the crust sinking in the intervals when no tangential pressure made itself felt, the collapse of geosynclines, the collapse of rift valleys etc; and even, as the most prominent consequence of the shrinking earth, the orogenies — as the advancing of the stable shields towards the sunken basins or oceans.

Even the bare outlines of the contraction theory as formulated here are sufficient to demonstrate its usefulness. It gives an excellent explanation of the fact that the crust possesses many zones where the total compression must be measured in at least many tens of miles, perhaps as much as 100 miles, whereas zones of dilatation are relatively scarce and never show more than a few miles maximum dilatation. Furthermore, the obvious submergences are explained in a satisfactory way, and the zoning of orogenies around the continental blocks is comprehensible only when a general stress condition on the whole surface is postulated, as does the contraction theory.

The objections which have been raised are very serious, however. First of all, there is overwhelming evidence that the earth's *crust* has *not* cooled since the Cambrian; the recurrence of ice ages and many other considerations point unequivocally to that conclusion. Secondly, it is very doubtful whether cooling would ever result in such a contraction; and thirdly, the cooling itself has become, to say the least, questionable, since the radioactive energy of the crust acts in the opposite direction.

Summarizing, one may evaluate the contraction theory as a theory which is very attractive as far as its consequences on the earth's crust are concerned, but very dubious in relation to its origin and to its motive force. No wonder that many well-known names of geotectonicians are amongst its adherents — Marcel Bertrand, Kober, T. C. Chamberlin, Stille, and many others; and if another adequate reason for a shrinking earth could be found, the reserve that many modern geologists feel against it for the reasons given above would vanish, and the contraction theory on a new base might reconquer the general acceptance it once held.

THE DRIFTING CONTINENTS

The theory of the wandering continents proposed by Wegener (1929) and defended fervently by du Toit (1927, 1937) originates in the remarkable similarity in the shapes of the west coast of Africa and the

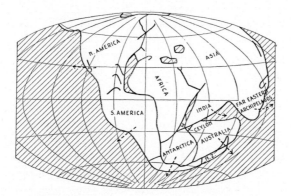

Fig. 304.   The continents joined together before they drifted apart at the end of the Mesozoic. *(After Wegener.)*

east coast of South America. If one could join them by shifting the two continents towards one another, very little space would be left void. Once this principle of drifting rigid floes of sialic matter on a viscous substratum is accepted, it becomes a kind of game to join all the pieces together as in a jigsaw puzzle; and its result can be checked by comparing the age and facies of the geological formations and disturbances on the pieces that have been joined together (Fig. 304). A remarkable fact then arises: marine sediments of the Cretaceous on both sides of the Atlantic Ocean join almost perfectly and the separation of the two continents is therefore believed to have happened after this period. The rift advanced northwards so that the American continent became separated from Europe only in the Tertiary, and Greenland drifted westwards only very recently. The westward drift is thought to have created the Pacific Cordilleras on the west coast of the American continents by friction of the continental shield on its sima bottom, causing a surge on its front.

The splitting up of the other continental areas mostly happened rather earlier, according to Wegener's theory; but as late as at the beginning of the Mesozoic all the continents still formed together one continuous shield, called Pangaea, on which a meridional epicontinental sea, the Tethys, had been formed. The Tethys geosyncline was later compressed by a northward drift of India. It would take us too far to quote all the arguments in favour of the theory, but obviously many difficulties connected with the distribution and similarity of faunas are solved by one stroke; nevertheless many dissimilarities replace them as unsolved questions.

The game of the jigsaw puzzle has been played by many geologists, of which Taylor (1923), Argand (1922), and Staub (1928), were perhaps the best-known representatives. Each of them had his own preferred solution of the puzzle, but it must be admitted that the greatest objection to the theory — that it was concerned only with the latest phase of the earth's history and left all the earlier developments alone — could never be met (cf. van Waterschoot v. d. Gracht, et al, symposium 1928).

Many other ideas were added to the original concept in the course of its relatively short but very lively span of life. In order to explain the distribution of ice-age climates and the climatological zoning of the Carboniferous, the Poles had to be shifted too. Furthermore, the shifting had to have a motive force, and this was found partly in the centrifugal force towards the Equator exerted on the continents by the rotation of the earth (Köppen, 1922), and in the westward drift due to the retardation caused by the tidal action of sun and moon. It has been proved without any doubt and with a very large margin that both forces are completely inadequate (Jeffreys, 1929). Other objections, mainly by tectonicians, can be found in the symposium of 1928, which more or less puts an end to the theory.

Although the theory has hardly any adherents now, it taught us two important principles, firstly, that continents need not be regarded as fixed forever in their present position since the birth of the crust, and secondly, that Pole-wandering could perhaps be admitted. The latter principle has since been proved to be non-existent for the Tertiary but probable in more remote times, and the first principle remains a real acquisition to geotectonic thought.

THE UNDATION AND OSCILLATION THEORY

The oscillation theory of Haarmann (1930) postulated vertical movements below the crust as a new principle for all structural deformations. It teaches that through the influence of some undefined cosmic factor a disequilibrium in the perfectly layered earth's crust could be established, and that this could be counteracted only by flow of subcrustal masses because the crust itself is rigid. Thus "geotumours" became established, separated by "geodepressions", by flow of vitreous sialic matter from the depressions to the tumours. The next stage in the development naturally became the erosion of tumours and sedimentation in the depressions. When the cosmic influence was moved in relation to the earth, the tumours had to move also and it was thought that an oscillating action of emergence and submergence was thus originated.

The sediments in the depression were lifted up, and consequently glided down the slopes of the new tumour; and later the folded and structurally accumulated rocks were lifted up again and became mountain chains.

In Haarmann's conception all structural deformation takes place in a depression and below sea level; he therefore distinguishes a "tectogenesis", the uplift followed by a folding process due to gliding, and an "orogenesis" the subsequent uplift that formed the mountain chains. Moreover, he distinguishes a "primary tectogenesis", the first geotumours, and a "secondary tectogenesis", the uplift of the primary geodepression filled with sediments.

The theory never found many supporters, principally because the mysterious cosmic influence could satisfy hardly anybody, and secondly because gliding tectonics as a universal cause of structural features were not found acceptable.

Nevertheless, the principle of geotumours and of subcrustal mass displacements is fascinating, and was soon adopted by van Bemmelen.

Before Haarmann proposed his theory, Bailey Willis (1929) had formulated another principle about the genesis of sialic crusts or continents. His starting point is the "planetesimal theory" of T. C. Chamberlin, in which the birth of the earth is seen as an accumulation of meteorites, or rather "planetesimals", which fused as a result of the gravitative pressure and then cooled again through loss of heat by radiation; it is a theory which never found much support with geologists, but geophysicists are more apt to refer to it. Differentiation of the basaltic magma into a granite layer is the core of Bailey Willis's conception. According to him the mantle of the earth consists of three shells, an inner highly elastic shell, the "stereosphere", 1,900 km thick, an intermediate non-elastic zone of 1,250 km thickness, the "asthenosphere", and an outer 60 km zone, the rigid crust. The asthenosphere receives more heat than it can transmit outwards, its temperature is raised and regions of molten magma are formed — the "asthenoliths", which are the cause of volcanic action, batholith intrusion etc., or, in other words, are the regions from which the granitic layer originates. The asthenoliths first grow in height, and then laterally; between them we find the basins, filled with sediments.

The new element in Willis's conception is the fundamental role of magmatic differentiation in structural deformation.

Van Bemmelen (1932, 1935) combined the elements of Willis's and Haarmann's theories by placing the magmatic differentiation that leads to granite in the centre of his undation theory, forming asthenolithic mountain roots, undations, from which, by a mechanism

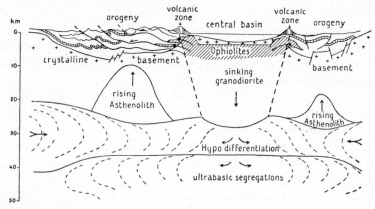

Fig. 305.   Section of the earth's crust in an orogeny according to the undation theory of van Bemmelen.

principally of subcrustal gliding, the superficial mountain chains were formed (Fig. 305). The fact that the undation theory was conceived in the East Indies explains why the role of volcanic differentiation and interpretation of gravimetric data is prominent in its reasoning.

The following table summarizes the zoning of the outer shell of the earth according to van Bemmelen.

Table XIV

		State and composition	Mechanical property	Thickness in km	Density	Velocity of long seismic waves
Silicate mantle	Tectonosphere	Epidermis	sediments	plastic	max. 10 km	2.0–2.8	4.25 km/sec
		Sial outer shell	crystalline granitic	zone of fracture	10–25	2.7–2.8	5.5–6.0
		Asthenolithic mountain root	magmatic, intermediate acid	flow no strength	max. 30	2.3–2.7	?
		Salsima, intermediate shell	upper part crystalline basalt	flow	15–30	2.7–3.0	± 6.5
			lower part vitreous basalt				
		Mohorovicic seismic discontinuity surface					
		Sima basement shell	partly crystalline ultrabasic	flow	50	3.2–3.4	± 8 km/sec
	Bathysphere	siferna substratum	vitreous, ultrabasic SiO_2 content diminishing with depth		down to —1200 km	3.4–4.4	7.9 increasing to 11.4 km/sec

The salsima of the intermediate shell is regarded as the parental magma zone, and in it is concentrated the origin of all the "equilibria-turbale" forces, the forces that disturb the equilibrium. The mechanism of this force is the formation of asthenoliths by a process of "hypo-differentiation", a splitting up into an ultrabasic sima and an acid granitic asthenolithic magma rich in volatiles. The volatile content lowers the specific density of the asthenolith, which rises and flows laterally outwards, causing salsima flow towards the centre. The asthenolith is the root of a mountain, or of the geanticline with geosynclines flanking it. During this stage of the hypo-differentiation the sialic crust above it was affected by a rising front of emanations and a femic front was formed, giving rise to ophiolitic magma of the initial magmatic phase. Later the asthenolith itself caused migmatization and batholithic intrusions.

The uplift of the geanticline, the lateral outward flow of the astheno-lith, caused gliding tectonics in the epidermis and these could reach very far out from the centre because the masses involved were large.

We cannot fully pursue the complete theory of van Bemmelen with all its intricate mechanisms of subcrustal flow, rising and subsiding masses etc.; let it suffice to state that he finally arrives at a central mass, characterized by a high gravity-anomaly due to a basic basement which replaced the original asthenolith, the latter having flowed away to two flanking zones of negative gravity-anomalies (Fig. 305).

Van Bemmelen's undation theory has won very little support, partly because of its unsurveyable complexity, partly because of the consequence of the secondary character of all lateral stress in the structural phenomena, partly because of the uncontrollable postulates on hypo-differentiation.

Nevertheless it merits a much closer study than we can devote to it since it establishes a close relation between the magmatic aspects and the structural aspects of mountain building. It is true that we know nothing for certain about the diffusion that might lead to granite differentiation from a basaltic parental magma, and that speculations about it are therefore premature; but neither can we be certain that it does *not* cause mass translations, which certainly might influence mountain building to a high degree.

From a structural point of view the absence of any primary lateral stress is inadmissible. We know too many examples of lateral stress deformation totally unconnected with any "tumours" or "undations". Moreover all gliding tectonics create, besides accumulation of crustal matter at one place, denudation at another place, and the latter are lacking in all simpler structures without an uplifted axial basement zone, and are often metamorphosed *in situ* instead of having been displaced in larger orogenies. Further, there is no reason why the asthenoliths should have a linear character; on the contrary they would tend to be circular, and therefore van Bemmelen prefers regions like the Banda arc or other Indonesian structures. But mountain chains are by nature linear structures and arcs of 270° like the Banda or Antillean arcs are exceptions.

Finally, van Bemmelen's sections, which join for instance the Alps with the northern Apennines or the Betic Cordilleras of Spain with the Oran Meseta of North Africa in one dual orogeny, link up so many completely incompatible features that their usefulness is seriously impaired.

THE THEORY OF CONVECTION CURRENTS

The theory of convection currents is at present the theory which doubtless finds more adherents and less contestants than any other theory. From the very beginning we must remember, however, that it is just another theory *ad hoc*, which nobody has ever succeeded in proving by independent measurements of any kind. The possibility of convection currents in the mantle of the earth has perhaps been demonstrated; they furnish an origin of the deformative forces which have crumpled the crust, but whether they are adequate is difficult to judge because we know very little about the absolute value of the physical properties of the crust and even less of the mantle material.

Heat-convection currents are generated by temperature differences, the hotter material having a smaller density than the cooler one, and they have the function of reestablishing the equilibrium in the temperature-distribution. The current itself is a gravitative function. In a good heat conductor, convection currents are less probable than in a bad one because the two methods of transmitting heat from the hot interior to the cooling surface have the same function. High viscosity will prevent convection currents, and large convection currents are more probable than small ones. A large temperature gradient favours them. Unfortunately we know very little about the temperature gradient in the mantle, and all we know about the viscosity is restricted to a zone just below the crust, where a viscosity of -10^{22} poises has been calculated from the supposed isostatic emergence of Scandinavia after the ice-cap melted off; but that was an exceptional occurrence.

Seismic evidence has proved that there exists a definite discontinuity surface at 2,900 km depth; hence convection currents can exist at present only in the mantle between 100 and 2,900 km depth, or between the Mohorovicic discontinuity and the surface of the core. There are many indications of other discontinuity surfaces: Gutenberg found three of them at 950, 1,900, and 2,150 km depth, and geophysicists finally agree on one second-order discontinuity, the Repetti surface, at 900 to 1,200 km depth; but none of them is very definite. But even in a slow convection current (its velocity is estimated at 1 to 5 cm per year) sudden changes in physical properties in the vertical column may exist without disturbing or preventing the currents if they are not of a permanent character.

Summarizing, we might say that convection currents in the mantle of the earth are not disproved by what we know of the physical circumstances in the mantle, but neither are they greatly favoured.

Vening Meinesz calculated that in the beginning of the history of the earth, before there was any question of a crust or a core, the most probable convection current system was a symmetrical double system as shown in Fig. 306a. Such a system could accumulate the lighter sialic components in a sialic continent in one hemisphere. How it subsequently generated the metallic (?) core rests unexplained, but a new system originated when this core became a fact; this could

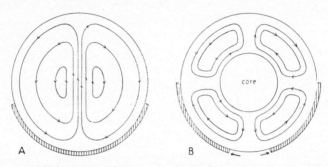

Fig. 306. The primeval convection current before—and the second-order convection current after—the formation of the core. *(After Vening Meinesz.)*

have the shape shown in Fig. 306b. Its system would have torn apart the great primeval continent and the fragments would have drifted towards the Equator.

With the generation of continents a new factor in the heat distribution below the crust is introduced. Because of the protection offered by a sialic crust and its generation of radioactive heat, there will arise a horizontal temperature gradient between the substratum below the continents and below the oceans. Very small gradients, for instance 1°–3° per km (Hales, 1936 and Pekeris, 1935), would be sufficient to set a horizontal current from continent to ocean in motion. The most probable, effective, and strongest convection current system would then be one with a current in every octant of the mantle.

Griggs (1939) pointed out that in order to sustain a permanent convection current system the cooling at the surface must be adequate, otherwise the downward stream would still be hot, and the convection would be stopped. Because the substratum has without doubt a certain strength, the heat difference can build up a considerable stress before the current is well under way, with the result that once it flows, it flows too quickly and is stopped. In this way the cyclic character of the crust movements which Umbgrove called the "pulse of the earth" can be explained as a phenomenon of convection currents.

Griggs (1939b) constructed a simple mechanism with which he demonstrated the action on a plastic crust of convection currents in a viscous substratum. With two turning drums in the substratum, he actually succeeded in forming a sialic bulge downwards in the "sima", representing the root of a mountain system, above the downward stream of the current.

The disadvantage of this point of view is that it neglects the horizontal temperature gradient between continent and ocean, and needs an upward stream both below the continent and below the ocean, and a downward stream below their boundary. The difference between ocean and continent therefore remains obscure in Grigg's conception.

Vening Meinesz has conceived a complex system of convection currents in order to explain most of the peculiarities of the Indonesian structure, its island arcs, geosynclinal basins, deep-sea basins, etc.

According to him there originated in the first place a large convection current, from the Asian continent towards the Pacific and Indian Oceans, and then downwards. The friction against the continental crust caused a stress in the continent which resulted in a downward bulge of the crust into the substratum, below the zone of negative

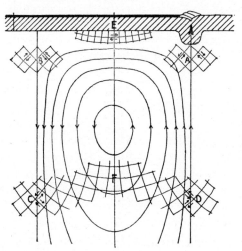

Fig. 307.   Small-size convection current next to a downward buckle. *(After Vening Meinesz.)*

gravity-anomalies. This sialic bulge created a disequilibrium in the heat distribution and generated a small convection current reaching to ± 700 km depth. At both sides of the bulge the substratum was heated by the radioactivity of the bulge and drifted sideways away from the bulge, thus creating an upward stream below the bulge and a downward stream below the basins behind the island arc (Fig. 307). Soon however the current would bring hot material from greater depth. Density difference between upward and downward stream disappears, and hence the current stops. Calculations showed that the radioactive heat of the bulge could not have penetrated deep enough below the crust to set up a convection current since a Pliocene folding phase, but would have had ample time since the great late-Miocene folding phase. The present gravity field with positive anomalies above the basins is explained by the greater density of the cooled downward stream, and this assumption also explains the submergence of the basin. Vening Meinesz even explains the distribution of earthquakes by the greater stress in the hinges of the convection current. Much of his reasoning is very opportunist because every feature has to be explained by the same mechanism. Moreover his calculations are based on assumptions of density variations due to temperature differences, of heat conductivity and heat capacity, of viscosity and strength and other properties, of a completely unknown substratum.

The broad concept of a large convection current from continent to ocean is mainly acceptable for the simple and negative reason that no other adequate source of horizontal orogenic stress has been proposed. That this stress results in folding located on the wedge of sialic crust is probable, and that a thickening of the crust, either by overthrusting or by simple thickening or by buckling, then occurs there is logical; but all this reasoning depends on the reality of convection currents, which from the very beginning are not favoured by the more or less vague seismic second-order discontinuity surfaces in the mantle and the increase in density downwards. Moreover, as stated before, convection currents are counteracted by restriction in size and increase of viscosity, two factors which certainly gained importance in the course of the earth's history. Hence we might expect that the original currents which followed on the chaotic stage were effectively stopped after a youthful stage of development. Finally, the magmatic phases of an orogeny suggest a stable substratum rather than steady flow.

CRITICAL REVIEW OF THEORIES

Every attempt to formulate a general theory about the historical development of the earth's crust is necessarily highly conjectural, because we suspect that the origin of its long and complicated history of deformation is not located in the crust itself, but in regions below it, regions which we have never seen, never touched with the hammer. As we have seen, we have nevertheless some information about the distribution of stress, temperature, and density in mantle and core, and their mechanical properties; but the effect of the combination of these physical properties together with the almost totally unknown chemical properties of matter in these circumstances can hardly be guessed. On the contrary we can be sure that unknown or unpredictable reactions can take place.

To take advantage of this ignorance by assuming reactions which are, unavoidably, extrapolations from reactions known to occur at the surface, is a hazardous procedure, but there is no other way open to us. Our ignorance ought to compel us however to observe the utmost modesty and simplicity in our assumptions, to avoid building a house of cards of assumptions, because otherwise we may be assured that at the slightest provocation it will topple down and leave us again with the chaos from which the earth was created.

I have tried to assemble the different theories discussed above in a comparative table, which enables us to formulate some conclusions about their merits and deficiencies. The contraction theory, taking the cooling of the earth as its fundamental principle, can no longer be upheld, because we know now that on one hand the radioactive energy of the crust makes cooling very doubtful, and on the other, cooling since the Pre-Cambrian is not reflected in any trend in the development of either the sediments or their organic content. Nevertheless the contraction theory offers one great advantage over all other theories and that is that a compression of one zone is not coupled with a stretching of another zone. The very simple and very obvious fact that zones of compression are numerous, frequent, and intense, whereas zones of tension are rare and small, is one of the major characteristics of the earth's crust distortion, and has been overlooked by most theories but not by the contraction theory.

With the drifting continents all the tension zones are conveniently located in the oceans, but we have to admit that this does not satisfy us and is contrary to almost everything we know about the oceans. There are many other objections to the theory; partly that the supposed origin of the force is completely inadequate, partly that the similarities are only apparent and that there are dissimilarities as well.

Both the undation, oscillation, and convection current theories have a

Table XV

	Contraction Theory	Drifting Continents
Origin of force	Cooling of the earth	Centripetal force from Pole to Equator and westward drift
Comments on origin of force	Principle of cooling is doubtful	Force is far too small to have any effect
Stress-field	Lateral stress, acting continuously	Lateral stress, quickly decreasing
Comments on stress-field	Cyclic development unexplained	Inadequate because dying out very quickly; no cyclic development
Adequacy in relation to: Absence of tensional regions	Accounts adequately for lack of tensional regions	Inadequate for both compression and tension
Folding	Adequate	Inadequate
Basin formation	Adequate	Inadequate
Faulting	Adequate	Adequate
Magmatic cycles	Inadequate	Inadequate
Main advantages	Explains absence of tensional regions	Explains striking similarities of shape of continents
Secondary advantages	Very simple and universal	
Main objections	Force altogether inadequate; no connexions magmatic orogenic cycles; not cyclic	Inadequate force and effect; not cyclic

Undation & Oscillation Theory	Convection Currents
Chemical reactions in upper mantle	Thermal gradients horizontal and vertical
Possible but very conjectural	Possibility decreasing with size and dependent on temperature gradient, viscosity etc., all ± unknown quantities
Vertical stress in cycles causing uplifts followed by gliding	Lateral stress in cycles
Gliding mechanism fully inadequate; cycles are possible	Inadequate because each feature requires its own current; cycles inadequately explained
Inadequate for absence of tensional region of the less intense structures	No explanation for absence of tensional regions
Inadequate	Adequate
Inadequate	Adequate
Inadequate	Adequate
Mainstay of theory	Somewhat forced
Correlation of magmatic cycles with orogenies	Large currents are probable and attractive in effect
Large intricate orogenies explained	Large and small orogenies are explained
Too complicated and construed; lateral stress inadequate, paratectonics unexplained	Too complicated for smaller structures; connexion magmatic cycles — orogenies inadequate; Repetti seismic discontinuity contradicts larger currents

great advantage over their predecessors in that they look for the origin of stress in the lower reaches of the crust or the mantle and not in the crust itself. When we realize that the order of size of the blocks is measured in thousands of miles and that of the orogenic belts in hundreds of miles, it becomes obvious that the origin of the crustal distortions cannot be located in the crust itself, which has a thickness of only tens of miles. In this respect the convection theory, by reaching deeper into the mantle, is preferable to the other theories, because it can postulate currents of continent or oceanwide size as Hess, Griggs, and Holmes do; but as soon as it requires a current for every basin and mountain chain it becomes self-contradictory. Either the big currents reach from core to crust, or the small ones reach just below the crust. The big ones fail to account for the linear and shifting pattern of mountain belts and chains, the small ones are inadequate in size and contradictory in position.

The undation and oscillation theories, which put the radial before the lateral forces, undoubtedly have advantages over the others. In many cases emergence does precede lateral compression, but in others the sequence is reversed. When major mountain chains with crystalline cores are concerned the universal lateral gliding motions towards the peripheries is not contradicted by the absence of tensional regions, but in less severely compressed chains there is no central emergence and there is no trace of tectonic denudation. Moreover, the postulates of the theory are too complex; there are too many assumptions, and far too often the actual facts about a specific mountain chain are not at all in harmony with the postulated general structure.

The main objection I have against these current theories and others less well known is that they make one or other of two errors. Either they wish to explain everything from one single point of view, or they introduce a new principle for every conspicuous feature.

When we contemplate from a distance the different theories about mountain building and the origin of oceans and continents, it strikes us as a peculiar fact that those theories which start from a purely conjectural origin of the forces are much more in discussion than those which try to start from the known pattern of these units in the earth's crust, and to deduce from that some sort of logical conclusion on the deformative forces.

These latter theories can be classified as follows:

1. Those which call attention to the fact that almost everywhere on the earth the antipode of a continent is an ocean, forming together a "rounded-off" tetrahedron.
2. Those which suspect that the great gap of the Pacific represents the scar left by the mass of the moon when it was torn away from the earth.
3. Those which discern on the earth's crust some kind of linear pattern, which is regarded as a set of fundamental shear-zones.

The first and second points of view start from real factual evidence. Only 1.4 % of the surface of the earth has land opposite land, and 95 % of the land is antipodal to the sea. No one has ever been able to suggest a physically acceptable reason for this argument. The theory that the moon was torn off the earth at a moment when the tidal period and the vibration of the mass of earth could resonate has been finally rejected by Jeffreys, because the internal friction would limit the extension to only 17 km. The peculiar round gap of the Pacific is nevertheless a fact, and must be regarded as a fundamental feature in the continent-ocean pattern.

The reality and significance of linear patterns on the contrary, are very doubtful from a global point of view. A modern view comes from Vening Meinesz, who constructed the kind of shear pattern which would be formed when the position of the Pole described a 90° arc on the surface of the globe, resulting from change of shape of the globe ellipsoid. This pattern, consisting of a set of intersecting lines of maximum shear, could be shifted over the surface of the earth until it coincided roughly with some coastal and other linear features. Whether the coincidence has a real value is still very doubtful because one is justified in presuming that any other kind of pattern could perhaps be fitted as well to other topographical features.

What we have to keep in mind, however, is that the earth's surface exhibits two major topographical features:

1. The Pacific with its circum-Pacific belts of folding.
2. The Tethys orogenic zone running from the Indonesian archipelago to the west, between the ancient moles of continents to the Caribbean archipelago, forming a buckle perpendicular to the Pacific belt.

These facts ought to be our starting point for any realistic analysis of the distortion of the earth's crust.

Chapter 34

Synthesis

THE STRESS-FIELD OF THE EARTH

When we try to look back along the road we have covered, nearing the end of our laborious travels over and underneath the much disturbed earth's surface, we feel the need to establish a high platform that will enable us to survey our experience in one sweeping glance. We wish to marshal all the pertinent facts into a synthesis that will give us a deeper insight into their relations. The reader will have noticed that I am dissatisfied with the trend that prevails in all theories of origin of diastrophic forces, mainly because they all are founded on a generalization of one particular favoured set of facts, and disregard any other set which is in conflict. A synthesis cannot properly be sought in that manner. On the contrary many factors together, interacting and interdependent, govern the development of the deformation of the earth's crust.

Stress and Resistance. In my description of the folding of various mountain chains and various basins we have learned that contraction in a cross-section can vary from a very mild degree of only a few per cent, to paroxysms in which more than 50 % overall contraction is noted.

Although we started from the presumption that there is a clear division between a mountain chain and a folded basin, we have to conclude from our experience that the subdivision is quite arbitrary, and is often more influenced by a post-orogenic elevation of the folded belt than by the folding itself. We should hardly classify the High Atlas as a mountain chain, for instance, if it had not been elevated to its present altitude long after the folding took place.

Nevertheless, we can make a distinction between mild or paratectonic folding and strong or orthotectonic folding, even if we recognize that there is considerable transition between these categories.

The really strong folding of a mountain chain is characterized by a

502

syntectonic magmatic phase; but even without that, in particular for the Alpine orogenies, strong folding shows low-angle thrusts of considerable width, or closely packed folds. We concluded that the onset of the folding was due either to a growing stress exceeding the yield point of the rock resistance, or to a decrease of resistance bringing the yield point below the stress, or both actions having effect at the same time.

Another question which we need to consider is why the folding stopped at all, and why it stopped in one case after mild folding, and in another case only after it had built up a real mountain chain. The first question is probably answered adequately by pointing out that when the stress-field achieved its purpose it ceased to exist, or in other words, when the disequilibrium that caused the stress had been wiped out the stress obviously subsided. This answer includes, however, the notion that the stress-field is not permanently at the same height, but that it grows and subsides. A folding phase should, therefore, be due to a rise of stress.

We may presume that in the case of the rise of stress accompanied by a fall in resistance we get a major orogeny, and in the case where the rise does not result in a decrease of resistance we get mild folding. The arrest of the folding in the mountain chain is then due to the subsidence of the stress; the arrest of the folding in a folded basin might be due to several factors, one of which might be a stiffening of the resistance; another, the yield of the stress-field in another area. In large-scale mountain building all these factors play a role when we consider particular zones of the structure. In one zone the folding starts, but stops because the yield is taken over by another zone where the resistance has dropped lower in the meantime; in another the start is relatively late in the period, and is due to growing resistance elsewhere, and the arrest is just the end of the whole contraction. Moreover, the yield in one cross-section will increase the stress to the left and right, and the folding will spread horizontally in the direction perpendicular to the stress. This principle of distribution of yield zones by variations in resistance can be applied to much larger areas than that of single mountain chains, and would imply a certain interdependence of different zones of yield, over large distances. We naturally apply this principle when we consider the American Cordilleran system, which is at least ten times larger than the Alps; and I would not hesitate to view the whole "Mediterranean" belt from Gibraltar to Australia from this point of view. I think that a world-

wide study of the interdependence of orogenies would yield remarkable
results, because we know already (through the Stille principle of
world-wide synchronization of orogenies, however defective its
formulation may have been) that an interaction does exist.

Stress and Time. Before we enter into speculations about the mechanism which regulates this relation between stress and folding, we have
to remember some of the salient facts about stress and time relations.
The most obvious common denominator for structural disturbances is
their timing. We have seen that we know of orogenic periods occurring
roughly each 200 million years since the Archean, and separated by
periods of quiescence. Further, we have seen that each period consists
of recurring folding phases which are perhaps irregularly distributed
when regarded from a global point of view, but which are more or less
regular, in periods of perhaps 10 million years, in one mountain belt.

I think we can break these intervening spaces of some 10 million
years down further, into smaller units; not from folds or faults themselves but by looking at the sedimentary history of sinking basins.
Each faunal break, disconformity or unconformity is in some way
related to crustal disturbance, and we have found some forty of them
in the Miocene of California. Each detailed section of each sedimentary
basin reveals the same frequency of disturbances. Even relatively
short intervals, minor unconformities of perhaps 500,000 years, may
be further broken down into even smaller units when we take into
account the remarkable sedimentary cycles known from coal-bearing
beds, for instance, or those very convincingly described by R. C.
Moore (1950), Wanless (1950), and Lombard (1953). The megacycles
of Moore are identical to what we have called minor unconformities.

The characteristic of earth disturbance in time, when considered in
this way, is that the energy distribution is not smooth but comes in
shocks, small shocks with small consequences in a quick succession,
big shocks with big consequences in a slow succession. The larger the
shock the larger is the time interval:

sedimentary cycles	sedimentary unconformities and megacycles	orogenic phases	orogenic periods in shocks
shocks of 25,000 years	in shocks of 500,000	in shocks of 10 million	of 200 million

Stress and Strain. In mountain building we can discern a space
distribution of the same character. The largest unit is the orogenic

belt, either circum-Pacific or equatorial, some 7,000 km length and some 500 km width. The next unit is the mountain chain some 800 km long and some 50 km wide. Still smaller is the single fold, with perhaps an average of 10 km length and a width of 2 km. In a major fold we can discern even smaller units when we consider microtectonics, with sedimentary folds of the order of 50 m width; microfolds of 10 cm width, and finally the smallest possible unit, which depends perhaps on the average grain size, let us say 0.1 mm. Not only do the strongly disturbed belts of the earth's crust show this sequence of diminishing sizes; blocks have the same habit. The largest blocks are the great blocks such as Gondwana, the Pacific and the northern hemisphere block (Canada–Greenland–Fennosarmatia–Angara). The next unit are blocks of the size of Fennosarmatia itself, the Sahara block, the Brazilian block. But even these blocks have been broken up into such smaller units as those of the North German blocks of Fig. 300. Still smaller blocks can be distinguished when we look to shattered areas. I think it would be futile to assign an average mass to any of these units; they vary too much. For the larger blocks and the smaller orogenic unit we can compare the cratogenic and orogenic elements:

Orogenic belts	Mountain chains	Single folds
Global blocks	Continental shields	Blocks

The Relation between Time and Space in Orogenic Processes. There is obviously a relation between spatial distribution and sequence in time; both come in definite quanta, which one could formulate by supposing that it takes an orogenic period of 200 million years to accumulate enough energy to move an orogenic belt or a global block, and 10 million years of accumulation of energy to form a mountain chain or move a continental shield, and so on.

The reason for this relation is perhaps rather simple. If we assume that the energy is steadily and evenly growing, it is the mass that regulates the release of potential energy into kinetic energy. If the proposed time and spatial relation between the shocks of energy release is real, it would imply that there is only one single source of energy in the earth's crust, a source which is, however, variable in its outward symptoms. The question "What is the mechanism that regulates this energy release?" can be answered when we recall the relation which we established between folds and secondary folds. I demonstrated that the smaller fold is directly induced by the larger one. The anticline which reached down to the bottom of a particular sedimentary base caused the formation of secondary folds whose size was again determined by the thickness of a single bed. The same relation exists between an orogenic belt and a mountain chain. When only the crust, of some 30 km depth, is concerned in the folding of a single mountain chain of some 50 to 60 km width, the orogenic belt of some 500 km width should reach down to at least 200 km depth and probably much deeper. Intermediate and deep-focus earthquakes, all connected with major orogenic belts, prove that such a depth is not in the least improbable. When we think of the extreme thinness of the crust as compared to the earth's diameter, a factor of 0.02, then it becomes quite plausible that the origin of a major disturbance of some 600 km width, 20 times the thickness of the crust, cannot be lodged in the crust itself. The mountain chain, on the other hand, could be an exclusively crustal feature.

If these considerations carry weight, we can suppose that the upper two or three hundred kilometres of the earth's crust possess some property which allows the slow accumulation of potential energy, during 200 million years, which is released in a much shorter period of some 50 million years. Once this release is effected the distribution of kinetic energy is regulated by the distribution of mass in these upper layers of the earth's mantle. The vitreous layer at 30 km depth is the cause of the mass distribution and therefore also of the time distribution involved in the mountain chains, in the same way as the limit between crystalline basement and sedimentary rocks determines, when the rocks are sufficiently plastic, the type and mass of the individual folds.

When we have to look so far below the crust for the origin of orogenic force, it becomes impossible in our present state of knowledge of the earth's interior to predict anything definite about its nature; but we can be convinced that all typical properties of the upper crust, such as the radioactivity of granite or contraction by cooling, ought to be disregarded.

From the available evidence we have concluded an omnipresence of the stress-field, growing when resisted, subsiding when the resistance yields. In my review of theories of orogeny I concluded that a contracting sphere offers the best starting point for such a stress-field.

In a contracting sphere we can expect an omnipresence of lateral stress on the surface; this stress does not become orientated unless yield sets in somewhere. Every heterogeneity in the crust will therefore orientate the stress, and as we presumed that in the early Archean the major features of heterogeneity of the crust were fixed once and for all, the stress-field direction also became fixed at that period. However, a uniform compression direction all over the earth's surface would not satisfy the stress-field, e.g. a shortening in a NS direction would not satisfy the EW stress, or, in other words, the yield in any direction round the earth would have to be roughly uniform. There are of course an infinite number of solutions to this problem. One could, for instance, imagine a multitude of contraction centres round which the compression took

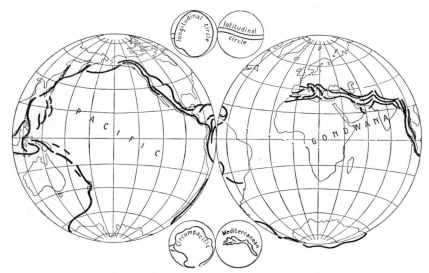

Fig. 308.   The circum-Pacific and Mediterranean orogenic belts of the earth's
crust.

place, or a multitude of straight lines orientated at random, or only a few lines which would have to have sufficiently different orientations and sufficient length to allow a uniform contraction. Even one NS line and one EW line, each a great circle, would satisfy the requirements, provided some minor adjustments at the corners were allowed for. I think we can perceive every one of these solutions — which by no means exclude one another — in the earth's crust; with, however, a preponderance of the last and simplest case of only two perpendicular lines. Without doubt we can distinguish one hemisphere with a NS contraction along an EW line, which would necessarily have to be about equatorial, and one hemisphere with an EW contraction along NS lines, e.g. the Eastern hemisphere with its Mediterranean folded belt and a Western hemisphere with its circum-Pacific folded belt (Fig. 308).

One sees no cogent reason why the major trends are orientated along the meridian and the parallel, but one can just feel that this orientation to the rotation axis of the earth is plausible.

As the contraction stress will be equally distributed over the earth's surface after a period of quiescence, any local disturbance of the stress-field by a yield will necessarily be followed by an increase of stress, and therefore by yield somewhere else in compensation. When this disturbance is small in extension it requires only a small compensating yield, of the same direction; but as soon as it has reached the extension of half the circumference of the earth a compensating contraction in a direction perpendicular to the first will be called for, and this in its turn will not finish until it has also spanned half the circumference.

In this mechanism of a trigger-action character — with one disturbance leading to a world-wide revolution — one finds the reason for the contemporaneity of the world revolutions, the orogenic periods. A certain divergence of contemporaneity is also inherent to the mechanism, and the orogenic phases of one period illustrate the mutual interdependence of the yield points distributed over the earth's surface.

The cyclic nature of the orogenic periods also finds ready explanation in the conception of a world-wide stress-field. Once the stress has worked out all over the world in a long succession of phases during one period, the necessary contraction has been achieved, and a long period of quiescence is needed to build up enough stress to start another world-wide revolution. This period of quiescence is not free from stress. On the contrary, from the very beginning the stress is already building up, and small readjustments may take place here and there continuously. An almost necessary result of this conception is that the elastic bending of the earth in the new geosynclines would proceed more slowly just after a major period, and considerably quicker just before a new period. Reviewing the general sequence of the sedimentation in a geosyncline, it is certainly true that the quick sinking of the basin, indicated by steepening of its margins and deep-water facies, i.e. by the flysch facies, is typical of the late geosynclinal periods although this rule is far from being universal. But the sinking of a basin is not only expressed by the depth of its axis but equally well by the rising of its borders; the facies changes can therefore differ considerably from one geosyncline to another. There is, however, one general rule of almost universal truth, and that is that the last lap of the geosynclinal stage is characterized first by a world-wide transgression followed immediately by a regression.

THE ORIGIN OF CONTRACTION IN THE EARTH

It is only with the greatest hesitation that I will advance, in the following pages, a new concept of the origin of the distortions of the earth's crust, for I am fully aware that it will be as vulnerable as any of the preceding theories. But as it certainly represents the keystone of my whole conception of the structural behaviour of the earth's crust as it has been sketched in the preceding chapters, I feel compelled to add it to the structure. On the other hand I hope that the reader will agree that the structure in itself is solid enough to stand up without this keystone, which fits in the place that has been prepared for it, but I emphatically agree that another keystone perhaps may fit as well and perhaps even better.

In this final concept I have started from some conditions to which it ought to conform. The basic idea should be very simple: it should be located far down in the mantle; it should combine vertical stress and lateral stress; it should not leave tensional regions in the crust unaccounted for by stressing the origin of the compressed areas only, and it should leave room for additional factors which might even predominate locally. In other words it should not be a universal theory that pretends to explain all distortions from one point of view leaving the many other known factors in the cold to shift for themselves.

In connexion with the famous law of Goldschmidt that the largest atoms have a tendency to accumulate in the lithosphere, and the smallest ones in the core (see Chapter 24), we may presume that there will be a tendency in the earth for dense molecules to descend and for voluminous molecules to ascend; or as an alternative, when new molecules form through chemical reactions dense ones will be preferred near the core and voluminous ones near the crust. As a result of this tendency the sialic crust is lighter than its basaltic substratum, and as we know that it is steadily increasing in thickness and area by the addition of granitic matter during every orogenic phase, we can state that this accumulation of light matter is still progressing. The opposite is also true; we know that in the core we have an accumulation of heavy material which is separated from the mantle by a discontinuity surface as well defined as that between the mantle and the crust. As we know that the discontinuity surface below the crust is constantly passed by light material added to the crust, we may assume without violating any principle of stability that the lower discontinuity surface, the core boundary, is also constantly passed by heavy material, the core accruing from the mantle material: it is the core that grows and is supplied by mantle material (cf. also the conception of Urey, 1952).

The contraction of the earth since the crust was formed and the continents and oceans were fixed approximately in their present position, let us say 2,000 million years ago, is due, according to this theory, to the compaction of matter, principally the siderophile elements, concentrated in the core. If we assume that the core had 3/4 of its present radius at that time, there has been some 800 km added to it in the last 2,000 million years. Assuming that the transformation of material from the mantle into a layer of 800 km of core was accompanied by a compaction of 1/5, the radius of the earth has been shortened in those 2,000 million years by 200 km. We may assume eight to ten orogenic periods in that long time interval, or 20 to 25 km radial shortening, or 125 to 150 km shortening of the earth circumference per major diastrophism. The actual shortening of a single mountain chain is already difficult to evaluate, and the difficulty of evaluating so much for the whole earth is correspondingly greater. In general, a maximum shortening of some 450 km is assumed for the Alps (480 km by Cadisch, 1953), but as can be demonstrated this figure is much too high, and I would not hesitate to limit it to some 150 km (cf. de Sitter, 1955). Together with the compression in the same orogeny on the southern margin of the Mediterranean, some 200 km would suffice for all the Alpine shortening in the direction of the meridian. Along the parallel a similar amount would be needed to account for both sides of the circum-Pacific belt. The assumed shrinking is therefore of the same order as the measured contraction and this theory meets no objection from this point of view.

The core is growing in size as the crust is growing in thickness. It is perfectly compatible with our general knowledge about the influence of hydrostatic pressure on chemical reactions to assume further that the volume of the newly formed heavy molecules added to the core is smaller than the space the same atoms occupied in their former position; or in other words that the total volume of core and that part of the mantle that is supplying it with new material is constantly decreasing by the formation of stress minerals, in the same way as is supposed for the genesis of eclogite. The growth of the core is accompanied by compaction. Only the siderophile elements rich in free electrons can comply with this law of concentration of matter in a smaller space; the lithophile elements with complete electronic shells are incapable of this kind of denser packing. This is all in accordance with the empirical law of Goldschmidt.

This theory of "polymorphism" as the cause of earth contraction has already been advanced by Brian Mason (1953) based on the assumptions of Birch (1952 and 1954) that the seismic second-order discontinuities were due to polymorphism of olivine, pyroxene, and SiO_2. Mason suggests that the process need not always have gone in the same direction, a reversal would cause a dilatation, which found its expression at the surface in the great rift valleys. This latter addition looks rather improbable because it is in contradiction with Goldschmidt's law.

If contraction through polymorphism is true we would have a contraction of core and of a considerable part of the mantle to which the upper part of the mantle and the crust would have to yield.

This concept is a revival of the contraction theory, with its merits and without its most obvious drawbacks. The origin of the force is adequate and located somewhere deep in the mantle. In the crust we have no longer to worry about any gaps of the same width as the contraction of a mountain chain would leave to be filled.

It is immaterial to our concept whether the transport of the lithophile elements upwards and of the siderophile elements downwards is effected by slow diffusion or by convection currents, or whether the chemical reactions are considered from the point of view of classical chemistry or atomic chemistry.

It is impossible to determine the upper boundary of the siderophile supplying part of the mantle; there need not even be any boundary at all; perhaps the whole thickness of the mantle is supplying the core with siderophile elements and the crust with lithophile elements – the effect would be the same as long as the denser packing near the core is predominant over the looser packing near the crust.

The only consequence of importance in connexion with our problem of the growth of the core is a general lateral stress in every part of the upper regions of the mantle and in the crust.

As Hales (1953) pointed out, the contraction of the crust through cooling, using Jeffreys' temperature distribution, would amount to only about 3.5 km in 200 million years, the asthenosphere being at a depth of 60 km only. But a much greater value of stress increase could be obtained if the lower mantle and the core were compressed as a result of cooling between the surface and a depth of 700 km; and failure would occur at depths of 250 to 600 km depth, with a periodicity of 200 million years.

I presume that the effect would be the same if the contraction of the core and mantle were primary and the contraction of the shell second-ary — instead of the case of compression of the core by a cooling outer shell 700 km thick. The conception of a growing core and crust is, however, applicable only to present circumstances. In the earliest stages of the earth's history there were no core and no mantle, and chaotic currents took care of the transport of heat from centre to surface and also of the separation of the elements into the hydrosphere and the body of the earth.

THE YOUTHFUL PHASE OF THE EARTH

During the first two milliard years of the earth's existence the crust was formed and the present configuration of oceans and conti-nents became fixed. How this came about can be understood from the point of view of convection currents, but other conceptions are perhaps preferable.

Vening Meinesz (1944) has proved that the most probable convection current for an earth without core and mantle would be one of the first order, i.e. one stream along the axis, plunging at one Pole and leaving it at the opposite one and returning along the surface. Slightly modi-fying his suggestion that this stream drove the floes of sialic matter, large and small, which condensed on the surface towards the North Pole, I suggest that it drove those floes to the South Pole, where they coagulated in one large blanket reaching almost to the Equator (Fig. 309). This thin blanket of sialic matter radiated heat as a result of its accumulation of radioactive elements, which were probably present in greater quantities than now, because many short-lived isotopes have disappeared altogether since then, and this heat eventually stopped the first large convection current. Sooner or later, it was replaced by an opposite current, flowing from beneath the heated blanket to the opposite Pole, i.e. from south to north, descending there, and arising again at the South Pole.

This second convection current broke up the blanket into large floes and drove these northwards, carried on the back of this mighty surface current. Each of the floes naturally had a long broad front and a tail-end tapering away to the south. They were floated northwards until their edges collided after having passed the Equator. With some shifting and squeezing they managed to reach quite a long way towards the north, but finally they stuck, and the North Pole remained free from any sialic cover but became surrounded by a barrier of floes formed by the broken sialic blanket that once covered the South Pole. The South Pole itself was still covered by the last remnant of that once extensive blanket, since a central rising current of this kind produces a dead spot without current where it starts turning to its lateral surface-flow. Antarctica is the only portion of the blanket that never left its original position. The same is true for the North Pole;

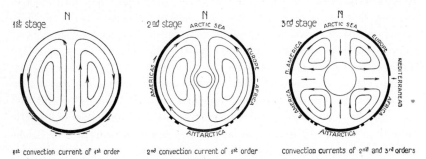

Fig. 309. Successive stages of convection currents in the youthful stage of the earth's development.

the surface current turns downwards long before it reaches the Pole, and has left it uncovered.

In the meantime, the core had started growing and was impeding the axial flow of the current. Simultaneously, the reversed position of the sialic cover again checked the convection current. After a period of quiescence, new convection currents started to move; but the space left for currents of this kind was now more restricted. The core was occupied by an immovable mass of heavy material, and the current had to split into smaller ones. According to the theory developed by Vening Meinesz, the most probable distribution was that each quadrant or octant of the earth now got its own current. It is tempting, of course, to play around with smaller convection currents here and there, and to explain every feature of the distribution of continents and oceans by currents towing one floe to this corner and another to that. An arrangement, for instance, that sweeps the Pacific clean of any remnants of the broken-up blanket could certainly be proposed as the next stage. Another set of currents could account for the breaking of each of the three great floes, i.e. the Americas, Europe-Africa and Asia-India-Australia, into two, thus separating the two Americas, Europe and Africa, Asia and Australia. For the sweep of the Pacific we should need a current that rose in the centre of the Ocean, flowed horizontally parallel to the Equator and then descended below its eastern and western borders. Its antipodal current or currents would rise in the Atlantic and Indian Oceans. The currents which broke up the great floes into a northern and southern half would need to be directed along the meridians, away from the Equator and descending at the Poles. These would create, once and for all, the Mediterranean zone of weakness. I must admit, however, that these speculations are too easy and leave too many alternatives to be very attractive. One could assume, for instance, as an alternative for the proposed sequence, that the pole of the first blanket covering the South Pole was not in its present position but somewhere much further north, in the present Indian Ocean. Proceeding from this assumption, it could be maintained that the cessation of the first current of the first order and the start of the second and opposite current of the first order evidently caused tremendous mass displacements, a revolution in the inner earth, which shifted the South Pole at the border of that blanket to its present position. If the original North Pole was situated in the northern Pacific, the clean sweep of the Pacific would be due to the first current of the first order, and not to some later current-distribution.

I would prefer to assume in a general way that subsequent convection currents of higher orders could easily account for any peculiarity of the present ocean and continent distribution on the surface of the earth, without specifying the role of each current.

In the meantime, however, the core kept on growing; additional sialic matter rose to the surface, and covered the empty spaces between the continents with a thin veneer, except where they were swept clean by convection currents. Thus we may expect that the first current that died was that of the Pacific, whereas the other ones continued somewhat longer still carrying sialic matter to the surface. Finally, however, the growth of the core stopped all convection currents, which, as the theory shows, become more and more improbable with decreasing size and decreasing temperature gradients.

Many conspicuous details of the pattern of island strings and smaller continental blocks on the earth's surface become comprehensible when seen from this point of view. For instance, the string of islands of the Falklands, connecting South America with Antarctica, is obviously a stretched and torn part of the sialic crust, formed when the continents were torn apart and the crust was still not quite solidified; the string of islands perhaps acquired its S-shaped swing through a swinging motion of the tail of the drifting continent. In the same way, some of the island arcs between North and South America and Asia and Australia were perhaps already formed when the large floe broke in two and drifted apart, swept away by currents of opposing direction.

Some small blocks broke off during the drift; Madagascar and Greenland are typical examples of these blocks. All this happened, however, in a very primitive state of the development of the earth's crust.

This part of the history of the earth was enacted and finished long before the end of the Pre-Cambrian. We have no means of fixing the limit of the end of this youthful stage, but it seems improbable that any of the orogenic cycles were involved, even those of the Pre-Cambrian. The youthful stage had its own periodicity, which was not necessarily that of the 200 to 250 million years which typifies the last 1,000 million years of the earth's history. We may eventually learn something about its rhythms, but the chance is small. So many revolutions have passed over it that little can be left unchanged; its rocks have been buried so many times below new loads of sediments which have become migmatized and replaced by granites that what is left is unrecognizable.

The middle-age of the earth started when the permanency of continents and oceans had been established. A constant lateral stress developed because of the shrinking of the earth, and made itself felt once a crust was formed. Other factors became active, and we are able to read the trend of its history in the rocks that are there to be interpreted. From then on we have a solid floor beneath our feet, and our method of interpretation has to change.

THE MIDDLE AGE OF THE EARTH

I need not elaborate in detail the development of the earth's crust after its consolidation, since the different aspects of this subject have already been treated extensively in the course of this book.

I concluded that there has been an omnipresent stress in the crust, causing its bending down in basins and geosynclines when the stress exceeded the elasticity limit; and causing strong folding in orogenic belts when the resistance dropped below the plasticity limit as a result of differential fusion at the bottom of the crust.

The pattern of the belts of least resistance on the globe is due to two factors: on one hand the need to attain an equal contraction of any great circle, and on the other the irregularities of the crust itself, its sialic continents, and its basaltic ocean bottom. The ocean bottom apparently forms the most rigid crust, and the boundaries of the old shields are the zones of least resistance.

Because the circum-Pacific zone absorbs most of the EW contraction, the rest of the globe is comparatively free from NS trending mountain chains; the Mediterranean and Antillean zones have remained the areas of most NS contractions because they are roughly equatorial, and were predisposed for this function by the original fixation of the continental shields. Every major orogenic period has necessarily to be world-wide, otherwise the stress-field would persist. Each local yield to stress induces other yields, first of all in an extension of its own direction, and later in a perpendicular direction also. Because considerable strain can be stored away by elastic bending, the actual orogenic phases can vary considerably in time and intensity from one place to another. And since rigid continental and oceanic blocks are apt to cause deviation in the main stress-direction, considerable variations in fold directions may be expected.

All epeirogenic and orogenic activity is accompanied by considerable elevations and subsidences, and although isostasy as a geophysical principle may be a fact, it is by no means clear how it can be brought into agreement with these radial movements. Large blocks sink and rise without any traceable connexion with isostatic adjustment, mountain chains rise and subside in an unaccountable way, great chunks of mountain chains are cut off by the present coast line, and the border zones of continents are curled up or bent down independently of any predictable isostatic influence. Consequently any hypothetical underflow in the substratum due to supposed isostatic adjustments or melting of supposed buckles must be considered to be highly conjectural.

It is thought that magmatic phases belonging to orogenic disturbances are a major factor in the development of mountain chains. They obviously play an important part as volcanic manifestations in the circum-Pacific island arcs, and the syntectonic magmatization phase is a deciding factor in any major orogeny. Both can perhaps be explained by the decrease of stress below an up-arched crustal strip combined with admixture of water from the metamorphosed sediments. The initial magmatic phase seems to be rather independent of the later ones, but its presence certainly tends to increase the intensity of folding. Whatever may be the true character of the relations between the magmatic phases and folding, it is certain that any theory on the mechanism of orogenic deformation has to take into account a close interdependence between magmatic activity and strain. The initial magmatic phase of ultrabasic intrusions and pillow lavas is perhaps less important in this respect than the syntectonic granitic phase. The late- and post-tectonic phases of batholith intrusions and volcanic activity are again not considered essential; they are effects and not causes.

In every orogeny we can distinguish several superposed tiers of deformation, distinguishable by their different mechanical mode of yield to the stress. The separation into tiers is due to several factors, among which the increase in temperature due to a central syntectonic phase is perhaps the most important. But besides this factor the increase of confining pressure downwards and the presence of particular incompetent layers are often deciding factors.

As a very rough approximation, the sequence from top to bottom is, concentric folding; cleavage folding; schistosity; flow-structure. But the greatly varying influence of stress on the varying material properties of rocks may bring about considerable variations in this schematic sequence. Each orogeny will therefore have its own peculiar development.

Further, this development is largely dependent on the preceding geosynclinal structure, and this is again dependent on the situation of the geosyncline in relation to the continent and ocean. As a general rule, but with many variations, I can state that a basin of short duration will engender a minor orogeny of paratectonic character, and an orthogeosyncline of long duration will be followed by a strong orogeny subdivided in several phases.

We found a remarkable rhythm in the development of circum-continental orthogeosynclines, shifting their axis of subsidence towards the continents in succeeding phases, a rhythm which is repeated in the succeeding orogenic phases. Each secondary geosyncline thus has its own tectonic style and orogenic phase, often influenced by a shifting of the stress-direction.

For all these reasons it is not surprising that a single prototype of an orogenic structure does not exist; each belt and each mountain chain has its own character. But on the other hand we can certainly discover particular tectonic styles, each determined by a particular combination of the factors mentioned above. The variation of combinations of different tectonic styles in one orogenic system results in the variety of characteristics of mountain chains which has been indicated.

The great African-European rift zone can also be seen as a result of a NS contraction in which the direction of the faults is largely determined by a conjugate set of tear-faults, and the dilatation in an EW direction is due to the NS contraction in a lower tier of the substratum.

The separation of the crust into horizontal layers, each representing a separate tier with its own mode of deformation, is repeated in the upper mantle. This is demonstrated by the greater frequency of deep-focus earthquakes on certain horizontal surfaces, and by the fact that in the island arc structures of the western Pacific margin, the main structural lines of the surface and of deeper horizons are shifted in relation to one another, and vary in shape though not in general outline.

All these considerations lead to the conclusion that there exists one fairly uniform and omnipresent stress-field, reaching many hundreds of kilometres down into the upper mantle. This stress-field has undoubtedly the property of contraction and we may suppose that it originates from a contraction of the core and lower mantle. This contraction may be due to further compaction of matter in this region of the globe, presumably accompanied by a growth of the core at the expense of the lower mantle.

List of References

ADAMS, F. D., An experimental contribution to the question of the depth of the zone of flow in the earth's crust. *Journ. of Geol.*, **20**, 97–118 (1912).
—— and J. A. BANCROFT, On the amount of internal friction developed in rocks during deformation and on the relative plasticity of different kinds of rocks. *Journ. of Geol.*, **25**, 592–97 (1917).
—— and J. T. NICHOLSON, An experimental investigation into the flow of marble. *Phil. Trans. R. Soc., London*, (A) **195**, 363–401 (1901).
AHRENS, L. H., Measuring geologic time by the strontium method. *Bull. Geol. Soc. Am.*, **60**, 218–66 (1949).
ANCION, CH., Etude géologique du Bassin houiller de Liége. La concession de Marihaye. *Ass. étude Pal. et strat. Houillères*, **3** (1948).
ANDERSON, E. M., The dynamics of Faulting. Oliver and Boyd, Edinburgh, 2nd ed. (1951).
—— and H. JEFFREYS, The dynamics of the formation of Cone-sheets, Ring-dykes, and Caldron-subsidence (A) with "Note on Fracture" (J). *Proc. R. Soc., Edin.*, **56** (2) 128–63 (1936).
APPALACHIAN GEOLOGICAL SOCIETY, In possible future petroleum provinces of North America, Appalachian region. *Bull. Am. Ass. Petr. Geol.*, **35**, 438–57 (1951).
APPLEBY, A. N., Joint patterns in highly folded and crystalline rocks of the New Jersey Highlands, etc. *Bull. Geol. Soc. Am.*, **51**, 1919 (1940).
ARBENZ, P., Probleme der Sedimentation und ihre Beziehungen zur Gebirgsbildung in den Alpen. *Heim-Festschr. Viertelj. Nat. f. Ges., Zürich*, **64** (1919).
ARGAND, E., Sur l'arc des Alpes occidentales. *Ecl. geol. Helv.*, **14**, 146–204 (1916).
——, La tectonique de l'Asie. *C.R. 13e Congr. géol. intern. Belgique*, (5) 171–372 (1922).
ASHAUER, H., Die östliche Endigung der Pyrenäen. *Gesell. Wiss. Göttingen, Math. phys. Kl., Abh.*, (3) **10**, 5–115 (1934).
AUBERT, D., Le Jura et la tectonique d'écoulement. *Bull. Lab. Géol. Univ. de Lausanne*, **83** (1945).

BACKLUND, H. G., On the stability of the earth's crust in Central Fennoscandia. *Fennia, Helsinki*, **50**, (25) 1–30 (1928).
——, Der "Magmaaufstieg" in Faltengebirgen. *C. R. Soc. Géol. Finl.*, **9** (1936).

——, Einblick in das geologische Geschehen des Präkambriums. *Geol. Rundschau*, 34, 2–6 (1943).

BAILEY, E. B., The geology of Ben Nevis and Glen Coe. *Mem. Geol. Survey of Scotland*, sheet 53 (1916).

——, Sedimentation in relation to tectonics. *Bull. Geol. Soc. Am.*, 47, 1713–26 (1936).

BALDRY, R. A., Slip planes and breccia zones in the Tertiary rocks of Peru. *Q. J. G. S.*, *London*, 94, 347–58 (1938).

BARAGWANATH, W., Ballarat. *Mem. Geol. Surv. Victoria*, 14, (1923).

BARRINGTON BROWN, CH., On a theory of gravitational sliding applied to the Tertiary of Ancon, Ecuador. *Q. J. G. S.*, *London*, 94, 359–70 (1938).

BARTRAM, J. G., Elk basin Oil and Gas field, in Typical American Oilfields, Vol. II. *Am. Ass. Petr. Geol.*, *Tulsa*, 577–88 (1929).

BEARTH, P., Ueber Gangmylonite der Silvretta. *Schweiz Min. Petr. Mitt.*, 13, 347–55 (1933).

BECKE, F., Über Mineralbestand und Struktur der kristallinen Schiefer. *Denkschr. Ak. Wiss.*, *Vienna*, 75 (1903).

BEHRMANN, R. B., Geologie und Lagerstätte des Oelfeldes Reitbrook bei Hamburg. *Erdöl. u. Tektonik in N.W. Deutschland*, 190–221 (1949).

BERTRAND, LÉON and L. MENGAUD, Sur l'existence de plusieurs nappes superposées dans la Cordillère Cantabrique entre Santander et Llanes. *C. R. Ac. Sci. Paris*, 155, 737 (1912).

BERTRAND, MARCEL, Structure des Alpes françaises et récurrence de certains facies sédimentaires. *C. R. Congr. géol. int.*, 161–77 (1897).

BILLINGS, M. P., Ring dikes and their origin. *Trans. N. Y. Ac. Sci.*, (2) 5 (6) 131–44 (1943), with literature references.

BIRCH, F., Elasticity and constitution of the Earth's interior. *J. Geophys. Res.*, 57, 227–86 (1952).

——, Earth's mantle. Elasticity and constitution. *Trans. Am. Geoph. Union*, 35, 75–85 (1953).

——, Elasticity and constitution of the earth. *Trans. Am. Geoph. Union*, 35, 79–85 (1954).

BÖKER, R., Die Mechanik der bleibenden Formänderungen in kristallinisch aufgebauten Körper. *Forsch. a. d. Geb. d. Ing. Wesen*, 175–6 (1915).

BÖRGER, H., Untersuchung der Tekt. Verhältnisse in der Umgebung von Ibbenbühren, etc. *Jahrb. Pr. G. Land. Anst.*, 49 (2), 801 (1928).

BORN, A., Über Druckschieferung im varistischen Gebirgskörper. *Fortschw. Geol. u. Pal.*, 7, 22 (1929).

BÖTTCHER, H., Die Bochumer Mulde der Karbonablagerung in der Gegend zwischen Dortmund und Bochum. Thesis, Bonn (1925). *cf.* also: Böttcher, *Glückauf* 61, 1145 (1925).

BOWEN, N. L., The Evolution of Igneous Rocks. Princeton University Press, Princeton, U.S.A. (1928).

BRILL, R., Die Tektonik an der Hauptrheintalverwerfung am Lorettoberg bei Freiburg i. Breisgau. *Geol. Rundsch.*, 23a (1933).

BROUWER, H. A., Geological expeditions to the lesser Sunda Islands, *Kon. Ak. v. Wetensch. N.-Holl.* Uitgev. Mij., Amsterdam (1942).

BROWN, R. W., Experiments relating to the results of horizontal shearing. *Bull. Am. Ass. Petr. Geol.*, **12**, 715 (1928a).

——, Experiments relating to factors causing localization of folds. *Bull. Am. Ass. Petr. Geol.*, **12**, 617–23 (1928b).

BROWN MONNET, V., Mississippian Marshall formation of Michigan. *Bull. Am. Ass. Petr. Geol.*, **32**, 629–88 (1948).

BRUYN, J. W. DE, Isogram maps of Caribbean Sea and surroundings, and of South-East Asia. Proc. 3rd World Petr. Congr., The Hague (1951).

BUCHER, W. H., Mechanical interpretation of joints. *Journ. of Geol.*, **28**, 707 and **29**, 1 (1920–21).

——, The deformation of the Earth's crust. Princeton University Press. Princeton, New Jersey (1933a).

——, Cryptovolcanic structures in the U. S. 16*th Inter. Geol. Congr.*, **2**, 1055–84 (1933b).

——, Geologic structures and orogenic history of Venezuela. *Geol. Soc. Am. Mem.* 49 (1952).

BULLARD, E. C., Gravity measurements in East Africa. *Phil. Trans. R. Soc.*, (A) **235**, 445 (1936).

BURGERS, W. G. and J. M., First report on viscosity and plasticity. *Verh. Kon. Ak. Wetensch.*, (1) **15** (3) 1–256 (1935).

BUXTORF, A., Geologische Beschreibung des Weissenstein-tunnels und seiner Umgebung. *Mat. crt. géol. Suisse*, **21** (1910).

——, Prognosen und Befunde beim Hauenstein-basis und Grenchenberg tunnel, und die Bedeutung der letzteren für die Geologie des Juragebirges. *Verh. Naturf. Ges. Basel*, **27** (1916).

CADELL, H. M., Experimental research in mountain-building. *Trans. R. Soc. Edinburgh*, **31**, 337–57 (1890).

CADISCH, J., Geologie der Schweizer Alpen. Wepf, Basel, 2nd ed. (1953).

CAHEN, L., Chronologie des terrains ante-Karroo de l'est du Basin de Congo. *Bull. Soc. Belge Géol.*, **60**, 97–113, 338–9 (1951).

——, Le Précambricum du Congo Belge et sa corrélation avec celui d'autres parties du monde. *Bull. Soc. Belge Géol.*, **62** (1953).

CARIBBEAN PETROLEUM COMPANY, Oilfields of Royal Dutch Shell group in Western Venezuela. *Bull. Am. Ass. Petr. Geol.*, **31**, 517–628 (1948).

CASTER, O. F., Coniaurum Mine. Struct. Geol. of Can. Ore Deposits. *Can. Inst. Min. Met., Montreal* (1948).

CASTERAS, M., Recherches sur la structure du versant Nord des Pyrénées centrales et orientales. *Bull. Serv. Crt. géol. France*, **36** (189) (1933).

CHOUBERT, G., Géologie du Maroc, 1 (1) Aperçu structural. *Monographes régionales* 19*th Congrès géol. Int.* (3) **6**, Histoire du domaine de l'Anti-Atlas, Rabat (1952).

CLOOS, E., Lineation. *Geol. Soc. Am. Mem.* 18 (1946).

——, Boudinage. *Trans. Am. Geoph. Union*, **28** (4) 626–32 (1947a).

——, Oolite deformation in the South Mountain-fold, Maryland. *Bull. Geol. Soc. Am.*, **58**, 843–918 (1947b).

—— and A. HIETANEN, Geology of the Marctic overthrust and the Glenarm series in Pennsylvania and Maryland. *Geol. Soc. Am.*, Sp. publ. 35 (1941).

—— and W. D. JOHNSTON, Structural history of the fracture systems of Grass Valley, California. *Econ. Geol.*, **29**, 39–54 (1934).

CLOOS, H., Tektonische Experimente und die Entstehung von Bruchlinien. *C. R. 15th Int. Geol. Congr. South Africa*, **2** (1929).

——, Künstliche Gebirge I & II. *Natur u. Mus.*, **5** (1929) **6** (1930).

——, Zur Experimentellen Tektonik I & II. *Die Naturwissenschaften*, **18** (34) 741–7, (1930); **19** (11) 1931.

——, Zur Mechanik grosser Brüche und Gräben. *Centr. bl. f. Min. etc.* (B) 273–86 (1932).

——, Einführung in die Geologie, 258–72. Borntraeger, Berlin (1936).

——, Hebung — Spaltung — Vulkanismus. *Geol. Rundsch. XXX.* (4a) (1939).

——, Gang und Gehwerk einer Falte. *Zeitschr. deutsch. Geol. Ges.*, **100**, 290–303 (1948).

COHEE, G. V., Cambrian and Ordovician rocks in Michigan basin and adjoining areas. *Bull. Am. Ass. Petr. Geol.*, **32**, 1417–48 (1948).

COOKE, H. C., The Canadian shield. *Geol. Surv. Can.* Econ. Geol. Ser. No. 1. 11–97 (1947).

CORNELIUS, H. P., Zur Auffassung der Ostalpen im Sinne der Deckenlehre *Zeitschr. Deutsch. Geol. Ges.*, **92**, (1940).

—— and M. FURLANI-CORNELIUS, Die Insubrische Linie vom Tessin bis zum Tonale pass. *Denkschr. Ak. Wiss. Math.-Naturw. Kl.*, **102** (1930).

COSIN, F., A propos du boudinage en Ardenne. *Soc. Belge. Géol.* **42**, 101–17 (1932).

CROSBY, W. O., The origin of parallel and intersecting joints. *Am. Geol.* **12**, 368–75 (1893).

DALY, R. A., Our mobile Earth. Charles Scribner's Sons, New York–London (1925).

——, Igneous rocks and the depths of the earth. McGraw-Hill Book Co. Inc., New York (1933).

——, Strength and structure of the earth. Prentice Hall, New York (1940).

DANA, JAMES, Geological results of the Earth's contraction in consequence of cooling. *Am. Journ. Sci.*, (2) **3**, 176–88 (1847).

DANA, J. D., On some results of the Earth's contraction on cooling. *Am. Journ. Sci.*, **5**, 423–43; **6**, 6–14, 104–15, 161–72 (1873).

DAPPLES, E. C., W. C. KRUMBEIN, and L. L. SLOSS, Tectonic control of lithologic associations. *Bull. Am. Ass. Petr. Geol.*, **32**, 1924–47 (1948).

DARTON, N. H., Some structural features of the Northern Coal Basin, Pennsylvania. *U. S. Geol. Surv.* Prof. Paper, 193 D (1940).

DAUBRÉE, A., Expériences tendant à uniter des formes diverses de ploiements, contournements et ruptures que présente l'écorce terrestre. *C. R. Ac. Sci.*, **86**, 733, 864, 928 (1878).

——, Etudes synthétiques de géologie expérimentale. Dunod, Paris (1879).

DAVID, T. W. E., The Geology of the Commonwealth of Australia. Arnold, London (1950).

DE BEAUMONT, ELIE, Notice sur les systèmes de montagnes. 3 vols, P. Bertrand, Paris (1852).

DEENEN, J. M., Breuken in kool en gesteente. *Med. Geol. Stichting, Heerlen,* (C. 1–2) 1 (1942).

DE JONG, J. D., On the structure of the preglacial Pleistocene of the Archemer- berg. Prov. of Overijsel, Netherlands. *Geol. en Mijnb.,* 14, 86–90 (1952).

DE SITTER, L. U., De begrippen plasticiteit en relaxatie. *Geol. en Mijnb.,* 16, 17–18 (1937).

——, Het verband tussen vervormingsproeven van gesteenten bij hoogen alzijdigen druk en tektoniek. *Geol. en Mijnb.,* n.s. 1, 233–9 (1939a).

——, Origin of oil in the Lower Oligocene of the Upper Rhine Valley, Pechelbronn field. *Geol. en Mijnb.,* 1, 221–30 (1939b).

——, Les porphyres luganois et leurs enveloppes, l'histoire géologique des Alpes tessinoises entre Lugano et Varese. *Leidse Geol. Med.,* 11, 1–61 (1939c).

——, The principle of concentric folding and the dependence of tectonic structure on original sedimentary structure. *Proc. Kon. Ak. Wetensch. Amsterdam,* 42, (5) 412–30 (1939d).

——, The Alpine geological history of the northern borders of the South Limburg coal district, Holland. *Med. Jaarversl. Geol. Bureau Heerlen,* 5–25 (1942).

——, De Keulsche Bocht en de horsten van de Peel en van Geldern-Crefeld. *Verh. Geol. Mijnb. Gen.,* 14 (1944–1945).

——, Antithesis Alps-Dinarides. *Geol. en Mijnbouw.* 9 (1), 1–13 (1947a).

——, Geophysical Survey of the South-east Netherlands, *Med. Geol. Stichting,* (C) 1–3 (1) (1947b).

——, Le style Nord-Pyrénéen dans les Alpes Bergamasques. *Soc. geol. France Bull.,* (5) 19, 617–21 (1949).

——, La tectonique d'écoulement dans les Alpes Bergamasques. *Geol. en Mijnb.,* 361–5 (1950).

——, Plissement croisé dans le Haut Atlas. *Geol. en Mijnb.,* 14, 277–82 (1952).

——, Essai de géologie structurale comparative de trois chaînes tertiaires, Alpes, Pyrénées et Haut-Atlas. *Bull. Soc. Belge de Géologie.* 63, (1) (1953).

——, La faille Nord-Pyrénéenne dans l'Ariège et la Haute Garonne. *Leidse Geol. Med.,* 18, 287–91 (1954).

——, Elastic or plastic buckling of the earth's crust. *Leidse Geol. Med.,* 20 (1955).

—— and C. M. DE SITTER-KOOMANS, Geology of the Bergamasc Alps. *Leidse Geol. Med.,* 14B, 1–257 (1949).

DESTOMBES, J. P., La couverture post-hercynienne du massif de l'Arize au pays de Serou (Ariège). *Bull. Soc. géol. France,* (3) 18, 327–40 (1948).

DIKKERS, A. J. and R. J. H. PATIJN, De Heerlerheide storing in het veld der Oranje Nassau mijnen. *Geol. en Mijnb.,* 6 N.S. (1944).

DINU, Y., Geol. Unters. der Beziehung zwischen Gesteinsspalten, etc. Pfälzer- wald. *Verh. Nat. Med. Ver., Heidelberg,* 11 (1912).

DIXIE, F. D., The Nyasa Rift Valley. *S. Afr., Geogr. Journal,* 23, 21 (1941).

————, Erosion and tectonics in the East African rift system. *Q. J. G. S.,* *London,* **102,** 339–79 (1946).

DOZY, J. J., Die Geologie der Catena Orobica zwischen Corno Stella und Pizo del Diavolo. *Leidse Geol. Med.,* **4,** 133–230 (1935).

DU TOIT, A. L., A geological comparison of South America with South Africa. *Carn. Inst. of Wash. Publ.,* **381,** 1–158 (1927).

————, Our wandering continents. Oliver and Boyd, Edinburgh (1937).

EARDLEY, A. J., Structure and Physiography of the southern Wasatch Mountains. *Papers Mich. Ac. Sc.,* **19** (1933).

————, Structural Geology of North America. Harper and Bros, New York (1951).

———— and M. G. WHITE, Flysch and Molasse. *Bull. Geol. Soc. Am.,* **38** (1947).

EBERT, A., Beiträge zur analytischen Tektonik etc. *Zeitschr. deutsche Geol. Ges.,* **75,** 46 (1923).

EDMUNDS, F. H., The Wealden district. British regional geology. *Geol. Survey,* London (1948).

ELLSWORTH, H. V., Rare element minerals of Canada. *Geol. Surv. Can.* Econ. Geol. Ser. No. 11, 105–6 (1932).

EMERY, W. B., Gas fields of Big Horn basin structural province, Wyoming and Montana. In Geology of Natural Gas, 277–96. *Am. Ass. Petr. Geol., Tulsa* (1935).

ENDE, K., Die Bildung von Schlechten und Bruchlagen in Steinkohlenflözen. *Glückauf,* **65,** 1635, 1693 (1929).

ENGSTLER, B., Geol. Untersuch. der Beziehung zwischen Gesteinspalten. etc. Östl. Mittelvogesen. *Verh. Nat. Med. Ver., Heidelberg,* **12** (1913).

ESCHER, B. G. and PH. H. KUENEN, Experiments in connection with saltdomes. *Leidse Geol. Med.,* **3,** 152–82 (1929).

ESKOLA, P., Ueber die Geologie Ostkareliens. *Geol. Rundschau,* **35** (2) 154–65 (1948).

ETZOLD, F., Die Braunkohlenformation Nordwest-sachsens. *Erl. geol. Sp. karte Königr. Sachsen, Leipzig,* **54** (1912).

EWING, M., Exploring the Mid-Atlantic Ridge. *Nat. Geogr. Mag.,* **94,** 275–94 (1948).

————, Seismic investigation in great ocean depths. *Ass. Oceanogr. Phys. Pr. Verb.,* **5,** 135–6 (1952).

————, Gravity anomalies and structure of the West Indies. *Bull. Geol. Soc. Am.* **65** (1954).

FAIRBAIRN, H. W., Structural Petrology of deformed rocks. Addison Wesley Cambridge, Mass. (1942).

FAIRBRIDGE, R. W., Possible causes of intraformational disturbances in the carboniferous varve rocks of Australia (with extensive bibliography). *Journ. & Proc. R. Soc. N. S. Wales,* **81,** 99–121 (1947).

————, Gravitational tectonics at Shorncliffe South-East Queensland. *Proc. R. Soc. Queensland,* **59,** 179–201 (1948).

FALLOT, P., Tectonique hercynienne et tectonique Alpine. *Bull. Soc. géol. France,* (5) **14** (1944).

————, Les chevauchements intercutanés de Roya. *Ann. Hébert et Hang.,* **7,** 161–9 (1949).

FATH, A. E., The origin of the faults, anticlines and buried "granite ridge" of the northern part of the Mid-Continent oil and gas field. *U. S. Geol. Survey*, Prof. Paper 128-A, 75–84 (1920).

FAVRE, A., Expériences sur les effets des refoulements ou écrasements latéraux en géologie. *Bibl. Univ. Genève Arch. des Sciences*, **66** (1878).

FELLOWS, R., Recrystallization and flowage in Appalachian quartzite. *Bull. Geol. Soc. Am.*, **54**, 1399–432 (1943).

FOLEY, L. L., The origin of the faults in Creek and Osage Counties, Oklahoma. *Bull. Am. Ass. Petr. Geol.*, **10**, 293 (1926).

FOURMARIER, P., Schistosité, foliation et microplissement. *Arch. des Sciences, Geneva*, **156**, 5–23 (1951).

——, Aperçu sur les déformations intimes des roches en terrains plissés. *Ann. Soc. Géol. Belg.*, **75**, 181–94 (1952).

——, Schistosité et phénomènes connexes dans les séries plissés. *Congr. géol. int. 19th sess.*, 3 (3), 117–31 (1953a).

——, Schistosité et grande tectonique. *Ann. Soc. Géol. Belg.*, **76**, 275–301 (1953b).

GÈZE, B., Etude géologique de la Montagne Noire et des Cévennes méridionales. *Soc. géol. France*, Mém. 62, 29 (1949).

GÈZE, B., L. U. DE SITTER, and R. TRÜMPY, Sur le sens du déversement des nappes de la Montagne Noire. *Bull. Soc. géol. France* (6) 2, 491–533 (1952).

GIGNOUX, M., La tectonique d'écoulement par gravité et la structure des Alpes. *Bull. Soc. Géol. France*, **18**, 739–61 (1948).

GILL, J. E., The Canadian Pre-Cambrian shield. Structural geology of Canadian ore deposits. *Can. Inst. Min. Met.* (1948).

——. Mountain building in the Precambrian shield. *Rep. 18th sess. Int. Geol. Congr.*, London, 1948, 13, 97–104 (1952).

GILLULY, J., Geology and ore deposits of the Stockton and Fairfield quadrangles, Utah. *U. S. Geol. Surv.* Prof. Pap. 173 (1932).

——, Distribution of mountain building in geologic time. *Bull. Geol. Soc. Am.*, **69**, 561–90 (1949).

GLAESSNER, M. F. and C. TEICHERT, Geosynclines: A fundamental concept in Geology. *Am. Journ. Science*, **245**, 463–82, 571–91 (1947).

GLANGEAUD, L., Le rôle des failles dans la structure du Jura externe. *Bull. Soc. Hist. Nat., Doubs*, **51**, 17 (1944).

——, Les caractères structuraux du Jura. *Bull. Soc. Géol.*, **5** (19) 669 (1949).

GOGUEL, J., Introduction à l'étude mécanique des déformations de l'écorce terrestre. *Mém. Carte géol. France*, 530 (1943).

——. Sur l'origine mécanique de la schistosité. *Bull. Soc. Géol. France*, (5) **15**. 519–22 (1945).

——, L'influence de l'échelle dans les phénomènes d'écoulement. *Geol. en Mijnb.* 12, 346–51 (1950).

——, Traité de Tectonique. Masson, Paris (1952).

GOLDSCHMIDT, V. M., Geochemische Verteilungsgesetze der Elemente. *Videnskaps Skr. Kristiania. Math. Nat. Kl.* (1924, 1925, 1926).

———, Geochemie. Handwörterbuch der Naturwissenschaften. Fischer, Jena, 2nd ed. (1933).

GORANSON, R. W., Flow in stressed solids; an interpretation. *Bull. Geol. Soc. Am.*, **51**, 1023–34 (1940).

GRABAU, A. W., The rhythm of the Ages. Henri Vetch, Peking (1940).

GREGORY, J. W., Rift Valleys and Geology of East Africa. Seeley, Service and Co., London (1921).

———, The Banda arc. *Geogr. Journ.*, **62** (1923).

GRIGGS, D., Deformation of rocks under high confining pressures. *Journ. of Geol.*, **44**, 541–77 (1936).

———, Deformation of single calcite crystals under high confining pressures. *Am. Mineral.*, **23**, 28–33 (1938).

———, Creep of rocks. *Journ. of Geol.*, **47** 225 (1939a).

———, A theory of mountain building. *Am. Journ. Sci.*, **237**, 611–50 (1939b).

———, Experimental flow of rocks under conditions favouring recrystallization. *Bull. Geol. Soc. Am.*, **51**, 1001–22 (1940).

———, Strength and plasticity. Handbook physical constants. *Geol. Soc. Am.*, Spec. Paper No. 36, 107–30 (1942).

——— and J. F. BELL, Experiments bearing on the orientation of quartz in deformed rocks. *Bull. Geol. Soc. Am.*, **49**, 1723–46 (1938).

GUTENBERG, B., Internal Constitution of the Earth. Dover Publications Inc., New York. 2nd ed. (1951).

——— and C. F. RICHTER, Seismicity of the Earth. *Geol. Soc. Am.*, Sp. Paper No. 34 (1941) and *Bull.*, **56**, 603–67 (1945).

——— and ———, Seismicity of the Earth and associated phenomena. Princeton University Press, Princeton (1949).

HAARMANN, E., Die Oscillationstheorie. Ferdinand Enke Verlag, Stuttgart (1930)

———, Um das geologische Weltbild. Ferdinand Enke Verlag, Stuttgart (1935)

HAAS, J. O. and C. R. HOFFMANN, Le gisement de calcaire asphaltique de Lobsann. *Bull. Serv. géol. Als.-Lorr.*, *Strassb.*, **1**, 277–301 (1928).

HALES, A. L., Convection currents in the Earth. *Geoph. suppl. Monthly Not. Astr. Soc.*, **3**, 372–79 (1936).

———, The thermal contraction theory of mountain building. *Geoph. suppl. Monthly Not. R. Astr. Soc.*, **6** (728) (1953).

HALL, A. L. and G. A. F. MOLENGRAAF, The Vredefort Mountainland in the Southern Transvaal and the Northern Orange Free State. *Verh. Kon. Ak. v. Wetensch.*, **24** (3) (1925).

HALL, J., On the vertical position and convolution of certain strata. *Trans. R. Soc. Edinburgh*, **7** (1813).

HALL, J., Natural History of New York, 3, Paleontology. Appleton, New York (1859).

HANNA, M. A., Geology of the Gulf Coast salt domes. Problems of Petr. Geology. *Am. Ass. Petr. Geol.*, *Tulsa*, 629–78 (1934).

HANZAWA, S., Geological history of the Riu-Kiu Islands. *Proc. Imp. Un., Tokyo*, **11** (1935).

HARRISON, J. V. and N. L. FALCON, Collapse structures. *Geol. Mag.*, **71**, 529–39 (1934).

—— and ——, Gravity collapse structures and mountain ranges as exemplified in south-western Iran. *Q. J. G. S., London,* **92,** 91–102 (1936).

Haug, E., Les géosynclinaux et les aires continentales. *Bull. Soc. Géol. France,* (3) **28,** 617–711 (1900).

Haughton, S., On slaty cleavage and the distortion of fossils. *Phil. Mag.,* **12,** 409–21 (1856).

Heim, A., Geologie der Schweiz (I) 613–23 (Jura wrench-faults), Leipzig (1919); (II) 1, 367–9 (Sax-Schwendi fault), Leipzig (1921).

Heiskanen, W., The gravity anomalies on the Japanese islands and in the waters east of them. *Pub. Isost. Inst. Int. Ass. Geodesy.* **13** (1945).

Herman, H., Structure of Bendigo Goldfield. *Bull. Geol. Survey, Victoria,* **47** (1923).

Hess, H. H., Gravity anomalies and island arc structure, with particular reference to the West Indies. *Proc. Am. Phil. Soc.,* **79,** 71–96 (1938).

——, Island arcs, gravity anomalies, and serpentinite intrusions. *17th Int. Geol. Congr., Moscow,* **2,** 263–83 (1939).

——, Appalachian Peridotite belt; its significance in sequence of events in mountain building (abstract). *Bull. Geol. Soc. Am.,* **51,** 1996 (1946).

——, Major structural features of the western North Pacific; an interpretation of H. O. 5485, bathymetric chart, Korea to New Guinea. *Bull. Geol. Soc. Am.,* **59** (5) 417–546 (1948).

——, Comment on Mountain Building. *Trans. Am. Geoph. Union,* **32,** 528–31 (1951).

Heybroek, P., The geology of the Dalskog Dals—Rostock region, Dalsland, Sweden, *Leidse Geol. Med.,* **16,** 55–195 (1950).

—— and J. Zwart, The overthrust between Teåkersjön and Marsjön, Dalsland. *Geol. För. Stockholm,* **71,** 425–34 (1949).

Hietanen, A., On the petrology of the Finnish quartzites. *Comm. géol. Finl. Bull.,* **122** (1938).

Hill, M. L. and T. W. Dibblee, Jr., San Andreas, Garlock, and Big Pine Faults, California. *Bull. Geol. Soc. Am.,* **64,** 443–58 (1953).

Hillenbrand, R., Kluftuntersuch. am Albrand von Ulm. Diss. Heidelberg (1934).

Hobbs, W. H., The asiatic arcs. *Bull. Geol. Soc. Am.,* **34** (1923).

——. Mountain growth, a study of the south-west Pacific region. *Proc. Am. Phil. Soc.,* **88** (1944).

Hollingworth, S. E., J. H. Taylor, and G. A. Kellaway, Large-scale superficial structures in the Northampton Ironstone Field. *Q. J. G. S., London,* **100,** 1–49 (1944).

Holmes, A., The sequence of the Pre-Cambrian orogenic belts in South and Central Africa. *C.R. 18th Int. Geol. Congr., London,* 1948 (1949).

—— and L. Cahen, African Geochronology. *Colonial Geol. and Min. Resources,* **5,** 3–38 (1955).

Holmquist, P. J., An interesting ladder-vein structure. *Geol. Fören. Stockholm,* **52,** 357–65 (1930).

528   LIST OF REFERENCES

———, On the relations of the boudinage structure. *Geol. Fören. Stockholm*,
        53, 193–208 (1931).
HOSPERS, J., Reversals of the main geomagnetic field. *Proc. Kon. Ak. Wetensch.
        Amsterdam*, (B), 56 (5) 57 (1953, 1954).
HOUWINK, R., Elasticity, plasticity and structure of matter. Cambridge
        University Press, Cambridge (1937).
HUBBERT, M. K., Scale models and geologic structures. *Bull. Geol. Soc. Am.*, 48,
        1459 (1937).
HULIN, C. D., Geology and ore deposits of the Randsburg Quadrangle (Garlock
        fault). *Bull. Cal. State Min. Bur.*, 95, 62 (1925).
HUMBLET, E., Le bassin houiller de Liége. *Revue Universelle des Mines* (8)
        17 (12) (1941).
HUNDT, R., Erdfalltektonik. Wilhelm Knapp, Halle (1950).
HUNT, C. B., Guidebook to the geology and geography of the Henry Mountain
        region, Utah. Guidebook to the geology of Utah, No. 1, Utah
        Geol. Soc. (1946).

IDE, J. M., The elastic properties of rocks; a correlation of theory and praxis.
        Proc. Nat. Ac. Sc., 32, 482–96 (1936).

JACOB, CH., Zone axiale, versant sud et versant nord des Pyrénées. *Soc. géol.
        France Bull.*, Livre jub., 389 (1930).
———, P. FALLOT, G. ASTRE, and R. CIRY, Observations tectoniques sur le
        versant méridional des Pyrénées centrales et orientales. 14e *Congr.
        géol. internat. Compte rendu*, 2, 235 (1927).
JEFFREYS, H., The Earth, Cambridge University Press, Cambridge, 2nd ed.
        (1929).
JOLY, J., Radioactivity and Geology. Constable, London (1909).
———, The surface history of the earth. Clarendon Press, Oxford (1925).
JONES, O. T., On the sliding and slumping of submarine sediments in Denbigh-
        shire, North Wales. *Q. J. G. S., London*, 93, 272–7 (1937).
———, The development of a geosyncline. *Q. J. G. S., London*, 94, IX–CX
        (1938).

KAISIN, F., Le problème tectonique de l'Ardenne. *Louvain Univ. Inst. géol.
        Mém.*, 11 (1936).
KAISIN, Jr, F., Le bassin houiller de Charleroi. *Louvain Univ. Inst. géol. Mém.*,
        15 (1947).
KAY, G. M., Development of the northern Alleghany synclinorium and adjoining
        regions. *Bull. Geol. Soc. Am.*, 53, 1601–58 (1942).
———, Geosynclinal nomenclature and the Craton. Geological note. *Bull.
        Am. Ass. Petr. Geol.*, 31, 1289–93 (1947).
———, North American geosynclines. *Geol. Soc. Am.*, Mem. 48 (1951).
KENNEDY, W. Q., Crustal layers and the origin of magmas. petrological aspects
        of the problem. *Bull. volcan.*, (2) 3 (1938).
———, The Great Glen fault. *Q. J. G. S., London*, 102, 41–76 (1946).
KEVERLING BUISMAN, A. S., Grondmechanica. Waltman, Delft (1940).

KING, PH. B., Tectonic framework of south-western United States. *Bull. Am. Ass. Petr. Geol.*, 34. 635–71 (1950).

KNOPF, E. B. and E. INGERSON, Structural petrology. *Geol. Soc. Am.*, Mem. 6 (1938).

KOBER, L., Der Bau der Erde. Borntraeger, Berlin. 2nd ed. (1928).

KONING, L. P. G., Over het mechanisme in de haard van diepe aardbevingen Diss. Amsterdam (1941)

———, Earthquakes in relation to their geographical distribution, depth, and magnitude. *Proc. Kon. Ak. Wetensch., Amsterdam* (B. 55) 60–70, 174–206, 263–92 (1952).

KÖPPEN. W., Über die Kräfte, welche die Kontinentverschiebungen und Polarwanderungen bewirken. *Geol. Rundschau,* 12, 314–20 (1922).

KOSSMAT, F., Das Erdbild und seine Veränderungen. Handb. der Experimental-physik 25/2. Akad. Verlagsgesellschaft, Leipzig, 1–66 (1931).

KRAUS, E., Die Baugeschichte der Alpen, 1 und 2. Akademie Verlag, Berlin (1951a).

———, Vergleichende Baugeschichte der Gebirge. Akademie Verlag, Berlin. (1951b).

KRUMBEIN. W. G., L. L. SLOSS, and E. C. DAPPLES, Sedimentary tectonics and sedimentary environments. *Bull. Am. Ass. Petr. Geol.*, 33, 1859–91 (1949).

KUENEN, PH. H., The Snellius Experiment. Geol. results (1) 5. Geological interpretation of the Bathymetrical results. Kemink en Zoon, Utrecht (1935).

———, The negative isostatic anomalies in the East Indies (with experiments). *Leidse Geol. Med.*, 8, 169–214 (1936).

———, Observations and experiments in ptygmatic folding. *C. R. Soc. Géol. Finl.*, (12) 11–28 (1938).

———, Slumping in the carboniferous rocks of Pembrokeshire. *Q. J. G. S., London,* 104. 365–85 (1949).

———, Slump structures in the Waitemata beds around Auckland. *Trans R. Soc. New Zealand*, 78, 467–75 (1950).

———, Significant features of graded bedding. *Bull. Am. Ass. Petr. Geol.,* 37, 1044–66 (1953).

——— and L. U. DE SITTER, Experimental investigation into the mechanism of folding. *Leidse Geol. Med.*, 10, 271–40 (1938).

——— and C. I. MIGLIORINI, Turbidity currents as a cause of graded bedding. *Journ. of Geol.*, 58, 91–127 (1950).

KUKUK, P., Geologie der Niederrheinisch-Westfälischen Steinkohlengebiete. Springer-Verlag, Berlin (1938).

KÜNDIG. E., Neue Gesichtspunkten in den Problemen der Tessiner Tektonik. *Ecl. geol. Helv.*, 27, 333–6 (1934).

LAHEE, F. H., Oil and Gas fields of the Mexia and Tehuancana fault zones, Texas. Typ. Am. Oilfields, Am. Ass. Petr. Geol., 1, 304, Tulsa (1929).

LAKE, PH., Island arcs and mountain building. *Geogr. Journ.,* 78 (1931).

LAWSON, H. C., Insular arcs, foredeeps and geosynclinal seas of the Asiatic coast. *Bull. Geol. Soc. Am.,* 43 (1932).

LEES, G. M., Persia. Science of Petroleum, 6, 73–82, Oxford University Press, London (1953).

LEHMANN, H., Die Gesteinsklüfte des östl. Harzvorlandes. *Geol. Arch.*, 1 (1923).

LEIDSE GEOLOGISCHE MEDEDELINGEN, "Pyrénées centrales" with articles by H. J. Zwart, L. U. de Sitter, and others, 18, (1954).

LEMKE, L., Der tektonische Bau des Gebietes zwischen Vogelsberg und Rhön. *Geotekt. Forsch.*, 1 (1937).

LEMOINE, P., Considérations sur la structure d'ensemble du bassin de Paris. Livre Jub. 1830–1930. *Soc. géol. France*, 2, 481–98 (1930).

LEUCHS, K., Ueber Breccien. *Geol. Rundschau*, 24, 273–81 (1933).

LIND, J. G., Geol. Unters. der Beziehung zwischen Gesteinspalten etc. bei Heidelberg. *Verh. Nat. Med. ver.*, *Heidelberg*, 9 (1910).

LINK, T. A., The origin and significance of epi-anticlinal faults as revealed by experiments. *Bull. Am. Ass. Petr. Geol.*, 11, 853–66 (1927).

——, Interpretations of foothills structures, Alberta. *Bull. Am. Ass. Petr. Geol.*, 33, 1175–501 (1949).

LOHEST, M., De l'origine des veines et des géodes des terrains primaires de Belgique. *Ann. Soc. Géol. Belgique*, 36 B, 275–82 (1909).

——, Expériences de tectonique. *Ann. Soc. Géol. Belgique*, 39, Mem. (1913).

LOMBARD, A. E., Appalachian and Alpine structures—a comparative study. *Bull. Am. Ass. Petr. Geol.*, 32, 709–44 (1948).

——, Rythmes sédimentaires et cyclothèmes dans le cadre de la sédimentation générale. *C. R. 3e Congr. Strat. Carb., Heerlen*, 415–21 (1951).

——, Les rythmes sédimentaires et la sédimentation générale. *Rev. Inst. Français Pétrole*, 8, 9–45 (1953).

LONGWELL, C. R., How old is the Colorado River? *Am. J. Sci.*, 244, 817–35 (1946).

LOTZE, FR., Zur Erklärung der Tekt. Klüfte. *Cent. bl. f. Min. usw.*, B, 193 (1933).

——, Das Problem der "saxonischen Faltung". *Geotekt. Forsch.*, 3, 73–84 (1938).

——, Einige Probleme der Osningtektonik. *Geotekt. Forsch.*, 9/10, 7–17 (1953).

LOVERING, T. S., The fracturing of incompetent beds. *Journ. of Geol.*, 36, 709 (1928).

LUGEON, M. and E. GAGNEBIN, Observations et vues nouvelles sur la géologie des Préalpes romandes. *Univ. Lausanne Lab. géol. Bull.*, 72 (1941).

MACGREGOR, A. M., Some milestones in the Pre-Cambrian of Southern Rhodesia. *Trans. and Proc. Geol. Soc. S. Africa*, 54, xxvii (1951).

MACGREGOR, M. and A. G., The Midland Valley of Scotland. British Regional Geology. Geological Survey and Museum, London, 73 (1948).

MAGNUSSON, N., Die Granitisationstheorie und deren Anwendung für Svionische Granite und Gneise Mittelschwedens. *Geol. För. Förh.*, 59, 525–47 (1937).

——, Die Genesis der svionischen Granite. *Geol. För. Förh.*, 60 (2) 285–316 (1938).

—— and P. GEYER, De mellansvenska järnmalmernas Geologi. *Sv. Geol. Unders.*, Avh. ser. Ca. No. 35 (1944).

—— and E. GRANLUND, Sveriges geologi. P. A. Norstedt, Stockholm (1936).

MALARODA, R., Revisione e aggiornamento della sistematica della tettoniti a deformazione post-cristallina. *Rendic. Soc. Min. It., Ann. III, 3,* 1–24, with exhaustive literature on mylonites (1946).

——, Studi petrografici nell'Adamello nord-orientale. *Mem. 1st. Geol. Univ. Padova,* 16, 1–111 (1948).

MARTINI, H. J., Groszschollen und Graben zwischen Habichtswald und Rheinischen Schiefergebirge. *Geotekt. Forsch.,* 1 (1937).

MASON, B., Polymorphism and orogeny. *Trans. Am. Geoph. Union,* 34, 921–3 (1953).

MAYO, E. B., Deformation in the interval Mount Lyell—Mount Whitney, California. *Bull. Geol. Soc. Am.,* 52, 1001–84 (1941).

MEAD, W. J., Notes on the mechanics of geologic structures. *Journ. of Geol.,* 28, 505–23 (1920).

MELTON, F. A., A reconnaissance of the joint systems in the Ouachita Mountains and central plains of Oklahoma. *Journ. of Geol.,* 37/8, 729–46 (1929).

MENGAUD, L., Recherches géologiques dans la région Cantabrique. Thèse. Paris, 370 (1920).

——, Sur la structure de la chaîne Cantabrique. *C. R. Ac. Sci., Paris.* 195. 1092 (1932).

——, Etudes géologiques dans la région de Gavarnie et du Mont Perdu. *Service Carte géol. France,* Bull., 199, 197–223 (1939).

MERLA, G., Geologia dell'Appennino settentrionale. *Soc. geol. Italiana Boll.,* 70, 95–382 (1951).

MIGLIORINI, C. I., Considerazioni su di particolare effetto dell'orogenesi. *Soc. geol. Italiana Boll.,* 52, 293–304 (1933).

——, Alcune questioni geologiche casentinesi. M. Ricci, Firenze (1936).

——, I cunei composti nell' orogenesi. *Soc. geol. Ital. Bol.,* 67, 31–142 (1948).

——, Sedimentazione delle brecciole calcarese e del Macigno. *Att. Soc. Toscana Sci. Nat Mem.,* (A) 56 (1949).

MILCH, L., Ueber dynamometamorphen Erscheinungen an einem nordischen Granitgneiss. *N. Jahr. f. Min.,* 2, 39–51 (1900).

MILLER, R. L. and J. O. FULLER, Geology and oil resources of the Rose Hill district — the Fenster area of the Cumberland overthrust, Lee County, Virginia. *Virginia Geol. Survey Bull.,* (71) (1955).

MISCH, P., Der Bau der mittleren Südpyrenäen. *Gesell. Wiss. Göttingen, Math.-phys. Kl., Abh..* (3) 12 (1934).

MOHR, O., Abhandlungen aus dem Gebiete der technischen Mechanik. W. Ernst & Sohn, Berlin, 2nd ed. (1914).

MONOD, TH., Sur quelques accidents circulaires du Sahara occidental. *19th Inter. Geol. Congr.,* 20, 85–93 (1954).

MOORE, R. C., Late Paleozoic Cyclic sedimentation in Central United States. *18th Int. Geol. Congr.* (4) 5–16 (1950).

MULLER, J. E., De post-carbonische tektoniek van het Z. Limburgse mijngebied, with English summary (4 p.). *Meded. Geol. Stichting,* (C) (I-1-No. 2) 1–32 (1945).

MURRAY, H. W., Profiles of the Aleutian trench. *Bull. Geol. Soc. Am.,* 56, 757–81 (1945).

NABHOLZ, W. K., Das mechanische Verkalten der granitischen Kernkörper der tiefen penninischen Decken bei der Alpinen Orogenese. *C. R. Congr. int. géol. Alger.* (3) **3**, 9–23 (1953).

NADAI, A., Plasticity. McGraw-Hill Book Co. Inc., New York (1931).

NATLAND, M. L. and PH. H. KUENEN, Sedimentary history of the Ventura basin, California. *Soc. Econ. Paleont. Min.*, Sp. Publ. no. 2, 76–107 (1951).

NEHM, W., Bewegungsvorgänge bei der Aufrichtung des Rheinisch-Westfälischen Steinkohlengebietes. *Glückauf*, **66**, 789 (1930).

NETTLETON, L. L., Recent experimental and geophysical evidence of mechanics of salt dome formation. *Bull. Am. Ass. Petr. Geol.*, **27**, 51–63 (1943).

NIGGLI, E., Zur Stereometrie und Entstehung der Aplit- Granit- und Pegmatitgänge im Gebiete von Sept-Laux (Belledonne massiv S.L.). *Leidse Geol. Med.*, **17**, 215–36 (1953).

NOBLE, L. F., The San Andreas rift and some other active faults in the desert region of south-eastern California. Carnegie Inst. Wash. Year Book 25, 415–28 (1926).

NOLAN, T. B., The Basin and Range province in Utah, Nevada and California., *U. S. Geol. Surv.* Prof. Paper 197 D, 141–96 (1943).

NORTON, W. M., A classification of breccias. *Journ. of Geol.*, **25**, 160 (1917).

OBERHOLZER, J., Geologie der Glarneralpen. *Beitr. geol. Karte Schweiz, neue Folge*, **28** (1933).

OBERSTE-BRINK, K. and K. HEINE, Klüfte und Schlechten in ihren Beziehungen zum geol. Aufbau des Ruhrkohlenbeckens. *Glückauf*, **70**, 102 (1934).

OFTEDAHL, C., Cauldron subsidence of the Oslo region. *Int. Geol. Congr. 18th Sess. London*, Part XIII (1952).

——, Studies in the igneous rock complex of the Oslo region. The Cauldrons. *Skrifter Norske Vidensk. Ak. Oslo I. Math. Naturw. Kl.*, No. 3 (1953).

OTUKA, Y., The geomorphology and geology of northern Idu peninsula, the earthquake figure of Nov. 26, 1930, and the Pre- and Post-seismic crust deformations. *Bull. Earthq. Res. Inst., Tokyo*, **11**, 530 (1933).

OULIANOFF, N., Infrastructure des Alpes et tremblement de terre du 25 janvier 1946. *Bull. Soc. Géol. France*, (5) **17** (1947).

OVEREEM, A. J. A., A section through the Dalformation. Thesis. Leiden (1948).

PARKER, J. M., Regional jointing systematic in slightly deformed sedimentary rocks. *Bull. Geol. Soc. Am.*, **53**, 381 (1942).

PEKERIS, C. L., Thermal convection in the interior of the earth. *Monthly Geoph. suppl. Not. R. Astr. Soc.*, **3**, 343–67 (1935).

PFANNENSTIEL, M., Vergleichende Unters. der Grund- und Deckgebirgsklüfte im Südl. Odenwald. *Ber. Naturf. Ges. Freiburg i. Breisgau*, **27**, 181–278 (1927).

PHILIPS, D. W., Contribution to the symposium on rock pressure. *Geol. en Mijnb.*, n.s. **10**, 216–39 (1948).

PINCUS, H. J., Statistical methods applied to the study of rock fractures. *Bull. Geol. Soc. Am.*, **62**, 81–130 (1951).

PRUVOST, P., Sédimentation et subsidence. *Soc. géol. France*. Livre jubilaire, 545–64 (1930).

————, Bassin houiller de a Sarre et de la Lorraine III. Description géologique. *Serv. Carte géol. Als. Lorr. Strassbourg* (1934).

QUENSEL, P., Zur Kenntniss der Mylonitbildung, erläutert an Material aus dem Kebnekaise Gebiet. *Bull. Geol. Ins:. Uppsala*, 15, 91–116 (1916).

RAAF, J. F. M., Rumania, in Science of Petroleum 6: The World's Oilfields, Part I. The Eastern Hemisphere 9–17 (1953).

RAGUIN, E., Contribution à l'étude des gneiss des Pyrénées. *Bull. Soc. Géol. France*, (5) 8 (1938).

RANKAMA, K. and TH. G. SAHAMA, Geochemistry University of Chicago Press, Chicago (1949).

READ, H. H., A note on ptygmatic folding in the Sutherland granite complex. *Summ. Progress. Geol. Survey for* 1927. Part II. 72 (1928).

REED. R. D., Geology of California. Am. Ass. Petr. Geologists, Tulsa (1933).

————, California's record in the Geologic history of the World. Dept. Nat. Resources. Bull. No. 118, 99–118 (1943).

———— and J. S. HOLLISTER, Structural evolution of Southern California. *Bull. Am. Ass. Petr. Geol.*, 20 (12) 1529–1721 (1936).

REEVES, FRANK. Geology and possible oil and gas resources of the faulted area south of the Bearpaw Mountains, Montana. *U. S. Geol. Survey Bull.* 751-C., 71–114 (1924).

————, Origin and mechanics of thrust faults adjacent to the Bearpaw Mountains, Montana. *Geol. Soc. America Bull.*, 57 1033–47 (1946).

REYNOLDS, S. H., Breccias. *Geol. Mag.*, 65. 97–108 (1928).

REID, J. A.. The California earthquake of April 18, 1906. *Rep. State Earthq. Inv. Comm.* State of California, 2: The mechanics of earthquakes.

RICH. J. L., Flow markings, groovings and intrastratal crumpling as criteria for recognition of slope deposits, with illustrations from Silurian rocks of Wales. *Bull. Am. Ass. Petr. Geol.*, 34, 717–41 (1950).

RICHEY, J. E., The dykes of Scotland. *Trans. Edin. Geol. Soc.*. 13 (4) 393 (1939).

RIEDEL, W., Zur Mechanik Geologischer Brucherscheinungen. *Centr. bl. Min. etc. Abt. B.*, 354–68 (1929).

RODGERS, J., Mechanics of Appalachian folding as illustrated by Sesquatchie anticline, Tennessee and Alabama. *Bull. Am. Ass. Petr. Geol.*, 34 672–81 (1950).

————, Absolute ages of radioactive minerals from the Appalachian region. *Am. J. of Science*, 250, 411–27 (1952).

————, Geologic map of East Tennessee with explanatory text. *Bull.* 58, Div. of Geology, State of Tennessee (1953a).

————, The folds and faults of the Appalachian Valley and Ridge province. *Kent. Geol. Survey, Sp. Publ.* No. 1, 150–66 (1953b).

ROEHRER, F., Geol. Unters. der Bez. etc. Nord Schwarzwald. Jahrb. d. Ober-rhein. *Naturw. ver. T. I.*, 2, 1922 (1916).

ROLL, A., Die strukturelle Entwicklung und die Geschichte der Salzstock-bildung im Hannoverischen Becken, in *Erdöl u. Tektonik in N.W. Deutschland*, 69–90 (1949).

RUNCORN, S. K., The earth's core. *Trans. Am. Geoph. Union*, 35, 49–63 (1954).

Russwurm, P., Braunkohlenformation und glaziale Lagerungstörung im Felde
    der Grube Merkur bei Drebkau. *Zeitschr. f. prak. Geol.*, 17, 87–102
    (1909).
Rutsch, F. R., Die Bedeutung der Fossil-deformation. *Bull. Ass. Suisse.
    géol. petr.*, 15 (49) with extensive literature (1948).
Rutten, L. M. R., Frequency and periodicity of orogenic movements. *Bull.
    Geol. Soc. Am.*, 60. 1755–70 (1949)
Rutten, M. G., Enkele gegevens over de helling van de Feldbiss. *Geol. en
    Mijnb.*, 5 N.S., 91–2 (1943).

Salomon, W., Die Bedeutung der Messung und Kartierung von gemeinen
    Klüften und Harnischen, mit besonderer Berücksichtigung des
    Rheintal-Grabens. *Zeitschr. der Deutsche Geol. Ges.*, 63, 496–521
    (1911).
——, Beobachtungen über Harnische. *Sitzungs. Ber. Heidelb. Ak. Wiss.
    Math-Naturw. Kl.*, (A) 1925, 4, 21 (1925).
——, Neue Kluft- und Harnischmessungen im südl. Odenwald. *Ber. Naturf.
    Ges. Freiburg i. Breisgau*, 27, 173–80 (1927).
Sampelayo, P. H., Discusión de algunos puntos de la Hoja geológica de Llanes
    (Asturias). *Notas y Comm. Inst. Geol. y Min Esp.*, 1 (1) (1928).
Sander, B., Gefügekunde der Gesteine. Springer Verlag, Vienna (1930).
——, Einführung in die Gefügekunde der geologischen Körper. I & II.
    Springer Verlag, Vienna (1950).
Sax, H. G., De tektoniek van het Carboon in het Zuid Limburgsch Mijngebied
    (with abridged English translation: The tectonics of the South
    Limburg Coalfield). *Med. Geol. Stichting* (C I-1) (3) (1946).
Schardt, H., Etudes sur le Pays d'Enhaut. *Bull. Soc. vand. des Sci. nat.*, 20,
    143–6 (1884).
Schlüter, H., Das Ölfeld Steimbke-Rodewald und die struktur Anderten-
    Lichtenhorst. *Erdöl und Tektonik in N.W. Deutschland*, 230–41
    (1949).
Schmidt, W., Tektonik und Verformungslehre. Borntraeger, Berlin (1932).
——, Festigkeit und Verfestigung von Steinsalz. *Zeitschr. f. angew. Min.*,
    1, 1 (1937).
Schnaebele, R., Carte structurale de la partie Nord du champ petrolifère de
    Pechelbronn. *C. R. 2e Congr. Mond. Pétr., Paris*, 1, 439–41 (1937).
Schneegans, D., La géologie des nappes de l'Ubaye-Embrunais entre la
    Durance et l'Ubaye. *Mem., Carte géol. de France* (1938).
Schuchert, C., Sites and nature of North American Geosynclines. *Bull. Geol.
    Soc. Am.*, 34, 151–230 (1925).
Schuppli, H. M., Erdölgeologische Untersuchungen in der Schweiz, 4. *Beiträge
    zur Geologie der Schweiz* (26) 4 (1952).
Schweizer Geologische Gesellschaft, Basel, Geologischer Führer der
    Schweiz, 1–14 (1934).
Schwinner, R., Vulkanismus und Gebirgsbildung. Ein Versuch. *Zeitschr.
    Vulk.*, 5, 175–230 (1919).
——, Scherung der Zentralbegriff der Tektonik. *Centr. bl. f. Min. usw.*,
    469–79 (1924).

SEDERHOLM, J. J., Ueber ptygmatische Faltungen. *N. Jahrb. f. Min. etc. Beilage Band* 36, 491–512 (1913).

——, On the geology of Fennoscandia. *Bull. Com. géol. Finl.*, 98, 5–30 (1932).

SELZER, G., Geologie der südpyrenäischen Sierren in Oberaragonien. *Neues Jahrb., Beilage-Band* 71, (B) 370–406 (1934).

SHACKLETON, R. M., The Tectonic Significance of Alkaline Igneous Activity, in *The Tectonic control of igneous activity.* Dept. of Geology, Univ. of Leeds (1954).

SHAND, J., The pseudotachylyte of Parijs (Orange Free State). *Q. J. G. S., London,* 72, 198–221 (1916).

SHAND, S. J., Rift valley impressions. *Geol. Mag.,* 123, 307 (1936).

SHARP, R. P., Basin-range structure of the Ruby East Humboldt Range, north-eastern Nevada. *Bull. Geol. Soc. Am.,* 50 (6) 881–915 (1939).

SHARPE, D., On slaty cleavage. *Q. J. G. S., London,* 5, 111–29 (1849).

SHELBY, T. H. Jr., Talco Field, in *Occurrence of oil and gas in N.E. Texas.* Univ. of Texas publ. No. 5116, 372–8 (1951).

SHELDON, P. G., Some observations and experiments on joint-planes. *Journ. of Geol.,* 20, 53 and 164 (1912).

SHERRILL, R. E., Origin of the en échelon faults in north central Oklahoma. *Bull. Am. Ass. Petr. Geol.,* 13, 31–7 (1929).

SHREVEPORT GEOLOGICAL SOCIETY, Reference report on certain Oil and Gas Fields of North Louisiana, South Arkansas, Mississippi, and Alabama, 1 and 2 (1945).

SLATER, G., On studies in drift deposits of south-west Suffolk. *Proc. Geol. Ass.,* 38, 157–216 (1927a).

——, Structure of the Mud Buttes and Tit Hills in Alberta. *Bull. Geol. Soc. Am.,* 38, 721–30 (1927b).

SMITH, K. G., Structure plan of clastic dikes. *Trans. Am. Geoph. Union,* 33/6 (1952).

SMITH, W. K., Quitman Field, in *Occurrence of oil and gas in N.E. Texas.* Univ. of Texas publ. No. 5116, 315–9 (1951).

SMOLUCHOWSKI. M., Ueber ein gewisses Stabilitätsproblem der Elastizitätslehre. *Anzeiger Ak. Wiss. Krakau Math. Phys. Kl.* (1909).

SOLLAS, W. J., The figure of the earth. *Q. J. G. S.. London,* 59, 180–8 (1903).

SORBY, H. C., On the theory of slaty cleavage. *Philos. Mag.,* 12. 127–9 (1856).

STAUB, R., Petrographische Untersuchungen im Westlichen Berninagebirge. *Vierteljahrschr. Naturf. Ges. Zürich,* 55–336 (1915).

——, Der Bau der Alpen. Versuch einer Synthese. *Beitr. Geol. Karte der Schweiz. N.F.* No. 52. Bern (1924).

——, Der Bewegungsmechanismus der Erde. Borntraeger, Berlin (1928).

STEINMANN, G., Alpen und Appennin. *Deutsche geol. Gesell. Monatsber.* 8/9 (1907).

STIELER, C., Ein Beitrag zum Kapitel "Klüfte" *Centr. bl. f. Min. usw.,* 664 and 703 (1922).

STILLE, H., Grundfragen der vergleichenden Tektonik. Borntraeger, Berlin (1924a).

——, Die Osning-Ueberschiebung, *Abh. Pr. geol. L-Anstalt, N.F.,* 95, 32–56 (1924b).

——, Die Entwickelung des amerikanischen Kordilleras systems in Zeit und Raum. *Sitz. ber. Preuss. Ak. Wiss.*, **15**, 134–55 (1936).

——, Einführung in den Bau Amerikas. Borntraeger, Berlin (1941).

STOCKWELL, C. H. and J. M. HARRISON, Structural control of ore deposits in Northern Manitoba. Struct. Geol. of Can. Ore Deposits. *Can. Inst. Min. Met., Montreal*, 284–91 (1948).

STOLZ, H. P., Long Beach Oilfield. *Bull.* 118. Dept. Nat. Resources. State Div. of Mines, 320–4 (1943).

SUESS, ED., Das Antlitz der Erde. Tempsky, Vienna (1909).

SWANSON, C. O., Notes on stress, strain, and joints. *Journ. of Geol.*, **35**, 193–223 (1927).

TABER, S., Fault troughs. *Journ. of Geol.*, **35**, 557–606 (1927).

TALIAFERRO, N. L., Geological history and structure of the Central Coast Ranges of California. *Bull. State Div. Mines Dept. Nat. Resources Bull.*, 118, 119–62 (1943a).

——, Franciscan —Knoxville problem. *Bull. Am. Ass. Petr. Geol.*, **27**, 109–219 (1943b).

TAYLOR, F. B., The lateral migration of land masses. *Proc. Wash. Acad. of Science*, **13** (29) 445–7 (1923).

TEALE, E. O., Provisional Geological map of Tanganyika. *Bulletin* No. 6, Dept. of Lands & Mines, Tanganyika (1936).

TERADA, T. and N. MYIABE, Experimental investigation on the mechanism of formation of step faults. *Bull. Earthq. Res. Inst., Tokyo*, **6**, 33 (1928).

—— and ——, Experimental investigation of the deformation of sand mass. *Bull. Earthq. Res. Inst., Tokyo*, **7**, 65–93 (1929).

TERCIER, J., Depots marins actuels et séries géologiques. *Ecl. géol. Helv.*, **32**, 47–100 (1940).

——, Le problème de l'origine des Préalpes. *Bull. Soc. Frib. Sc. nat.*, **37**, 125–40 (1945).

——, Le Flysch dans la sédimentation alpine. *Ecl. géol. Helv.*, **40**, 164–98 (1948).

THOMAS, D. E., Notes on the Chewton gold field. *Min. Geol. Journ. Victoria*, **2**, 11, 91, and 219 (1939–1941).

TILLEY, C. E., The dunite mylonites of St Paul's rocks (Atlantic). *Am. Journ. Sci.*, **245**, 483–91 (1947).

TOKUDA, S., On the échelon structure of the Japanese archipelagoes. *Jap. J. Geol. Geogr.*, **5**, 41–76 (1927).

TÖRNEBOHM, A. E., Grunddragen av det centrala skandinaviens byggnad. *K. Sv. Ventensk. Ak. Handl.*, **28**, (5) (1896).

TREVISAN, L., Il Gruppo di Brenta. *Mem. Ist. Geol. R. Univ. Padova*, **13**, 1–128 (1939).

——, L'Elba orientale e la sua tettonica di scivolamento per gravita. *Padua Univ. Inst. geol. Mem.*, **16**, 1–40 (1950).

TURNER, F. J., Mineralogical and structural evolution of the metamorphic rocks. *Geol. Soc. Am.*, Mem. 30 (1948).

—— and J. VERHOOGEN, Igneous and Metamorphic Petrology. McGraw-Hill Book Co. Inc., New York (1951).

TYRREL, G. W., Flood basalts and fissure eruptions. *Bull. volc.*, (2) 1, 89–111 (1937).

UMBGROVE, J. H. F., Geological history of the East Indies. *Bull. Am. Ass. Petr. Geol.*, 22, 1–70 (1938).
——, Different types of island arcs in the Pacific. *Geogr. Journ.*, 106 (5–6) 198–209 (1945).
——, The Pulse of the Earth. Nijhoff, The Hague, 2nd ed. (1947).
——, Structural History of the East Indies. Cambridge University Press, Cambridge (1949).
UREY, H. C., The Planets. Yale University Press, New Haven (1952).

VAN BEMMELEN, R. W., De Undatie theorie, hare afleiding en toepassing op het westelijk deel van de Soenda boog. *Nat. Tijdschr. v. Ned. Indië*, 92 (1) 85–242 (1932).
——, Ein Beispiel für Sekundärtektogenese auf Java. *Geol. Rundschau* (25) 175–94 (1934).
——, The Undation theory on the development of the earth's crust. *Proc. 16th Int. Geol. Congr. Washington*, 2, 965–82 (1935).
——, Examples of gravitational tectogenesis from central Java. *De Ing. in Ned. Indië*, 4, 55–65 (1937).
——, The geology of Indonesia, vol. IA. Govt. Printing Office, The Hague (1949).
——, On the origin of the Pacific magma types in the volcanic inner-arc of the Soenda mountain system. *De Ing.· Ned. Indië*, 5 (4) Mijnb. en Geol., 1–14 (1938a).
——, The distribution of the regional isostatic anomalies in the Malayan Archipelago. *De Ing. Ned. Indië.*, 5 (4) Mijnb. en Geol., 61–7 (1938b).
VAN DER FLIERT, J. R., Tectonique d'écoulement et Trias diapir au Chettaaba, sud-ouest de Constantine (Algérie): 19e *Cong. Géol. Internat.* (1952) Compte rendue, (3) 3, 63–80 (1953).
VAN WATERSCHOOT V. D. GRACHT, W. A., Theory of continental drift; a symposium in the origin and the movement of land masses both intercontinental and intracontinental. Am. Ass. Petr. Geol., Tulsa (1928).
VAYRYNEN, H., Ueber die Stratigraphie der Karelischen Formationen. *Bull. Comm. Géol. Finlande*, 101 (1933).
VENING MEINESZ, F. A., Gravity expeditions at sea 1923–1932, 2, 47–51. Netherlands Geodetic Commission (1934).
——, The earth's crust deformation in the East Indies. *Proc. Kon. Ak. v. Wetensch.,· Amsterdam*, 43, 278–93 (1940).
——, De verdeeling van continenten en oceanen over het aardoppervlak. *Versl. Kon. Ak. Wet., Amsterdam*, 53 (4) (1944).
——, A third arc in many Island Arc Areas. *Proc. Kon. Ak. v. Wetensch., Amsterdam*, 54 (5) 433–42 (1951).
——, Convection-currents in the earth and the origin of the continents, 1. *Proc. Kon. Ak. v. Wetensch., Amsterdam* (B), 55 (5) 527–54 (1952).

VERHOOGEN, J., Petrological evidence on temperature distribution in the mantle of the earth. *Trans. Am. Geoph. Union*, **35**, 85–92 (1954).

VERSTEEG, K., Jointing in the central coal beds of Ohio. *Econ. Geol.*, **37**. 305 (1942).

VISSER, S. W., Aardbevingen met zeer diepe haard. *Tydschrift Kon. Nederl Aardr. Gen.*, **54**, 313–35 (1937).

——, Seismic isobaths in the East Indian Archipelago. *Gerl. Beitr. Geoph.*, **53**, 389–91 (1938).

VOELCKER, ILSE, Vergleichende Unters. der Grund- und Deckgebirgsklüfte im Südl. Odenwald. *Jahrber. d. Oberrh. Geol. Ver.*, N.F. **17**, 54–96 (1927).

VON BUBNOFF, S., Grundproblemen der Geologie. Borntraeger, Berlin (1931).

——, Fennosarmatia. Akademie Verlag, Berlin (1952).

VON KÁRMÁN, TH., Festigkeitsversuche unter allseitigem Druck. *Zeitschr. Ver. deutsch. Ing.* **55**, 1749–57 (1911).

WADATI, K., On the activity of deep-focus earthquakes in the Japanese islands. *Geoph. Mag., Tokyo*, **8**, 305–25 (1934).

WAGER, L. R., Jointing in the Great Scar Limestone of Craven and its relation to the Tectonics of the Area. *Q. J. G. S., London*, **87**, 392–420 (1931).

——, The stratigraphy and tectonics of Knud Rasmussens Land and the Kangerdlugssuag region. *Med. om Grønland*, **134** (5) 1–62 (1947).

—— and W. A. DEER, A dyke swarm and crustal flexure in East Greenland. *Geol. Mag.*, **75**, 39–46 (1938).

WALLACE, R. E., Structure of a portion of the San Andreas Rift in Southern California. *Bull. Geol. Soc. Am.*, **60**, 781–806 (1949).

WALLS. R., A new record of boudinage structure from Scotland. *Geol. Mag.*, **74**, 325–32 (1937).

WANLESS. H. R., Late Paleozoic Cycles of sedimentation in the United States. *18th Int. Geol. Congr.*, Part 4, 17–28 (1950).

WATERS, A. C. and C. D. CAMPBELL, Mylonites from the San Andreas fault zone. *Am. Journ. of Sci.*, (5) **29**, 473–503 (1935).

WEGENER, A., Die Entstehung der Kontinente und Ozeane. Friedr. Vieweg, Braunschweig, 4th ed. (1929).

WEGMANN, C. E., Über die Tektonik der jüngeren Faltung in Ostfinland. *Fennia*, **50**, (16) 22 (1928).

——, Über Diapirismus. *Bull. de la Comm. Géol. Finl.* (92) 58–76 (1930).

——, Note sur le boudinage. *Bull. Soc. Géol. France*, (5) **2**, 477–89 (1932).

——, Zur Deutung der Migmatite. *Geol. Rundschau*, **26**, 305–50 (1935).

—— and E. H. KRANCK. Beiträge zur Kenntniss der Svecofenniden in Finnland, Parts I and II. *Bull. de la Com. Géol. Finl.*, **89**, 1–107 (1931).

WENK, E., Principelles zur geologisch-tektonischen Gliederung des Penninikums im zentralen Tessin. *Ecl. geol. Helv.*, **46**, 9–22 (1953).

WENTLANDT, E. A., "Hawkinsfield" in *Occurrence of oil and gas in north-east Texas*. University of Texas Publication No. 5116, 153–8 (1951).

WILLEMS, H. W. V., On the magmatic provinces in the Netherlands East Indies. *Verh. Geol. Mijnb. Gen. Geol. Serie*, **12** (1940).

WILLIAMS, H., Calderas and their origin. Univ. of Calif. Publ. Dept. Geol. Sci. 25, (6) (1941).

WILLIS, B., The mechanics of Appalachian structures. 13th ann. rep. U. S. Geological Survey 2, 211–83 (1893).

——, Continental genesis. Bull. Geol. Soc. Am., 40, 281–336 (1929).

——, East African Plateaux and Rift Valleys. Carnegie Institute, Publication No. 470 (1936).

——, Geologic observations in the Philippine archipelago. Nat. Research Council, Philipp. Isl. Bull. No. 13 (1937).

——, San Andreas Rift in California. Journ. of Geol., 46, 793–827 (1938a).

——, San Andreas Rift in south-western California. Journ. of Geol., 46, 1017–57 (1938b).

WILSON, G., The relationship of slaty cleavage and kindred structures to tectonics. Proc. Geol. Ass., 62, 263–302 (1946).

——, Ptygmatic structures and their formation. Geol. Mag., 89, 1–21 (1952).

——, Mullion and rodding structures in the Moine series of Scotland. Proc. Geol. Ass., 64 (2) 118–51 (1953).

WILSON, M. E., The Canadian Shield. Geologie der Erde. Geology of North America, ed. by R. Ruedeman and R. Balk. Borntraeger, Berlin (1939).

——, An approach to the structure of the Canadian shield. Trans. of Am. Geoph. Union., 29, 691–726 (1948).

——, Some major structures of the Canadian shield. Trans. Can. Inst. Min. Met., 52, 231–42 (1949).

WINTERTHURN, R., Wilmington Oilfield, Bull. 118, Dept. Nat. Res., State Div. of Mines, California, 301–5 (1943).

WÖLK, E., Zur Klüfttektonik des Niederrheinischen Haupt-Braunkohlenflözes, Zeitschr. deutsch. Geol. Ges., 91/2, 109 (1937).

WOODRING, W. P. and R. STEWART, Geologic map of Kettleman Hills, California. U. S. Geological Survey (1934).

WOODWORTH, J. B., Fracture system of joints. Boston Soc. Nat. Hist., 27, 163 (1896).

WYOMING GEOLOGICAL ASSOCIATION, Field Guide Book. Big Horn Basin (1947).

——, Field Guide Book. Wind River Basin (1948).

YABE, H., The latest land connection of the Japanese islands to the Asiatic continent. Proc. Imp. Ac., 5, 167–9 (1929).

ZIJLSTRA, G., De Permschubben van de Salmurano culminatie. Geol. en Mijnb., 3 N.S. (1941).

——, Enige gegevens over de Feldbiss. Geol. en Mijnb., 6 N.S. (1944).

ZWART, H. J., Breuken en diaklazen in Robin Hood's Bay. Geol. en Mijnb., 13, 1–4 (1951).

——, La géologie du Massif du St Barthélemy. L. Geol. Med., 18, 1–228 (1954).

——, Sur les herzolites et ophites des Pyrénées. L. Geol. Med., 18, 281–6 (1954).

Index

A

Aar massif, 280, 281, 290, 394
    diag., 268
Acadian orogenic belt, 436
Achondrites, 341
Adamello massif,
    diag., 85
Adamello Mountains, 167
Adams, F. D.,
    cit., 47, 50
Affines, 105
African continent, 487
African-European rift zone, 518
African rift system, 467, 469
African rift zone, 143
African shield, 442–5
Ahr river, 310
Airy's columns, 330, 331
Alabaster, 51, 52, 53, 57, 58, 59
Algeria,
    anticlines, 257–8
    coast, 357
    fault patterns in, 123–5
    gliding in, 275–6
    Morsott anticline, 130
Algoman, 433
Algonkian, 437–8, 439
Algonkian Dal-formation, 361
"Alpides", 177
Alpine belts, 472
Alpine Molasse, 296
Alpine mountain chains, 474
Alpine orogenies, 375
    diag., 441
Alpine period, 471–2
Alpine structure, 344–9
Alps, 146, 165, 166, 167, 177–9, 188,
    213, 243, 244, 266, 291, 352, 353,
    354, 358, 362, 378–9, 383–4, 428,
    467, 477, 480, 481, 503, 510
    diags, 312, 478
    facies, 293
    folding, 192–3, 268, 319, 320
    gliding, 268, 276–82, 290
    history, 348, 384–92
    Nevada orogeny and, 403
    structure, 235–7

Åmålformation, 439
America,
    orogenic periods, 328
Anatolia, 362
Anderson, E. M.,
    cit., 43, 124, 135, 151
Andes, 291
Andesite line, 337, 371
    defined, 410
Anisotropy, 73, 77
Anti-Atlas, 369
    sills, 139
Antillean arc, 416, 427–8, 492
Appalachian basin,
    diag., 4
Appalachian (Hercynian) system, 404
Appalachians, 9, 12, 178, 246, 296,
    329, 352, 361, 362, 430, 434,
    475, 476, 477, 478, 480
    history, 403–9
Appenines, 268, 290, 299
    gliding in, 286–8
Apsheron peninsula, 242
Apuane Alps, 286, 287, 288
Aquitainian basin, 456
Arbenz, P.,
    cit., 293
Arbuckle–Wichita belt, 43
Archean orogenies, 474
Arcs. See Island arcs
Arctic climates, 300
Ardennes, 149, 458, 472
Argand, E.,
    cit., 116, 187, 319, 392
Argille scagliose, 268, 290, 291, 299
    composition and origin, 286–8
Arkansas, 150
Arkoses, 299
Armorican mountains, 149
Ascension, 372
Asthenoliths, 490, 491, 492
Asthenosphere, 333, 486, 490, 511
Asturian-Cantabric mountain chain,
    473
Asturian folding, 186
Atlantic Ocean, 338, 339, 357, 372,
    488, 514
Atlantic ridge, 372

Atlas Mountains, 179, 187, 237, 472–3
  diag., 238
  folding, 315–7
  gliding, 269
  grain, 319
  slumping, 306
Aubert, D.,
  cit., 319
Augen-gneiss, 86, 103, 381
Australia, 424–5
Azores, 372

B

Backlund, H. G.,
  cit., 437
  phases, 374
Baerum cauldron, 264
Baldry, R. A.,
  cit., 272
Balearic Islands, 358
Ballarat East Goldfield,
  cleavage folding, 218
Baltic shield, 431, 436–42, 457
Banda arc, 424–5, 427, 492
Banda geosyncline, 421, 422
Barbers Hill salt-dome,
  diag., 259
Barrádos Valley, 95, 96–7, 98
Bartlett trough,
  wrench-fault, 416
Basaltic rocks, 138–9, 337, 338, 371–2
  continental, 373–4
  flood, 372–3
Basin and Range fault system, 155–8
Basins, 2–7, 297, 317–22, 332–3, 347,
    349, 350–2, 370, 399–402, 436,
    447–60, 462, 465, 517
  defined, 354
Bathyal facies, 295
Bavarian basin, 456
Bearpaw Mountains, 272
  gliding, 269–70
Beaumont, Elie de,
  contraction theory, 485–7
Bedding, 102
Beds, 300–06
Belgian coal district, 187
  folding in, 222–4
Bemmelen, van. *See* van Bemmelen
Bendigo goldfield,
  cleavage folding, 218
  saddle reefs, 219–20
Beneo, E.,
  cit., 249
Bergamasc Alps, 192, 193
  gliding in, 277
  structure, 235–6
Bertrand, Marcel,
  cit., 293
Betic Cordillera, 346, 428

Big Bad Lands,
  elastic dikes, 141–2
Bijlaard, P. P.,
  cit., 414
Bingham formula, 42
Birch, F.,
  cit., 336
Block-faulted regions, 15
Blocks, 351, 354, 461–70, 505
Blue Ridge Province, 406–7
Böker, R.,
  cit., 47
Bore-holes, 304
Borislaw oilfield, 213
Borna–Gnandorf mine,
  diag., 305
Boudinage, 87–8
Bou Khadra structure,
  diag., 262
Brabant massif, 250, 458, 465
Brecciation, 85, 86, 294
Brenta Mountain,
  wrench-faults, 167–9
Brittany, 357
Brown, B.,
  cit., 272
Brown, R. W.,
  cit., 191
  wrench-fault experiments, 173
Bubnoff, von. *See* von Bubnoff
Buckling hypothesis, 416–21
Bucher, W. H.,
  cit., 43, 164
Bulawayan system, 443
  diag., 444
Bullard, E. C.,
  cit., 143
"Bündnerschiefer", 475
Burgers, W. G.,
  cit., 50
Buxtorf, A.,
  cit., 187, 241, 242, 246, 248, 319

C

Calcite crystal, 54, 87
Calcium, 445
Calderas. *See* Cauldrons
Caledonian mountain chain, 356–7
Caledonides, 472
California, 504
  basins, 448–52, 460, 477
  coastal ranges, 398–400
Canada,
  Archean rocks, 103
Canadian shield, 351, 353, 430–4
Cantabric nappes, 7–8
Capistrano embayment, 449, 451
Carbon, 298

Dikkers, A. J.,
cit., 148
Dilatation zones, 467–9
"Dinarides", 177
Dislocation lines, 178–9
Djebel Def salt-dome, 258
Djebel Friktia,
gliding in, 275
Djebel Saghro, 139
Djembangan Mountain range, 272
Dôle-Champagnole fault, 169
Dolerites, 139, 140
Dolomites, 188
Domaniale colliery,
diag., 223
Domes, 201, 204, 263, 287
Bearpaw Mountains, 269–70
Kettleman Hills, 209–10
Drag, 98, 99
Dunites, 360
du Toit, A. L.,
drifting continents theory, 487–9

E

Eardley, A. J.,
cit., 155–6
Earth. *See also* Crust
ages, 512–18
chemical composition, 340–2
convection currents, 492–6
core, 338–9, 494, 510–11, 513
density, 340
disturbances, 504
interior, 333–43
layers, 337–8
magnetic field, 342–3
mantle, 338–9
pulse, 494
stress-field, 502–8
surface, 336, 501
temperature, 339–40
Earth Valley fault, 156–7
Earthquakes, 416
Japanese, 419
Earthquakes (1906),
San Andreas fault and, 164, 165
Earthquakes (1930), 518
faults and, 165
East Asturian fold,
diag., 198
East Greenland,
dike swarms, 139
Eastern Alps, 388
Egge rift,
diag., 154
Eifel fault, 250
Elastic flow, 56, 57, 73, 74
Elastic yield, 44–6
Elasticity limit, 45

Elba, 286, 287, 358
Elk Basin oilfield,
faults, 207, 208, 213
Ellipsoid. *See* Strain Ellipsoid
Epeirogenesis,
defined, 325, 326
Erosion, 193–5
facies and, 294
gliding and, 269
Escher. B. G.,
cit., 71, 116
Eurasia, 440–2
Europe,
folding, 322
mountains, 116
orogenic periods, 328
European rift system, 469
Ewing, M.,
cit., 423

F

Facies,
epeirogenic and geosynclinal,
297–9
molasse, 295–7
orogenic, 293–5
Falkland Island arc, 428
Falkland Islands, 514–5
Fallot, P.,
cit., 286, 471–2
Fars series, 273–5
Fath, A. E.,
cit., 173
Faults, 43, 74, 183, 254, 259–60, 313,
319
Alpine, 467
antithetic, 153–5
Apennine, 248–50
Basin and Range, 155–7
Bearpaw thrust-, 270
cauldron, 262–3
crest, 201–6
cross-, 206–11
defined, 118–20
experimental, 70
flat planar thrust planes, 246–50
fundamental, 175–9
glacial sand, 305–6
gliding and thrust, 288–91
Javanese, 272
joints and, 122–42
mingling of. 320–1
model, 67
normal, 143–58
oil conduit, 212–3
Paris basin, 459
rifts and, 468, 469
Rockies, 401–2
Schuld flexure, 311

Drukkerij Holland N.V., Amsterdam